Psalms for All Seasons
A Complete Psalter for Worship

Psalms for All Seasons
A Complete Psalter for Worship

Calvin Institute of
Christian Worship
for the study and renewal of worship

FAITH
ALIVE®
Christian Resources

BrazosPress
a division of Baker Publishing Group

Psalms for All Seasons is copublished by

Calvin Institute of Christian Worship
1855 Knollcrest Circle SE, Grand Rapids, MI 49546
phone: 616-526-6088
fax: 616-526-7168
email: worship@calvin.edu
website: worship.calvin.edu

Faith Alive Christian Resources
2850 Kalamazoo Ave. SE, Grand Rapids MI 49560
phone: 800-333-8300
fax: 616-224-0834
email: info@faithaliveresources.org
website: www.FaithAliveResources.org

Brazos Press, a division of Baker Publishing Group
P.O. Box 6287, Grand Rapids, MI 49516
website: www.brazospress.com

ISBN 978-1-59255-444-7

10 9 8 7 6 5 4 3 2

Table of Contents

Introduction

This Psalter is designed to promote faithful and fruitful use of the biblical psalms in Christian worship. It arises out of a sense of wonder at the psalms' spiritual vitality, rugged beauty, and enduring pastoral relevance for communities all over the world. It is guided by three overarching commitments: *to encourage thoughtful and faithful engagement with the text of each psalm; to feature musical choices that are singable and accessible; and to be hospitable to a relatively wide range of traditions and cultures.*

It is composed of contributions from the long history of Christian psalmody as well as from the recent outpouring of new psalm settings from a wide range of Christian traditions and cultures. Whereas most collections of psalmody focus on one approach, this volume draws freely from a wide variety of approaches and styles, providing multiple options and making it possible to easily compare the strengths of each.

For each of the Bible's 150 Psalms, this volume includes:

- *the complete New Revised Standard Version* (NRSV) *text of the psalm*, presented with alternating regular and boldfaced type for responsive readings and red markings that enable the chanting of the psalm

- *a Christian prayer* that responds to a theme, imagery, or basic intent of the psalm;

- *a brief footnote* which identifies the psalm's genre or type, highlights significant features of its form or imagery, and suggests a range of uses in Christian worship

- *one or more settings of the psalm*, most of which are musical settings for congregational use

This range of material means that the book is well-suited to a variety of uses.

This book is designed for use in ***corporate worship***—to be placed in the hands of worship leaders, choirs, and, ideally, all worshipers. Most congregations across the wide spectrum of approaches to worship will be able to find at least 100 settings in this book accessible and fitting for their own approach, another 100 that they can easily learn, and then several dozen (or hundred!) more to stretch them in new directions. This means that the book is useful, even if a given community is not attracted to or able to sing the full range of material. Wise use of the materials in this book will require careful thought about which settings are most appropriate in a given congregation and what kind of introduction will help people engage each setting thoughtfully.

This volume is also designed for communities or groups committed to services of ***daily prayer*** at morning, noon, evening, and/or night. The inclusion of simple liturgies for these traditional services means that a community could celebrate daily prayer using only this book and a Bible. (For daily lectionary texts, see *www.psalmsforallseasons.org*.) This book is ideal for ***personal and family devotion***. It belongs on pianos and music stands of those with musical abilities. The texts alone provide a treasury of material for daily contemplation and prayer.

This Psalter is also a resource for ***Bible study***, particularly as an anthology for courses on the book of Psalms. For pastors preparing to preach on a given psalm, it can function as a ***commentary*** on the book of Psalms. Each musical setting of a psalm is, in its own way, a miniature sermon or interpretation of the psalm. Comparing the range of approaches to a given psalm offers an insightful introduction to the challenges and possibilities of the biblical psalms in guiding the Christian life.

Finally, this book is intended to ***inspire composers*** in a wide range of cultures and traditions to imagine new, vital, and faithful ways of rendering psalms. Many settings in this book are suggestive of new approaches that might develop and mature over the next several years—a task that calls for deep and creative engagement by the next generation of pastoral composers and text-writers.

MULTIPLE APPROACHES TO THE USE OF THE PSALMS

The overarching lesson of this book is that the biblical psalms can be legitimately appropriated in a variety of ways in Christian worship. This can only happen through attentive study of each psalm and thoughtful pastoral leadership.

1. *Excerpts versus Entire Psalms:* Psalm excerpts have been prominent in both historic liturgical introits and in contemporary praise choruses. Complete psalms have been prominent as both preaching texts and stand-alone, hymn-like responses with various liturgical functions. Both appropriations can be legitimate, provided that they do not close off a community from realizing the value of the other practice. This Psalter pays special attention to complete settings of psalms. It also includes some musical selections that dwell on a single verse, often suggesting ways to use these as refrains or frames around either complete psalms or large portions of a given psalm.

2. *Range of Interpretive Freedom:* The long history of psalm usage includes both practices that follow the form, content, and imagery of a given psalm very closely, and those that exercise greater interpretive freedom. An example of this interpretive freedom can be found in Scripture itself: Mary's song (Luke 1) is an improvisation that is based on, but also different from, Hannah's song (1 Sam. 2). This volume includes examples of a wide range of approaches. Chanting or reading a psalm draws the tightest connection between the text on the page and the contemporary rendering of the text (though even here, the choice of chant tones or tone of voice can suggest strikingly different interpretations of the text). Metrical psalms vary widely from those that follow the contours of a psalm closely to those that focus on a central theme or image in the psalm. Some examples are independent enough from the psalm that they might better be called "hymns" rather than "metrical psalms." Users of this book are encouraged to pay close attention to the relative distance or gap between the actual psalm text and the text of any given psalm setting.

3. *Function or Genre:* The book of Psalms includes texts that perform a range of functions: praying, teaching, blessing, testifying, and exhorting. For this reason the settings in this Psalter fulfill multiple functions in Christian worship services— some are prayers, some are exhortations, some are prophetic announcements. This is a more expansive approach than is found within any single tradition, where the psalms may be used primarily as a response to an Old Testament reading or almost exclusively as texts for preaching or prayer.

4. *Options for Imagining Our Relationship with the Text:* We might speak, pray, or sing a psalm in one or more of the following modes:

- As an expression of our own experience: *"Given our despair over the persecution we face, let us sing Psalm 22 together— as our own prayer, testimony, and vow."*

- As a text which we do not yet experience fully, but which we are growing into: *"Let us sing Psalm 116 as a way of stretching ourselves toward the kind of thanksgiving and dedication to God we desire to exhibit as God's covenant people."*

- As a way of praying in solidarity with those whose experience is quite different from our own: *"Let us sing Psalm 22 in solidarity with all those who are facing persecution today."*

- As a way of entering into or responding to a particular biblical narrative: *"Let us sing Psalm 22 as way of entering into the drama of Jesus' passion."* or *"Let us sing Psalm 38 in order to sense the despair experienced by the prophet Jeremiah."*

- As a way of contemplating or wrestling with a given text without committing to a particular way of understanding our relationship to it: *"As we read Psalm 41 together, consider whether this text describes our experience of betrayal, or if it might be prayed by others who have been betrayed by us."*

- As a way of distancing ourselves from the text, in light of our wrestling with another part of scripture: *"We read Psalm 109 not only to sense the anger and frustration that the ancient people experienced, but also to mark the stunning contrast with Jesus' response to those who crucified him."*

In some circumstances, we may approach the text in more than one way at the same time. For example, as we are praying a text in solidarity with others, we may discover that it also expresses a deep part of our own experience. Or, as we are praying a text that expresses our own experience, we may discover that part of the text does not express our own experience. In other circumstances, we may approach the text without specifying this relationship—the text is simply presented, read, or sung without explanation, creating juxtapositions with other texts and themes that evoke new insights, questions, and dispositions. The psalms are poignant both when they reflect and name our experience, and when they stretch the range of our expression and experience. When we take words upon our lips that do not express something we feel—or perhaps have never felt—it is then that the psalms may have the greatest capacity to help us see the world in a new way, experience new things, and identify with people different from ourselves.

5. *Understanding the Psalms in an Old Testament Context or a New Testament Context:* Some Christian commentators have wisely insisted that we understand the essentially Jewish origin and context of the book of Psalms, having integrity in its own right apart from its relationship with the New Testament. For example, Psalm 54 stands on its own as a powerful record of the experience of an Old Testament figure—the kind of experience of betrayal felt by Jacob or Joseph. Engaging Psalm 54 in worship does not require us to explicitly link the psalm with the person of Jesus or a New Testament text. At the same time, Christian interpreters, preachers, theologians, and worshipers wisely acknowledge how the New Testament has shaped our view of the psalms. Some psalms present promises that are fulfilled in the New Testament. Some psalms develop types, analogies, or themes that recur in the New Testament (e.g. the shepherd of Ps. 23 developed in John 10:11). Some psalms are quoted in the New Testament—at times in contexts that significantly shape how we receive and understand them (e.g., Ps. 22:1 on the lips of Jesus). Other psalms present images, themes, or sentiments that stand in contrast to various New Testament themes or passages (e.g., the contrast between Jesus' prayers for his enemies and the psalmodic imprecations against the enemy).

6. *Christological interpretation:* Special mention should also be made regarding Christological approaches to the book of Psalms—approaches that explore how the person and work of Jesus affect our encounter with a psalm text. A Christological approach to the psalms may refer to any of four distinct approaches, all of which have merit:

- Focusing on how a given psalm expresses aspects of Jesus' experience (especially psalms traditionally linked with Jesus' passion, Pss. 22 and 31 but also 70, 71, and 88)

- Focusing on how Jesus fulfills specific Messianic prophesies in the psalms or on the way in which references to the king and the king's son are fulfilled by Jesus' role as king and representative of Israel (e.g., Pss. 2, 20, 72, and 110)

- Focusing on the correspondence between a primary theme of a psalm and a particular description of Jesus or event in Jesus' ministry (e.g., Ps. 29 with Jesus' Baptism)

- Focusing on the way in which every psalm prayed by the church is, in fact, a cry of "the body of Christ" offered "in the name of Christ," an echo of the way Jesus himself prayed these texts while living on earth

There are settings in this volume that correspond to each of these uses. Arguably the greatest barrier to the strong functioning of the psalms in worship is lack of clarity about the many ways a single text could function. Every psalm should be contemplated and studied. Pastors, worship leaders, and musicians should take great care both in selecting psalms for worship as well as in preparing the congregation to understand how and why they are used.

MULTIPLICITY OF FORMS AND STYLES

This volume also arises out of the conviction that the richness of the psalms and different ways they function commend the use of a wide variety of musical, textual, and artistic forms for rendering them. Each approach has unique strengths. *The reading or chanting of a psalm* is ideal for engaging with the text in an unobtrusive way, free from the constraints of any single interpretative move. *Metrical psalms*, with regular meter and often rhyme set to familiar hymn tunes, are ideal for encouraging congregational singing. Their regularity improves their accessibility and facilitates their memorization. *Responsorial psalms*, with a repeated refrain sung by the congregation, are ideal for directing the congregation to a central thrust of the psalm. They allow for both congregational participation and the unique contribution that a soloist, cantor, or choir can offer in exploring a given text. *Improvisational prayers* based on psalms are especially ideal for contextually applying the psalms to present circumstances (see 126C). *A dramatic reading* of the psalm may be ideal for highlighting the implicit script in a psalm, a literary feature that is obscured in other forms. Drawing upon sources from a *different cultural, historical, or ethnic context* invites us to pray the text in solidarity with others.

As you encounter examples throughout this book, pause to consider the unique strengths, and corresponding weaknesses, of each type of setting. Note also that this volume includes some examples that push beyond standard approaches. Psalms with dramatic turns pose particular challenges. While most approaches to psalmody are good at establishing a mood, rhythm, and ethos, they are not necessarily well suited to conveying the abrupt changes or pivot points that are found in several psalms. This volume presents several examples (e.g., Pss. 22 and 73) which feature musical 'gearshifts' that correspond with the form of the psalm.

Several examples in this Psalter were crafted out of concern both to faithfully reflect the themes of a psalm and to connect the psalm with a particular occasion. For example, the text of 132B was created for a tune with powerful Christmas associations. In this case and many others, the tune and its associations becomes an interpretative resource, helping worshipers enter into the meaning of the psalm more fully. At other times, well known hymns or spirituals are placed in juxtaposition to the psalm (e.g., 74A). These songs become musical dialogue partners for the psalm text. The familiar song allows for greater accessibility to the less familiar psalm.

DIFFICULT, NEGLECTED, AND MISUNDERSTOOD PSALMS

As a complete Psalter, this volume offers many opportunities to engage with psalms that are often neglected, misunderstood, or even intentionally ignored.

Royal and Zion Psalms refer explicitly to Israel's king, temple, and holy city—Jerusalem or Zion. Christians have traditionally appropriated these psalms in three distinct ways: to enter into the drama of God's story with the people of Israel; to address Christ as the King, the true representative of Israel (e.g., Ps. 21 on Ascension Day) or the locus of God's dwelling; and to test our own political sensibility. Psalm 45 offers a particularly interesting example—and challenge. It certainly could be used in conjunction with an Old Testament reading about life in the royal court. It could be sung allegorically as a way of depicting the marriage of Jesus, "the bridegroom," to the church, "the bride of Christ." And it could be appropriated as a way to address those in contemporary positions of political power, reminding them (and us) of the God-centered righteousness we are all called to emulate. This Psalter includes a range of examples for psalms like this, inviting users into the long, centuries-old conversation about which approaches are most faithful and illuminating.

Psalms that Express Innocence or Integrity may seem arrogant, especially from cultural contexts that emphasize humility. How can we possibly pray Psalm 26 or Psalm 101 in light of all that the Bible itself teaches about human limitations and sinfulness? Three considerations may help. First, in certain circumstances, claims of innocence are an act of truth telling, especially for those who are unjustly imprisoned, tortured, or mistreated. Second, at times we are called to speak words that describe the deep intentions of our hearts, even when we are unable to live up to these ideals fully. Even as we can testify, "I believe, help my unbelief," so too we can pray "I am innocent; help me in my failings." Third, at times we are called to pray in language that is formative rather than expressive. Like the petitions "your kingdom come" or "forgive us our sins as we forgive those who sin against us," so too the claim of innocence is something we are learning to pray and to live into more fully over time.

Psalms that discuss the godless, the enemy, especially psalms of vengeance and imprecation, including those that wish harm upon the enemy, are rarely used in public worship in the majority of Christian traditions. Reading or singing these texts without care has both implicitly and explicitly reinforced Christian participation in inter-religious violence—in direct opposition to Jesus' command to "love your enemies" and his own prayer that God would forgive his enemies (Matt. 5:44, Luke 23:34). They seem to violate Paul's injunction to "bless, and not curse" (Rom. 12:14). At the same time, these texts have too often been simply ignored or dismissed with little care to their significance and meaning. It is important to learn from the vast array of Christian commentary on these texts, including the following approaches:

- Many imprecations were simply requests that the normal justice system in Israel would work (e.g., Deut. 19:16-21, Deut. 32). It would be akin to someone today saying, "may the person who broke into my home be caught and punished appropriately."

- Imprecations hand over vengeance to God (e.g., Deut. 32:35). By asking for divine retribution, these texts also reject human revenge. In psalms of vengeance, the psalmist channels feelings into a prayer rather than into actions. Confidence in God's ultimate work of justice ultimately frees us to extend love and hospitality to the enemy.

- Such candid prayers are a powerful witness to God's desire to hear honest prayer in all circumstances. This transparency inside the divine-human covenantal relationship makes it possible for a temporary expression of anger to be transformed into other, more emphatic and gracious expressions.

- While it may be typical to approach these imprecations by identifying with the victim who is crying, it is also helpful to imagine identification with the oppressor—and imagine people praying these words against us.

- Imprecations point us to the resolve needed in the face of wickedness. Just as Paul and Peter lamented those who pervert the gospel of Christ (Gal. 1:8-9, Acts 8:20), and just as Jesus cursed the fig tree (Mark 11:14), we must continue to combat the forces of evil and repudiate systems of injustice in every guise.

The prayers and musical settings associated with imprecatory psalms in this volume reflect a variety of approaches. They help us contemplate the meaning and significance of these psalms and help us discern how to draw upon these texts in wise, challenging, and pastorally sensitive ways.

CHANTING THE PSALMS

The Psalms have been chanted by cantors, choirs, and congregations for centuries. Indeed, of all the modes of singing the Psalms, chanting comes closest to the ancient practice. Recently the chanting of psalms has been fused with jazz, modern, and popular genres. Sometimes chant is cast in conventional notation (e.g., the Orthodox setting of the Lord's Prayer on p. 1034). In other instances the text may be set with musical notation using flexible chant melodies either for unison singing (e.g., 3A), or for singing in harmony (e.g., 46E). In either case, the singing should always be fluid, taking its cue from the pace of natural speech.

In this book the chanted texts are most often provided with red marks that serve as musical markers. This presentation is commonly referred to as *'pointed psalmody.'* Though perhaps puzzling for the uninitiated, the formula is intuitive. The practice is better 'caught' than taught. The explanation of the pointing (in the next paragraph) can be both distracting and intimidating for congregations. Most assemblies do best when simply encouraged to chant with the cantor or an initiated group of singers.

Each pointed verse is divided into two half verses that correspond to the two parts of the *Tone* melody. The second half verse is indented. Each half verse has a dot within it indicating when the singers move from the reciting tone (⦀◖◗⦀) and continue with the rest of the melody. Occasionally a slur is placed under two syllables indicating that both syllables are to be sung with one black note (*Example 1*). Two red dots above one syllable indicate that this single syllable is held over two black notes (*Example 2*). It is important to remember that the tone melody is in no way a metrical interpretation of the text. Rhythmically, they are neutral conduits for the natural expression of the words.

Example 1

·

Israel
‿

Example 2

··

Praise

Each psalm leads off with the complete text from the NRSV. This translation purposes to provide a faithful and accurate rendering of the original Hebrew text, but not necessarily in a form suitable for chanting. The use of regular and boldface type is provided for the purpose of responsive reading. Nevertheless, these texts have also been pointed in order to make it possible for every psalm to be chanted. When chanting from the NRSV, any of the refrains and tones found throughout the book may be used. (See also the general refrains provided on p. 1054.) Though there are no *Refrain* indications in the NRSV text, a worship leader may gesture to the congregation when the singing of the refrain is desired. It is also possible for a refrain or song to frame the chanting of a psalm. Each psalm verse is divided into two parts by a red asterisk (*) which allows for antiphonal chanting, alternating at the half verse.

An additional pointed setting is included for each psalm or portion of psalm found in the three-year cycle of the *Revised Common Lectionary*. These texts are drawn from *Evangelical Lutheran Worship* (Augsburg Fortress Press), which contains translations of the psalms particularly suited for chanting. They may be chanted by a solo voice with all joining at the singing of the refrain, or the entire congregation may chant the psalm. When the entire congregation chants the psalm, this can be done either antiphonally (e.g., two parts of the congregation alternating at the half verse) or together throughout, with or without the refrains.

With regard to the refrains, this Psalter draws from a number of sources and traditions. Some are very short phrases intended to punctuate the chanted psalm. These might be drawn from the psalm itself or from a well-known hymn text. Others might employ a spiritual or a longer chorus. All reflect a theme in the psalm and suggest possible functions of the psalm in the liturgy. For some psalms, more than one refrain is suggested to allow for greater flexibility. For example, the two refrains provided for Psalm 22 (pp. 122 and 125) allow for use during either Holy Week or Eastertide. (A note at the bottom of the page indicates the lectionary use of the psalm.) The *General Refrains Appendix* (p. 1054) provides shorter options that may be used across the spectrum of the Psalter.

ADDITIONAL EDITORIAL NOTES

1. *Translations:* This volume draws upon multiple translations, representing a variety of Christian traditions:

- The initial presentation of a psalm text is taken from the *New Revised Standard Version* (NRSV).

- Lectionary-based responsorial psalms are taken from *Evangelical Lutheran Worship* (Augsburg Fortress Press), a text used in a wide variety of ecumenical settings.

- Other translations or paraphrases include the *New International Version* (NIV), the *New Living Translation* (NLT), Eugene Peterson's *The Message*, Calvin Seerveld's *Voicing God's Psalms* (Eerdman's Publishing Company), the *Book of Common Prayer* (BCP), *Common Worship: Daily Prayer*, and the *Psalter for the Christian People*, each of which is identified.

2. *Use of LORD and Lord:* Modern Bible translations indicate the use of the Tetragrammaton (the four-letter Hebrew name for God, "YHWH") using all capital letters, as in LORD. When the sources of the musical settings indicated the use of the Tetragrammaton with LORD or GOD, this was maintained. When text writers did not intend to make such distinctions, no further editorial attempts were made to reconcile their versification to the use of the Tetragrammaton in the psalm. The use of the word "Jehovah" has been avoided.

3. *Use of the Gloria Patri:* In some traditions it is customary to conclude each psalm with the singing of the *Gloria Patri (Glory to the Father, and to the Son and to the Holy Spirit...).* In most cases when the *Gloria Patri* was found in the original source, it was maintained in this book. Where possible (i.e., when it is set as an additional stanza or as a coda) the text is presented in italics, indicating that its singing is optional.

4. *Psalm Prayers:* A Christian prayer in a communal voice is provided at the end of each NRSV setting of the psalm. These prayers are not so general as to be appropriate for all contexts. Rather, they were prepared to model the full spectrum of possible prayer responses to the various psalms. (See *Options for Imagining Our Relationship with the Text* on p. *iii*.) Care should be taken to ensure that the prayer is appropriate for the way in which the psalm is being used in worship. For example, if the psalm prayer takes the approach of being in solidarity with others who are suffering, it may need to be adapted in order fit a context where the psalm and the prayer express the community's own suffering.

5. *Chords for Guitar and Keyboard:* Chord symbols have been provided for nearly all of the musical settings. These chords are for use by both guitar and keyboard players. Every attempt has been made to accommodate both users. For most settings chords are inserted at a pace that is logical for the use of guitar. No attempt was made to represent each change in the given harmony. Usually this will allow for the use of guitar and keyboard harmony together. The use of added tones (e.g., Am6 or Asus) or indications of bass notes (e.g., Am/C) are more useful to keyboard players and bass players who play using the chord symbols. On the whole, guitarists can ignore these marks and drop the numeral or the suspension. Some settings in this Psalter, however, include suspended chords that are followed by a minor chord (e.g., Dsus followed by a Dm, see 70B, p. 431). These chords should either be played as suspended chords or as minor chords. In other instances a chord is followed by the instruction 'no3.' The third should be dropped from these chords. If the third is added to the chord it cannot be assumed that this is a major chord. Guitar players need to determine

from the context whether a major or minor chord is most suitable. (See p. 1055 ff. for further explanation of chord symbols.)

6. *Performing Songs with Refrains:* The approach to songs with refrains varies widely from one tradition to the next. Many of the settings arise from traditions where a solo voice or an ensemble sings the stanzas or verses and the congregation only joins in the singing of the refrain. In other traditions, the entire congregation is accustomed to singing stanzas or verses and the refrain. Recognizing the spectrum of approaches to these songs, most 'solo voice,' 'cantor,' or 'ensemble' designations have been removed from the score. Leaders must consider each musical setting in light of the congregational context when determining whether or not the congregation will share in the singing of the stanzas or verses.

7. *Use of Time Signatures and Barlines:* Many songs were not composed with time signatures or regular barlines (e.g., plainchant, Genevan psalms, Lutheran chorales, and some contemporary hymn tunes). In most cases no attempt was made to add time signatures to these settings. The phrase markings in these settings are designed to allow for flexibility of interpretation. In instances without a time signature, a regular barline through the staff indicates that the rhythm should continue normally (see 33C where each third phrase ends with a regular barline). A small 'tick' in the staff (*Example 1*) indicates that the rhythm might be stretched in order to allow the singers to take a breath (see 10A). A vertical line that strikes through the middle of the staff (*Example 2*) can be interpreted in different ways: it may be interpreted as a half note rest (a measured rest for the singers), or simply as a breath mark without a rest. The tune GENEVAN 134/OLD HUNDREDTH (100A) provides an excellent case in point. Congregations who know this tune well will intuitively sense whether they will elongate the end of each phrase or keep the pulse and continue. The vertical mark serves as a neutral indicator allowing for either interpretation. In instances where the tune is not as well known, the musical introduction must make clear for the singers how these phrases will be interpreted. When led by a contemporary band, these vertical marks can indicate short instrumental interludes. (For examples of leading in this way see *www.thepsalmproject.com.*)

8. *Performance Notes:* Helpful guides and suggestions for leading many of the psalm settings are provided on p. 1077. For expanded performance notes see *www. psalmsforallseasons.org.*

9. *Lectionary Use:* References to those psalms or psalm portions found in the three-year cycle of the *Revised Common Lectionary* are noted after the psalm tones of responsorial settings. This indicates that the psalm verses covered in that instance match the verses selected in the lectionary. It does not suggest that this particular musical setting is preferred over the others provided for that psalm.

10. *Indexes:* In the *Index of First Lines and Common Titles* most settings are referenced by their instance number followed by the page number in parenthesis: 23A (130). In the case of the New Testament canticles and settings embedded within the prayer services, only the page number is indicated. The *Index of Subjects and Seasons* refers to the biblical psalm number. One should explore that particular psalm for the most appropriate setting (e.g., Ps. 118 is generally associated with Easter, however, settings 118 I and 118 J are especially appropriate for an Easter celebration.) All other indexes refer to page numbers. The entire three year cycle for the *Revised Common Lectionary* is included, as well an index of all the lectionary psalms or portions of psalms arranged in biblical order. (For the two year cycle of daily lectionary readings see *www.psalmsforallseasons.org.*)

11. *Additional Resources:* Despite its size, this volume includes only a small portion of all of the psalm settings for congregational use that are in print today. Several hundred composers and poets have written individual psalm-based compositions for

congregational use, several dozen have published complete volumes of material, and some have produced anthologies of material on nearly the entire Psalter. For more complete information about available psalm settings see *www.psalmsforallseasons.org* and John D. Witvliet, *The Biblical Psalms in Christian Worship* (Eerdmans, 2008).

This book provides a feast of resources. When we sit down to a festive meal we can approach the abundance with such enthusiasm and consume so much at one time that we lose our appetite for more. Or we can approach the feast with wisdom, taking only as much as we can enjoy, savoring each taste. You are encouraged to take the second approach. Begin where you and your community are most comfortable. Explore in small doses approaches outside your comfort zone. Savor the feast.

Acknowledgments

We are grateful for the many people who participated in the gathering and preparing of this collection.

The psalm chant tones, unless otherwise noted, were prepared by Paul Detterman, Emily Brink, and Martin Tel. The psalm prayers were prepared by Paul Detterman with contributions from Leonard Vander Zee and Martin Tel. The psalm notes were prepared by John D. Witvliet. The responsive readings, voicing, and pointing for the NRSV psalms were prepared by Melissa Haupt.

We would also like to express our profound thanks to Melissa Haupt, assistant to the editor; Paul Detterman, Emily Brink, Bert Polman, Patrick Miller, Greg Scheer, and Dean Wiers-Windemuller, reviewers; Diane Dykgraaf and Rebecca Hoeksema, copyrights; Sarah Hong, page designer; Bethany Vrieland and Linda Missad, music engravers; Carol Bechtel and Leonard Vander Zee for participating in a two-year process of reviewing and selecting materials; Princeton Theological Seminary for releasing Martin Tel from his duties to work on this project and for the staff who filled in during his absence; family who were gracious when our time and attention was given to this project and who encouraged us in our work; and the staff of the Calvin Institute of Christian Worship and Faith Alive Christian Resources who supported this project.

Not to us, O LORD, not to us, but to your name be the glory.

Joyce Borger
Faith Alive Christian Resources

Martin Tel (Senior Editor)
Princeton Theological Seminary

John D. Witvliet
Calvin Institute of Christian Worship

Psalms

Trees

1. (Ps. 1) Tree of Wis-dom, fruit-ful, green, flour-ish-ing be - side the stream;
2. (Ps. 26) Tree of Jus-tice, ev - er bless; shade me with your right-eous-ness.
3. (Ps. 52) Tree of Plen-ty, feed my soul; nur-ture me, and make me whole.

spread your knowl-edge day and night; make your law my true de - light.
Teach me how to live your ways, and my lips shall sing your praise.
Give me strength, cast fear a - side; let me in your love a - bide.

Fash-ion me, O Lord, to be strong and splen-did as a tree.
Fash-ion me, O Lord, to be ev - er branch-ing as a tree.
Fash-ion me, O Lord, to be firm - ly plant-ed as a tree.

(Ps. 92)

4 Tree of Promise, keep your vow:
with me then, and with me now.
Springtime blossoms, winter tears,
mark the seasons of my years.
Fashion me, O Lord, to be
always changing as a tree.

5 Like a forest all around,
so the gifts of grace abound:
flowing waters, fertile sod,
sunlit dawn, the Word of God.
Fashion me, O Lord, to be
living, giving as a tree.

Words: Michael Morgan from Psalms 1, 26, 52, and 92 © 2011 Michael Morgan, admin. Faith Alive
Christian Resources
Music (DIX 7.7.7.7.7.7): Conrad Kocher, 1838; adapt. William H. Monk, 1861, P.D.

Psalm 1

¹ Happy are those who do not follow the advice of the wicked, *
    or take the path that sinners tread, or sit in the seat of scoffers;

² **but their delight is in the law of the LORD, ***
    and on his law they meditate day and night.

³ **They are like trees planted by streams of water,**
    which yield their fruit in its season, and their leaves do not wither. *
    In all that they do, they prosper.

⁴ The wicked are not so, *
    but are like chaff that the wind drives away.

⁵ Therefore the wicked will not stand in the judgment, *
    nor sinners in the congregation of the righteous;

⁶ **for the LORD watches over the way of the righteous, ***
    but the way of the wicked will perish.

Lord our God, giver of blessing and judgment, your Son Jesus lived the only true life.
Because of him, we can know you, love you, and delight in you.
Keep us watered by your grace and rooted in your Spirit
so that our ears will hear your voice and our feet will follow your path,
giving glory to you alone. **Amen.**

Psalm 1 describes and contrasts two pathways: righteousness and wickedness. Such imagery recurs throughout the psalms and other parts of the Bible (e.g., Jer. 17:5-8). Like Pss. 19 and 119, it celebrates the significance of God's law as a source of wisdom and blessing. Early church theologian Jerome called this "the main entrance to the mansion of the Psalter." Much of what follows in the Psalter either expresses or appeals to its message. *Use in Worship: preparing for or responding to the reading and preaching of God's Word.*

For an additional setting of Ps. 1 see 28B.

1A The One Is Blest

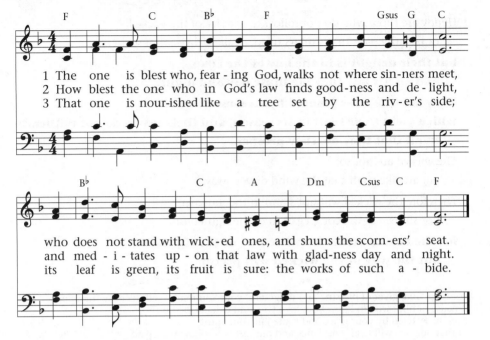

1 The one is blest who, fear-ing God, walks not where sin-ners meet,
2 How blest the one who in God's law finds good-ness and de-light,
3 That one is nour-ished like a tree set by the riv-er's side;

who does not stand with wick-ed ones, and shuns the scorn-ers' seat.
and med-i-tates up-on that law with glad-ness day and night.
its leaf is green, its fruit is sure: the works of such a-bide.

4 The wicked, like the driven chaff,
are swept from off the land;
they shall not gather with the just,
nor at the judgment stand.

5 The LORD will guard the righteous well,
their way to God is known;
the way of sinners, far from God,
shall surely be o'erthrown.

Guitar chords do not correspond with keyboard harmony.

Words: *Psalter*, 1912, alt. 1985, P.D.
Music (WINCHESTER OLD 8.6.8.6): attr. George Kirbye, 1592, P.D.

Psalm 1 | A Responsorial Setting **1B**

Refrain

Hap-py are they who trust, who trust in the LORD.

Refrain

1. Happy are they who have not walked in the counsel of the wicked,
   nor lingered in the way of sinners, nor sat in the seats of the scornful!

2. Their delight is in the law of the LORD,
   and they meditate on God's teaching day and night.

3. They are like trees planted by streams of water,
   bearing fruit in due season, with leaves that do not wither;
   everything they do shall prosper. *Refrain*

4. It is not so with the wicked;
   they are like chaff which the wind blows away.

5. Therefore the wicked shall not stand upright when judgment comes,
   nor the sinner in the council of the righteous.

6. For the LORD knows the way of the righteous,
   but the way of the wicked shall be destroyed. *Refrain*

Tone

Lectionary: Ordinary Time after Epiphany (C); Eastertide (B); Ordinary Time after Pentecost (A,B,C).

Words and Music: Robert J. Thompson © 1986 GIA Publications, Inc.; arr. Emily R. Brink (b. 1940) © GIA Publications, Inc.
Psalm Text: from *Evangelical Lutheran Worship* © 2006 Evangelical Lutheran Church in America, admin. Augsburg Fortress Publishers
Tone: © 2011 Faith Alive Christian Resources

1C Happy Are They Who Walk in God's Wise Way

| Thai | Khwaam suk yeun yong khong maa suu phuu tham chop, |

English
1 Hap - py are they who walk in God's wise way;
2 Theirs is the life where du - ty and de - light
3 Fret - ful and an - xious are the sin - ner's days,
4 Lord, in your mer - cy spare me, keep me still;

| phuu kawb duai jai - man nai sat thaa |

hap - py who shun the sin - ful choice;
nour - ish each oth - er bliss - ful - ly;
bar - ren and lone - ly is their path;
let me not choose the sin - ner's way;

| phaa jai doen taam ban yat phra yaa - ho - waa |

hap - py who find their plea - sure in God's law;
as when be - side a broad and gen - erous stream
like wind on dust the judg - ment of the Lord
prom - ise and law you e - qual - ly have given:

| doen nai man khaa puang saa thu chon. |

hap - py who heed God's right - eous voice.
proud - ly stands ev - er green the tree.
scat - ters their pride in sud - den wrath.
let them be my de - light to - day.

Finger Cymbals (+ = closed o = open)

simile

Drum

simile

Words: Psalm 1; Thailand; tr. and para. Erik Routley © 1976 Hinshaw Music, Inc.
Music (SRI LAMPANG 10.8.10.8): traditional melody, Thailand; acc. I-to Loh (b. 1936) © 2011 Hinshaw Music, Inc.

A Litany for the Renewal
of Baptismal Vows

The congregation sings, reads or chants Psalm 1.

The leader reads Romans 6:3-4 (or vv. 3-11).

As God's baptismal people, do you renounce Satan and all the spiritual forces
of evil that rebel against God?
We renounce them!

Do you renounce all sinful desires that draw you from the love of God?
We renounce them!

Do you turn to Jesus Christ?
Yes! We trust in him as our Lord and Savior.

Do you intend to be Christ's faithful disciples, trusting his promises, obeying
his Word, honoring his church, and showing his love, as long as you live?
Yes! God helping us.

Let us pray.
O Lord, uphold us by your Holy Spirit.
Daily increase in us your gifts of grace:
the spirit of wisdom and understanding,
the spirit of counsel and might,
the spirit of knowledge and the fear of the Lord,
the spirit of joy in your presence.
Plant us by the streams of living water.
Amen.

The leader reads Romans 12:9.

May the blessing of God Almighty be with us always.
Amen.

The psalm refrain or a stanza of the metrical setting used earlier may be repeated.

1E Feliz la gente / How Blest the People

Refrain

Fe - liz se - rá,
How blest they are,

fe - liz se - rá,
how blest they are,

fe - liz se - rá.
how blest they are.

(⌢ last time)

Spanish

3 Feliz la gente que no sigue los caprichos de la moda,
  ni hace caso de anuncios engañosos,
  ni se deja llevar por charlatanes.   *Refrain*

4 Feliz la gente que no vende su inquietud ante amenazas,
  ni claudica de su rumbo ya trazado,
  ni se hunde en el silencio de los cómplices.   *Refrain*

5 Feliz la gente que encamina sus pasos por tus sendas;
  serán como un árbol grande y fuerte,
  que da sombra y alegría al caminante.   *Refrain*

English

3 How blest the people who disdain to live their lives as slaves of fashion,
  or incline their ears to gossip or to scandal;
  who are not swayed by deceit, lying, or scheming.   *Refrain*

4 How blest the people who decline to sell their souls in spite of danger,
  those whose course in times of trouble never wavers,
  and whose voice, fearless and strong, will not be silenced.   *Refrain*

5 How blest the people who direct their every step on holy pathways.
  God will make them like a tree, green and majestic,
  that gives shade and joyful rest to weary travelers.   *Refrain*

Words: Juan A. Espinosa © 1990 Juan A. Espinosa, admin. OCP Publications; tr. Mary Louise Bringle (b. 1953)
© 1990 Juan A. Espinosa, admin. OCP Publications
Music (FELIZ EL HOMBRE): Juan A. Espinosa © 1990 Juan A. Espinosa, admin. OCP Publications; arr.
Marcus Hong © 2011 OCP Publications

1F Happy Is the One

1 Hap - py   is   the one who does not   take   bad ad -
2 Hap - py   is   the one who takes de - light in   the
3 Such   a   one   as this is   like a   tree   by   the
4 Not   so   the wick - ed's fate; for they, like chaff which the
5 Nor   will sin - ners walk a - mong the_as - sem - bly of

vice   for   a   guide,   nor walks   the   path   on which
law   of   the LORD,   and med - i -   tates on it
nour - ish - ing streams, which yields its   fruit when the
wind   blows a - way,   will nev - er   stand and be
God's   own   folk;   for wick - ed   ways   are all

sin - ners have trod,   nor sits where the cyn - ics   mock.
both   day and night, and pros - pers in   ev - ery   way.
sea - son is   right   and bears leaves that nev - er   fade.
con - fi - dent on God's great   judg - ment day.
doomed by the Lord   who bless - es the   hon - est   path.

Words: The Iona Community © 1993 Wild Goose Resource Group, Iona Community, Scotland, GIA
Publications, Inc., exclusive North American agent
Music (BENEDICTUS PRIMUS 5.10.10.6): The Iona Community © 1993 Wild Goose Resource Group, Iona
Community, Scotland, GIA Publications, Inc., exclusive North American agent

¹ Why do the nations conspire, *
  and the peoples plot in vain?

² The kings of the earth set themselves, and the rulers take counsel together, *
  against the LORD and his anointed, saying,

³ "Let us burst their bonds asunder, *
  and cast their cords from us."

⁴ He who sits in the heavens laughs; *
  the LORD has them in derision.

⁵ Then he will speak to them in his wrath, *
  and terrify them in his fury, saying,

⁶ "I have set my king on Zion, *
  my holy hill."

⁷ I will tell of the decree of the LORD: *
  He said to me, "You are my son; today I have begotten you.

⁸ Ask of me, and I will make the nations your heritage, *
  and the ends of the earth your possession.

⁹ You shall break them with a rod of iron, *
  and dash them in pieces like a potter's vessel."

¹⁰ Now therefore, O kings, be wise; *
  be warned, O rulers of the earth.

¹¹ Serve the LORD with fear, *
  with trembling ¹² kiss his feet,

or he will be angry, and you will perish in the way;
for his wrath is quickly kindled. *
  Happy are all who take refuge in him.

Mighty God and Creator of all, we are made in your image,
yet many deny you and despise the Messiah who is your Son.
By your Spirit, keep us humble and faithful
so that our lives may proclaim our Savior's love
and inspire others to find their refuge in you.
We pray in Jesus' name. **Amen.**

Psalm 2 is a dramatic text, likely used for the coronation of a king. It speaks of the folly of human power and the importance of serving the Lord with fear (v. 10). References to the divine son (vv. 7-9) describe God's anointed king of Israel. Christians have long interpreted these verses as pointing toward Christ as Messiah. Remembering that God is King leads us to take refuge in him (v. 12b). Despite the chaos and tension of multiple claims on authority, the psalm ends with God's authoritative kingship, in which all may repose. Taken together, Pss. 1 and 2 indicate the significance of God's law and God's reign as the twin themes that will recur throughout the Psalter. *Use in Worship: services focusing on the proper exercise of human governance; celebrations of Christ's holy reign (Transfiguration, Easter, and Ascension); call to confession.*

2A Why Do the Nations Rage

1 Why do the na-tions rage a - gainst God's right-eous reign,
2 For by di-vine de - cree heaven's pur - pose is made known:
3 Give hon-or to the Son: be wise, and seek his face,

as - sum-ing that the law is some re - stric-tive chain?
God's one and on - ly Son now sits on Zi - on's throne;
for those who spurn God's law risk judg - ment and dis - grace—

En - throned on high, God hears their cry—
his ma - ny foes he o - ver - throws
so come, draw near in rev - erent fear,

and knows their threats are all in vain.
and claims the na - tions as his own.
and he will be your hid - ing - place.

Words: Martin Leckebusch © 2003 Kevin Mayhew Ltd.
Music (GRANT PARK 6.6.6.6.4.4.8): Roy Hopp © 2011 Roy Hopp

Psalm 2 | A Dramatized Reading

The wise cantor:

1 Why do the peoples of the world rage about like madmen?
Why in the world do the different nations keep on thinking up stupid schemes?
2 Earth kings get together "for a consultation"—
important rulers hold conferences all together
against the LORD God and against God's anointed one (*mashiach*).
These earthly rulers say:
3 "Let us smash the chains of this God that hold us down!
Let us throw off the reins of God's 'anointed one'!"

Another liturgete, perhaps a priest:

4 The One who sits enthroned in heaven begins to laugh,
my LORD mimics their foolish bluster;
5 and then God turns to them in holy anger,
stops the upstarts short with God's fierce outrage:
6 "It was I! It is I who have set up my anointed king
on Zion, my set-apart mountain."

Princely ruler taking official part in the liturgy:

7 Yes, I will recite the decisive appointment by the LORD God.
God said to me:
"You are my son. Today is the day I have borne you.
8 Ask it of me and I will give you peoples of the world for your heritage;
the most distant nations of the earth will be yours to tend.
9 You may have to break them with a rod of iron.
You may have to smash them for remolding
as a sculpting potter reshapes her clay dish—"

[The congregation stands]

Wise cantor again:

10 So now, you small-time little rulers, you had better wise up!
You who only judge on the earth, hadn't you better get the point?
11 Serve the LORD God with an attentive awe—
Take joy *in your task only* with trembling—
Give homage to this *adopted* son *of God too*—
lest he also get worked up, and you obliterate any way for you to walk,
for God's anger can flash up like lightning. . . .

Congregated chorus:

12 Blessèd are all those who have run to take shelter with the anointed one.
Blessèd are all those who have run to take shelter with the anointed one.
Blessèd are all those who have run to take shelter with the anointed one.

2C Why This Dark Conspiracy

1 Why this dark con-spir-a-cy, na-tions plot-ting to be free?
2 On this Cor-o-na-tion Day, God's dear Son holds king-ly sway.
3 Now his king-ship ful-ly won, God af-firms him as the Son,
4 All con-spir-a-cies are vain: God's Mes-si-ah comes to reign.

Fool-ish-ly they rid-i-cule God's most wise and right-eous rule.
His the hon-or, his the worth, his the na-tions of the earth!
say-ing: "Rule with pru-dent hand each pos-ses-sion, ev-ery land."
Prin-ces, peo-ples, heed this call: Hon-or Christ as Lord of all.

Lord, have mer-cy! Lord, have mer-cy; Christ, have mer-cy;
Al-le-lu-ia! Al-le-lu-ia! Al-le-lu-ia!
Al-le-lu-ia! Al-le-lu-ia! Al-le-lu-ia!
Al-le-lu-ia! Al-le-lu-ia! Al-le-lu-ia!

Lord, have mer-cy! Fool-ish-ly they rid-i-cule
Al-le-lu-ia! His the hon-or, his the worth,
Al-le-lu-ia! Now his king-ship ful-ly won,
Al-le-lu-ia! Prin-ces, peo-ples, heed this call:

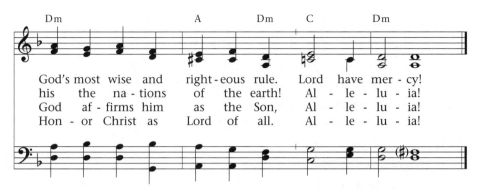

God's most wise and right-eous rule. Lord have mer - cy!
his the na - tions of the earth! Al - le - lu - ia!
God af - firms him as the Son, Al - le - lu - ia!
Hon - or Christ as Lord of all. Al - le - lu - ia!

Words: Norman J. Goreham © 2010 Norman J. Goreham, admin. Faith Alive Christian Resources
Music (CHRIST IST ERSTANDEN 7.7.7.7.4 with refrain): J. Klug's *Geistliche Lieder*, 1533; harm. Dale
Grotenhuis © 1987 Faith Alive Christian Resources

Psalm 2 | A Responsorial Setting 2D

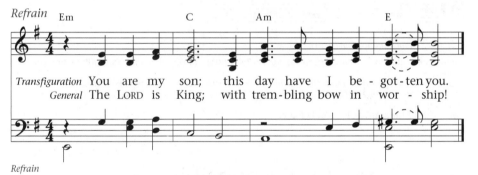

Refrain

Transfiguration You are my son; this day have I be - got-ten you.
General The LORD is King; with trem-bling bow in wor - ship!

Refrain

1 Why are the nations in an uproar?

Why do the peoples mutter empty threats?

2 Why do the kings of the earth rise up in revolt, and the princes plot together,

against the LORD and against the LORD's anointed? *Refrain*

3 "Let us break their yoke," they say;

"let us cast off their bonds from us."

4 God whose throne is in heaven is laughing;

the LORD holds them in derision.

5 Then in wrath God speaks to them

and in rage fills them with terror.

6 "As for me, I have anointed my king

upon Zion, my holy mountain." *Refrain*

(continues)

7 Let me announce the decree of the LORD,

who said to me, "You are my son; this day have I begotten you.

8 Ask of me, and I will give you the nations for your inheritance

and the ends of the earth for your possession.

9 You shall crush them with an iron rod

and shatter them like a piece of pottery." *Refrain*

10 And now, you kings, be wise;

be warned, you rulers of the earth.

11 Submit to the LORD with fear,

and with trembling bow in worship;

12 lest the LORD be angry, and you perish in a sudden blaze of wrath.

Happy are all who take refuge in God! *Refrain*

Tone

Lectionary: Transfiguration Sunday (A).

Words: transfiguration, Psalm 2:7; general, Martin Tel © 2011 Martin Tel, admin. Faith Alive Christian Resources
Music: Robert Wetzler from *Psalter for Worship, Cycle A* © 1998 Augsburg Fortress Publishers
Psalm Text: from *Evangelical Lutheran Worship* © 2006 Evangelical Lutheran Church in America, admin. Augsburg Fortress Publishers
Tone: © 2011 Faith Alive Christian Resources

2E A Litany for Responsible Exercise of Authority

God of justice and mercy,

we pray for the outpouring of the Spirit of your anointed Son

upon all the peoples of the earth.

May all those in authority **submit and take refuge in God.**

May the rulers of the nations **submit and take refuge in God.**

May our own elected officials **submit and take refuge in God.**

May all citizens, in the exercise of their responsibility,

submit and take refuge in God.

We long for uncommon wisdom and lasting peace. **Amen.**

John D. Witvliet, 2011, © Creative Commons Attribution-NonCommercial-ShareAlike

Psalm 3

A Psalm of David, when he fled from his son Absalom.

1 O LORD, how many are my foes! *
    Many are rising against me;

2 many are saying to me, *
    "There is no help for you in God." *Selah*

3 But you, O LORD, are a shield around me, *
    my glory, and the one who lifts up my head.

4 **I cry aloud to the LORD,** *
    and he answers me from his holy hill. *Selah*

5 **I lie down and sleep;** *
    I wake again, for the LORD sustains me.

6 **I am not afraid of ten thousands of people** *
    who have set themselves against me all around.

7 Rise up, O LORD! Deliver me, O my God! *
    For you strike all my enemies on the cheek;
    you break the teeth of the wicked.

8 **Deliverance belongs to the LORD;** *
    may your blessing be on your people! *Selah*

Eternal God and author of salvation, no matter what each new day may bring,
keep our eyes focused on you and our hearts immersed in your Word
so that we will not fear our enemies but rather rejoice in your presence
and find peace in the promise of your love.
We ask this in Jesus' name. **Amen.**

Psalm 3 is an expression of profound trust in God as a source of hope in time of turmoil. In contrast to the opening lament about the taunts of the enemy that there is no help in God (v. 2), the psalmist confidently concludes that God will deliver (v. 8). The psalm develops this theme using a striking set of images of God as a shield (v. 3), as one who listens to and answers prayer (v. 4), as one who offers protection during sleep (v. 5), and as an aggressive warrior (v. 7). *Use in Worship: morning or evening prayer services (references to sleeping and waking).*

3A You, O LORD, Are My Glory!

Refrain

You, O LORD, are my glo - ry!

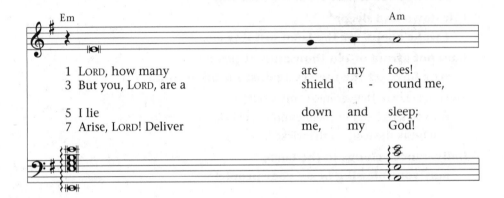

1 LORD, how many　　　are　my　foes!
3 But you, LORD, are a　shield　a - round me,

5 I lie　　　　　　　down　and　sleep;
7 Arise, LORD! Deliver　me,　my　God!

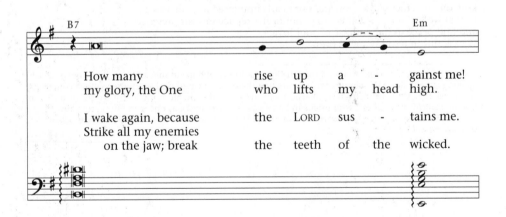

How many　　　rise　up　a - gainst me!
my glory, the One　who　lifts　my　head high.

I wake again, because　the　LORD　sus - tains me.
Strike all my enemies
　on the jaw; break　the　teeth　of　the　wicked.

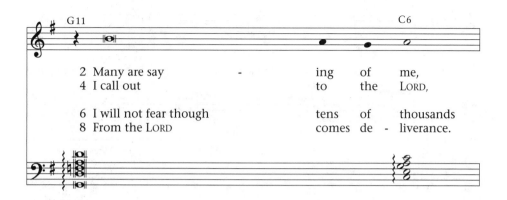

3B A Shield About Me

You, O Lord, are a shield a-bout me. You're my glo - ry; you're the lift - er of my head. head. Hal - le - lu - jah, hal - le - lu - jah, hal - le - lu - jah, you're the lift - er of my head. head.

Psalm 4

To the leader: with stringed instruments. A Psalm of David.

1 Answer me when I call, O God of my right! *
>   You gave me room when I was in distress.
>   Be gracious to me, and hear my prayer.

2 How long, you people, shall my honor suffer shame? *
>   How long will you love vain words, and seek after lies? *Selah*

3 **But know that the Lord has set apart the faithful for himself; ***
>   **the Lord hears when I call to him.**

4 When you are disturbed, do not sin; *
>   ponder it on your beds, and be silent. *Selah*

5 **Offer right sacrifices, ***
>   **and put your trust in the Lord.**

6 There are many who say, "O that we might see some good! *
>   Let the light of your face shine on us, O Lord!"

7 **You have put gladness in my heart ***
>   **more than when their grain and wine abound.**

8 **I will both lie down and sleep in peace; ***
>   **for you alone, O Lord, make me lie down in safety.**

Righteous God who answers prayer,
you have chosen us to be your children and have begun a good work in us.
Help us to trust you so completely with whatever we face
that we may sleep in peace and wake again with confident joy.
We pray in the name of Jesus. **Amen.**

Psalm 4 is a psalm of prayer, lament, and trust, which asks for God's deliverance (v. 1), exhorts others to trust in God (vv. 2-5), and concludes with a statement of trust in God (vv. 6-8). Experiencing inner joy (v. 7), the psalmist confidently asks for God's deliverance, evocatively described as a move from being constrained to an experience of spaciousness (v. 1b). *Use in Worship: night prayer.*

4A O God, Defender of the Poor

1 O God, de-fend-er of the poor, have
2 How long will peo-ple choose vain things, love
3 The saints, O Lord, you set a-part by
4 While man-y pray that you will bless and

mer-cy when I pray: you lis-tened to my
emp-ty words and wrong? They scorn to serve the
grace to be your own: let sin-ners trem-ble,
bring them all they need, un-less they long for

prayer be-fore—Lord, hear my prayer to-day, you lis-tened
King of kings— O liv-ing God, how long? They scorn to
search their hearts, and bow be-fore your throne; let sin-ners
hol-i-ness, their prayers are vain in-deed; un-less they

to my prayer be-fore—Lord, hear my prayer to-day!
serve the King of kings— O liv-ing God, how long?
trem-ble, search their hearts, and bow be-fore your throne.
long for hol-i-ness, their prayers are vain in-deed.

(continues)

5 Your light, O LORD, let us receive; your face within us shine,
   for richer is the joy you give than all their grain and wine;
   for richer is the joy you give than all their grain and wine.

6 And even when I turn to sleep your blessings still increase,
   for you alone, O LORD, will keep your child in perfect peace;
   for you alone, O LORD, will keep your child in perfect peace.

Words: Christopher Idle © 1986 The Jubilate Group, admin. Hope Publishing Company
Music (BROTHER JAMES' AIR 8.6.8.6.8.6): J. L. Macbeth Bain (ca. 1840-1925); harm. Gordon Jacob (1895-1984). Reproduced by permission from Oxford University Press.

Psalm 4 | A Responsorial Setting 4B

Refrain (or stanza 1 of Alternate Refrain)

1 Answer me when I call, O God, defender of my cause;
   you set me free when I was in distress;
   have mercy on me and hear my prayer.

2 "You mortals, how long will you dishonor my glory;
   how long will you love illusions and seek after lies?"

3 Know that the LORD does wonders for the faithful;
   the LORD will hear me when I call.   *Refrain (or stanza 2 of Alternate Refrain)*

4 Tremble, then, and do not sin;
   speak to your heart in silence upon your bed.

5 Offer the appointed sacrifices,
   and put your trust in the LORD.   *Refrain (or stanza 3 of Alternate Refrain)*

6 Many are saying, "Who will show us any good?"
   Let the light of your face shine upon us, O LORD.

7 You have put gladness in my heart,
   more than when grain and wine abound.

8 In peace, I will lie down and sleep;
   for you alone, O LORD, make me rest secure.   *Refrain (or stanza 4 of Alternate Refrain)*

(continues)

23

Tone

Lectionary: Eastertide (B).

Words and Music: Anthony Teague © 1986 Westminster John Knox Press
Psalm Text: from *Evangelical Lutheran Worship* © 2006 Evangelical Lutheran Church in America, admin.
Augsburg Fortress Publishers
Tone: © 2011 Faith Alive Christian Resources

Alternate Refrain

1 Night has fal - len. Night has fal - len.
2 You have kept us, Lord. You have kept us, Lord.
3 We will trust in you. We will trust in you.
4 Night has fal - len. Night has fal - len.

God our ma - ker, guard us sleep - ing.

Alternate Tone

Words: Malawi; trans. Tom Colvin © 1969 Hope Publishing Company
Music (NIGHT HAS FALLEN): Malawian traditional; adapt. Tom Colvin; arr. John L. Bell (b. 1949) © 1969
Hope Publishing Company
Tone: © 2011 Faith Alive Christian Resources

Psalm 5

To the leader: for the flutes. A Psalm of David.

1 Give ear to my words, O LORD; *
   give heed to my sighing.

2 **Listen to the sound of my cry, my King and my God, ***
   for to you I pray.

3 **O LORD, in the morning you hear my voice; ***
   in the morning I plead my case to you, and watch.

4 For you are not a God who delights in wickedness; *
   evil will not sojourn with you.

5 The boastful will not stand before your eyes; *
   you hate all evildoers.

6 You destroy those who speak lies; *
   the LORD abhors the bloodthirsty and deceitful.

7 **But I, through the abundance of your steadfast love,**
   will enter your house, *
   I will bow down toward your holy temple in awe of you.

8 **Lead me, O LORD, in your righteousness because of my enemies; ***
   make your way straight before me.

9 For there is no truth in their mouths; their hearts are destruction; *
   their throats are open graves; they flatter with their tongues.

10 Make them bear their guilt, O God; let them fall by their own counsels; *
   because of their many transgressions cast them out,
   for they have rebelled against you.

11 **But let all who take refuge in you rejoice; let them ever sing for joy. ***
   Spread your protection over them,
   so that those who love your name may exult in you.

12 **For you bless the righteous, O LORD; ***
   you cover them with favor as with a shield.

O Lord our God, your mercy greets us when we rise
and your grace attends us when we return to our rest.
Help us to live each waking moment assured of your protection and your love.
We pray rejoicing in the power of your Spirit, through Jesus Christ our Lord. **Amen.**

Psalm 5 is a prayer for God's attention (v. 1), guidance (v. 8), retribution (v. 10), and protection (v. 11). It echoes the imagery of Ps. 1, contemplating both the wisdom of righteousness and the folly of sinfulness, especially boasting, deceit, and flattery (vv. 4-5, 9). *Use in Worship: morning prayer; morning psalm reading; as a counterpart to Ps. 141 (an evening psalm that explores much of the same imagery).*

5A Hear, O LORD, My Urgent Prayer

1 Hear, O LORD, my ur - gent prayer as I
2 You do not de - light in sin or in
3 By your mer - cy and your grace I will

come to seek your care. With each morn - ing
tales that li - ars spin. Haugh - ty ones you
come be - fore your face. Fear - ing foes, I

light I raise voice and heart in prayer and praise.
will de - feat with all those who love de - ceit.
bow to pray: lead me, LORD, make straight my way.

4 Save me from deceitful ways;
liars' throats are open graves.
Make them bear their guilt, O LORD,
for by choice they spurn your word.

5 Let those trusting you sing praise;
grant them joy to fill their days.
Those who always seek the right
are protected by your might.

This tune in a higher key: p. 112.

Words: Marie J. Post, 1983, © 1987 Faith Alive Christian Resources
Music (TEBBEN 7.7.7.7): Timothy Hoekman, 1979, © 1987 Faith Alive Christian Resources

Psalm 5:1-8 | A Responsorial Setting 5B

Refrain

Give ear to our words, O Lord: give heed to our sigh- ing cries. Please hear us, O God, to you do we pray. Each morn-ing we plead to you.

Refrain

1 Give ear to my words, O LORD;
    give heed to my sighing.

2 Listen to my cry for help, my king and my God,
    for I plead to you.

3 In the morning, LORD, you hear my voice;
    early in the morning I make my appeal and watch for you.   *Refrain*

4 For you are not a God who takes pleasure in wickedness,
    and evil cannot dwell with you.

5 Braggarts cannot stand in your sight;
    you hate all those who work wickedness.

6 You destroy those who speak lies;
    the bloodthirsty and deceitful, O LORD, you abhor.   *Refrain*

7 But as for me, through the abundance of your steadfast love
  I will go into your house;
    I will bow down toward your holy temple in awe of you.

8 Lead me, LORD, in your righteousness, because of those who lie in wait for me;
    make your way straight before me.   *Refrain*

(continues)

5B (continued)

Tone

Lectionary: Ordinary Time after Pentecost (C).

Words: Luke Hyder © 2006 Luke Hyder, admin. Faith Alive Christian Resources
Music: Luke Hyder © 2006 Luke Hyder, admin. Faith Alive Christian Resources; arr. Marcus Hong © 2011
Luke Hyder, admin. Faith Alive Christian Resources
Psalm Text: from *Evangelical Lutheran Worship* © 2006 Evangelical Lutheran Church in America, admin.
Augsburg Fortress Publishers
Tone: © 2011 Faith Alive Christian Resources

5C Hear My Words, O Lord

Hear my words, O Lord. Hear the
Hear my prayer, my God. Hear the

sound of my sigh - ing.
sound of my cry - ing. I of - fer up my

fear and trust to your un - end - ing care.

Refrain

Narrator 1 (with a hint of disdain):

For you are not a God who is pleased with wickedness;
   with you, evil people are not welcome.
The arrogant cannot stand in your presence.
You hate all who do wrong; you destroy those who tell lies.
The bloodthirsty and deceitful you, LORD, detest.

Narrator 2 (more peacefully):

But I, by your great love, can come into your house;
   in reverence I bow down toward your holy temple.
Lead me, LORD, in your righteousness
   because of my enemies—make your way straight before me.

Refrain

Narrator 1 (accusingly):

Not a word from their mouth can be trusted;
   their heart is filled with malice.
Their throat is an open grave; with tongues they tell lies.
Declare them guilty, O God!
Let their intrigues be their downfall.
Banish them for their many sins, for they have rebelled against you.

Narrator 2 (confident, joyous):

But let all who take refuge in you be glad;
   let them ever sing for joy.
Spread your protection over them,
   that those who love your name may rejoice in you.
Surely, LORD, you bless the righteous;
   you surround them with your favor as with a shield.

Refrain

Vamp on these two bars underneath Narrator 1.
Vamp on these two bars underneath Narrator 2.
These two bars signal the return of the Refrain. *To Refrain*

Words and Music: Greg Scheer © 2007 Greg Scheer

Psalm 6

To the leader: with stringed instruments; according to The Sheminith. A Psalm of David.

1 O LORD, do not rebuke me in your anger, *
   or discipline me in your wrath.

2 **Be gracious to me, O LORD, for I am languishing;** *
   O LORD, heal me, for my bones are shaking with terror.

3 **My soul also is struck with terror,** *
   while you, O LORD—how long?

4 Turn, O LORD, save my life; *
   deliver me for the sake of your steadfast love.

5 For in death there is no remembrance of you; *
   in Sheol who can give you praise?

6 **I am weary with my moaning;** *
   every night I flood my bed with tears;
   I drench my couch with my weeping.

7 **My eyes waste away because of grief;** *
   they grow weak because of all my foes.

8 Depart from me, all you workers of evil, *
   for the LORD has heard the sound of my weeping.

9 **The LORD has heard my supplication;** *
   the LORD accepts my prayer.

10 **All my enemies shall be ashamed and struck with terror;** *
   they shall turn back, and in a moment be put to shame.

Compassionate Healer,
you know the depths of human grief and the intensity of human pain.
Jesus suffered in agony on the cross so that we could know the extent of your love.
You hear our prayer. Support us as we wait for your healing.
We pray in Jesus' name. **Amen.**

Psalm 6, the first of the Psalter's seven penitential psalms, is a cry for deliverance. The psalmist experiences God's rebuke and discipline (v. 1), is physically weak and in need of healing (v. 2), is afraid of death (v. 5), is exhausted with grief (v. 6), and is weakened in vision (v. 7). The psalm takes a dramatic turn between vv. 7 and 8, testifying to God's response and warning offending enemies. *Use in Worship: prayer of complaint and supplication; call to confession.*

LORD, Chasten Not in Anger 6A

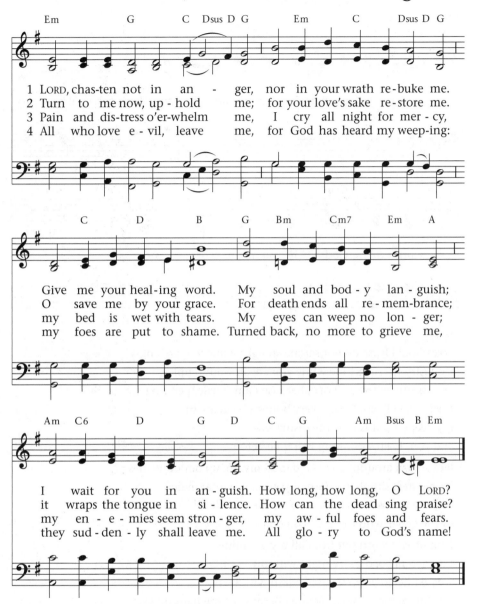

1 LORD, chas-ten not in an - ger, nor in your wrath re-buke me.
2 Turn to me now, up - hold me; for your love's sake re-store me.
3 Pain and dis-tress o'er-whelm me, I cry all night for mer - cy,
4 All who love e - vil, leave me, for God has heard my weep-ing:

Give me your heal-ing word. My soul and bod - y lan - guish;
O save me by your grace. For death ends all re - mem-brance;
my bed is wet with tears. My eyes can weep no lon - ger;
my foes are put to shame. Turned back, no more to grieve me,

I wait for you in an - guish. How long, how long, O LORD?
it wraps the tongue in si - lence. How can the dead sing praise?
my en - e - mies seem stron - ger, my aw - ful foes and fears.
they sud - den - ly shall leave me. All glo - ry to God's name!

Guitar chords do not correspond with keyboard harmony.

Words: Clarence P. Walhout, 1982, © 1987 Faith Alive Christian Resources
Music (GENEVAN 6 | 7.7.6.7.7.6): *Genevan Psalter*, 1542; harm. Howard Slenk, 1985, © 1987 Faith Alive Christian Resources

6B Psalm 6 | A Responsorial Setting

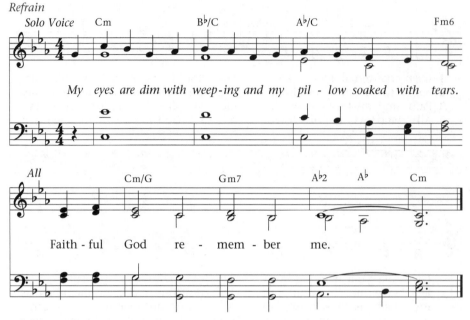

Refrain

My eyes are dim with weep-ing and my pil - low soaked with tears.

Faith - ful God re - mem - ber me.

Refrain

1 LORD God! Please do not set me straight while you are angry!
   Don't try to correct me while you are all wound up!

2 Deal gently with me, LORD, because I am fragile, petering out, really—
   Heal me, O LORD, for my very bones are caving in,

3 my deepest self is horribly disturbed—
   and you, LORD, how long will it be before . . .   *Refrain*

4 Please turn around, LORD God, pull my life up out of its mess;
   set me free! simply because of your covenantal mercy,

5 because no one remembers you if they are dead!
   In the grave, who can give you praise?   *Refrain*

6 I am utterly worn out from all my groaning:
   I drench my bed every night with my crying,
   where I lie down to sleep is awash with tears.

7 My appearance is wasting away because of the hard times;
   I look old simply because of my constantly being buffeted and maligned.   *Refrain*

8 Get away from me, all you doers of what's crooked,

for the LORD God has heard the cry of my weeping!

9 The LORD has heard my plea for help.

The LORD God has accepted my importunate praying:

10 all my enemies shall be shamed and disoriented;

those evildoers shall be spun around without warning

and be brought to shame. *Refrain*

Alternate Refrain

Heal-er of our ev-ery ill, light of each to-mor-row,

give us peace be-yond our fear and hope be-yond our sor-row.

6C A Prayer of Lament in Solidarity with Sufferers

Refrain 1

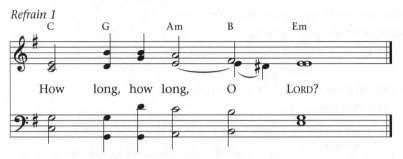

How long, how long, O Lord?

Our hearts cry out, to you, O Lord.
Those whom we love [,_____,] struggle in fear and pain.
They feel abandoned.
Their eyes—and ours—are filled with tears.

Repeat Refrain 1

Silence for reflection.

Lord God, may they experience the answer to their prayers,
a strong sense of your presence with them,
a cry of praise in their hearts.
Help them—and us—to sing:

Refrain 2

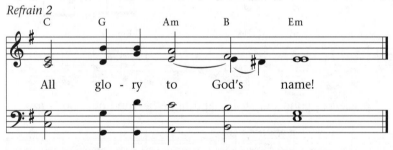

All glo - ry to God's name!

Psalm 7

A Shiggaion of David, which he sang to the LORD concerning Cush, a Benjaminite.

Voice 1:

1 O LORD my God, in you I take refuge; *
    save me from all my pursuers, and deliver me,

2 or like a lion they will tear me apart; *
    they will drag me away, with no one to rescue.

Voice 2:

3 O LORD my God, if I have done this, *
    if there is wrong in my hands,

4 if I have repaid my ally with harm *
    or plundered my foe without cause,

5 then let the enemy pursue and overtake me, *
    trample my life to the ground, and lay my soul in the dust.   *Selah*

6 **Rise up, O LORD, in your anger;**
  lift yourself up against the fury of my enemies; *
    awake, O my God; you have appointed a judgment.

7 **Let the assembly of the peoples be gathered around you, ***
    and over it take your seat on high.

Voice 1:

8 The LORD judges the peoples; *
    judge me, O LORD, according to my righteousness
    and according to the integrity that is in me.

9 **O let the evil of the wicked come to an end, ***
    but establish the righteous, you who test the minds and hearts,
    O righteous God.

10 God is my shield, *
    who saves the upright in heart.

11 God is a righteous judge, *
    and a God who has indignation every day.

12 If one does not repent, God will whet his sword; *
    he has bent and strung his bow;

13 he has prepared his deadly weapons, *
    making his arrows fiery shafts.   (continues)

Voice 2:

14 See how they conceive evil, *

 and are pregnant with mischief, and bring forth lies.

15 They make a pit, digging it out, *

 and fall into the hole that they have made.

16 Their mischief returns upon their own heads, *

 and on their own heads their violence descends.

17 I will give to the LORD the thanks due to his righteousness, *

 and sing praise to the name of the LORD, the Most High.

O righteous God, remove from our lives all duplicity.
Help us to disentangle guilt from grief so that we may truly confess our sins
and then walk in paths of righteousness, peace, and joy,
following the way of our Savior, Jesus Christ. **Amen.**

Psalm 7 is a plea for justice from a faithful servant of God who has been unjustly attacked. It features a wide variety of expressions: trust in God (vv. 1, 10-11), claims of human innocence (vv. 3-5), pleas for divine intervention (vv. 1-2, 6-9), reflections on the folly of the faithless (vv. 12-16), and a vow to praise God (v. 17)—the very kind of juxtaposing thoughts that often swirl around in the mind in situations of despair. The psalm asks God to intervene against the attacker (vv. 6-7) but also acknowledges that foolish attackers at times cause their own downfall (vv. 15-16). *Use in Worship: partner reading to biblical narratives depicting attacks on God's people.*

Plaintive Is the Song I Sing 7A

1 Plain-tive is the song I sing, woe-ful the la-
2 My pur-su-ers take de-light in their mal-ice
3 Try me, put me to the test: If I ev-er

ment I bring; all my an-guish I lay bare:
and their spite. They ac-cuse me with-out cause,
have op-pressed those who taunt me and de-ride,

God, my Sav-ior, hear my prayer.
held as in a li-on's claws.
then they might be jus-ti-fied.

4 Seated on your lofty throne,
   summon all the lands, each one;
   hold high court, lay motives bare,
   give just judgment, firm but fair,

5 Leading to a different way,
   where revenge no more holds sway,
   and where Christ will set us free,
   free to build community.

Words: Norman J. Goreham © 2010 Norman J. Goreham, admin. Faith Alive Christian Resources
Music (NUN KOMM DER HEIDEN HEILAND 7.7.7.7): *Enchiridia*, Erfurt, 1524; harm. Seth Calvisius, 1594, P.D.

Psalm 8

To the leader: according to The Gittith. A Psalm of David.

¹ O LORD, our Sovereign, how majestic is your name in all the earth! *
  You have set your glory above the heavens.

² Out of the mouths of babes and infants you have founded a
  bulwark because of your foes, *
    to silence the enemy and the avenger.

³ **When I look at your heavens, the work of your fingers, ***
  the moon and the stars that you have established;

⁴ **what are human beings that you are mindful of them, ***
  mortals that you care for them?

⁵ Yet you have made them a little lower than God, *
  and crowned them with glory and honor.

⁶ You have given them dominion over the works of your hands; *
  you have put all things under their feet,

⁷ all sheep and oxen, *
  and also the beasts of the field,

⁸ the birds of the air, and the fish of the sea, *
  whatever passes along the paths of the seas.

⁹ **O LORD, our Sovereign, ***
  how majestic is your name in all the earth!

Creator God, heavenly Father,
you alone know why you love your people, and in you alone we can love one another.
By your Spirit, help us to find our true worth, not in other created things, but in you.
Keep us faithful in our care for your world and in our compassion for your people.
We pray this in the name of Jesus, creation's Redeemer. **Amen.**

Psalm 8 is a grand hymn of praise for the glory and grandeur of God's creation. The psalm expresses wonder at God's regard for human beings and the authority and freedom God gives them (vv. 3-8). While some psalms lament the fleeting nature and seeming insignificance of human life (e.g., Ps. 39), this psalm affirms the value of human life and the place of the human creature in the created order. The NT quotes this text (1 Cor. 15:27, Heb. 2:6-8) in order to reflect on the meaning and significance of Jesus' life. *Use in Worship: services focusing on creation or vocation.*

LORD, Our Lord, Your Glorious Name 8A

1 LORD, our Lord, your glo - rious name all your
2 In - fant voic - es chant your praise, tell - ing
3 Moon and stars in shin - ing height night - ly
4 Who are we that we should share in your

won - drous works pro - claim; in the heavens with
of your glo - rious ways; weak - est means work
tell their Mak - er's might; when I view the
love and ten - der care— raised to an ex -

ra - diant signs ev - er - more your glo - ry shines.
out your will, might - y en - e - mies to still.
heavens a - far, then I know how small we are.
alt - ed height, crowned with hon - or in your sight!

5 With dominion crowned, we stand
  o'er the creatures of your hand;
  all to us subjection yield,
  in the sea and air and field.

6 LORD, our Lord, your glorious name
  all your wondrous works proclaim,
  yours the name of matchless worth,
  excellent in all the earth.

For another setting of this text see 8B.

Words: *Psalter*, 1912, alt., P.D.
Music (GOTT SEI DANK DURCH ALLE WELT 7.7.7.7): J. Freylinghausen's *Gesangbuch*, 1704, P.D.

8B LORD, Our Lord, Your Glorious Name

1 LORD, our Lord, your glo - rious name all your won - drous
2 In - fant voic - es chant your praise, tell - ing of your
3 Moon and stars in shin - ing height night - ly tell their

works pro - claim; in the heavens with ra - diant signs
glo - rious ways; weak - est means work out your will,
Mak - er's might; when I view the heavens a - far,

ev - er - more your glo - ry shines.
might - y en - e - mies to still. How great your name!
then I know how small we are.

Refrain

LORD, our Lord, in all the earth, how great your name!

Yours the name of match - less worth, ex - cel - lent in

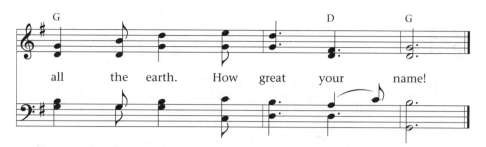

all the earth. How great your name!

4 Who are we that we should share
in your love and tender care—
raised to an exalted height,
crowned with honor in your sight!
How great your name! *Refrain*

5 With dominion crowned, we stand
o'er the creatures of your hand;
all to us subjection yield,
in the sea and air and field.
How great your name! *Refrain*

For another setting of this text see 8A.

Words: *Psalter*, 1912, alt., P.D.
Music (EVENING PRAISE 7.7.7.7.4 with refrain): William F. Sherwin (1826-1888), 1877, P.D.

Chorus: O Lord, Our Lord, 8C
How Excellent Is Thy Name

O Lord, our Lord, how ex-cel-lent is thy name.

O Lord, our Lord, how ex-cel-lent is thy name.

Words: Psalm 8:1
Music: Richard Smallwood (b. 1948); arr. Stephen Key © 2000 GIA Publications, Inc.

8D O Lord, Our Lord, Throughout the Earth

1 O Lord, our Lord, through-out the earth how
2 When I look up and see the skies which
3 Yet such as us you made and meant just

glo - rious is your name, and glo - rious
your own fin - gers made, and won - der
less than gods to be; with hon - or

too where un - seen heavens your maj - es - ty pro -
at the moon and stars, each per - fect - ly dis -
and with glo - ry, Lord, you crowned hu - man - i -

claim. On in - fant lips, in chil - dren's song a
played; then must I ask, "Why do you care? Why
ty. And then do - min - ion you be - stowed for

strong de-fense you raise to coun-ter en - e-
love hu - man - i - ty? And why keep ev - ery
all made by your hand, all sheep and cat - tle,

my and threat, and foil the re - bel's ways.
mor - tal name fixed in your mem - o - ry?"
birds and fish that move through sea or land.

4 O LORD, our Lord, through-out the earth

how glo - rious is your name.

Words: John L. Bell (b. 1949) © 1993 Wild Goose Resource Group, Iona Community, Scotland, GIA Publications, Inc., exclusive North American agent
Music (TRAMPS AND HAWKERS 8.6.8.6 D with refrain): arr. John L. Bell (b. 1949) © 1993 Wild Goose Resource Group, Iona Community, Scotland, GIA Publications, Inc., exclusive North American agent

8E Psalm 8 | A Responsorial Setting

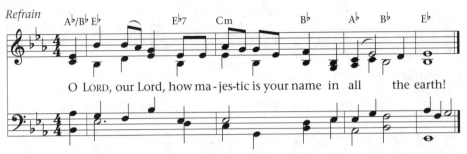

Refrain

O LORD, our Lord, how ma-jes-tic is your name in all the earth!

Refrain

¹ O LORD our Lord,

how majestic is your name in all the earth!—

² you whose glory is chanted above the heavens
out of the mouths of infants and children;

you have set up a fortress against your enemies,
to silence the foe and avenger. *Refrain*

³ When I consider your heavens, the work of your fingers,
the moon and the stars you have set in their courses,

⁴ what are mere mortals that you should be mindful of them,
human beings that you should care for them? *Refrain*

⁵ Yet you have made them little less than divine;
with glory and honor you crown them.

⁶ You have made them rule over the works of your hands;
you have put all things under their feet:

⁷ all flocks and cattle,
even the wild beasts of the field,

⁸ the birds of the air, the fish of the sea,
and whatever passes along the paths of the sea.

⁹ O LORD, our Lord,
how majestic is your name in all the earth! *Refrain*

Tone

Lectionary: *Christmastide (A,B,C); Ordinary Time after Pentecost (A,B,C).*

Words: Psalm 8:1
Music: Alfred V. Fedak (b. 1953) © 1998 GIA Publications, Inc.
Psalm Text: from *Evangelical Lutheran Worship* © 2006 Evangelical Lutheran Church in America, admin.
Augsburg Fortress Publishers
Tone: © 2011 Faith Alive Christian Resources

Chorus: O Lord, How Excellent

Words and Music: Brenda Joyce Moore © 1989 Brenda Joyce Moore

Psalm 9

To the leader: according to Muth-labben. A Psalm of David.

¹ I will give thanks to the LORD with my whole heart; *
  I will tell of all your wonderful deeds.

² **I will be glad and exult in you; ***
  I will sing praise to your name, O Most High.

³ When my enemies turned back, *
  they stumbled and perished before you.

⁴ For you have maintained my just cause; *
  you have sat on the throne giving righteous judgment.

⁵ You have rebuked the nations, you have destroyed the wicked; *
  you have blotted out their name forever and ever.

⁶ The enemies have vanished in everlasting ruins; *
  their cities you have rooted out; the very memory of them has perished.

⁷ **But the LORD sits enthroned forever, ***
  he has established his throne for judgment.

⁸ **He judges the world with righteousness; ***
  he judges the peoples with equity.

⁹ **The LORD is a stronghold for the oppressed, ***
  a stronghold in times of trouble.

¹⁰ **And those who know your name put their trust in you, ***
  for you, O LORD, have not forsaken those who seek you.

¹¹ Sing praises to the LORD, who dwells in Zion. *
  Declare his deeds among the peoples.

¹² For he who avenges blood is mindful of them; *
  he does not forget the cry of the afflicted.

¹³ **Be gracious to me, O LORD. ***
  See what I suffer from those who hate me;
  you are the one who lifts me up from the gates of death,

¹⁴ **so that I may recount all your praises, ***
  and, in the gates of daughter Zion, rejoice in your deliverance.

¹⁵ The nations have sunk in the pit that they made; *
  in the net that they hid has their own foot been caught.

¹⁶ The LORD has made himself known, he has executed judgment; *
  the wicked are snared in the work of their own hands.   *Higgaion. Selah*

¹⁷ The wicked shall depart to Sheol, *
  all the nations that forget God.

¹⁸ For the needy shall not always be forgotten, *

nor the hope of the poor perish forever.

¹⁹ **Rise up, O Lord! Do not let mortals prevail; ***

let the nations be judged before you.

²⁰ **Put them in fear, O Lord; ***

let the nations know that they are only human.   *Selah*

Eternal God, righteous Judge,
rule this world with truth and grace.
Inspire your people to such joyful praise
that every nation will proclaim your glory and every knee will bow before your Son,
who is our Lord and Savior Jesus Christ. **Amen.**

Psalm 9 is an acrostic poem in which every second verse begins with a subsequent letter of the Hebrew alphabet. (The acrostic is completed in Ps. 10.) The psalm is an urgent plea for God's deliverance (vv. 13, 19-20), which is introduced by a commitment to praise God and statements of trust in God (vv. 1-12). The psalm pays special attention to the broken, weak, and needy (vv. 9, 12, 18). Beginning with worshipful thanksgiving and ending with a prayer for God's just rule, the psalm contrasts the folly of human governance with God's faithfulness and integrity. *Use in Worship: a prayer for God's rule and care to be fully realized; an act of praise.*

Psalm 9:9-20 | A Responsorial Setting **9A**

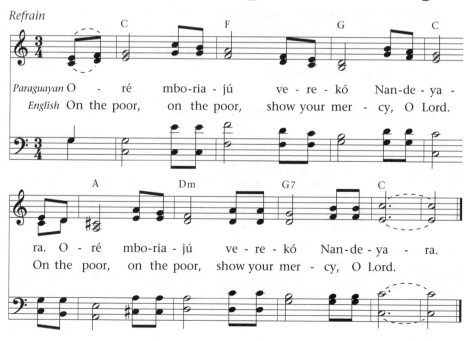

(continues)

Refrain

⁹ You, O Lᴏʀᴅ, will be a refuge for the oppressed,
  a refuge in time of trouble.

¹⁰ Those who know your name will put their trust in you,
  for you never forsake those who seek you, O Lᴏʀᴅ.

¹¹ Sing praise to the Lᴏʀᴅ, who dwells in Zion;
  proclaim to the peoples the things God has done.

¹² The avenger of blood will remember them
  and will not forget the cry of the afflicted.

¹³ Be gracious to me, O Lᴏʀᴅ;
  see the misery I suffer from those whose hate me,
  you that lift me up from the gates of death;

¹⁴ so that I may tell of all your praises and rejoice in your salvation
  in the gates of the city of Zion.   *Refrain*

¹⁵ The nations have fallen into the pit they dug;
  in the snare they set, their own foot is caught.

¹⁶ The Lᴏʀᴅ is revealed in acts of justice;
  the wicked are trapped in the works of their own hands.

¹⁷ The nations go down to the grave,
  all the peoples that forget God.

¹⁸ For the needy shall not always be forgotten,
  nor shall the hope of the poor be taken away.   *Refrain*

¹⁹ Rise up, O Lᴏʀᴅ, let not mortals have the upper hand;
  let the nations be judged before you.

²⁰ Put them in fear, O Lᴏʀᴅ;
  let the nations know they are but mortal.   *Refrain*

Tone

Lectionary: Ordinary Time after Pentecost (B).

Words: traditional Paraguayan; adapt. liturgical text
Music: as taught by Pablo Sosa (b. 1933); arr. John L. Bell (b. 1949) © 1991 Wild Goose Resource Group, Iona Community, Scotland, GIA Publications, Inc., exclusive North American agent
Psalm Text: from *Evangelical Lutheran Worship* © 2006 Evangelical Lutheran Church in America, admin. Augsburg Fortress Publishers
Tone: © 2011 Faith Alive Christian Resources

Sing Praise to God, Whose Mighty Acts 9B

1 Sing praise to God, whose might-y acts still strong in mem-ory stand
2 Though mon-u-ments of e - vil rise in mar - ble, gilt, and stone,
3 Rise up, O God, re - claim the power u - surped by mor - tal pride,

to give us hope when e - vil seems to gain the up - per hand.
time's search will find their boasts un-true, their mak - ers' names un-known.
de - flate the hol - low pomp of those whom rank and ti - tles hide.

Give thanks for deeds of stead-fast love, for won - ders new and old:
Mute av - e - nues of ruins will mark where once proud cit - ies stood,
Let not the need - y cry un-heard, the suf-fering hope in vain;

for fire and cloud, for dai - ly food, for mer - cies yet un - told.
but from de - struc-tion God will save the faith - ful, just, and good.
re - store the fal - len, bless the meek, till peace and jus - tice reign.

Words: Carl P. Daw Jr. (b. 1944) © 1996 Hope Publishing Company
Music (SALVATION 8.6.8.6 D): *Kentucky Harmony*, 1816; harm. Kenneth Munson (1916-1988), P.D.

9C Come, Sing to God with All Your Heart

1 Come, sing to God with all your heart; give
2 For, Ho - ly One, you take our part; your
3 You are a shel - ter for the poor, a

thanks to God, Most High, who makes the ruth - less
ways are al - ways just. You stop the ty - rants
strong-hold in dis - tress. You care for all who

fall from power and res - cues those who cry.
in their tracks and turn their names to dust.
trust in you and all who are op - pressed.

4 The violent move in vicious stealth
 to dig their victims' grave.
 Come, snare them in the nets they cast.
 Come, Mighty God, and save!

5 Rise up, O God; our blood cries out.
 Bring justice! Raise your hand!
 Then we will tell how you have saved.
 Your praise will fill the land.

Words: Ruth C. Duck © 2011 GIA Publications, Inc.
Music (MORNING SONG/CONSOLATION 8.6.8.6): J. Wyeth's *Repository of Sacred Music*, 1813, P.D.; harm.
Jack Grotenhuis, 1983, © 1987 Faith Alive Christian Resources

Optional stanzas from Psalm 10

1 Why stand so far away, my God?
 Why hide in times of need?
 The proud, unbridled, chase the poor,
 and curse you in their greed.

2 Why do you hide when, full of lies,
 they murder and betray?
 They wait to pounce upon the weak
 as lions stalk their prey.

(continues)

3 The weak are crushed and fall to earth;
the wicked strut and preen.
Why in these cruel, chaotic times
cannot your face be seen?

4 In ages past you heard the voice
of those the proud oppress.
Remember those who suffer now,
who cry in deep distress.

5 Arise, O God, and lift your hand;
bring justice to the poor.
Come, help us stop the flow of blood!
Let terror reign no more!

Words: Ruth C. Duck © 1992 GIA Publications, Inc.

Psalm 10

1 Why, O LORD, do you stand far off? *
Why do you hide yourself in times of trouble?

2 **In arrogance the wicked persecute the poor— ***
let them be caught in the schemes they have devised.

3 For the wicked boast of the desires of their heart, *
those greedy for gain curse and renounce the LORD.

4 **In the pride of their countenance the wicked say,**
"God will not seek it out"; *
all their thoughts are, "There is no God."

5 Their ways prosper at all times; *
your judgments are on high, out of their sight;
as for their foes, they scoff at them.

6 **They think in their heart, "We shall not be moved; ***
throughout all generations we shall not meet adversity."

7 Their mouths are filled with cursing and deceit and oppression; *
under their tongues are mischief and iniquity.

8 **They sit in ambush in the villages;**
in hiding places they murder the innocent. *
Their eyes stealthily watch for the helpless;

9 they lurk in secret like a lion in its covert;
they lurk that they may seize the poor; *
they seize the poor and drag them off in their net.

10 **They stoop, they crouch, ***
and the helpless fall by their might.

(continues)

11 They think in their heart, "God has forgotten, *
    he has hidden his face, he will never see it."

12 Rise up, O Lord; O God, lift up your hand; *
    do not forget the oppressed.

13 Why do the wicked renounce God, *
    and say in their hearts, "You will not call us to account"?

14 But you do see! Indeed you note trouble and grief,
    that you may take it into your hands; *
        the helpless commit themselves to you;
        you have been the helper of the orphan.

15 Break the arm of the wicked and evildoers; *
    seek out their wickedness until you find none.

16 The Lord is king forever and ever; *
    the nations shall perish from his land.

17 O Lord, you will hear the desire of the meek; *
    you will strengthen their heart, you will incline your ear

18 to do justice for the orphan and the oppressed, *
    so that those from earth may strike terror no more.

Timeless and mysterious God, we cannot begin to understand your ways,
but we trust your justice and your mercy.
Help us to face the unbelief and injustice in our day
with strength from your Holy Spirit and confidence in your ultimate redemption.
We pray in the name of Jesus. **Amen.**

Psalms 9 and 10 together form an acrostic poem in which alternating lines begin with successive letters of the Hebrew alphabet. Psalm 10 echoes the themes of Ps. 9 in lamenting oppression (vv. 1-11), asking for divine intervention on behalf of the needy (vv. 12-15), and concluding with statements of trust in God (vv. 16-18). *Use in Worship: intercessory prayer.*

For an additional setting of Ps. 10 see 9C.

When Trouble Looms 10A

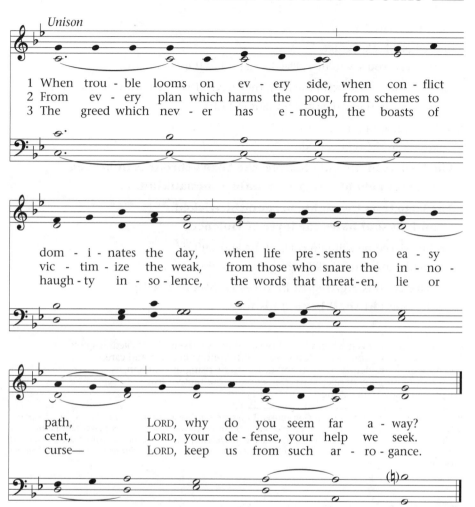

1 When trou-ble looms on ev-ery side, when con-flict
2 From ev-ery plan which harms the poor, from schemes to
3 The greed which nev-er has e-nough, the boasts of

dom-i-nates the day, when life pre-sents no ea-sy
vic-tim-ize the weak, from those who snare the in-no-
haugh-ty in-so-lence, the words that threat-en, lie or

path, LORD, why do you seem far a-way?
cent, LORD, your de-fense, your help we seek.
curse— LORD, keep us from such ar-ro-gance.

4 Some think that you are blind to sin;
some live as though you were not there;
some treat your justice with contempt;
LORD, surely you both see and care!

5 You call the wicked to account;
you champion the victim's cause;
you silence mortal taunts and threats;
LORD, heaven's eternal throne is yours.

Words: Martin Leckebusch © 2006 Kevin Mayhew Ltd.
Music (JESU DULCIS MEMORIA 8.8.8.8): Plainsong, mode I; acc. McNeil Robinson II © 1984 Church Pension Group/Church Publishing, Inc.

Psalm 11

To the leader. Of David.

¹ In the LORD I take refuge; *
> how can you say to me, "Flee like a bird to the mountains;

² for look, the wicked bend the bow, they have fitted their arrow to the string, *
> to shoot in the dark at the upright in heart.

³ If the foundations are destroyed, *
> what can the righteous do?"

⁴ **The LORD is in his holy temple; the LORD's throne is in heaven.** *
> **His eyes behold, his gaze examines humankind.**

⁵ **The LORD tests the righteous and the wicked,** *
> **and his soul hates the lover of violence.**

⁶ On the wicked he will rain coals of fire and sulfur; *
> a scorching wind shall be the portion of their cup.

⁷ **For the LORD is righteous; he loves righteous deeds;** *
> **the upright shall behold his face.**

Loving God,
you are our shelter even when your whole creation is shaken and wickedness prevails.
No one—helpless, orphaned, or oppressed—is beyond your reach and care.
You have given us victory over sin and death in the rising of your Son.
Let the surpassing joy of his resurrection conquer our present fear.
We pray in Jesus' name. **Amen.**

Psalm 11 is a statement of trust in God spoken in response to advice to flee oppression (v. 1). The psalm acknowledges the threat of faithless people (vv. 2-3) but expresses trust in God's power and faithfulness in the face of injustice (vv. 4-7). Its most dramatic imagery depicts God as being against those dedicated to violence (vv. 5-6). *Use in Worship: a prayer in solidarity with those experiencing oppression; times of violent oppression.*

11A O Lord, Be Our Refuge

1 O Lord, be our refuge, when evils assail;
  your justice is sure, and your strength will prevail.
  Yet wicked ones rise and the good are laid low.
  Your mercy reveal and your righteousness show.

2 O God, send your fire, come to judge humankind,
  our evil consume and our virtue refine.
  Then crowns of oppression will fall to the dust,
  and saints will delight in the reign of the just.

3 How firm a foundation we find in God's Word!
  We fashion our lives in the way of the Lord.
  When all else gives way, God's salvation remains;
  and even in death, God's great glory sustains.

Tune: FOUNDATION on facing page.

Hymn: How Firm a Foundation 11B

1 How firm a foun-da-tion you saints of the Lord,
2 "Fear not, I am with you, O be not dis-mayed,
3 "The soul that on Je-sus has leaned for re-pose

is laid for your faith in his ex-cel-lent Word!
for I am your God and will still give you aid;
I will not, I will not de-sert to its foes;

What more can he say than to you he has said,
I'll strength-en you, help you, and cause you to stand,
that soul, though all hell should en-deav-or to shake,

to you who for ref-uge to Je-sus have fled? *Read Ps. 11:1-3*
up-held by my right-eous, om-nip-o-tent hand. *Read Ps. 11:4-7*
I'll nev-er, no nev-er, no nev-er for-sake!"

Alternate harmonization on p. 276.

Words: Isaiah 43:1-5; J. Rippon's *Selection of Hymns*, 1787, alt., P.D.
Music (FOUNDATION 11.11.11.11): J. Funk's *A Compilation of Genuine Church Music*, 1832; harm. Dale Grotenhuis, 1985, © 1987 Faith Alive Christian Resources

Psalm 12

To the leader: according to The Sheminith. A Psalm of David.

1 Help, O Lord, for there is no longer anyone who is godly; *
 the faithful have disappeared from humankind.

2 They utter lies to each other; *
 with flattering lips and a double heart they speak.

3 **May the Lord cut off all flattering lips,** *
 the tongue that makes great boasts,

4 **those who say, "With our tongues we will prevail;** *
 our lips are our own—who is our master?"

5 "Because the poor are despoiled, because the needy groan, *
 I will now rise up," says the Lord;
 "I will place them in the safety for which they long."

6 **The promises of the Lord are promises that are pure,** *
 silver refined in a furnace on the ground, purified seven times.

7 **You, O Lord, will protect us;** *
 you will guard us from this generation forever.

8 On every side the wicked prowl, *
 as vileness is exalted among humankind.

O God of justice and truth, chaos often clouds the day and fears command the night.
Remind us always of your promise to guard and protect your people,
and of your perfect, holy love revealed to us in Jesus Christ our Redeemer.
We pray this in Jesus' name. **Amen.**

Psalm 12 addresses the predicament caused by the way the wicked speak and prowl, featuring both a cry to God for help (v. 1) and God's promise of deliverance (v. 5), along with a poignant contrast between two kinds of speech: the empty boasts of the faithless (vv. 2-4, 8) and the sure promises of God (v. 6). *Use in Worship: intercession for those who suffer by the words of the faithless; confession of our participation in inflicting such suffering on others; affirmation of confidence in the God who delivers.*

Lying Lips

Words: Adam M. L. Tice © 2011 GIA Publications, Inc.
Music (CAPTIVITY/KAS DZIEDAJA 8.7.8.7): Latvian melody; harm. Geoffrey Laycock (b. 1927), P.D.

Psalm 13

To the leader. A Psalm of David.

1 How long, O LORD? Will you forget me forever? *
   How long will you hide your face from me?

2 **How long must I bear pain in my soul,
   and have sorrow in my heart all day long?** *
   How long shall my enemy be exalted over me?

3 Consider and answer me, O LORD my God! *
   Give light to my eyes, or I will sleep the sleep of death,

4 and my enemy will say, "I have prevailed"; *
   my foes will rejoice because I am shaken.

5 **But I trusted in your steadfast love;** *
   my heart shall rejoice in your salvation.

6 **I will sing to the LORD,** *
   because he has dealt bountifully with me.

Loving God,
in Jesus Christ you have come so near
that our hearts can sing even when we feel most alone.
Guard our thoughts, guide our steps, and help us to put our trust in no one but you. **Amen.**

Psalm 13 is a simple but urgent psalm of lament. Its three-part form is theologically and psychologically significant, moving from lament (vv. 1-2) to petition (vv. 3-4) to a vow to praise God (vv. 5-6). Each section acknowledges God: God is the one to whom we cry in lament, whom we rely upon to change lamentable circumstances, and whom we praise for deliverance. In order to slow down the pace of our encounter with this psalm and to live into the dramatic change of emotion between vv. 4 and 5, the psalm could guide a three-part prayer that unfolds over the space of a few minutes, hours, or even days. *Use in Worship: prayer of lament.*

For an additional setting appropriate for use with Ps. 13 see 107B.

13A A Prayer of Distress

God—are you there?
It seems so long since I have felt the comfort of your presence
and even longer since I have experienced the assurance of your blessing.
I do not like the thoughts in my own heart, let alone the words of my enemies.
Come, Lord Jesus, to this dark place in me.
Let me know the joy of your presence again.
With you, I have all I need. Help me to want nothing else.

How Long Will You Forget Me 13B

1 How long will you for - get me, Lord,
2 Look on my need, O Lord my God,
3 Look on their threats and hear my cry,
4 Lord, in your mer - cy is my trust;

and hide your face a - way?
who grants my ev - ery breath;
and an - swer when I call:
I shall be glad and free:

How long shall e - vils tear my heart
give light that I may see your light,
or they will claim the vic - to - ry
then shall I sing with all my heart

and trou - bles fill my day?
nor sleep the sleep of death.
who long to see me fall.
how you have dealt with me.

Words: Christopher Idle © 1990 The Jubilate Group, admin. Hope Publishing Company
Music (MARTYRDOM 8.6.8.6): Hugh Wilson, ca. 1800; adapt. Robert Smith, 1825, P.D.; arr. Nolan Williams Jr. (b. 1969) © 2000 GIA Publications, Inc.

13C How Long, O Lord

(continues)

Words: Brian Doerksen, Steve Mitchinson, Karen Mitchinson, Daphne Rademaker © 2002 Integrity's Hosanna! Music, admin. EMI CMG Publishing
Music: Brian Doerksen, Steve Mitchinson, Karen Mitchinson, Daphne Rademaker © 2002 and arr. Eelco Vos © 2011 Integrity's Hosanna! Music, admin. EMI CMG Publishing

How Long, O Lord, Will You Forget 13D

1 How long, O Lord, will you for-get an an-swer to my
2 How long, O Lord, will you for-sake and leave me in this
3 How long, O Lord? But you for-give with mer-cy from a-

prayer? No to-kens of your love I see,
way? When will you come to my re-lief?
bove. I find that all your ways are just,

your face is turned a - way from me; I wres-tle with des-pair.
My heart is o - ver-whelmed with grief, by e - vil night and day.
I learn to praise you and to trust in your un - fail - ing love.

Words: Barbara Woollett © 1990 The Jubilate Group, admin. Hope Publishing Company
Music (HOW LONG 8.6.8.8.6): Christopher Norton (b. 1953) © 1993 HarperCollins Religious, admin.
Music Services, Inc.

13E Psalm 13 | A Responsorial Setting

Refrain

1 O Lord, hear my prayer, O Lord, hear my prayer;
2 The Lord is my song, the Lord is my praise.

when I call an - swer me. O Lord, hear my prayer, O
All my hope comes from God. The Lord is my song, the

Lord, hear my prayer; come and lis - ten to me.
Lord is my praise. God, the well-spring of life.

Refrain (sing stanza 1)

1 How long, O LORD? Will you forget me forever?
    How long will you hide your face from me?

2 How long shall I have perplexity in my mind,
    and grief in my heart, day after day?
        How long shall my enemy triumph over me?   *Refrain (sing stanza 1)*

3 Look upon me and answer me, O LORD my God;
    give light to my eyes, lest I sleep in death;

4 lest my enemy say, "I have defeated you,"
    and my foes rejoice that I have fallen.   *Refrain (sing stanzas 1 and 2)*

5 But I trust in your unfailing love;
    my heart is joyful because of your saving help.

6 I will sing to the LORD,
    who has dealt with me richly.   *Refrain (sing stanza 2)*

Tone

Lectionary: Ordinary Time after Pentecost (A).

Words: Psalm 102:1-2; adapt. The Community of Taizé © 1991 Ateliers et Presses de Taizé, Taizé Community, France, GIA Publications, Inc., exclusive North American agent
Music: Jacques Berthier (1923-1994) © 1991 Ateliers et Presses de Taizé, Taizé Community, France, GIA Publications, Inc., exclusive North American agent
Psalm Text: from *Evangelical Lutheran Worship* © 2006 Evangelical Lutheran Church in America, admin. Augsburg Fortress Publishers
Tone: © 2011 Faith Alive Christian Resources

Psalm 14

To the leader. Of David.

¹ Fools say in their hearts, "There is no God." *
   They are corrupt, they do abominable deeds; there is no one who does good.

² **The Lord looks down from heaven on humankind ***
   to see if there are any who are wise, who seek after God.

³ **They have all gone astray, they are all alike perverse; ***
   there is no one who does good, no, not one.

⁴ Have they no knowledge, all the evildoers *
   who eat up my people as they eat bread, and do not call upon the Lord?

⁵ **There they shall be in great terror, ***
   for God is with the company of the righteous.

⁶ You would confound the plans of the poor, *
   but the Lord is their refuge.

⁷ **O that deliverance for Israel would come from Zion! ***
   When the Lord restores the fortunes of his people,
   Jacob will rejoice; Israel will be glad.

Patient and loving Lord,
in a world where many deny your very existence and fearlessly break your laws,
we trust that you are God Most High and that you will judge the world with justice.
You are sovereign—we are not; you are holy—we are not.
Help us to see the foolishness of earthly wisdom.
Through Jesus Christ, lead us home to you. **Amen.**

Psalm 14, which is nearly identical to Ps. 53, is a wisdom psalm that exposes the folly and pervasiveness of unbelief and faithlessness, particularly the failure to acknowledge God (v. 1), human corruption (v. 1) and oppression (v. 4). It culminates with a strong expression of desire for God to deliver and restore the people (v. 7). The psalm is quoted by Paul (Rom. 3:10-12) to demonstrate the universality of human sin. *Use in Worship: services that identify with the oppression of God's people, lamenting the godlessness that leads to oppression; a call for God's people to confess living as though "there is no God."*

For an additional setting of Ps. 14 see 53A.

14A Oh, That Your Salvation and Your Rescue

Refrain

Oh, that your sal - va - tion and your res - cue would
swift - ly come to re - new your peo - ple. -new your peo - ple.

To Stanzas / Final Ending

Stanzas

1 The fools have said in their heart: "There is no God": they are cor -
4 All glo - ry be to the Fa - ther and to the Son and to the

rupt, their deeds are all loath-some; not one of them does good.
Ho - ly Spir - it both now and through-out e - ter - ni - ty.

To Refrain

Words: David Lee © 2010 David Lee
Music (based on the tune RORATE CAELI): David Lee © 2010 David Lee

14B Psalm 14 | A Responsorial Setting

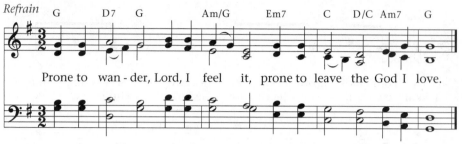

Refrain

Prone to wan-der, Lord, I feel it, prone to leave the God I love.

Refrain

¹ Fools say in their hearts, "There is no God."

They are corrupt, every deed is vile; there is no one who does any good.

² The LORD looks down from heaven upon us all,

to see if there is anyone who is wise, who seeks after God.

³ They have all proved faithless; all alike have turned bad;

there is none who does good; no, not one.   *Refrain*

⁴ Have they no knowledge, all those evildoers

who eat up my people like bread and do not call upon the LORD?

⁵ See how they tremble with fear,

because God is in the company of the righteous.

⁶ Your aim is to confound the plans of the afflicted,

but the LORD is their refuge.   *Refrain*

⁷ Oh, that Israel's deliverance would come out of Zion!

When the LORD restores the fortunes of the people,

Jacob will rejoice and Israel will be glad.   *Refrain*

Tone

Lectionary: Ordinary Time after Pentecost (B,C).

Words: Robert Robinson, 1758, alt., P.D.
Music (BEACH SPRING fragment): *The Sacred Harp*, Philadelphia, 1844; harm. A. Royce Eckhardt, 1972,
© 1972, 1996 Covenant Publications
Psalm Text: from *Evangelical Lutheran Worship* © 2006 Evangelical Lutheran Church in America, admin.
Augsburg Fortress Publishers
Tone: © 2011 Faith Alive Christian Resources

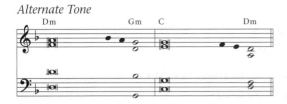

Alternate Tone

The alternate tone may be used with the refrain of 14A.

Tone: © 2011 Faith Alive Christian Resources

A Prayer of Confession 14C

Prayer of Confession

Let us pray.
Holy Wisdom, Almighty God,
with our lips we acclaim you as Lord,
yet often in our hearts and lives we deny your reign.
We confess our foolishness in wandering from your ways,
in wasting your gifts, in forgetting your love.
According to your abundant mercy forgive us our sins,
and clothe us in the righteousness of Christ
so that we may delight in your will and walk in your ways,
to the glory of Jesus Christ, our Savior. Amen.

Assurance of Pardon

There is no one righteous, not even one.   *Romans 3:10* (NIV)
For all have sinned and fall short of the glory of God,
and all are justified freely by his grace
through the redemption that came by Christ Jesus.   *Romans 3:23-24* (NIV)
Blessed are those
whose transgressions are forgiven,
whose sins are covered.
Blessed is the one
whose sin the Lord will never count against them.   *Romans 4:7-8* (NIV)

Hymn of Response

This or another Hymn of Response may be sung:

Oh, to grace how great a debtor daily I'm constrained to be!
Let that grace, now, like a fetter, bind my wandering heart to thee:
prone to wander, Lord, I feel it, prone to leave the God I love;
here's my heart, O take and seal it, seal it for thy courts above.

For accompaniment see p. 295.

Prayer: Martin Tel, 2011, © Creative Commons Attribution-NonCommercial-ShareAlike
Hymn: Robert Robinson, 1758, alt., P.D.

Psalm 15

A Psalm of David.

1 O LORD, who may abide in your tent? *

  Who may dwell on your holy hill?

2 **Those who walk blamelessly, and do what is right,** *

  and speak the truth from their heart;

3 **who do not slander with their tongue,**

  and do no evil to their friends, *

  nor take up a reproach against their neighbors;

4 in whose eyes the wicked are despised,

  but who honor those who fear the LORD; *

  who stand by their oath even to their hurt;

5 **who do not lend money at interest,**

  and do not take a bribe against the innocent. *

  Those who do these things shall never be moved.

Holy God, through your Word and your Son you have taught us to love you
with our heart, and soul, and mind, and to love our neighbors as ourselves.
Pour out your Spirit upon us so that we may joyfully obey you
and live today with confident praise.
We pray in Jesus' name. **Amen.**

Psalm 15 is a liturgy of entrance or procession. It echoes the themes of Ps. 24, contrasting the beauty of obedience with the folly of disobedience. It is also the first of an artfully-shaped set of nine psalms in chiastic (or mirror-like) form with the following pairings: Pss. 15 and 24 (entrance liturgies), 16 and 23 (trust), 17 and 22 (lament), 18 and 20-21 (psalms about victory of the king). Psalm 19, a psalm of creation and Torah, stands at the center. *Use in Worship: preparation for worship; a call to faithful obedience.*

LORD, Who Are They That May Dwell 15A

1 LORD, who are they that may dwell
2 They lead an in-cor-rupt life
3 They do no wrong to their friends

with-in the courts of your house? And by what
and do the thing that is right. They speak the
and will not slan-der their name. They scorn the

lives do they show they dwell on your ho-ly hill?
truth from their heart and use not their tongue for harm.
one who is false but love those who fear the LORD.

4 They stand by what they have vowed,
   although it be to their hurt.
   They do no sin with their wealth
   and will not be swayed with bribes.

5 Now these are they who may dwell
   within the courts of the LORD.
   Their lives shall never be moved;
   they stand in their God, secure.

Words: James E. Seddon, 1971, alt. © 1973 The Jubilate Group, admin. Hope Publishing Company
Music (STELLA CARMEL 7.7.7.7): Norman L. Warren, 1971, © 1973 The Jubilate Group, admin. Hope
Publishing Company

15B Lord, Who Shall Be Welcome

Words and Music: Steven C. Warner © 2006 World Library Publications

Psalm 15 | A Responsorial Setting 15C

Refrain

I'm gon-na live so God can use me an-y-where, Lord,
live so

an-y-time! I'm gon-na live so God can
an-y-time! *live so*

use me an-y-where, Lord, an-y-time!
my Lord, *an-y-time!*

Refrain

¹ LORD, who may dwell in your tabernacle?
Who may abide upon your holy hill?

² Those who lead a blameless life and do what is right,
who speak the truth from their heart;

³ they do not slander with the tongue, they do no evil to their friends;
they do not cast discredit upon a neighbor.   *Refrain*

⁴ In their sight the wicked are rejected, but they honor those who fear the LORD.
They have sworn upon their health and do not take back their word.

⁵ They do not give their money in hope of gain,
nor do they take bribes against the innocent.
Those who do these things shall never be overthrown.   *Refrain*   (continues)

Tone

Lectionary: Ordinary Time after Epiphany (A); Pentecost (B,C).

Words: Afro-American spiritual, P.D.
Music (I'M GONNA LIVE): traditional; arr. Wendell Whalum (1932-1987) © the Estate of Wendell Whalum
Psalm Text: from *Evangelical Lutheran Worship* © 2006 Evangelical Lutheran Church in America, admin.
Augsburg Fortress Publishers
Tone: © 2011 Faith Alive Christian Resources

Alternate Tone

The alternate tone may be used with the refrain of 15B.

Tone: © 2011 Faith Alive Christian Resources

15D LORD, Who May Dwell Within Your House

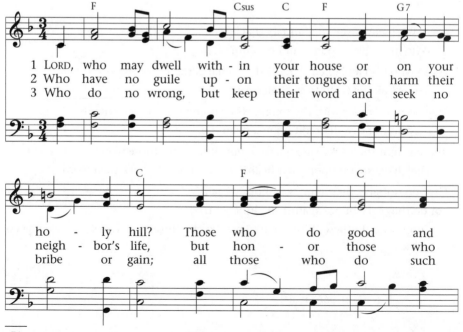

1 LORD, who may dwell with-in your house or on your
2 Who have no guile up-on their tongues nor harm their
3 Who do no wrong, but keep their word and seek no

ho - ly hill? Those who do good and
neigh - bor's life, but hon - or those who
bribe or gain; all those who do such

speak	the	truth,	whose	lives	are	blame -	less	still;
fear	the	LORD	and	turn	a -	way	from	strife;
things	shall	live	and	safe	from	harm	re -	main.

Alternate tune: TALLIS ORDINAL, p. 647.

Words: Christopher L. Webber © 1986 Christopher L. Webber
Music (CRIMOND 8.6.8.6): Jessie Seymour Irvine, 1872; harm. David Grant, 1872, P.D.

A Prayer of Confession **15E**

God of truth and grace,
we confess that we have strayed like sheep,
we have turned, each one of us, to our own way.
We pray your forgiveness for the times
when we have not spoken the truth,
when we have not loved our neighbor,
when we have brought dishonor to your people.
So shepherd us, we pray,
that we may follow you in paths of righteousness.
Enable us to live with such integrity
so that others may see you shining through us and glorify you.
In your goodness and mercy lead us to dwell in your house
where we may rest securely forever.
Amen.

All Sing:

Your goodness and your gracious love
pursue me all my days;
your house, O LORD, shall be my home—
your name, my endless praise.

For accompaniment use 15D.

Prayer: Martin Tel, 2011, © Creative Commons Attribution-NonCommercial-ShareAlike
Hymn: Christopher Idle, 1977, © 1982 The Jubilate Group, admin. Hope Publishing Company

Psalm 16

A Miktam of David.

1 Protect me, O God, *
> for in you I take refuge.

2 **I say to the Lord, "You are my Lord; ***
> **I have no good apart from you."**

3 **As for the holy ones in the land, they are the noble, ***
> **in whom is all my delight.**

4 Those who choose another god multiply their sorrows; *
> their drink offerings of blood I will not pour out
> or take their names upon my lips.

5 **The Lord is my chosen portion and my cup; ***
> **you hold my lot.**

6 The boundary lines have fallen for me in pleasant places; *
> I have a goodly heritage.

7 **I bless the Lord who gives me counsel; ***
> **in the night also my heart instructs me.**

8 I keep the Lord always before me; *
> because he is at my right hand, I shall not be moved.

9 **Therefore my heart is glad, and my soul rejoices; ***
> **my body also rests secure.**

10 For you do not give me up to Sheol, *
> or let your faithful one see the Pit.

11 **You show me the path of life. ***
> **In your presence there is fullness of joy;**
> **in your right hand are pleasures forevermore.**

God of unending abundance,
in you alone we find all we need in this life and even more in the life to come.
Open our eyes to see your glory and our ears to hear your Word
until our hearts burn with the joy of your presence
and our lives proclaim the power of your love.
We pray in Jesus' name. **Amen.**

Psalm 16, like Ps. 23, is a psalm of trust that expresses utter dependence on God (vv. 1-2, 9), a love for God's people (v. 3), and gratitude for God's instruction (v. 7) and guidance (vv. 8, 11). The psalm includes a compelling description of God as "portion" and "cup" (v. 5). For Christians, it is an apt Easter testimony because of its poignant description of life in the face of death (vv. 10-11; see Acts 2:25-31, 13:35, Rom. 6:3-4). *Use in Worship: services of baptism or remembrance of baptism (especially on the basis of the imagery of life arising from death coupled with the profound testimony of trust in God).*

When in the Night I Meditate

16A

1 When in the night I med-i-tate on
2 For-ev-er in my thought the LORD be-
3 My in-most be-ing thrills with joy and

mer-cies mul-ti-plied, my grate-ful heart in-
fore my face shall stand; se-cure, un-moved, I
glad-ness fills my breast; be-cause on him my

spires my tongue to bless the LORD, my guide.
shall re-main, with him at my right hand.
trust is stayed, my flesh in hope shall rest.

4 I know that I shall not be left
forgotten in the grave,
that from corruption, thou, O LORD,
thy holy one wilt save.

5 The path of life thou showest me;
of joy a boundless store
is ever found at thy right hand,
and pleasures evermore.

Words: *Psalter,* 1912, P.D.
Music (MAITLAND 8.6.8.6): George N. Allen, 1850, P.D.

16B Harbor of My Heart

Refrain

Har-bor of my heart, I take ref-uge in you, preserve me, O God! My joy is in you a - lone.

1 Pre-serve me, O God, my Sav - ior; I take
2 He has put in-to my heart a won-drous love for the

3 My des-ti-ny, O Lord, is my de-light; how I
4 The path-way of my life will be shown to me, the

ref - uge with - in your em - brace. I say to the Lord, "You are my
faith - ful who dwell in your land. It is you, O Lord, who are my

wel - come your will for me! I will bless the Lord who gives me
full - ness of joy in your pres - ence. At your side, my soul will sing for-

Cm7   Fm   Ab   Bbm

To Refrain

God. My joy a - lone is found in you."
cup, you a - lone, my por - tion and my prize.

coun - sel, who at night is the com - pass of my heart.
ev - er to the One who brought life un - to my spir - it.

Ebsus   Bbm   Eb   Fsus   Fm

Words and Music: Steven C. Warner © 1995 World Library Publications

16C Protect Me, God: I Trust in You

1 Pro - tect me, God: I trust in you.   I tell you now,
2 Your peo - ple are   a cho-sen race,   and I de -light
3 LORD God, you are   my food and drink;   my work for you
4 Thank you, my LORD,   for warn-ing me;   by night and day

"You are my Lord;   on you my hap - pi - ness de - pends."
in faith-ful friends,   but pa - gan ways I will not share.
is joy in - deed;   glad is the her - i - tage that's mine.
you guide my thoughts.   With you be - fore me, I stand firm.

Refrain

Pro - tect me, God: I trust in you.

5 So now I'm glad in heart and soul,
   for I have found security—
   among the dead I shall not lie.
   Refrain

6 Not death, but life, shall be my path;
   abundant joy your presence grants,
   an honored place, and happiness.
   Refrain

Words: Michael Saward © 1973 The Jubilate Group, admin. Hope Publishing Company
Music (MEPHIBOSHETH 8.8.8 with refrain): Christian Strover © 1973 The Jubilate Group, admin. Hope Publishing Company

Psalm 16 | A Responsorial Setting 16D

Refrain

Pro - tect me, God: I trust in you.

Refrain

1 Protect me, O God, for I take refuge in you;
   I have said to the LORD, "You are my Lord, my good above all other."

2 All my delight is in the godly that are in the land,
   upon those who are noble among the people.

3 But those who run after other gods
   shall have their troubles multiplied.

4 I will not pour out drink offerings to such gods,
   never take their names upon my lips.   *Refrain*

5 O LORD, you are my portion and my cup;
   it is you who uphold my lot.

6 My boundaries enclose a pleasant land;
   indeed, I have a rich inheritance.

7 I will bless the LORD who gives me counsel;
   my heart teaches me night after night.

8 I have set the LORD always before me;
   because God is at my right hand, I shall not be shaken.   *Refrain*

9 My heart, therefore, is glad, and my spirit rejoices;
   my body also shall rest in hope.

10 For you will not abandon me to the grave,
   nor let your holy one see the pit.

11 You will show me the path of life;
   in your presence there is fullness of joy,
   and in your right hand are pleasures forevermore.   *Refrain*

Tone

Lectionary: Easter Vigil (A,B,C); Eastertide (A); Ordinary Time after Pentecost (B,C).

For accompaniment see facing page.

Words: Michael Saward © 1973 The Jubilate Group, admin. Hope Publishing Company
Music (MEPHIBOSHETH fragment): Christian Strover © 1973 The Jubilate Group, admin. Hope Publishing Company
Psalm Text: from *Evangelical Lutheran Worship* © 2006 Evangelical Lutheran Church in America, admin. Augsburg Fortress Publishers
Tone: © 2011 Faith Alive Christian Resources

(continues)

Alternate Refrain

My heart is glad and my spir - it re-joic - es; my bod - y shall rest in hope.

Alternate Tone

Words: Psalm 16
Music: William Beckstrand from *Psalter for Worship, Cycle B* © 1996 Augsburg Fortress Publishers
Tone: © 2011 Faith Alive Christian Resources

A Prayer of David.

¹ Hear a just cause, O L ORD; attend to my cry; *
   give ear to my prayer from lips free of deceit.

² **From you let my vindication come; ***
   let your eyes see the right.

³ If you try my heart, if you visit me by night, *
   if you test me, you will find no wickedness in me;
   my mouth does not transgress.

⁴ As for what others do, by the word of your lips *
   I have avoided the ways of the violent.

⁵ My steps have held fast to your paths; *
   my feet have not slipped.

⁶ **I call upon you, for you will answer me, O God; ***
   incline your ear to me, hear my words.

⁷ **Wondrously show your steadfast love, ***
   O savior of those who seek refuge from their adversaries
   at your right hand.

⁸ **Guard me as the apple of the eye; ***
   hide me in the shadow of your wings,

⁹ **from the wicked who despoil me, ***
   my deadly enemies who surround me.

¹⁰ They close their hearts to pity; *
   with their mouths they speak arrogantly.

¹¹ They track me down; now they surround me; *
   they set their eyes to cast me to the ground.

¹² They are like a lion eager to tear, *
   like a young lion lurking in ambush.

¹³ **Rise up, O L ORD, ***
   confront them, overthrow them!
   By your sword deliver my life from the wicked, *
   ¹⁴ from mortals—by your hand, O L ORD—
   from mortals whose portion in life is in this world.   (continues)

May their bellies be filled with what you have stored up for them; *

    may their children have more than enough;

    may they leave something over to their little ones.

¹⁵ As for me, I shall behold your face in righteousness; *

    when I awake I shall be satisfied, beholding your likeness.

God of unfailing love,
like David we cry out to you, knowing that you hear and answer prayer.
Our enemies are very real—around us and within us.
By the power of your Spirit, make your love revealed in Jesus more real to us each day.
We pray in Jesus' name. **Amen.**

Psalm 17, like Ps. 22, is an urgent prayer for God's attention and deliverance (vv. 1-2, 6-9, 13-15). The psalmist calls to mind God's past faithfulness (vv. 3-5) and the current lamentable conditions (vv. 10-12). The psalm reflects the contrast between good and evil first established in Ps. 1. It is filled with bodily imagery: God's ears, eyes, lips, right hand, wings, and face meet the psalmist's voice, lips, mouth, and feet and confront the enemies' face, heart, mouth, eyes, and belly. This realistic imagery testifies to the psalmist's belief in God's personal interaction with the world, in contrast to that of the idols that have eyes, ears, and mouths but cannot see, hear, or speak (Pss. 115, 135). The concluding image of "seeing God's face" is particularly compelling in light of Aaronic blessing (see Num. 6:24-26 and Ps. 67:1). *Use in Worship: in conjunction with intercessory prayer; services focusing on justice and holiness; vv. 1, 8, and 15 together comprise a responsive call to prayer for services at the close of the day, also known as Compline.*

17A Psalm 17:1-9, 15 | A Responsorial Setting

Refrain

Descant

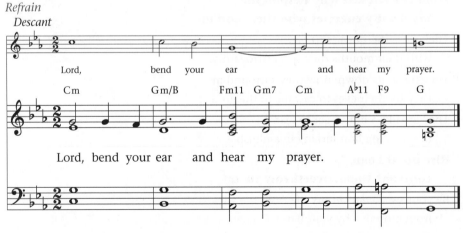

Refrain

¹ Hear a just cause, O Lord; give heed to my cry;

    listen to my prayer, which does not come from lying lips.

² Let my vindication come forth from your presence;

    let your eyes be fixed on justice.

³ Examine my heart, visit me by night,

    melt me down; you will find no impurity in me.   *Refrain*

4 I have not regarded what others do;

at the word of your lips I have avoided the ways of the violent.

5 My footsteps hold fast to your well-worn path;

and my feet do not slip.

6 I call upon you, O God, for you will answer me;

incline your ear to me and hear my words.

7 Show me your marvelous lovingkindness,

O Savior of those who take refuge at your right hand

from those who rise against them.   *Refrain*

8 Keep me as the apple of your eye;

hide me under the shadow of your wings,

9 from the wicked who assault me,

from my deadly enemies who surround me.

15 But at my vindication I shall see your face;

when I awake, I shall be satisfied, beholding your likeness.   *Refrain*

Tone

Optional vamp during the reading of the psalm

Lectionary: vv. 1-7, 15 Ordinary Time after Pentecost (A); vv. 1-9 Ordinary Time after Pentecost (C).

Words: from *Lectionary for Mass* © 1969, 1981, 1997, International Commission on English in the Liturgy Corporation
Music (refrain and vamp, alt.): Jeffrey Honoré © 1994 World Library Publications
Psalm Text: from *Evangelical Lutheran Worship* © 2006 Evangelical Lutheran Church in America, admin. Augsburg Fortress Publishers
Tone: © 2011 Faith Alive Christian Resources

17B Lord, Bend Your Ear

Refrain

Descant

Lord, bend your ear and hear my prayer.

Cm Gm A♭9 B♭6 Cm A♭9 F9 G

(⌢ *last time*)

Lord, bend your ear and hear my prayer.

Cm   Gm   A♭9   B♭6

1 I am in - no-cent, O Lord! I   pray, I beg for
2 O   God I pray to you, for   you a - lone can
3 O   keep me   as the   ap - ple of your

Cm   A♭maj7   B♭6   G7   Cm   *To Refrain*

help! Won't you lis-ten?   For   I have fol-lowed you.
help.   Lis-ten   and an-swer my   prayer!
eye;   hide me in the shad-ow of your wings.

Words: Jeffrey Honoré © 1994 World Library Publications; ref. from *Lectionary for Mass* © 1969, 1981, 1997
International Commission on English in the Liturgy Corporation
Music: Jeffrey Honoré © 1994 World Library Publications

LORD, Listen To My Righteous Plea   **17C**

1 LORD, lis - ten to my right - eous plea; you
2 LORD, as the ap - ple of your eye may
3 For your own peo - ple you pro - vide; with

will not find de - ceit in me as my prayers rise.
I be kept in safe - ty by your might - y hand.
gifts their chil - dren you sup - ply from your great store.

Ex - am - ine me and probe my heart to
Be - neath the shad - ow of your wings pro -
At dawn I will be sat - is - fied, when

see that I have kept a - part from ways of sin.
tect me from all e - vil things sur - round - ing me.
I in right - eous - ness a - bide be - fore your face.

Words: Helen Otte (b. 1931) © 1987 Faith Alive Christian Resources
Music (ROSALIE MCMILLAN 8.8.4 D): James Ward, 1984, © 1987 Music A. D.

Psalm 18

To the leader. A Psalm of David the servant of the LORD, who addressed the words of this song to the LORD on the day when the LORD delivered him from the hand of all his enemies, and from the hand of Saul. He said:

Voice 1:

¹ I love you, O LORD, my strength. *

　² The LORD is my rock, my fortress, and my deliverer,

　my God, my rock in whom I take refuge, *

　　my shield, and the horn of my salvation, my stronghold.

³ **I call upon the LORD, who is worthy to be praised, ***

　　so I shall be saved from my enemies.

⁴ The cords of death encompassed me; *

　　the torrents of perdition assailed me;

⁵ the cords of Sheol entangled me; *

　　the snares of death confronted me.

⁶ **In my distress I called upon the LORD; to my God I cried for help. ***

　　From his temple he heard my voice,

　　and my cry to him reached his ears.

Voice 2:

⁷ Then the earth reeled and rocked; *

　　the foundations also of the mountains trembled and quaked,

　　because he was angry.

⁸ Smoke went up from his nostrils, and devouring fire from his mouth; *

　　glowing coals flamed forth from him.

⁹ **He bowed the heavens, and came down; ***

　　thick darkness was under his feet.

¹⁰ He rode on a cherub, and flew; *

　　he came swiftly upon the wings of the wind.

¹¹ **He made darkness his covering around him, ***

　　his canopy thick clouds dark with water.

¹² Out of the brightness before him there broke through his clouds *

　　hailstones and coals of fire.

¹³ **The LORD also thundered in the heavens, ***

　　and the Most High uttered his voice.

¹⁴ **And he sent out his arrows, and scattered them; ***

　　he flashed forth lightnings, and routed them.

¹⁵ Then the channels of the sea were seen,

　　and the foundations of the world were laid bare *

　　　at your rebuke, O LORD, at the blast of the breath of your nostrils.

Voice 1:

16 He reached down from on high, he took me; *
    he drew me out of mighty waters.

17 **He delivered me from my strong enemy,**
    and from those who hated me; *
        for they were too mighty for me.

18 They confronted me in the day of my calamity; *
    but the Lord was my support.

19 **He brought me out into a broad place; ***
    he delivered me, because he delighted in me.

Voice 2:

20 The Lord rewarded me according to my righteousness; *
    according to the cleanness of my hands he recompensed me.

21 **For I have kept the ways of the Lord, ***
    and have not wickedly departed from my God.

22 For all his ordinances were before me, *
    and his statutes I did not put away from me.

23 **I was blameless before him, ***
    and I kept myself from guilt.

24 Therefore the Lord has recompensed me according to my righteousness, *
    according to the cleanness of my hands in his sight.

Voice 1:

25 With the loyal you show yourself loyal; *
    with the blameless you show yourself blameless;

26 with the pure you show yourself pure; *
    and with the crooked you show yourself perverse.

27 **For you deliver a humble people, ***
    but the haughty eyes you bring down.

28 **It is you who light my lamp; ***
    the Lord, my God, lights up my darkness.

29 By you I can crush a troop, *
    and by my God I can leap over a wall.

30 **This God—his way is perfect; the promise of the Lord proves true; ***
    he is a shield for all who take refuge in him.

(continues)

Voice 2:

³¹ For who is God except the L<small>ORD</small>? *
    And who is a rock besides our God?—

³² the God who girded me with strength, *
    and made my way safe.

³³ He made my feet like the feet of a deer, *
    and set me secure on the heights.

³⁴ He trains my hands for war, *
    so that my arms can bend a bow of bronze.

³⁵ **You have given me the shield of your salvation,**
  and your right hand has supported me; *
    your help has made me great.

³⁶ **You gave me a wide place for my steps under me,** *
    and my feet did not slip.

³⁷ I pursued my enemies and overtook them; *
    and did not turn back until they were consumed.

³⁸ I struck them down, so that they were not able to rise; *
    they fell under my feet.

³⁹ **For you girded me with strength for the battle;** *
    you made my assailants sink under me.

⁴⁰ **You made my enemies turn their backs to me,** *
    and those who hated me I destroyed.

⁴¹ They cried for help, but there was no one to save them; *
    they cried to the L<small>ORD</small>, but he did not answer them.

⁴² I beat them fine, like dust before the wind; *
    I cast them out like the mire of the streets.

Voice 1:

⁴³ You delivered me from strife with the peoples;
  you made me head of the nations; *
    people whom I had not known served me.

⁴⁴ As soon as they heard of me they obeyed me; *
    foreigners came cringing to me.

⁴⁵ Foreigners lost heart, *
    and came trembling out of their strongholds.

⁴⁶ **The L<small>ORD</small> lives! Blessed be my rock,** *
    and exalted be the God of my salvation,

47 the God who gave me vengeance *
    and subdued peoples under me;

48 who delivered me from my enemies;
    indeed, you exalted me above my adversaries; *
        you delivered me from the violent.

49 **For this I will extol you, O Lord, among the nations,** *
    and sing praises to your name.

50 **Great triumphs he gives to his king,** *
    and shows steadfast love to his anointed,
    to David and his descendants forever.

We sing your praise, O God, for you alone are our protection and our freedom.
By the power of your Spirit, may your strength enable our strength
and your Word shape our words.
Enable us to love you, serve you, and follow you
so that our lives may proclaim the redeeming love of Jesus,
in whose name we pray. **Amen.**

Psalm 18 is a psalm of testimony and commitment associated with God's deliverance of David in a military battle. It features an outpouring of images for God's deliverance, describing God as a crag, stronghold, deliverer, rock, shield, and horn. Vertical imagery is especially prominent, contrasting the heights of God's love with the depths of human plight. God's actions raise up the lowly and put down the enemy, themes that echo in the canticles of Hannah and Mary. The psalm speaks about God's intervention in and through human battles. *Use in Worship: a narration of the story of David (see 2 Sam. 22); a prophecy of Christ's liberation of humanity through his victory over death and hell; an allegory of battles against spiritual forces; a testimony for celebrating God's providential care in the context of battle.*

18A Refuge and Rock

1 Ref - uge   and   Rock,   Shield and   De - liv - erer!
2 Earth - quake   and   fire,   thun - der   and   light - ning!
3 Faith - ful   and   pure,   blame - less   and   per - fect—

I   love you, LORD,   for   your   un - fail - ing   care:
Clothed   in   such   ar - mor   you   sprang to   my   aid;
yet   to   the   crook - ed   you   show your - self   shrewd.

fac - ing   the   grave,   fear - ing   de - struc - tion,
part - ing   the   heavens,   burst - ing   with   splen - dor,
Your   ho - ly   light   shines   on   my   dark - ness;

I   called   to   you   and   you   an - swered   my   prayer:
you   left your   foes   ov - er - whelmed and   dis - mayed.
my   steps   are   guid - ed,   my   vig - or   re - newed.

I was dis - tressed— you heard my voice;
Your awe - some power, your ten - der grace
Your law will shape my heart and mind,

I will re - joice for you saved me.
gave me a place where I flour - ish.
let - ting me find rich - est bless - ing.

4 Wisdom and strength, honor and triumph!
Such are the gifts you are eager to give:
strength for the fight; wisdom to lead me;
triumph and more for as long as I live;
honor indeed to make it known
that you alone are eternal.

5 Worship and thanks, reverence and glory
be to the LORD I am honored to know;
saved from my foes, called to your service,
I will extol you wherever I go.
Your love surrounds me all my days:
therefore I praise you, my Savior.

Guitar chords do not correspond with keyboard harmony.

Words: Martin Leckebusch © 2003 Kevin Mayhew Ltd.
Music (EARTH AND ALL STARS 4.5.10.4.5.10.8.8): David N. Johnson (1922-1987), 1968, © 1968 Augsburg
Fortress Publishers; harm. Dale Grotenhuis, 1984, © Augsburg Fortress Publishers

18B How I Love You, Lord My God

1 How I love you, Lord, my God, you, my rock and
for - tress strong; con - stant ref - uge, might - y shield—
I will praise you in my song. Snares of death en -
tan - gled me, hell - ish tor - rents fright-ened me; but you

2 All God's prom - i - ses are sure. Who is God be -
sides the Lord? He is per - fect in his ways.
Who the Rock ex - cept our God? It is God who
gives me strength; he en - a - bles me to stand high a -

heard my des-perate cry, and your hand has set me free.
bove the bat - tle - field, held up by his power-ful hand.

Words: Ada Roeper-Boulogne, 1985, © 1987 Faith Alive Christian Resources
Music (ABERYSTWYTH 7.7.7.7 D): Joseph Parry, 1879, P.D.

Psalm 19

To the leader. A Psalm of David.

¹ The heavens are telling the glory of God; *
  and the firmament proclaims his handiwork.
² Day to day pours forth speech, *
  and night to night declares knowledge.
³ **There is no speech, nor are there words; ***
  their voice is not heard;
⁴ **yet their voice goes out through all the earth,**
  and their words to the end of the world. *
  In the heavens he has set a tent for the sun,
⁵ which comes out like a bridegroom from his wedding canopy, *
  and like a strong man runs its course with joy.
⁶ Its rising is from the end of the heavens, and its circuit to the end of them; *
  and nothing is hid from its heat.
⁷ **The law of the LORD is perfect, reviving the soul; ***
  the decrees of the LORD are sure, making wise the simple;
⁸ **the precepts of the LORD are right, rejoicing the heart; ***
  the commandment of the LORD is clear, enlightening the eyes;
⁹ **the fear of the LORD is pure, enduring forever; ***
  the ordinances of the LORD are true and righteous altogether.

(continues)

¹⁰ More to be desired are they than gold, even much fine gold; *

    sweeter also than honey, and drippings of the honeycomb.

¹¹ Moreover by them is your servant warned; *

    in keeping them there is great reward.

¹² **But who can detect their errors?** *

    Clear me from hidden faults.

¹³ Keep back your servant also from the insolent;

    do not let them have dominion over me. *

        Then I shall be blameless, and innocent of great transgression.

¹⁴ **Let the words of my mouth**

    and the meditation of my heart be acceptable to you, *

        O Lord, my rock and my redeemer.

Amazing God, your glory is revealed in your creation and law,
and your love is revealed in Jesus Christ, the Word made flesh.
You have freed us from sin and death.
You have given us wisdom and joy.
Now, by the power of your Spirit,
make our words and thoughts worthy offerings of praise.
We pray in Jesus' name. **Amen.**

Psalm 19 is a poetic masterpiece that celebrates God's mighty creation (vv. 1-6) and life-giving law (vv. 7-11) as the basis for a humble and faithful piety (vv. 12-14). It celebrates both modes of God's revelation—through creation and through the written Word—and describes the fitting response to this twofold gift. Its poignant images (the eloquent heavens, the racing sun, the honeysweet law) are especially memorable. *Use in Worship: services focusing on themes of creation, divine instruction, and humble piety; an act of preparation for prayer, for hearing God's Word, or for worship itself.*

The Stars Declare His Glory 19A

1 The stars de-clare his glo-ry; the vault of heav-en
2 The dawn re-turns in splen-dor, the heav-ens burn and
3 So shine the Lord's com-mand-ments to make the sim-ple
4 So or-der too this life of mine, di-rect it all my

springs mute wit-ness of the Mas-ter's hand in
blaze, the ris-ing sun re-news the race that
wise; more sweet than hon-ey to the taste, more
days; the med-i-ta-tions of my heart be

all cre-a-ted things, and through the si-lenc-
meas-ures all our days, and writes in fire a-
rich than an-y prize, a law of love with-
in-no-cence and praise, my rock and my re-

es of space their sound-less mu-sic sings.
cross the skies God's maj-es-ty and praise.
in our hearts, a light be-fore our eyes.
deem-ing Lord, in all my words and ways.

Words: Timothy Dudley-Smith (b. 1926) © 1981 Hope Publishing Company
Music (DEERFIELD 7.6.8.6.8.6): David Haas (b. 1957) © 1986 GIA Publications, Inc.

19B God's Glory Fills the Heavens

1 God's glo - ry fills the heavens with hymns;
2 God's per - fect law re - vives the soul;
3 God's ser - vant may I ev - er be:

the domed sky bears the Mak - er's mark.
its pre - cepts make the sim - ple wise.
this world my joy, that word my guide.

New prais - es sound from day to day
Its just com-mands re - joice the heart;
O cleanse me, LORD, from se - cret sin;

and ech - o through the know - ing dark.
its truth gives light un - to the eyes.
de - liv - er me from self - ish pride.

Words: Carl P. Daw Jr. (b. 1944) © 1989 Hope Publishing Company
Music: (CREATION 8.8.8.8 D): Franz Joseph Haydn (1732-1809), 1798, P.D.

19C Psalm 19 | A Responsorial Setting

Refrain

Through the wit-ness of cre-a-tion, through the glo-ry of the Word, you show the way to the king-dom of light, you show the way to e-ter-nal life.

Refrain

¹ The heavens declare the glory of God,
  and the sky proclaims its maker's handiwork.

² One day tells its tale to another,
  and one night imparts knowledge to another. *Refrain*

³ Although they have no words or language,
  and their voices are not heard,

⁴ their sound has gone out into all lands,
  and their message to the ends of the world,
    where God has pitched a tent for the sun.

⁵ It comes forth like a bridegroom out of his chamber;
  it rejoices like a champion to run its course.

⁶ It goes forth from the uttermost edge of the heavens
  and runs about to the end of it again;
    nothing is hidden from its burning heat. *Refrain*

⁷ The teaching of the LORD is perfect and revives the soul;
   the testimony of the LORD is sure and gives wisdom to the simple.

⁸ The statutes of the LORD are just and rejoice the heart;
   the commandment of the LORD is clear and gives light to the eyes.

⁹ The fear of the LORD is clean and endures forever;
   the judgments of the LORD are true and righteous altogether.

¹⁰ More to be desired are they than gold, more than much fine gold,
   sweeter far than honey, than honey in the comb.   *Refrain*

¹¹ By them also is your servant enlightened,
   and in keeping them there is great reward.

¹² Who can detect one's own offenses?
   Cleanse me from my secret faults.

¹³ Above all, keep your servant from presumptuous sins;
   let them not get dominion over me;
   then shall I be whole and sound, and innocent of a great offense.

¹⁴ Let the words of my mouth
   and the meditation of my heart be acceptable in your sight,
   O LORD, my strength and my redeemer.   *Refrain*

Tone

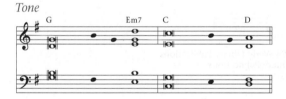

Lectionary: Ordinary Time after Epiphany (C); Lent (B); Easter Vigil (A,B,C); Ordinary Time after Pentecost (A,B); vv. 7-14 Ordinary Time after Pentecost (B).

Words and Music: Gregg DeMey © 2011 Re:Create Music; arr. Paul Detterman © 2011 Re:Create Music
Psalm Text: from *Evangelical Lutheran Worship* © 2006 Evangelical Lutheran Church in America, admin.
Augsburg Fortress Publishers
Tone: © 2011 Faith Alive Christian Resources

(continues)

Alternate Refrain
May be sung in canon

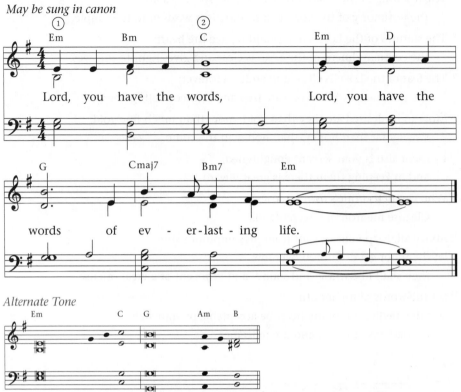

Lord, you have the words, Lord, you have the words of ev - er-last - ing life.

Alternate Tone

Words: John 6:68; Ann Celeen Dohms © 1994 World Library Publications
Music: Ann Celeen Dohms © 1994 World Library Publications
Tone: © 2011 Faith Alive Christian Resources

The Heavens Declare Your Glory 19D

1 The heavens de - clare your glo - ry, the fir - ma - ment your power;
2 The sun with roy - al splen - dor goes forth to chant your praise,
3 All heaven on high re - joic - es to do its Mak - er's will;

day un - to day the sto - ry re - peats from hour to hour.
and moon-beams soft and ten - der their gen - tler an - them raise.
the stars with sol - emn voic - es re - sound your prais - es still.

Night un - to night re - ply - ing, pro - claims in ev - ery land,
O'er ev - ery tribe and na - tion the mu - sic is out-poured,
So let my whole be - hav - ior, each thought, each deed I do,

O LORD, with voice un - dy - ing, the won - ders of your hand.
the song of all cre - a - tion to you, cre - a-tion's Lord.
be, LORD, my strength, my Sav - ior, a cease - less song to you.

Words: Thomas R. Birks, 1874, alt., P.D.
Music (FAITHFUL 7.6.7.6 D): Johann S. Bach (1685-1750); adapt. from 'My Heart Ever Faithful,' *Cantata 68*, P.D.

19E May the Words of My Mouth

Refrain

May the words of my mouth and the med - i - ta - tion
of my heart be ac - cept-a - ble in your sight, O
Lord, my strength and my re - deem - er.

1 The law of the Lord is per - fect, re -
2 The rule of the Lord is gra - cious, re -
3 The fear of the Lord is ho - ly, en -

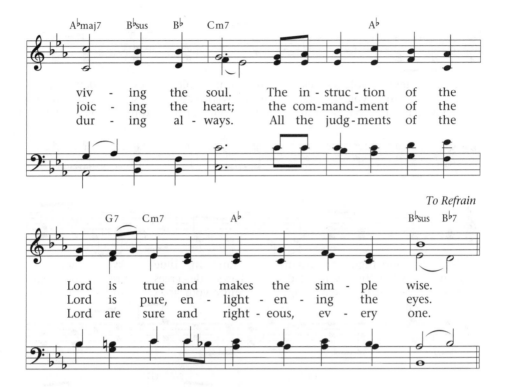

viv - ing the soul. The in - struc - tion of the
joic - ing the heart; the com-mand-ment of the
dur - ing al - ways. All the judg-ments of the

To Refrain

Lord is true and makes the sim - ple wise.
Lord is pure, en - light - en - ing the eyes.
Lord are sure and right - eous, ev - ery one.

4 Your laws are more sweet than honey
and prized more than gold;
and from them your servant shall be taught:
in them is great reward. *Refrain*

5 For sins of my own commission
forgive me, I pray;
and for all those sins I know not of
forgive me, make me clean. *Refrain*

Words and Music: David Lee © 1996, 2001 David Lee

1 Si - lent voic - es, un - heard voic - es, day to day and night to night. Sun in blue sky, stars in black sky: sing-ing, speak - ing, tell - ing light. Ev - ery - thing that God has made tells his glo - ry, tells his glo-ry.

2 Hu - man voic - es, well-loved voic - es, tell a - gain what they were told. Laws, de - crees, pre - cepts, com - mand-ments: next to these what good is gold? Ev - ery - thing the Lord has said, sweet as hon - ey, sweet as hon-ey.

3 Light from na - ture, light from scrip - ture; yet the heart sings bro - ken songs. Shine your grace in - to our shad - ows, sav-ing us from hid - den wrongs. Let our dai - ly lives, O Lord, tell your glo - ry, tell your glo-ry.

Guitar chords do not correspond with keyboard harmony.

Music: Richard Leach, 2006, © 2006 Selah Publishing Company, Inc.
Music (SILENT VOICES 8.7.8.7.7.4.4): Iteke Prins, 2006, © 2006 Selah Publishing Company, Inc.

To the leader. A Psalm of David.

1 The LORD answer you in the day of trouble! *
   The name of the God of Jacob protect you!

2 May he send you help from the sanctuary, *
   and give you support from Zion.

3 **May he remember all your offerings, ***
   and regard with favor your burnt sacrifices.   *Selah*

4 **May he grant you your heart's desire, ***
   and fulfill all your plans.

5 May we shout for joy over your victory,
   and in the name of our God set up our banners. *
   May the LORD fulfill all your petitions.

6 **Now I know that the LORD will help his anointed; ***
   he will answer him from his holy heaven
   with mighty victories by his right hand.

7 Some take pride in chariots, and some in horses, *
   but our pride is in the name of the LORD our God.

8 They will collapse and fall, *
   but we shall rise and stand upright.

9 **Give victory to the king, O LORD; ***
   answer us when we call.

God of every age, you watch nations rise and fall.
May our leaders be led by your wisdom.
When we turn from your way,
help us to repent so that we might be transformed by your forgiveness.
Guide us with your light and truth,
through Jesus Christ, who is Lord of all and light of the world. **Amen.**

Psalm 20 is a psalm of blessing that weaves together three modes of communication: expressions of desire for God's blessing ("may God bless you"), statements of confident assurance ("I know that the Lord will help"), and petitions for God's deliverance ("answer us when we call"). In its original context the psalm focused on blessings for God's anointed, the king (vv. 6, 9). Christians have viewed this as an appropriate blessing for all of God's anointed ones, including Jesus, God's anointed King, and all believers who share in Christ's anointing. *Use in Worship: celebrating Christ's lordship; tempering our reliance on military might; a blessing at celebrations of baptism, baptismal renewal, or other significant moments in the life of an individual or congregation.*

20A El nombre de Dios te ampare / May God's Holy Name Uphold You

Unison

C / Dm / G

Spanish
1 El nom-bre de Dios te_am-pa - re cuan-do_a-prie-te la re-
2 Que cum-pla to-dos tus sue-ños, que lle-ne tus es-per-

English
1 May God's ho-ly name up-hold you when dis-tress and cares sur-
2 May all of your dreams be grant-ed, as you reap what hope has

C / Dm

frie - ga; so - bre ti su gra - cia llue-va, que su_a-
an - zas; que un dí - a nues-tra_a - la - ban-za pue - da
round you; may God's grace rain down up - on you, may God's
plant - ed. May the ban-ners of cre - a - tion wave on

G7 / C / A♭ / B♭

yu - da te de-fien - da; re - ci - ba_el Se - ñor tu_o-
con - tar tu vic - to - ria; fes - te - jar de Dios la
might-y arm de-fend you; may God bless the gifts you
high in cel - e - bra - tion; may shouts of joy greet each

E♭ / G7 / *Last time to Coda* / C

fren - da en el dí - a de tu_en - tre - ga.
glo - ria, que_ha_es-cu - cha-do tus de - man-das.
of - fer on the day you are de - liv - ered.
vic - tory as to God be all the glo - ry.

Spanish

3 Ahora sé que nuestro Dios
  su triunfo te_ha otorgado,
  desde su cielo sagrado
  el Señor te_ha respondido;
  su fuerza te_ha protegido,
  su diestra te_ha salvado.

4 Algunos sólo confían
  en sus potros y_en sus lanzas,
  nosotros nuestra_esperanza
  la ponemos sólo_en Dios;
  veremos cual de los dos
  pesa más en la balanza.
  To Coda

English

3 One thing that I know most surely:
  we may rest in God securely.
  At the time God has appointed
  grace will come to God's anointed;
  for God's strong right hand that made you
  is the same hand that will save you.

4 Some people put trust in weapons,
  but we trust the Lord of heaven.
  Foolish faith will cause their falling
  while God answers to our calling.
  Their fortresses and their towers
  are no match for heaven's powers.
  To Coda

Coda

Dá - le, Se - ñor, la vic - to - ria; res - pón - de - le_a su lla - ma - do.

Hear, Lord, our in - ter - ced - ing; an - swer now your peo - ple's plead - ing.

Words: Mamerto Menapace © Brother Mamerto Menapace; tr. Mary Louise Bringle (b. 1953), 2011
Music (8.8.8.8.8.8 with coda): Homero Perera © Homero Perera

20B Psalm 20 | A Responsorial Setting

Refrain

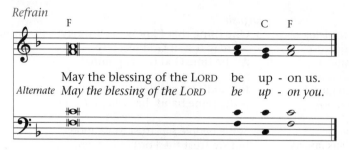

May the blessing of the Lᴎᴀᴀ be up - on us.
Alternate *May the blessing of the Lᴎᴀᴀ be up - on you.*

Refrain

¹ May the Lᴎᴀᴀ answer you in the day of trouble,
    the name of the God of Jacob defend you;

² send you help from the sanctuary
    and strengthen you out of Zion;

³ may the Lᴎᴀᴀ remember all your offerings
    and accept your burnt sacrifice;

⁴ grant you your heart's desire
    and prosper all your plans.   *Refrain*

⁵ We will shout for joy at your victory
  and unfurl our banners in the name of our God;
    may the Lᴎᴀᴀ grant all your requests.

⁶ Now I know that the Lᴎᴀᴀ gives victory to the anointed one;
    God will answer out of holy heaven,
    gaining victory with a strong right hand.   *Refrain*

⁷ Some trust in chariots and some in horses,
    but we rely on the name of the Lᴎᴀᴀ our God.

⁸ They collapse and fall down,
    but we will arise and stand upright.

⁹ O Lᴎᴀᴀ, give victory to the king
    and answer us when we call.   *Refrain*

Tone

Lectionary: Ordinary Time after Pentecost (B).

Words: Psalm 20
Music: Byzantine chant, P.D.
Psalm Text: from *Evangelical Lutheran Worship* © 2006 Evangelical Lutheran Church in America, admin.
Augsburg Fortress Publishers
Tone: © 2011 Faith Alive Christian Resources

Alternate Refrain

Alternate Tone

20C May the Lord God Hear You Pray

1 May the Lord God hear you pray, may God's strength be
2 May God give you all you need, may God make your
3 Now we see the Lord can save, now the trem - bling

yours to - day; may God bless you from a - bove,
plans suc - ceed; may God guide you all your days,
heart is brave; now we know that Love will hear:

lift - ing up your heart in love.
fill - ing all our hearts with praise:
wor - ship now, for God is near!

This tune in a lower key: p. 26.

Words: Michael Perry © 1990 The Jubilate Group, admin. Hope Publishing Company
Music (TEBBEN 7.7.7.7): Timothy Hoekman, 1979, © 1985 Faith Alive Christian Resources

Psalm 21

To the leader. A Psalm of David.

1 In your strength the king rejoices, O Lord, *
   and in your help how greatly he exults!

2 **You have given him his heart's desire, ***
   and have not withheld the request of his lips.   *Selah*

3 **For you meet him with rich blessings; ***
   you set a crown of fine gold on his head.

4 He asked you for life; you gave it to him—*
   length of days forever and ever.

5 **His glory is great through your help; ***
   splendor and majesty you bestow on him.

6 **You bestow on him blessings forever; ***
   you make him glad with the joy of your presence.

7 For the king trusts in the Lord, *
   and through the steadfast love of the Most High he shall not be moved.

8 **Your hand will find out all your enemies; ***
   your right hand will find out those who hate you.

9 You will make them like a fiery furnace when you appear. *
   The Lord will swallow them up in his wrath, and fire will consume them.

10 You will destroy their offspring from the earth, *
   and their children from among humankind.

11 **If they plan evil against you, ***
   if they devise mischief, they will not succeed.

12 For you will put them to flight; *
   you will aim at their faces with your bows.

13 **Be exalted, O Lord, in your strength! ***
   We will sing and praise your power.

Almighty God, you have given victory to Christ, your Anointed One.
Keep us from stumbling into lesser loyalties and give us strength to stand firm,
trusting in the grace and peace of Jesus Christ our Lord. **Amen.**

Psalm 21 is a royal psalm that praises God for blessing the righteous king (vv. 1-7) and for conquering those opposed to divine rule (vv. 8-12). It echoes the "two ways" imagery of Ps. 1 in a manner particularly suited for a coronation. *Use in Worship: Ascension Day; celebrations of the lordship of Christ (vv. 1-6 offer an apt depiction of Christ, the King).*

To Your Unequaled Strength

1 To your un - e - qualed strength, O Lord, your
2 The rul - ers of the Lord's e - lect wear
3 The ones who hon - or you as Lord, to
4 In wrath our en - e - mies will fall, your

cho - sen ones as - pire; bring to the just sure
crowns of fin - est gold; their lives, once emp - ty,
such shall hon - or come; and those in whom good-
arm puts them to flight; we gain our bless - ings

vic - to - ry, and grant their hearts' de - sire.
now through faith shall burst with wealth un - told.
will a - bides in you will find a home.
by your grace, and vic - tory through your might.

Alternate harmonization on p. 869.

Words: Michael Morgan © 1999, 2011 Michael Morgan, admin. Faith Alive Christian Resources
Music (DETROIT 8.6.8.6): *Supplement to Kentucky Harmony*, 1820; harm. Hal H. Hopson © 2002 Selah
Publishing Company, Inc.

Psalm 22

To the leader: according to The Deer of the Dawn. A Psalm of David.

1 My God, my God, why have you forsaken me? *
   Why are you so far from helping me, from the words of my groaning?

2 O my God, I cry by day, but you do not answer; *
   and by night, but find no rest.

3 **Yet you are holy,** *
   enthroned on the praises of Israel.

4 **In you our ancestors trusted;** *
   they trusted, and you delivered them.

5 **To you they cried, and were saved;** *
   in you they trusted, and were not put to shame.

6 But I am a worm, and not human; *
   scorned by others, and despised by the people.

7 All who see me mock at me; *
   they make mouths at me, they shake their heads;

8 "Commit your cause to the LORD; let him deliver— *
   let him rescue the one in whom he delights!"

9 **Yet it was you who took me from the womb;** *
   you kept me safe on my mother's breast.

10 **On you I was cast from my birth,** *
   and since my mother bore me you have been my God.

11 **Do not be far from me, for trouble is near** *
   and there is no one to help.

12 Many bulls encircle me, *
   strong bulls of Bashan surround me;

13 they open wide their mouths at me, *
   like a ravening and roaring lion.

14 **I am poured out like water, and all my bones are out of joint;** *
   my heart is like wax; it is melted within my breast;

15 **my mouth is dried up like a potsherd,**
   and my tongue sticks to my jaws; *
   you lay me in the dust of death.

16 For dogs are all around me; a company of evildoers encircles me. *
   My hands and feet have shriveled;

17 I can count all my bones. *
   They stare and gloat over me;

18 they divide my clothes among themselves, *
   and for my clothing they cast lots.

(continues)

¹⁹ But you, O LORD, do not be far away! *

O my help, come quickly to my aid!

²⁰ Deliver my soul from the sword, *

my life from the power of the dog!

²¹ Save me from the mouth of the lion! *

From the horns of the wild oxen you have rescued me.

²² **I will tell of your name to my brothers and sisters;** *

in the midst of the congregation I will praise you:

²³ You who fear the LORD, praise him! *

All you offspring of Jacob, glorify him;

stand in awe of him, all you offspring of Israel!

²⁴ For he did not despise or abhor the affliction of the afflicted; *

he did not hide his face from me, but heard when I cried to him.

²⁵ **From you comes my praise in the great congregation;** *

my vows I will pay before those who fear him.

²⁶ The poor shall eat and be satisfied; those who seek him shall praise the LORD. *

May your hearts live forever!

²⁷ **All the ends of the earth shall remember and turn to the LORD;** *

and all the families of the nations shall worship before him.

²⁸ For dominion belongs to the LORD, *

and he rules over the nations.

²⁹ **To him, indeed, shall all who sleep in the earth bow down;** *

before him shall bow all who go down to the dust,

and I shall live for him.

³⁰ **Posterity will serve him;** *

future generations will be told about the Lord,

³¹ **and proclaim his deliverance to a people yet unborn,** *

saying that he has done it.

Merciful God, some of your children are joyfully singing your praise.
Others are languishing in despair.
Through Jesus you are acquainted with our grief
and in him we have resurrection hope.
Bind up those who are broken, bless those who are dying, shield those who are joyous,
and lead us all to your house, where we may feast together at your table. **Amen.**

Psalm 22 is a poignant individual lament and cry for help (vv. 1-21) which, after a dramatic pivot, concludes with a hymn of praise (vv. 22-31). This hymn is a beautiful psalm in itself, paying special attention to God's provision for the weak and needy (vv. 24, 26) and speaking of the praise of God that future generations will offer (v. 31). Psalms 22 and 23, when taken together, form a beautiful triptych that moves from restless lament through restorative praise to calm trust. Christians frequently approach Ps. 22 Christologically, especially because two of its verses are quoted in the gospel narrative of Jesus' suffering and death (vv. 1,18). *Use in Worship: Good Friday; services focusing on Jesus' passion; services of baptism; funerals; services exploring union with Jesus in his death and resurrection (see Rom. 6:3-4).*

My God, My God, 22A
Why Have You Forsaken Me?

Words: Susan Sayers (b. 1946) © 1995 Kevin Mayhew Ltd.
Music: Andrew Moore © 1995 Kevin Mayhew Ltd.

22B Lord, Why Have You Forsaken Me

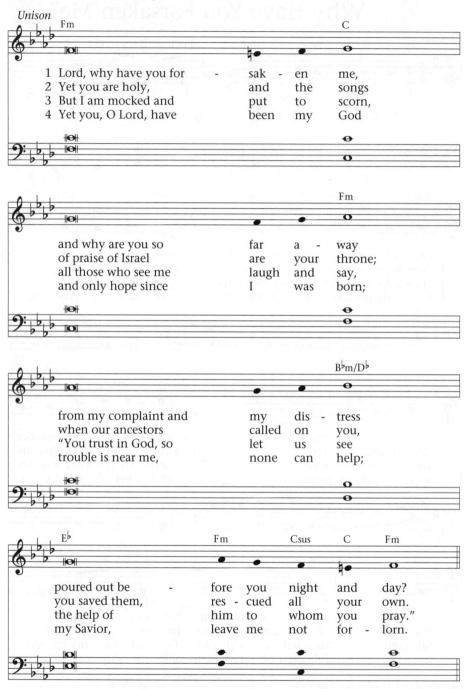

Unison

1 Lord, why have you for - sak - en me,
2 Yet you are holy, and the songs
3 But I am mocked and put to scorn,
4 Yet you, O Lord, have been my God

and why are you so far a - way
of praise of Israel are your throne;
all those who see me laugh and say,
and only hope since I was born;

from my complaint and my dis - tress
when our ancestors called on you,
"You trust in God, so let us see
trouble is near me, none can help;

poured out be - fore you night and day?
you saved them, res - cued all your own.
the help of him to whom you pray."
my Savior, leave me not for - lorn.

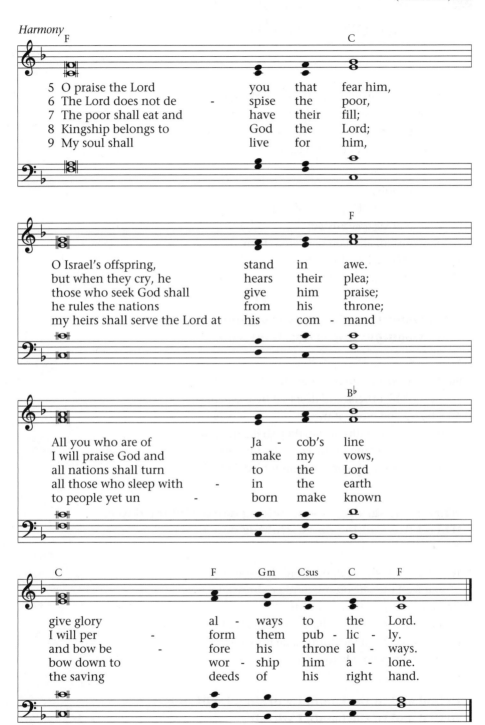

Harmony

5 O praise the Lord you that fear him,
6 The Lord does not de - spise the poor,
7 The poor shall eat and have their fill;
8 Kingship belongs to God the Lord;
9 My soul shall live for him,

O Israel's offspring, stand in awe.
but when they cry, he hears their plea;
those who seek God shall give him praise;
he rules the nations from his throne;
my heirs shall serve the Lord at his com - mand

All you who are of Ja - cob's line
I will praise God and make my vows,
all nations shall turn to the Lord
all those who sleep with - in the earth
to people yet un - born make known

give glory al - ways to the Lord.
I will per - form them pub - lic - ly.
and bow be - fore his throne al - ways.
bow down to wor - ship him a - lone.
the saving deeds of his right hand.

Words: Christopher L. Webber © 1986 Christopher L. Webber, admin. Church Pension Group/Church Publishing, Inc.
Music (HARVEY'S CHANT alt. 8.8.8.8): William B. Bradbury (1816-1868); adapt. Martin Tel © 2011 Faith Alive Christian Resources

22C Psalm 22:1-11, 22-29
A Scripted Reading

Psalm reading may begin with WONDROUS LOVE *refrain played on an instrument or hummed by the congregation.*

Voice 1:

¹ My God, my God, why have you forsaken me?
Why are you so far from helping me, from the words of my groaning?
² O my God, I cry by day, but you do not answer;
and by night, but find no rest.

Voice 2:

³ Yet you are holy,
enthroned on the praises of Israel.
⁴ In you our ancestors trusted;
they trusted, and you delivered them.
⁵ To you they cried, and were saved;
in you they trusted, and were not put to shame.

All Sing

What wondrous love is this, O my soul, O my soul?
What wondrous love is this, O my soul?

Voice 1:

⁶ But I am a worm, and not human;
scorned by others, and despised by the people.
⁷ All who see me mock at me;
they make mouths at me, they shake their heads;
⁸ "Commit your cause to the LORD; let him deliver—
let him rescue the one in whom he delights!"

All Sing

When I was sinking down, sinking down, sinking down,
When I was sinking down, sinking down . . .

Voice 2:

⁹ Yet it was you who took me from the womb;
you kept me safe on my mother's breast.
¹⁰ On you I was cast from my birth,
and since my mother bore me you have been my God.
¹¹ Do not be far from me, for trouble is near
and there is no one to help.

All Sing

To God and to the Lamb, I will sing, I will sing.
To God and to the Lamb, I will sing.

Voice 1:

²² I will tell of your name to my brothers and sisters;

  in the midst of the congregation I will praise you:

²³ You who fear the LORD, praise him!

  All you offspring of Jacob, glorify him;

  stand in awe of him, all you offspring of Israel!

Voice 2:

²⁴ For he did not despise or abhor the affliction of the afflicted;

  he did not hide his face from me, but heard when I cried to him.

²⁵ From you comes my praise in the great congregation;

  my vows I will pay before those who fear him.

²⁶ The poor shall eat and be satisfied; those who seek him shall praise the LORD.

  May your hearts live forever!

Voices 1 and 2 together:

²⁷ All the ends of the earth shall remember and turn to the LORD;

  and all the families of the nations shall worship before him.

²⁸ For dominion belongs to the LORD,

  and he rules over the nations.

²⁹ To him, indeed, shall all who sleep in the earth bow down;

  before him shall bow all who go down to the dust,

  and I shall live for him.

All Sing

And when from death I'm free, I'll sing on, I'll sing on!

And when from death I'm free, I'll sing on!

Optional Accompaniment

Words: S. Mead's *A General Selection*, 1811, P.D.
Music (WONDROUS LOVE fragment): W. Walker's *Southern Harmony*, 1835; harm. Emily R. Brink (b. 1940), 1986, © 1987 Faith Alive Christian Resources
Text: Psalm 22, New Revised Standard Version © 1989 Division of Christian Education of the National Council of the Churches of Christ in the United States of America. Used by permission. All rights reserved.

Refrain

1 My God, my God, why have you forsaken me?
    Why so far from saving me, so far from the words of my groaning?

2 My God, I cry out by day, but you do not answer;
    by night, but I find no rest.

3 Yet you are the Holy One,
    enthroned on the praises of Israel.

4 Our ancestors put their trust in you,
    they trusted, and you rescued them.

5 They cried out to you and were delivered;
    they trusted in you and were not put to shame.

6 But as for me, I am a worm and not human,
    scorned by all and despised by the people.

7 All who see me laugh me to scorn;
    they curl their lips; they shake their heads.

8 "Trust in the LORD; let the LORD deliver;
    let God rescue him if God so delights in him."

9 Yet you are the one who drew me forth from the womb,
    and kept me safe on my mother's breast.

10 I have been entrusted to you ever since I was born;
    you were my God when I was still in my mother's womb.   *Refrain*

11 Be not far from me, for trouble is near,
    and there is no one to help.

12 Many young bulls encircle me;
    strong bulls of Bashan surround me.

13 They open wide their jaws at me,
    like a slashing and roaring lion.

14 I am poured out like water; all my bones are out of joint;
    my heart within my breast is melting wax.

15 My strength is dried up like a potsherd;
  my tongue sticks to the roof of my mouth;
    and you have laid me in the dust of death.   *Refrain*

16 Packs of dogs close me in, a band of evildoers circles round me;
    they pierce my hands and my feet.

17 I can count all my bones
    while they stare at me and gloat.

18 They divide my garments among them;
    for my clothing, they cast lots.

19 But you, O LORD, be not far away;
    O my help, hasten to my aid.

20 Deliver me from the sword,
    my life from the power of the dog.

21 Save me from the lion's mouth!
    From the horns of wild bulls you have rescued me.

22 I will declare your name to my people;
    in the midst of the assembly I will praise you.   *Refrain*   (continues)

²³ You who fear the LORD, give praise! All you of Jacob's line, give glory.
    Stand in awe of the LORD, all you offspring of Israel.

²⁴ For the LORD does not despise nor abhor the poor in their poverty;
    neither is the LORD's face hidden from them;
        but when they cry out, the LORD hears them.

²⁵ From you comes my praise in the great assembly;
    I will perform my vows in the sight of those who fear the LORD.

²⁶ The poor shall eat and be satisfied.
    Let those who seek the LORD give praise! May your hearts live forever!   *Refrain*

²⁷ All the ends of the earth shall remember and turn to the LORD;
    all the families of nations shall bow before God.

²⁸ For dominion belongs to the LORD,
    who rules over the nations.

²⁹ Indeed, all who sleep in the earth shall bow down in worship;
    all who go down to the dust, though they be dead,
        shall kneel before the LORD.

³⁰ Their descendents shall serve the LORD,
    whom they shall proclaim to generations to come.

³¹ They shall proclaim God's deliverance to a people yet unborn,
    saying to them, "The LORD has acted!"   *Refrain*

Tone

Lectionary: Good Friday (A,B,C); vv. 1-15 Ordinary Time after Pentecost (B); vv. 19-28 Ordinary Time after Pentecost (C); vv. 23-31 Lent (B); vv. 25-31 Eastertide (B).

Words: Psalm 22
Music: Val Parker © 2005 Val Parker, admin. OCP Publications
Psalm Text: from *Evangelical Lutheran Worship* © 2006 Evangelical Lutheran Church in America, admin. Augsburg Fortress Publishers
Tone: © 2011 Faith Alive Christian Resources

Alternate Refrain

All the ends of the earth shall re-mem-ber and turn to the LORD.

Alternate Tone

Words: Psalm 22
Music: Lorraine Brugh from *Psalter for Worship, Cycle B* © 1996 Augsburg Fortress Publishers
Tone: from *Psalter for Worship, Cycle B* © 1996 Augsburg Fortress Publishers

22E Amid the Thronging Worshipers

1 A - mid the throng-ing wor-ship-ers the Lord, our God, I bless;
2 The bur-den of the sor-row-ful the Lord will not de-spise;
3 He feeds with good the hum-ble soul and sat-is-fies the meek,

be - fore his peo-ple gath-ered here his name will I con-fess.
he has not turned from those who mourn, he lis-tens to their cries.
and they shall live and praise the Lord who for his mer-cy seek.

Come, praise him, all who fear the Lord, the chil-dren of his grace;
His good-ness makes me join the throng where saints his praise pro-claim,
The ends of all the earth will hear, the na-tions seek the Lord;

with rev-erence sound his glo-ries forth and bow be-fore his face.
and there will I ful-fill my vows with those who fear his name.
they wor-ship him, the King of kings, in earth and heaven a-dored.

Words: *Psalter*, 1912, P.D.
Music (BOVINA 8.6.8.6 D): Laura A. Tate, 1912, P.D.

In the Presence of Your People 22F

1 In the pres-ence of your peo - ple I will praise your name,
2 All who love you sing your prais - es and pro-claim your power,
3 All who seek your rule will praise you and be sat - is - fied;

for a - lone you are ho - ly, en-throned on the prais-es of Is - ra - el.

Let us cel - e - brate your good-ness and your stead-fast love;
You have not ig-nored our suf-fering but have heard our cry;
All the peo-ples of the na - tions will bow down to you;

may your name be ex-al - ted here on earth and in heaven a - bove.

Descant

Lai, lai, lai...

Words: st. 1 Brent Chambers (b. 1948) and sts. 2-3 Bert Polman © 1977 Universal Music—Brentwood-Benson Publishing
Music (CELEBRATION): Brent Chambers (b. 1948), 1977, © 1977 Universal Music—Brentwood-Benson Publishing

22G The Ends of All the Earth

1 The ends of all the earth shall hear and turn un-to the
2 His is the king-dom, his of right; he rules the na-tions
3 Both rich and poor, both bond and free shall wor-ship him on
4 The Lord's un-fail-ing right-eous-ness all gen-er-a-tions

Lord in fear; all kin-dreds of the earth shall own
by his might. All earth to him her hom-age brings,
bend-ed knee, and chil-dren's chil-dren shall pro-claim
shall con-fess; from age to age they shall be taught

Refrain

and wor-ship him as God a-lone.
the Lord of lords, the King of kings.
the glo-rious hon-or of his name. All earth to him
what won-drous works the Lord has wrought.

her hom-age brings, the Lord of lords, the King of kings.

Words: *Psalter*, 1912, P.D.
Music (VISION 8.8.8.8 with refrain): William H. Doane (1832-1915), P.D.

Psalm 23

A Psalm of David.

1 The LORD is my shepherd, *
   I shall not want.

2 **He makes me lie down in green pastures; ***
   he leads me beside still waters;

3 he restores my soul. *
   He leads me in right paths for his name's sake.

4 **Even though I walk through the darkest valley, I fear no evil; ***
   for you are with me; your rod and your staff—they comfort me.

5 You prepare a table before me in the presence of my enemies; *
   you anoint my head with oil; my cup overflows.

6 **Surely goodness and mercy shall follow me all the days of my life, ***
   and I shall dwell in the house of the LORD my whole life long.

Jesus, loving shepherd, we hear your voice,
and we know the price you paid because of your love for us.
Help us to move beyond hearing and knowing
to accepting the life you offer us and committing ourselves to serving others,
giving you all honor, glory, and praise. **Amen.**

Psalm 23, like Ps. 16, is a psalm of trust. It is filled with memorable imagery: grassy pastures, restful waters, dark valleys, the protecting and correcting rod and staff, sumptuous feasts, and fragrant oil. It makes a journey from "rest" to "shadow" to "feast," narrating God's presence in moments of orientation, disorientation, and reorientation. *Use in Worship: funerals; celebrations during the season of Easter focused on the image of the good shepherd (see Ezek. 34, John 10); services marking a stage in life's journey.*

23A My Shepherd Will Supply My Need

1 My Shep-herd will sup-ply my need; the LORD God is his name:
2 When I walk through the shades of death your pres-ence is my stay;
3 The sure pro-vi-sions of my God at-tend me all my days;

in pas-tures fresh he makes me feed, be-side the liv-ing stream.
one word of your sup-port-ing breath drives all my fears a-way.
O may your house be my a-bode, and all my work be praise.

He brings my wan-dering spir-it back, when I for-sake his ways;
Your hand, in sight of all my foes, shall still my ta-ble spread;
There would I find a set-tled rest, while oth-ers go and come;

and leads me, for his mer-cy's sake, in paths of truth and grace.
my cup with bless-ings o-ver-flows, your oil a-noints my head.
no more a strang-er or a guest, but like a child at home.

Words: Isaac Watts (1674-1748), 1719, alt., P.D.
Music (RESIGNATION 8.6.8.6 D): W. Walker's *Southern Harmony*, 1835; harm. *Hymnal for Colleges and Schools*, 1956, © 1956 Yale University Press

The LORD, My Shepherd, Rules My Life 23B

Descant

5 Your good - ness and your gra - cious love pur -

1 The LORD, my shep - herd, rules my life and
2 The LORD re - vives my fail - ing strength, he
3 Though in a val - ley dark as death, no

sue me all my days; your house, O LORD, shall

gives me all I need; he leads me by re -
makes my joy com-plete; and in right paths, for
e - vil makes me fear; your shep - herd's staff pro -

be my home— your name, my end - less praise.

fresh - ing streams; in pas - tures green I feed.
his name's sake, he guides my fal - tering feet.
tects my way, for you are with me there.

4 While all my enemies look on,
you spread a royal feast;
you fill my cup, anoint my head,
and treat me as your guest.

5 Your goodness and your gracious love
pursue me all my days;
your house, O LORD, shall be my home—
your name, my endless praise.

Words: Christopher Idle © 1982 The Jubilate Group, admin. Hope Publishing Company
Music (CRIMOND 8.6.8.6): Jessie Seymour Irvine, 1872; harm. David Grant, 1872; desc. W. Baird Ross (1871-1950), P.D.

23C The LORD's My Shepherd

1 The LORD's my shep-herd; I'll not want. He
2 My soul he doth re-store a-gain, and
3 Yea, though I walk in death's dark vale, yet

makes me down to lie in pas-tures green; he
me to walk doth make with-in the paths of
will I fear no ill; for thou art with me,

lead-eth me the qui-et wa-ters by; he
right-eous-ness, e'en for his own name's sake; with-
and thy rod and staff me com-fort still; for

lead-eth me, he lead-eth me the qui-et wa-ters by.
in the paths of right-eous-ness, e'en for his own name's sake.
thou art with me, and thy rod and staff me com-fort still.

4 My table thou hast furnishéd
 in presence of my foes;
 my head thou dost with oil anoint,
 and my cup overflows;
 my head thou dost with oil anoint,
 and my cup overflows.

5 Goodness and mercy all my life
 shall surely follow me,
 and in God's house forevermore
 my dwelling place shall be;
 and in God's house forevermore
 my dwelling place shall be.

Spanish

1 Es el Señor mi buen pastor y no me faltará;
  por verdes prados con amor él me conducirá.
  Por verdes prados con amor él me conducirá.

2 Junto a aguas frescas con bondad haráme reposar;
  por sendas justas y de paz su mano me guiará.
  Por sendas justas y de paz su mano me guiará.

3 Y cuando_el valle de dolor o muerte deba andar,
  no sentiré ningún temor pues él me guardará.
  No sentiré ningún temor pues él me guardará.

4 Es sabio_y fiel mi buen pastor; jamás me dejará;
  con su cayado mi Señor aliento me dará.
  Con su cayado mi Señor aliento me dará.

5 Hasta_el final me seguirán misericordia_y bien;
  y de mi Padre_en el hogar por siempre moraré.
  Y de mi Padre_en el hogar por siempre moraré.

Korean

1 주 나의 목자 되시니 부족함 없도다
  푸른 풀밭 호숫가로 날 인도하시네
  푸른 풀밭 호숫가로 날 인도하시네

2 내 영혼 소생시키며 그 이름 위하여
  늘 의로운 길 걷도록 날 인도하시네
  늘 의로운 길 걷도록 날 인도하시네

3 나 어둠 골짝 지나도 두려움 없겠네
  주 막대기와 지팡이 날 안위하시네
  주 막대기와 지팡이 날 안위하시네

4 주 나의 원수 앞에서 내 상을 베푸사
  머리에 기름 부으니 내 잔이 넘치네
  머리에 기름 부으니 내 잔이 넘치네

5 선함과 인자하심이 내 평생 따르리
  여호와 전에 영원히 나 거하리로다
  여호와 전에 영원히 나 거하리로다

Alternate tune: CRIMOND, p. 131.
(When singing this text to CRIMOND do not repeat the last two lines of text.)

Words: English, *Scottish Psalter*, 1650, P.D.; Spanish, tr. Federico J. Pagura; Korean tr. The United Methodist Korean Hymnal Committee © 2001 The United Methodist Publishing House, admin. The Copyright Company Music (BROTHER JAMES' AIR 8.6.8.6.8.6): J. L. Macbeth Bain (1840-1925); harm. Gordon Jacob (1895-1984). Reproduced by permission of Oxford University Press.

23D The King of Love My Shepherd Is

1 The King of love my Shep-herd is, whose good-ness
2 Where streams of liv-ing wa-ter flow my ran-somed
3 Per-verse and fool-ish oft I strayed, but yet in
4 In death's dark vale I fear no ill with thee, dear

fail-eth nev-er; I noth-ing lack if
soul he lead-eth, and where the ver-dant
love he sought me, and on his shoul-der
Lord, be-side me; thy rod and staff my

I am his and he is mine for-ev-er.
pas-tures grow, with food ce-les-tial feed-eth.
gent-ly laid, and home, re-joic-ing, brought me.
com-fort still, thy cross be-fore to guide me.

5 Thou spreadst a table in my sight;
thy unction grace bestoweth;
and, oh, what transport of delight
from thy pure chalice floweth!

6 And so through all the length of days
thy goodness faileth never;
Good Shepherd, may I sing thy praise
within thy house forever.

Alternate tune: DOMINUS REGIT ME, see facing page.

Words: Henry Williams Baker, 1868, P.D.
Music (ST. COLUMBA 8.7.8.7): Ancient Irish melody, P.D.

Such Perfect Love My Shepherd Shows 23E

1 Such per-fect love my Shep-herd shows, whose
2 Where streams of liv-ing wa-ter flow, my
3 When vain and fool-ish I have strayed, you,
4 I do not fear death's shad-owed vale when

good-ness fails me nev - er, whose hand all things I
lov - ing Shep-herd leads me, and where the ver-dant
faith - ful Shep-herd, sought me, and on your shoul-der
you are here be - side me; your rod and staff and

need be - stows and watch - es me for - ev - er.
pas - tures grow with food from heav-en feeds me.
gent - ly laid, then home, re - joic-ing, brought me.
strength pre - vail to com - fort and to guide me.

5 You spread a table in my sight,
  your gifts of grace bestowing;
  and from your chalice I delight
  to taste your mercy flowing.

6 And so through all the length of days
  your goodness fails me never;
  Good Shepherd, may I sing your praise
  within your house forever

Alternate tune: ST. COLUMBA, see facing page.

Words: Henry Williams Baker, 1868, alt., P.D.
Music (DOMINUS REGIT ME 8.7.8.7): John B. Dykes (1823-1876), 1868, P.D.

Descant (with Refrain)

I will trust, I will trust in you.

Eb   Bb7   Eb

1 The Lord's my shep - herd, I'll not want. He makes me
2 He guides my ways in right-eous - ness, and he a-
3 And though I walk the dark - est path, I will not

Refrain And I will trust in you a - lone. And I will

I will trust, I will trust in you.

Ab/C   Bbsus   Bb

lie in pas - tures green. He leads me
noints my head with oil, and my
fear the e - vil one, for you are

trust in you a - lone, for your

End - less mer - cy fol - lows me, your

Ab   Bbsus   Bb7   Eb   Ab2/C

by the still, still wa - ters, his
cup, it o - ver - flows with joy, I
with me, and your rod and staff are the

end - less mer - cy fol - lows me, your

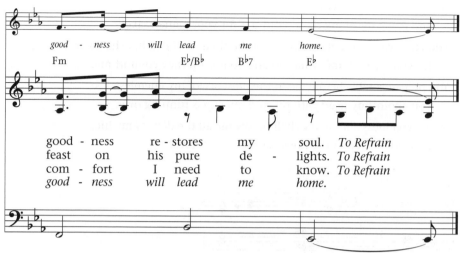

good - ness will lead me home.

good - ness re - stores my soul. *To Refrain*
feast on his pure de - lights. *To Refrain*
com - fort I need to know. *To Refrain*
good - ness will lead me home.

Words: Psalm 23:1-6; 36:8; 56:3
Music: Stuart Townend © 1996 ThankYou Music, admin. by worshiptogether.com songs/EMI CMG
Publishing, excl. UK and Europe, admin. by Kingsway Music/www.kingswaysongs.com

Psalm 23 | A Responsorial Setting 23G

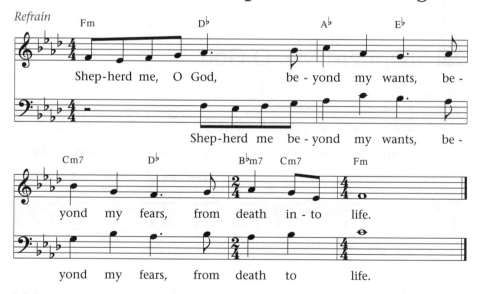

Refrain

Shep-herd me, O God, be - yond my wants, be -

Shep-herd me be - yond my wants, be -

yond my fears, from death in - to life.

yond my fears, from death to life.

Refrain

¹ The LORD is my shepherd;
   I shall not be in want.

² The LORD makes me lie down in green pastures
   and leads me beside still waters. *Refrain*

(continues)

³ You restore my soul, O LORD,

and guide me along right pathways for your name's sake.

⁴ Though I walk through the valley of the shadow of death, I shall fear no evil;

for you are with me; your rod and your staff, they comfort me. *Refrain*

⁵ You prepare a table before me in the presence of my enemies;

you anoint my head with oil, and my cup is running over.

⁶ Surely goodness and mercy shall follow me all the days of my life,

and I will dwell in the house of the LORD forever. *Refrain*

Lectionary: Lent (A); Eastertide (A,B,C); Ordinary Time after Pentecost (A,B).

For accompaniment see p. 140.

23H Shepherd Me, O God

rest in the mead-ows of faith-ful-ness and love, I
lead me by path-ways of right-eous-ness and truth, my
fear no e - vil, for you are at my side, your

walk by the qui - et wa - ters of peace. *To Refrain*
spir - it shall sing the mu - sic of your name. *To Refrain*
rod and your staff, my com - fort and my hope. *To Refrain*

4 You have set me a ban-quet of love in the face of ha-tred,

crown-ing me with love be-yond my power to hold. *To Refrain*

5 Sure - ly your kind-ness and mer - cy fol-low me

all the days of my life; I will

dwell in the house of my God for-ev - er - more. *To Refrain*

Keyboard accompaniment on p. 140.

Words: Marty Haugen (b. 1950) © 1986 GIA Publications, Inc.
Music (SHEPHERD ME): Marty Haugen (b. 1950) © 1986 GIA Publications, Inc.

Accompaniment

Music (SHEPHERD ME): Marty Haugen (b. 1950) © 1986 GIA Publications, Inc.

231 El Señor es mi pastor / My Shepherd Is the LORD

Refrain

Spanish: El Se-ñor es mi pas-tor; na-da me pue-de fal-tar.
English: My shep-herd is the LORD; noth-ing in-deed shall I want.

1 El Se-ñor es mi pas-tor. ¿Qué me pue - de fal-tar?
1 The LORD is my shep-herd; there is noth - ing I want.
2 The LORD re-stores my soul and guides me in the right;
3 In the sight of my foes you pre-pare a feast for me.

En pra-de-ras des-cu-bier-tas él me lle-va a des-can-sar.
God leads me in green pas-tures and be-side qui-et wa-ters.
e-ven though I walk near death, noth-ing e-vil shall I fear.
You a-noint my head with oil, and my cup ov-er-flows.

2 El me guía en sus senderos por amor de su nombre.
Aunque cruce a oscuras ningún mal temeré. *To Refrain*

3 Tú preparas una mesa frente a mis enemigos;
tú perfumas mi cabeza y mi copa rebosa. *To Refrain*

Words: Ricardo Villarreal, 1975; tr. *Psalter Hymnal*, 1987, © 1987 Faith Alive Christian Resources
Music (PASTOR): Ricardo Villarreal, 1975; harm. Delbert Asay, 1975

The God of Love My Shepherd Is 23J

1 The God of love my shep - herd is, and
2 He leads me to the ten - der grass, where
3 Or if I stray, he doth con - vert and
4 Yea, in death's sha - dy black a - bode well

he that doth me feed: while he is mine and
I both feed and rest; then to the streams that
bring my mind in frame: and all this not for
may I walk, not fear: for thou art with me;

I am his, what can I want or need?
gent - ly pass: in both I have the best.
my de - sert, but for his ho - ly name.
and thy rod to guide, thy staff to bear.

5 Nay, thou dost make me sit and dine,
e'en in my enemy's sight:
my head with oil, my cup with wine
runs over day and night.

6 Surely thy sweet and wondrous love
shall measure all my days;
and as it never shall remove,
so neither shall my praise.

Words: George Herbert (1593-1633), P.D.
Music (RIDGEMOOR 8.6.8.6): Roy Hopp, 1992, © 1992 Selah Publishing Company, Inc.

The Lord Is My Shepherd

Second piano part, for playing as a duet:

Repeat through the entire song.
May also be played on Orff instruments.

Words: Psalm 23:1-2
Music: Folk melody; arr. Charlotte Larsen, 1992, © 1994 Faith Alive Christian Resources

Of David. A Psalm.

¹ The earth is the LORD's and all that is in it, *
  the world, and those who live in it;

² for he has founded it on the seas, *
  and established it on the rivers.

³ Who shall ascend the hill of the LORD? *
  And who shall stand in his holy place?

⁴ **Those who have clean hands and pure hearts, ***
  who do not lift up their souls to what is false,
  and do not swear deceitfully.

⁵ **They will receive blessing from the LORD, ***
  and vindication from the God of their salvation.

⁶ **Such is the company of those who seek him, ***
  who seek the face of the God of Jacob.   *Selah*

⁷ Lift up your heads, O gates! and be lifted up, O ancient doors! *
  that the King of glory may come in.

⁸ Who is the King of glory? *
  The LORD, strong and mighty, the LORD, mighty in battle.

⁹ Lift up your heads, O gates! and be lifted up, O ancient doors! *
  that the King of glory may come in.

¹⁰ Who is this King of glory? *
  The LORD of hosts, he is the King of glory.   *Selah*

Creator of all things,
keep us alert to the signs of Christ's return and attentive to the needs of your people,
so that we may live with joy and purpose and eagerly welcome the King of Glory.
We pray in Jesus' name. **Amen.**

Psalm 24 is a psalm of testimony that announces three basic themes: our world belongs to God (vv. 1-2), true worship is offered by people of integrity and holiness (vv. 3-6, see also Ps. 15), and the world should welcome the coming of the sovereign and mighty Lord (vv. 7-10). It can be understood chronologically: God made the world in the past, is worshiped now by people of integrity and holiness, and is coming to redeem the world. Thus, the psalm insists that holiness is the proper response to the God of creation and future redemption. *Use in Worship: call to worship (especially vv. 1-6); during the season of Advent (vv. 7-10); services focusing on a call to holiness, justice, and integrity; services emphasizing the overarching drama of Scripture from creation to new creation.*

24A The Earth, with All That Dwell Therein

1 The earth, with all that dwell there-in, with all its
2 Oh, who shall stand be-fore the Lord on Zi-on's
3 Lo, such are they that seek the Lord, and blest by

wealth un-told, be-longs to God who found-ed it up-
ho-ly hill? The clean of hand, the pure of heart, the
God they live; to them the Lord's pure right-eous ways the

on the seas of old, up-on the seas of old.
just who do God's will, the just who do God's will.
God of grace will give, the God of grace will give.

4 O everlasting doors, give way;
lift up your head, O gates!
For now, behold, to enter in,
the King of glory waits,
the King of glory waits.

5 Who is this glorious King that comes
to sit upon the throne?
All hail the Lord of Hosts who is
our glorious King alone,
our glorious King alone.

Guitar chords do not correspond with keyboard harmony.

Words: *Psalter*, 1912, alt., P.D.
Music (LOBT GOTT, IHR CHRISTEN 8.6.8.6.6): Nikolaus Herman (1480-1561), P.D.

Lift Up Your Heads, O Gates 24B

Guitar chords do not correspond with keyboard harmony.

Words: Bert Polman, 1986, © 1987 Faith Alive Christian Resources
Music (VINEYARD HAVEN 6.6.8.6 with refrain): Richard Dirksen, 1974, © 1974, 1987 Harold Flammer,
a division of Shawnee Press; arr. © 2011 Harold Flammer, a division of Shawnee Press, Inc., reprinted by
permission of Hal Leonard Corporation

24C The Earth Is the Lord's

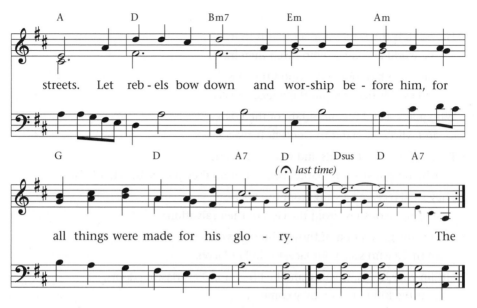

streets. Let reb-els bow down and wor-ship be-fore him, for all things were made for his glo - ry. The

Words and Music: Graham Kendrick © 1986 Thankyou Music, admin. EMI CMG Publishing

Psalm 24 | A Responsorial Setting **24D**

Refrain

The king-dom of God is jus-tice and peace and joy in the Ho-ly Spir-it. Come, Lord, and o-pen in us the gates of your king-dom.

(continues)

Refrain

1 The earth is the LORD's and all that is in it,
    the world and those who dwell therein.

2 For the LORD has founded it upon the seas
    and established it upon the rivers.   *Refrain*

3 Who may ascend the mountain of the LORD,
    and who may stand in God's holy place?

4 Those of innocent hands and purity of heart,
    who do not swear on God's being, nor do they pledge by what is false.

5 They shall receive blessing from the LORD
    and righteousness from the God of their salvation.

6 Such is the generation of those who seek you, O LORD,
    of those who seek your face, O God of Jacob.   *Refrain*

7 Lift up your heads, O gates; and be lifted up, O everlasting doors,
    that the King of glory may come in.

8 Who is this King of glory?
    The LORD, strong and mighty, the LORD, mighty in battle!

9 Lift up your heads, O gates; and be lifted up, O everlasting doors,
    that the King of glory may come in.

10 Who is this King of glory?
    Truly, the LORD of hosts is the King of glory.   *Refrain*

Tone

Lectionary: Ordinary Time after Pentecost (B); All Saints' Day (B).

The tone may also be used with the refrain of 24E.

Words and Music: The Community of Taizé © 2007 Ateliers et Presses de Taizé, Taizé Community, France, GIA Publications, Inc., exclusive North American agent
Psalm Text: from *Evangelical Lutheran Worship* © 2006 Evangelical Lutheran Church in America, admin. Augsburg Fortress Publishers
Tone: © 2011 Faith Alive Christian Resources

Lift Up the Gates Eternal **24E**

Refrain

Lift up the gates e-ter-nal, lift up your voic - es;

the King of glo - ry comes, the na - tion re - joic - es. *Fine*

1 See, all the earth is God's, its peo - ple and na - tions;
2 Who can go up this moun - tain, who stand in prais - ing?
3 They shall re - ceive for - give - ness, and have God's bless - ing

God built it on the deeps and laid its foun - da - tions.
Those who are pure, who come with clean hands up - rais - ing.
if they will search for God, their Sav - ior con - fess - ing. *To Refrain*

4 Come, lift your voices high,
   be lifted to glory;
   the Lord our God approaches,
   come, shout the story.

5 Who is this glorious one,
   for whom we are waiting?
   We wait the mighty Lord,
   our God celebrating. *To Refrain*

6 Come, lift your heads with joy;
   come, lift up your tower;
   the King of glory comes in
   full might and power.

7 Who is this King of glory
   of whom we're singing?
   Our God, the Lord of Hosts,
   the victory is bringing. *To Refrain*

Words: sts. Arlo D. Duba © 1986 Arlo D. Duba; ref. Willard F. Jabusch © 1966 Willard F. Jabusch, admin.
OCP Publications
Music (PROMISED ONE 12.12.12.12): Israeli folk melody; arr. John Ferguson © 1974 United Church Press

Psalm 25

Of David.

1 To you, O LORD, *

  I lift up my soul.

2 O my God, in you I trust; *

  do not let me be put to shame; do not let my enemies exult over me.

3 Do not let those who wait for you be put to shame; *

  let them be ashamed who are wantonly treacherous.

4 **Make me to know your ways, O LORD; ***

  teach me your paths.

5 **Lead me in your truth, and teach me,**

  for you are the God of my salvation; *

  for you I wait all day long.

6 Be mindful of your mercy, O LORD, and of your steadfast love, *

  for they have been from of old.

7 Do not remember the sins of my youth or my transgressions; *

  according to your steadfast love remember me,

  for your goodness' sake, O LORD!

8 **Good and upright is the LORD; ***

  therefore he instructs sinners in the way.

9 **He leads the humble in what is right, ***

  and teaches the humble his way.

10 **All the paths of the LORD are steadfast love and faithfulness, ***

  for those who keep his covenant and his decrees.

11 For your name's sake, O LORD, *

  pardon my guilt, for it is great.

12 Who are they that fear the LORD? *

  He will teach them the way that they should choose.

13 **They will abide in prosperity, ***

  and their children shall possess the land.

14 **The friendship of the LORD is for those who fear him, ***

  and he makes his covenant known to them.

15 My eyes are ever toward the LORD, *

  for he will pluck my feet out of the net.

16 **Turn to me and be gracious to me, ***

  for I am lonely and afflicted.

17 **Relieve the troubles of my heart, ***

  and bring me out of my distress.

¹⁸ **Consider my affliction and my trouble, ***
   and forgive all my sins.

¹⁹ Consider how many are my foes, *
   and with what violent hatred they hate me.

²⁰ O guard my life, and deliver me; *
   do not let me be put to shame, for I take refuge in you.

²¹ **May integrity and uprightness preserve me, ***
   for I wait for you.

²² **Redeem Israel, O God, ***
   out of all its troubles.

Loving God,
you teach us, you lead us, you protect us, you forgive us.
Help us to trust you more each day,
Father, Son, and Holy Spirit, now and forever. **Amen.**

Psalm 25 is an acrostic in which each verse begins with a subsequent letter in the Hebrew alphabet. Like other acrostic or alphabetical psalms, it includes an anthology of prayers that arise out of quite different life circumstances and express quite different emotions. It alternates between testimonies (vv. 1-3, 8-10, 12-15) and petitions (for guidance, vv. 4-5; for remembrance, vv. 6-7; for comfort and forgiveness, vv. 11, 16-18; and for strength and rescue, vv. 19-21). The psalm is unified in its depiction of life as a journey and its celebration of divine instruction on "the way." *Use in Worship: during the season of Advent; services marking a stage in the journey of life for individuals or a community; services exploring the interrelationship between testimony and prayer.*

Psalm 25:1-10 | A Responsorial Setting 25A

(continues)

Refrain

1 To you, O LORD,

   I lift up my soul.

2 My God, I put my trust in you; let me not be put to shame,

   nor let my enemies triumph over me.

3 Let none who look to you be put to shame;

   rather let those be put to shame who are treacherous.   *Refrain*

4 Show me your ways, O LORD,

   and teach me your paths.

5 Lead me in your truth and teach me,

   for you are the God of my salvation; in you have I trusted all the day long.

6 Remember, O LORD, your compassion and love,

   for they are from everlasting.

7 Remember not the sins of my youth and my transgressions;

   remember me according to your steadfast love

   and for the sake of your goodness, O LORD.   *Refrain*

8 You are gracious and upright, O LORD;

   therefore you teach sinners in your way.

9 You lead the lowly in justice

   and teach the lowly your way.

10 All your paths, O LORD, are steadfast love and faithfulness

   to those who keep your covenant and your testimonies.   *Refrain*

Tone

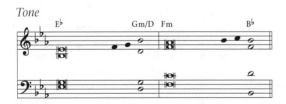

Lectionary: vv. 1-9 Ordinary Time after Pentecost (A); vv. 1-10 Lent (B), Advent (C), and Ordinary Time after Pentecost (C).

LORD, I Gladly Trust 25B

1 LORD, I glad-ly trust in you: let me not be
2 In your hands I place my past: all my sins you
3 Teach me what is true and good; let me hear and
4 When my trou-bles mul-ti-ply you a-lone can

put to shame. As I look up toward your throne
know so well. Your for-give-ness, LORD, I need,
un-der-stand! In the choic-es I must make
bring me through: so with all your saints I say,

make your gra-cious pro-mise known: God my ref-uge
for my guilt is great in-deed; ev-en great-er
show my heart the way to take, so that I may
"Be my strength and shield to-day." Since I know you

and my hope, your pro-tect-ive care I claim.
is your love— mer-cy more than I can tell.
al-ways tread on the path which you have planned.
hear my prayer, LORD, I glad-ly trust in you.

Guitar chords do not correspond with keyboard harmony.

This tune in a higher key: p. 346.

Words: Martin Leckebusch © 2006 Kevin Mayhew Ltd.
Music (REDHEAD 76 | 7.7.7.7.7.7): Richard Redhead, 1853, P.D.

25C To You, O God, I Lift Up My Soul

Refrain

To you, O God, I lift up my soul;

lift up my spir-it to my Lord.

1

2 (⌢ *last time*)

To you I lift up my soul.

1 Make me to know your ways, O God;
2 Good and up - right our gra - cious God,
3 Stead - fast and kind your ways, O God;

teach me your paths, guide me.
show - ing the way, guid - ing the
all who re - vere your cov - e - nant

You are my Sav - ior.
hum - ble to jus - tice.
know your friend - ship.

To Refrain

25D LORD, to You My Soul Is Lifted

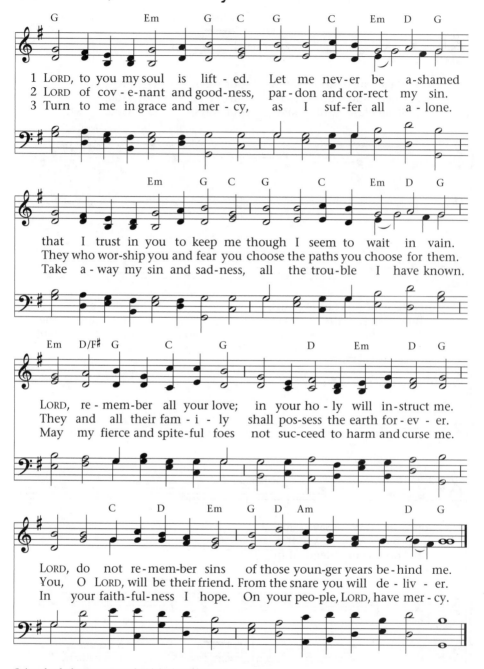

1 LORD, to you my soul is lift-ed. Let me nev-er be a-shamed
2 LORD of cov-e-nant and good-ness, par-don and cor-rect my sin.
3 Turn to me in grace and mer-cy, as I suf-fer all a-lone.

that I trust in you to keep me though I seem to wait in vain.
They who wor-ship you and fear you choose the paths you choose for them.
Take a-way my sin and sad-ness, all the trou-ble I have known.

LORD, re-mem-ber all your love; in your ho-ly will in-struct me.
They and all their fam-i-ly shall pos-sess the earth for-ev-er.
May my fierce and spite-ful foes not suc-ceed to harm and curse me.

LORD, do not re-mem-ber sins of those youn-ger years be-hind me.
You, O LORD, will be their friend. From the snare you will de-liv-er.
In your faith-ful-ness I hope. On your peo-ple, LORD, have mer-cy.

Guitar chords do not correspond with keyboard harmony.

Words: Stanley Wiersma (1930-1986), 1980, © 1987 Faith Alive Christian Resources
Music (GENEVAN 25 | 8.7.8.7.7.8.7.8): Louis Bourgeois (ca. 1510-1561), 1551; harm. Howard Slenk, 1985,
© 1987 Faith Alive Christian Resources

Psalm 26

Of David.

1 Vindicate me, O Lord, for I have walked in my integrity, *
   and I have trusted in the Lord without wavering.

2 **Prove me, O Lord, and try me; ***
   test my heart and mind.

3 **For your steadfast love is before my eyes, ***
   and I walk in faithfulness to you.

4 I do not sit with the worthless, *
   nor do I consort with hypocrites;

5 I hate the company of evildoers, *
   and will not sit with the wicked.

6 **I wash my hands in innocence, ***
   and go around your altar, O Lord,

7 **singing aloud a song of thanksgiving, ***
   and telling all your wondrous deeds.

8 **O Lord, I love the house in which you dwell, ***
   and the place where your glory abides.

9 Do not sweep me away with sinners, *
   nor my life with the bloodthirsty,

10 those in whose hands are evil devices, *
   and whose right hands are full of bribes.

11 **But as for me, I walk in my integrity; ***
   redeem me, and be gracious to me.

12 **My foot stands on level ground; ***
   in the great congregation I will bless the Lord.

O God, our Judge and Redeemer, we want to build our house on the rock.
Grant us wisdom to anchor our lives in your love
and the perseverance to live each day in joyful obedience,
no matter what challenges may come.
We ask this in Jesus' name. **Amen.**

Psalm 26 is a prayer for justice and vindication that includes a strong assertion of innocence. Echoing the language of Ps. 1, it serves as a model response of faith for all who hear the injunction of Ps. 1 to affirm the way of righteousness and reject evil. While different in tone, it is reminiscent of other scriptural testimonies of faith, including those of Joshua ("as for me and my house, we will serve the lord") and Thomas ("I believe, help my unbelief"). Christian interpreters have noted the value of this psalm not only to express the confidence of those with a sturdy faith but also as a formative text to grow into by those who aspire to that integrity. *Use in Worship: prayer of dedication; prayer for deliverance.*

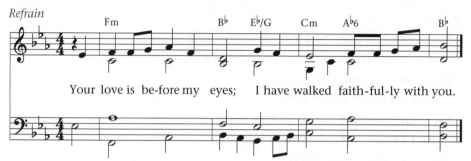 26A Psalm 26 | A Responsorial Setting

Refrain

Your love is be-fore my eyes; I have walked faith-ful-ly with you.

Refrain

1 Give judgment for me, O Lord, for I have lived with integrity;
    I have trusted in the Lord and have not faltered.

2 Test me, O Lord, and try me;
    examine my heart and my mind.

3 For your steadfast love is before my eyes;
    I have walked faithfully with you. *Refrain*

4 I have not sat with the worthless,
    nor do I consort with the deceitful.

5 I have hated the company of evildoers;
    I will not sit down with the wicked. *Refrain*

6 I will wash my hands in innocence, O Lord,
    that I may go in procession round your altar,

7 singing aloud a song of thanksgiving
    and recounting all your wonderful deeds.

8 Lord, I love the house in which you dwell
    and the place where your glory abides. *Refrain*

9 Do not sweep me away with sinners,
    nor my life with those who thirst for blood,

10 whose hands are full of evil plots,
    and their right hands full of bribes.

11 As for me, I will live with integrity;
    redeem me, and be gracious to me.

12 I take my stand on level ground;
    in the full assembly I will bless the Lord. *Refrain*

Tone

Lectionary: Ordinary Time after Pentecost (B); vv. 1-8 Ordinary Time after Pentecost (A).

Words and Music: John W. Becker from *Psalter for Worship, Cycle A* © 1998 Augsburg Fortress Publishers
Psalm Text: from *Evangelical Lutheran Worship* © 2006 Evangelical Lutheran Church in America, admin.
Augsburg Fortress Publishers
Tone: from *Psalter for Worship, Cycle A* © 1997 Augsburg Fortress Publishers

Let This Be My Supreme Desire 26B

1 Let this be my su - preme de - sire, my ob - ject
2 To lead a blame - less life, O Lord, to trust you
3 To walk be - fore you in the truth, to shun all
4 Let this be my su - preme de - sire, my ob - ject

and my prayer, un - til I stand be -
with - out fear, to bring my hum - ble
e - vil ways, to come in - to your
and my prayer, un - til I stand be -

fore your throne to glo - ri - fy you there:
heart to you and know your love is near:
house to pray and shout a - loud your praise:
fore your throne to glo - ri - fy you there!

For guitar chords see p. 4.

Words: Michael Perry © 1989 The Jubilate Group, admin. Hope Publishing Company
Music (WINCHESTER OLD 8.6.8.6): attr. George Kirbye, 1592, P.D.

Psalm 27

Of David.

1 The LORD is my light and my salvation; whom shall I fear? *
> **The LORD is the stronghold of my life; of whom shall I be afraid?**

2 When evildoers assail me to devour my flesh— *
> my adversaries and foes—they shall stumble and fall.

3 Though an army encamp against me, my heart shall not fear; *
> though war rise up against me, yet I will be confident.

4 **One thing I asked of the LORD, that will I seek after: ***
> **to live in the house of the LORD all the days of my life,**
> **to behold the beauty of the LORD, and to inquire in his temple.**

5 **For he will hide me in his shelter in the day of trouble; ***
> **he will conceal me under the cover of his tent;**
> **he will set me high on a rock.**

6 Now my head is lifted up above my enemies all around me,
> and I will offer in his tent sacrifices with shouts of joy; *
> I will sing and make melody to the LORD.

7 **Hear, O LORD, when I cry aloud, ***
> **be gracious to me and answer me!**

8 **"Come," my heart says, "seek his face!" ***
> **Your face, LORD, do I seek.**

9 Do not hide your face from me.
> Do not turn your servant away in anger, you who have been my help. *
> Do not cast me off, do not forsake me, O God of my salvation!

10 If my father and mother forsake me, *
> the LORD will take me up.

11 **Teach me your way, O LORD, ***
> **and lead me on a level path because of my enemies.**

12 Do not give me up to the will of my adversaries, *
> for false witnesses have risen against me,
> and they are breathing out violence.

13 **I believe that I shall see the goodness of the LORD ***
> **in the land of the living.**

14 **Wait for the LORD; ***
> **be strong, and let your heart take courage; wait for the LORD!**

Light of the world, shine in our darkness.
Savior of the world, come into our hearts.
There is much we should fear if we faced this day alone.
But you, O Lord, are with us; thanks be to God! **Amen.**

Psalm 27 is a confident profession of faith and declaration of trust in God. The psalmist is profoundly aware of the enemy's threats but is even more aware of God's ultimate protection and the beauty of ongoing communion with God. The psalm deftly interweaves two contrasting sets of images: one focusing on perception (God as light, beholding God's beauty, seeing God's goodness) and the other on deliverance (God as salvation and shelter). *Use in Worship: funerals; pastoral care of the sick and distressed.*

For a setting of Ps. 27:4 see 84B.

The Lord Is My Light 27A

Words and Music: The Community of Taizé © 1991 Ateliers et Presses de Taizé, Taizé Community, France, GIA Publications, Inc., exclusive North American agent

27B The Lord Is My Light

1 The Lord is my light and my sal - va - tion, the
3 Wait on the Lord and be of good cour - age, oh,

Lord is my light and my sal - va - tion, the Lord is my
wait on the Lord and be of good cour - age, wait on the

light and my sal - va - tion; whom shall I fear?
Lord and be of good cour - age; he shall strength - en thy heart.

Refrain
Whom shall I fear, whom shall I fear?

The Lord is the strength of my life;

27C O Lord, You Are My Light

1 O Lord, you are my light and my sal-va-tion near:
2 My one re-quest has been and still this prayer I raise;
3 When trou-bles round me swell, when fears and dan-gers throng,
4 Up-lift-ed on a rock a-bove my foes a-round,

then who will cause me fright or fill my heart with fear?
that I may live with-in God's house for all my days.
se-cure-ly I will dwell in his pa-vil-ion strong.
a-mid the bat-tle shock my song shall still re-sound.

While God my strength, my life sus-tains, se-cure from fear
God's glo-rious beau-ty to ad-mire, and in his tem-
With-in the shel-ter of God's tent he hides me till
Then joy-ful of-ferings I will bring; the Lord God's praise

my soul re-mains, se-cure from fear my soul re-mains.
ple to in-quire, and in his tem-ple to in-quire.
the storm is spent, he hides me till the storm is spent.
my heart shall sing, the Lord God's praise my heart shall sing.

Words: st. 1 *Psalter*, 1887; sts. 2-4 *Psalter*, 1912, alt., P.D.
Music (RHOSYMEDRE 6.6.6.6.8.8 with repeat): John D. Edwards, ca. 1840, P.D.

God Is My Strong Salvation **27D**

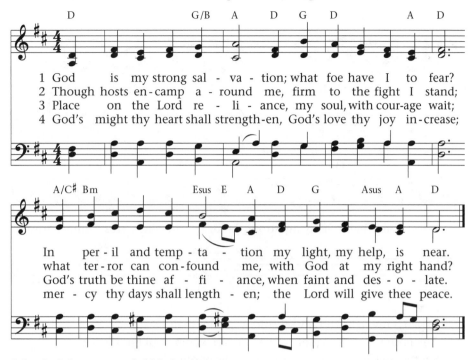

1 God is my strong sal - va - tion; what foe have I to fear?
2 Though hosts en - camp a - round me, firm to the fight I stand;
3 Place on the Lord re - li - ance, my soul, with cour-age wait;
4 God's might thy heart shall strength-en, God's love thy joy in-crease;

In per - il and temp - ta - tion my light, my help, is near.
what ter - ror can con - found me, with God at my right hand?
God's truth be thine af - fi - ance, when faint and des - o - late.
mer - cy thy days shall length - en; the Lord will give thee peace.

Guitar chords do not correspond with keyboard harmony.

Words: James Montgomery, 1822, alt. 1988, P.D.
Music (CHRISTUS, DER IST MEIN LEBEN 7.6.7.6): Melchoir Vulpius, 1609, P.D.

An Accompaniment for Reading **27E**

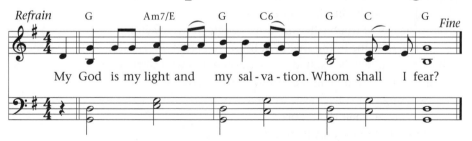

My God is my light and my sal - va - tion. Whom shall I fear?

Sing softly or hum during spoken verses.

Whom shall I fear? (My)

Bells or harmony for Refrain

God is my light. I'll not fear.

Words: Julie Howard © 1992 Liturgical Press
Music: Julie Howard; arr. Vera Lyons © 1992 Liturgical Press

Refrain

The LORD is my light and my strong-hold, in him I trust, him I trust. The LORD is my light and my strong-hold, in him I trust, him I trust.

Refrain

1 The LORD is my light and my salvation—whom shall I fear?
 The LORD is the stronghold of my life—of whom shall I be afraid?
2 When the wicked advance against me to devour me,
 it is my enemies and my foes who will stumble and fall.
3 Though an army besiege me, my heart will not fear;
 though war break out against me, even then I will be confident. *Refrain*
4 One thing I ask from the LORD, this only do I seek:
 that I may dwell in the house of the LORD all the days of my life,
 to gaze on the beauty of the LORD
 and to seek him in his temple.
5 For in the day of trouble he will keep me safe in his dwelling;
 he will hide me in the shelter of his sacred tent and set me high upon a rock.
6 Then my head will be exalted above the enemies who surround me;
 at his sacred tent I will sacrifice with shouts of joy;
 I will sing and make music to the LORD.
7 Hear my voice when I call, LORD;
 be merciful to me and answer me. *Refrain*
8 My heart says of you, "Seek his face!"
 Your face, LORD, I will seek.
9 Do not hide your face from me,
 do not turn your servant away in anger;
 you have been my helper.
 Do not reject me or forsake me, God my Savior.
10 Though my father and mother forsake me,
 the LORD will receive me. *Refrain*

¹¹ Teach me your way, LORD;

    lead me in a straight path because of my oppressors.

¹² Do not turn me over to the desire of my foes,

    for false witnesses rise up against me, spouting malicious accusations.

¹³ I remain confident of this:

    I will see the goodness of the LORD in the land of the living.

¹⁴ Wait for the LORD;

    be strong and take heart and wait for the LORD.   *Refrain*

Accompaniment for spoken verses

Words and Music: Daniel Richardson and Angel Napieralski © 2010 Daniel Richardson and Angel Napieralski, admin. Faith Alive Christian Resources
Text: Psalm 27 © THE HOLY BIBLE, NEW INTERNATIONAL VERSION®, NIV® Copyright © 1973, 1978, 1984, 2011 by Biblica, Inc.™ Used by permission. All rights reserved worldwide.

El Señor es mi luz / The Lord Is My Light

Refrain

Spanish El Se-ñor es mi luz y mi sal-va-ción. El Se-ñor es la de-
English The Lord is my light, my help and sal-va-tion. The Lord is the

fen-sa de mi vi-da. Si el Se-ñor es mi luz, ¿a
strong-hold of my life. If the Lord is my light, what

quién te-me-ré? ¿Quién me ha-rá tem - blar? *Fine*
then shall I dread? Whom shall I fear?

1 U - na co-sa pi-do al Se-ñor: ha-bi-tar por
1 One re-quest, Lord, I make of you: to a-bide in

siem - pre en su ca-sa, go - zar de la dul-zu-ra del Se-
your house for - ev - er, to re-flect up-on your beau-ty with de-

ñor con-tem-plan-do su tem-plo san-to.
light and to in-quire with-in your tem-ple.

Additional Stanzas

2 No me_es-con-das tu ros-tro, Se-ñor; bus-ca-ré to-do_el
2 Turn your face not a-way from me, Lord, for your face is the

dí-a tu ros-tro. Si mi pa-dre_y mi ma-dre me_a-ban-
light that I long for. If my fa-ther or moth-er should for-

do-nan, el Se-ñor me_a-bra-za-rá.
sake me, still you hold me in your care.

3 Oh Se-ñor, en-sé-ña-me_el ca-mi-no; guí-a-me por la
3 Teach me, Lord, the way that I should fol-low; guide my steps in the

sen-da ver-da-de-ra. Go-za-ré de la dul-zu-ra del Se-
way of truth and good-ness. I shall tell of your bless-ings all my

ñor en la tie-rra de la vi-da.
days through the lands of the liv-ing.

Words: Psalm 27 © 1970 Comisión Episcopal Española de Liturgia; tr. Mary Louise Bringle (b. 1953), 2011
Music: Father Alberto Taulé; arr. Gerhard Cartford © 1982 Fr. Alberto Taulé, admin. OCP Publications

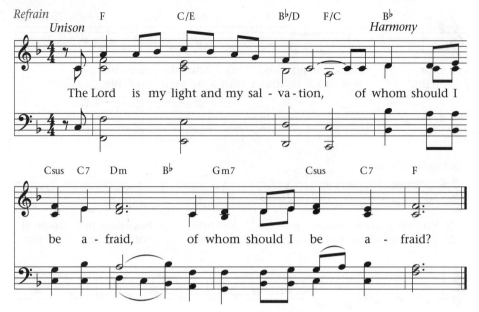

Refrain

[1] The LORD is my light and my salvation; whom then shall I fear?
   The LORD is the stronghold of my life; of whom shall I be afraid?

[2] When evildoers close in against me to devour my flesh,
   they, my foes and my enemies, will stumble and fall.

[3] Though an army encamp against me, my heart will not fear.
   Though war rise up against me, my trust will not be shaken.   *Refrain*

[4] One thing I ask of the LORD; one thing I seek;
   that I may dwell in the house of the LORD all the days of my life;
   to gaze upon the beauty of the LORD and to seek God in the temple.

[5] For in the day of trouble God will give me shelter,
   hide me in the hidden places of the sanctuary, and raise me high upon a rock.

[6] Even now my head is lifted up above my enemies who surround me.
   Therefore I will offer sacrifice in the sanctuary, sacrifices of rejoicing;
   I will sing and make music to the LORD.   *Refrain*

[7] Hear my voice, O LORD, when I call;
   have mercy on me and answer me.

[8] My heart speaks your message— "Seek my face."
   Your face, O LORD, I will seek.

[9] Hide not your face from me, turn not away from your servant in anger.
   Cast me not away—you have been my helper;
   forsake me not, O God of my salvation.   *Refrain*

¹⁰ Though my father and mother forsake me,
  the LORD will take me in.

¹¹ Teach me your way, O LORD;
  lead me on a level path, because of my oppressors.

¹² Subject me not to the will of my foes,
  for they rise up against me, false witnesses breathing violence.

¹³ This I believe—that I will see the goodness of the LORD
  in the land of the living!

¹⁴ Wait for the LORD and be strong.
  Take heart and wait for the LORD!   *Refrain*

Tone

Lectionary: Lent (C); vv. 1, 4-9 Ordinary Time after Epiphany (A).

Words: Psalm 27:1 © 1983 GIA Publications, Inc.
Music: David Haas (b. 1957) © 1983 GIA Publications, Inc.
Psalm Text: from *Evangelical Lutheran Worship* © 2006 Evangelical Lutheran Church in America, admin.
Augsburg Fortress Publishers
Tone: © 2006 Augsburg Fortress Publishers

Alternate Refrain

The Lord is my light and my Sav - ior;

whom   shall I fear?

Alternate Tone

Words and Music: from *The Divine Liturgy: An Anthology for Worship* © Metropolitan Andrey Sheptytsky
Institute of Eastern Christian Studies
Tone: © 2011 Faith Alive Christian Resources

271 One Thing I Ask

1 One thing I ask, one thing I seek,
2 Hear me, O Lord, hear me when I cry;

that I may dwell in your house, O Lord,
Lord, do not hide your face from me:

all of my days, all of my
you have been my strength, you have been my

life that I may see you,
shield, and you will lift me

Lord.

up. One thing I ask, one

thing I de - sire is to see you,

is to see you.

Words and Music: Andy Park © 1987 Mercy/Vineyard Publishing & Vineyard Songs (Canada), admin. Music Services o/b/o Vineyard Music USA

27J The Lord Is My Light

1 The Lord is my light, my light and my sal - va - tion. With God pro - tect - ing me from ev - ery dan - ger, whom shall I fear?

2 Should e - vil powers ad - vance, should ar - mies try to kill, let them sur - round me and let them at - tack me; I'll still trust God.

3 One thing I ask the Lord, this on - ly I de - sire: Al - ways in wor - ship to gaze at God's good - ness and seek his aid.

4 Pre - served by God from harm, se - cure in him a - lone, I will re - joice in the face of af - flic - tion and sing God's song.

Guitar chords do not correspond with keyboard harmony.

Words: Psalm 27; para. The Iona Community © 1990 Wild Goose Resource Group, Iona Community, Scotland, GIA Publications, Inc., exclusive North American agent
Music (CZECHOSLOVAKIA): Czechoslovakian hymn tune (17th c.), P.D.

Psalm 28

Of David.

1 To you, O LORD, I call; my rock, do not refuse to hear me, *
   for if you are silent to me, I shall be like those who go down to the Pit.

2 **Hear the voice of my supplication, as I cry to you for help,** *
   as I lift up my hands toward your most holy sanctuary.

3 Do not drag me away with the wicked, with those who are workers of evil, *
   who speak peace with their neighbors, while mischief is in their hearts.

4 Repay them according to their work, and according to the evil of their deeds; *
   repay them according to the work of their hands;
   render them their due reward.

5 Because they do not regard the works of the LORD, or the work of his hands, *
   he will break them down and build them up no more.

6 **Blessed be the LORD,** *
   for he has heard the sound of my pleadings.

7 **The LORD is my strength and my shield; in him my heart trusts;** *
   so I am helped, and my heart exults,
   and with my song I give thanks to him.

8 The LORD is the strength of his people; *
   he is the saving refuge of his anointed.

9 **O save your people, and bless your heritage;** *
   be their shepherd, and carry them forever.

God our Rock, you are life and truth.
Before his arrest, your Son prayed for the protection of your flock.
Deliver us, we pray, from the evil that is around us and within us.
And, by the power of your Holy Spirit,
help us to live and serve you as those who know your salvation.
We pray in Jesus' name. **Amen.**

Psalm 28 features a dramatic pivot from a plea for God's deliverance and retribution against the enemies (vv. 1-5) to a grateful response for answered prayer (vv. 6-7). The psalm looks beyond the immediate circumstances by concluding with an expansive prayer for God to be a shepherd to the people forever (vv. 8-9). The prayers for deliverance are particularly concerned with wily evildoers whose peaceful speech masks evil intent (v. 3). The psalm can be appropriated both by identifying with the experience of the author as victim and, more provocatively, by identifying with the victimizer, realizing that faithful people may be compelled to pray this in light of how they have been victimized by us. *Use in Worship: prayer of petition; call to confession.*

28A I Call to You, My Rock

1 I call to you, my Rock: Lord, hear my ear-nest prayer—
2 May I be spared the fate of those who cling to sin,
3 But you have heard my prayer; in you I will be strong:

if you ig-nore my plea how can I not de-spair?
whose friend-ly words be-lie mal-i-cious thoughts with-in—
since I re-ly on you my heart is filled with song.

As I reach out, make this the place of fresh en-coun-ters
would ru-in not be my re-ward if I should dis-re-
Yes, Lord, I sing to you, my Rock: e-ter-nal Shep-herd,

with your grace, of fresh en-coun-ters with your grace.
gard you, Lord, if I should dis-re-gard you, Lord?
guard your flock, e-ter-nal Shep-herd, guard your flock.

Words: Martin Leckebusch © 2002, 2011 Kevin Mayhew Ltd.
Music (RHOSYMEDRE 6.6.6.6.8.8 with repeat): John D. Edwards, ca. 1840, P.D.

178

A Scripted Reading of Psalms 1 and 28

Voice 1:

The Word of the Lord from Psalms 1 and 28.

Happy are they who have not walked in the counsel of the wicked, nor lingered in the way of sinners, nor sat in the seats of the scornful! Their delight is in the law of the LORD, and on this law they meditate day and night. They are like trees planted by streams of water, bearing fruit in due season, with leaves that do not wither; everything they do shall prosper.   *Psalm 1:1-3*

Voice 2:

O LORD, I call to you; my Rock, do not be deaf to my cry; lest, if you do not hear me, I become like those who go down to the pit. Hear the voice of my prayer when I cry out to you, when I lift up my hands to your holy of holies.   *Psalm 28:1-2*

Voice 1:

It is not so with the wicked; they are like chaff which the wind blows away. Therefore the wicked shall not stand upright when judgment comes, nor the sinner in the council of the righteous. For the LORD knows the way of the righteous, but the way of the wicked is doomed.   *Psalm 1:4-6*

Voice 2:

Do not snatch me away with the wicked or with the evildoers, who speak peaceably with their neighbors, while strife is in their hearts. Repay them according to their deeds, and according to the wickedness of their actions. According to the work of their hands repay them, and give them their just deserts.   *Psalm 28:3-5*

Silence for reflection

Voice 2:

Blessed is the LORD! for you have heard the voice of my prayer.

The LORD is my strength and my shield; my heart trusts in you, and I have been helped. Therefore my heart dances for joy, and in my song I will praise you. You, O LORD, are the strength of your people, a safe refuge for your anointed. Save your people and bless your inheritance; shepherd them and carry them forever.   *Psalm 28:7-11*

Text: Psalms 1 and 28, from *Psalter for the Christian People* © Liturgical Press

28C O LORD My Rock, to You I Cry Aloud

1 O LORD my rock, to you I cry a - loud to hear my
2 Praise to the LORD, who is my strength and shield; he hears my

plea; I shall be lost, if you stay si - lent now and
cry! God is my help; my heart will give him thanks and

deaf to me. I lift my hands to your most ho - ly place;
leap for joy. Strength of his peo - ple, for - tress for his king;

do not with - hold your mer - cy, love and grace!
our Shep - herd, save us! All your praise we sing.

Guitar chords do not correspond with keyboard harmony.

Words: Christopher Idle © 1996 The Jubilate Group, admin. Hope Publishing Company
Music (SANDON 10.4.10.4.10.10): Charles H. Purday, 1860, P.D.

A Psalm of David.

1 Ascribe to the LORD, O heavenly beings, *
   ascribe to the LORD glory and strength.

2 Ascribe to the LORD the glory of his name; *
   worship the LORD in holy splendor.

3 **The voice of the LORD is over the waters;** *
   the God of glory thunders, the LORD, over mighty waters.

4 **The voice of the LORD is powerful;** *
   the voice of the LORD is full of majesty.

5 The voice of the LORD breaks the cedars; *
   the LORD breaks the cedars of Lebanon.

6 He makes Lebanon skip like a calf, *
   and Sirion like a young wild ox.

7 **The voice of the LORD** *
   flashes forth flames of fire.

8 The voice of the LORD shakes the wilderness; *
   the LORD shakes the wilderness of Kadesh.

9 **The voice of the LORD causes the oaks to whirl,**
   and strips the forest bare; *
   and in his temple all say, "Glory!"

10 The LORD sits enthroned over the flood; *
   the LORD sits enthroned as king forever.

11 **May the LORD give strength to his people!** *
   May the LORD bless his people with peace!

Lord God Almighty,
by the power of your Spirit we can sing "Glory!" with the angels
and praise you with all of creation.
Holy God, receive the worship of those for whom you sent your Son,
Jesus Christ our Lord, in whose name we pray. **Amen.**

Psalm 29 is a meditation on the splendor of God's voice as it speaks through creation and elicits the response of God's people gathered for worship. The final verses offer an assurance that God sits enthroned as King forever and will strengthen and bless the congregation of the faithful, emphasizing that the one who strengthens and blesses is none other than the one whose power is seen in creation. *Use in Worship: in conjunction with celebrations of Jesus' baptism (emphasis on the voice of God); call to worship for services focusing on creation or God's ongoing, active, and personal presence in the world; preparation for the benediction at the conclusion of worship.*

29A All on Earth and All in Heaven

1 All on earth and all in heav - en, raise to
2 Trees shall bow in awe and won - der, bend their

God a song on high; strength un - mea - sured,
branch - es to the ground; from God's lips one

love un - bound - ed, God a - lone we glo - ri - fy.
word in an - ger wreaks de - struc - tion all a - round.

At God's voice the clouds as - sem - ble, thun - der roars and
But the Word which sets in mo - tion such tra - vails can

tor - rents fall; earth shall quake be - fore God's
make them cease; that same voice which tu - mult

pres - ence, moun - tains trem - ble at God's call.
beck - ons in a gen - tler breath speaks peace.

Guitar chords do not correspond with keyboard harmony.

Words: Michael Morgan © 2011 Michael Morgan, admin. Faith Alive Christian Resources
Music (EBENEZER 8.7.8.7 D): Thomas J. Williams, 1890, P.D.

Refrain

Spanish: Hi - jos de Dios, den glo - ria al Se - ñor. Re-co-
English: An - gels on high and peo - ples on earth give

noz - can su glo - ria y su po - der.
glo - ry to God, praise God's splen - dor and might.

Fine

Spanish

1 Tri - bu - ten glo - ria al nom - bre del Se - ñor, a-
2 So - bre las a - guas la voz del Se - ñor re-
3 Y a su pueb - lo fuer - za da - rá y

dó - ren - lo en___ su san - tua - rio.
tum - ba el true - no de Dios.
ben - di - cio - nes___ de paz.

To Refrain

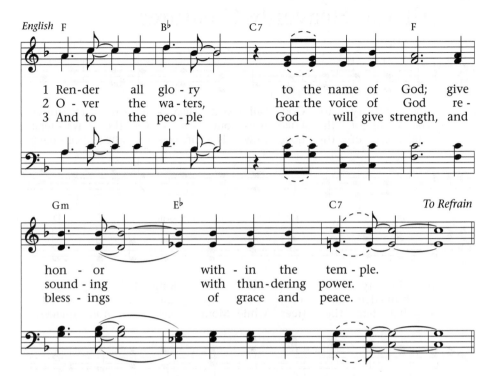

English

1 Ren-der all glo - ry to the name of God; give
2 O - ver the wa - ters, hear the voice of God re -
3 And to the peo - ple God will give strength, and

hon - or with - in the tem - ple.
sound - ing with thun-dering power.
bless - ings of grace and peace.

29C Give Glory to God, All You Heavenly Creatures

1 Give glo - ry to God, all you heav - en - ly crea-tures;
2 The voice of the LORD rolls out o - ver the wa - ters;
3 The voice of the LORD now is break - ing the ce - dars;

all glo - ry and pow - er be - long to the LORD!
it thun - ders and ech - oes his glo - ry a - broad.
he shat - ters the trees while Mount Leb - a - non quakes.

So drop to your knees and re - spect what is ho - ly,
The voice of the LORD is ma - jes - tic and might - y;
God speaks: all the hills jump like an - te-lopes star - tled—

be qui - et and lis - ten: the voice of the LORD!
its pow - er re - sounds, and his crea - tures are awed.
the voice of the LORD makes us crea - tures to shake.

(continues)

4 The voice of the LORD whips out lightning-like flashes.
The voice of the LORD makes the desert to reel.
The voice of the LORD sets the oak tree awhirling.
God strips forests bare by the force of his gale.

5 The creatures now worship the God of all power;
all creatures respond, "May God's glory increase."
The LORD gives his people their strength and all blessing;
the LORD shall encircle his people with peace.

Words: Calvin Seerveld © 1983 Calvin Seerveld
Music (ARLES 12.11.12.11): Charles H. Gabriel (1856-1932), P.D.

Psalm 29 | A Responsorial Setting 29D

Refrain

Your voice, O LORD, is a voice of splen - dor.

Refrain

¹ Ascribe to the LORD, you gods,
   ascribe to the LORD glory and strength.

² Ascribe to the LORD the glory due God's name;
   worship the LORD in the beauty of holiness. *Refrain*

³ The voice of the LORD is upon the waters; the God of glory thunders;
   the LORD is upon the mighty waters.

⁴ The voice of the LORD is a powerful voice;
   the voice of the LORD is a voice of splendor.

⁵ The voice of the LORD breaks the cedar trees;
   the LORD breaks the cedars of Lebanon;

⁶ the LORD makes Lebanon skip like a calf,
   and Mount Hermon like a young wild ox. *Refrain*   (continues)

7 The voice of the LORD
  bursts forth in lightning flashes.

8 The voice of the LORD shakes the wilderness;
  the LORD shakes the wilderness of Kadesh.

9 The voice of the LORD makes the oak trees writhe and strips the forests bare.
  And in the temple of the LORD all are crying, "Glory!" *Refrain*

10 The LORD sits enthroned above the flood;
   the LORD sits enthroned as king forevermore.

11 O LORD, give strength to your people;
   give them, O LORD, the blessings of peace. *Refrain*

Tone

Lectionary: Baptism of the Lord (A,B,C); Trinity Sunday (B).

The tone may also be used with the alternate refrain.

Words and Music: Martin Tel © 2011 Martin Tel, admin. Faith Alive Christian Resources
Psalm Text: from *Evangelical Lutheran Worship* © 2006 Evangelical Lutheran Church in America, admin.
Augsburg Fortress Publishers
Tone: © 2011 Faith Alive Christian Resources

Alternate Refrain

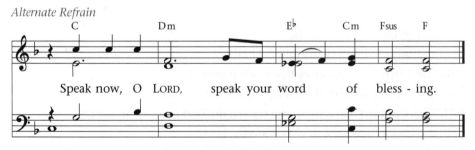

Speak now, O LORD, speak your word of bless-ing.

Words and Music: Martin Tel © 2011 Martin Tel, admin. Faith Alive Christian Resources

Psalm 30

A Psalm. A Song at the dedication of the temple. Of David.

1 I will extol you, O LORD, for you have drawn me up, *
   and did not let my foes rejoice over me.

2 **O LORD my God, I cried to you for help, ***
   and you have healed me.

3 **O LORD, you brought up my soul from Sheol, ***
   restored me to life from among those gone down to the Pit.

4 Sing praises to the LORD, O you his faithful ones, *
   and give thanks to his holy name.

5 For his anger is but for a moment; his favor is for a lifetime. *
   Weeping may linger for the night, but joy comes with the morning.

6 **As for me, I said in my prosperity, ***
   "I shall never be moved."

7 **By your favor, O LORD, you had established me as a strong mountain; ***
   you hid your face; I was dismayed.

8 To you, O LORD, I cried, *
   and to the LORD I made supplication:

9 "What profit is there in my death, if I go down to the Pit? *
   Will the dust praise you? Will it tell of your faithfulness?

10 Hear, O LORD, and be gracious to me! *
   O LORD, be my helper!"

11 **You have turned my mourning into dancing; ***
   you have taken off my sackcloth and clothed me with joy,

12 **so that my soul may praise you and not be silent. ***
   O LORD my God, I will give thanks to you forever.

O God, our healer and our help,
we will never face a challenge or a need that surpasses your provision and your love.
Fill our hearts with thankful praise, and use us to draw others close to you,
so that after the night of sorrow they too may rejoice in the Dayspring from on high,
your Son, our Lord Jesus Christ, in whose name we pray. **Amen.**

Psalm 30 is a testimony of gratitude for God's deliverance and restoration. The psalm preserves the testimony of someone who once prayed a lament (vv. 8-10) but now has experienced God's favorable answer to that prayer. It begins and ends with a commitment to praise God based on the remembrance of the outcome of God's deliverance (vv. 2-3) and the narrative of the journey from well-being through trouble to restoration (vv. 6-7). The middle of the psalm features a kernel of timeless wisdom about the enduring mercy of God (vv. 4-5). The psalm's imagery features polar opposites (put down/brought up, anger/mercy, weeping/rejoicing, mourning/dancing, sackcloth/joy) that suggest the dramatic nature of God's deliverance. *Use in Worship: celebrations of God's deliverance, either of individual persons or of an entire community.*

30A I Worship You, O Lord

1 I wor-ship you, O Lord, for you have raised me up;
2 Sing prais-es to the Lord, all those who know his name;
3 I said, "I am so strong, I nev-er shall be moved";

I cried to you for help, and you re-stored my life.
for while his wrath is brief, his fa-vor knows no end.
but you, Lord, shook my life— my heart was in dis-tress.

You brought me back from death and saved me from the grave.
Though tears flow for a night, the morn-ing brings new joy.
I cried out for your help and plead-ed for your grace:

4 "What good am I when dead,
while lying in the grave?
Can dust recount your love,
the grave proclaim your praise?
O hear me, gracious Lord,
in mercy be my aid!"

5 My mourning you have turned
to dancing and to joy;
my sadness you dispelled
as gladness filled my soul.
And so I'll sing your praise,
my God, through all my days.

Words: sts. 1-3, 5 James E. Seddon © 1973 The Jubilate Group, admin. Hope Publishing Company; st. 4
Calvin Seerveld © 1982 Calvin Seerveld
Music (BISHOP TUCKER 6.6.6.6.6.6): Norman L. Warren © 1990 The Jubilate Group, admin. Hope
Publishing Company

Psalm 30 | A Responsorial Setting 30B

Refrain

Spanish: Te en - sal - za - ré,   Se - ñor.   Te en -
English: I   will   praise you,   O   Lord.   I

sal - za - ré,   Se - ñor,   por - que   me has   li -
will   praise you,   O   Lord;   you lift - ed   me   from

bra - do,   por - que   me has   li - bra - do.
dan - ger.   You lift - ed   me   from dan - ger.

Refrain

1 I will exalt you, O LORD, because you have lifted me up
   and have not let my enemies triumph over me.

2 O LORD my God, I cried out to you,
   and you restored me to health.

3 You have brought me up, O LORD, from the dead;
   you restored my life as I was going down to the grave.   *Refrain*

4 Sing praises to the LORD, all you faithful;
   give thanks in holy remembrance.

5 God's wrath is short; God's favor lasts a lifetime.
   Weeping spends the night, but joy comes in the morning.   *Refrain*

6 While I felt secure, I said,
   "I shall never be disturbed.

7 You, LORD, with your favor, made me as strong as the mountains."
   Then you hid your face, and I was filled with fear.   (continues)

⁸ I cried to you, O LORD;

    I pleaded with my Lord, saying,

⁹ "What profit is there in my blood, if I go down to the pit?

    Will the dust praise you or declare your faithfulness?

¹⁰ Hear, O LORD, and have mercy upon me;

    O LORD, be my helper."

¹¹ You have turned my wailing into dancing;

    you have put off my sackcloth and clothed me with joy.

¹² Therefore my heart sings to you without ceasing;

    O LORD my God, I will give you thanks forever.   *Refrain*

Lectionary: Ordinary Time after Epiphany (B); Eastertide (C); Ordinary Time after Pentecost (B,C).

Words and Music: John L. Bell (b. 1949) © 1999 GIA Publications, Inc.
Psalm Text: from *Evangelical Lutheran Worship* © 2006 Evangelical Lutheran Church in America, admin.
Augsburg Fortress Publishers
Tone: © 2011 Faith Alive Christian Resources

30C All with Joyful Exultation

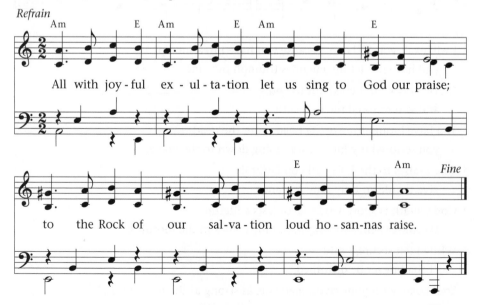

1 Lord, we sing with joy - ful voic - es; your great power can
2 Praise to you, our sure sal - va - tion, you, the Ho - ly
3 Change our sor - row to re - joic - ing, clothe with glad - ness
4 Dry our tears we shed in mourn-ing, give us stead - fast

lift and save; by your heal - ing touch, re - vive us,
One a - bove. End the night so dimmed by an - guish,
all de - spair; cause un - stead - y feet that stum - ble
hope al - ways; fill our hearts with ex - pec - ta - tion;

life re - store be - yond the grave.
with your light of peace and love.
now to dance be - neath your care.
fill our songs with thanks and praise.

To Refrain

Words: sts. Michael Morgan © 1999, 2011 Michael Morgan, admin. Faith Alive Christian Resources; ref. Hal
H. Hopson © 2008 Birnamwood Publications, a division of MorningStar Music Publishers, Inc.
Music (YISRAEL V'ORAITA 8.7.8.7 with refrain): traditional Hasidic melody; arr. © 2006 Augsburg Fortress
Publishers

30D O choro pode durar / Though Weeping and Deepest Sorrow

Refrain

Portuguese: O cho - ro po - de du-rar, u - ma noi - te_in - tei - ra, mas a a - le - gri - a vem pe - la - ma - nhã.

English: Though weep - ing and deep-est sor - row may re-main all night long, with the dawn of morn-ing sad - ness turns to joy.

Fine

1 I will praise you, O my God, for you
2 I will praise you, O my God, you pro-
3 I will praise you, O my God, for you
4 I will praise you, O my God, I will

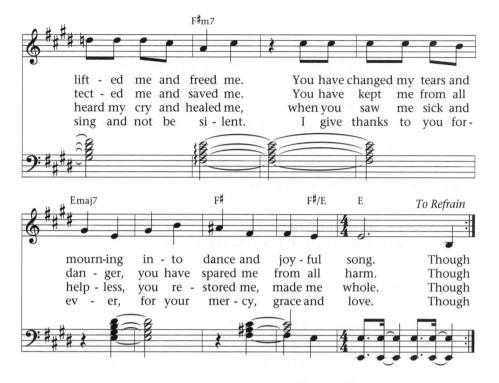

F#m7

lift - ed me and freed me. You have changed my tears and
tect - ed me and saved me. You have kept me from all
heard my cry and healed me, when you saw me sick and
sing and not be si - lent. I give thanks to you for -

Emaj7   F#   F#/E   E   *To Refrain*

mourn-ing in - to dance and joy - ful song. Though
dan - ger, you have spared me from all harm. Though
help - less, you re - stored me, made me whole. Though
ev - er, for your mer - cy, grace and love. Though

Portuguese Stanzas

1 Eu te exaltarei ó Deus,
   porque tu me libertaste:
   converteste o meu pranto
   em folguedos e canções.
   Refrain

2 Eu te exaltarei ó Deus,
   porque tu me protegeste,
   quando muitos me humilhavam
   e zombavam do que fiz.
   Refrain

3 Eu te exaltarei ó Deus,
   porque tu me socorreste,
   quando estava enfermo e triste
   e com tanta precisão.
   Refrain

4 Ouve, ó Deus, o meu clamor,
   que levanto em esperança.
   Quero agradecer, agora,
   tua grande compaixão.
   Refrain

Optional instruments for Refrain
Triangle

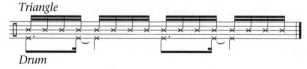

Drum

Words and Music: Simei Monteiro © 2000 Simei Monteiro, admin. General Board of Global Ministries t/a GBGMusik

Psalm 31

Voice 1:

¹ In you, O Lᴏʀᴅ, I seek refuge; do not let me ever be put to shame; *
   in your righteousness deliver me.

² **Incline your ear to me; rescue me speedily. ***
   Be a rock of refuge for me, a strong fortress to save me.

³ You are indeed my rock and my fortress; *
   for your name's sake lead me and guide me,

⁴ take me out of the net that is hidden for me, *
   for you are my refuge.

⁵ **Into your hand I commit my spirit; ***
   you have redeemed me, O Lᴏʀᴅ, faithful God.

Voice 2:

⁶ You hate those who pay regard to worthless idols, *
   but I trust in the Lᴏʀᴅ.

⁷ I will exult and rejoice in your steadfast love, *
   because you have seen my affliction; you have taken heed of my adversities,

⁸ and have not delivered me into the hand of the enemy; *
   you have set my feet in a broad place.

Voice 1:

⁹ Be gracious to me, O Lᴏʀᴅ, for I am in distress; *
   my eye wastes away from grief, my soul and body also.

¹⁰ **For my life is spent with sorrow, and my years with sighing; ***
   my strength fails because of my misery, and my bones waste away.

¹¹ I am the scorn of all my adversaries, a horror to my neighbors,
   an object of dread to my acquaintances; *
   those who see me in the street flee from me.

¹² **I have passed out of mind like one who is dead; ***
   I have become like a broken vessel.

¹³ For I hear the whispering of many—terror all around!— *
   as they scheme together against me, as they plot to take my life.

¹⁴ **But I trust in you, O Lᴏʀᴅ; ***
   I say, "You are my God."

Voice 2:

¹⁵ My times are in your hand; *
   deliver me from the hand of my enemies and persecutors.

¹⁶ **Let your face shine upon your servant; ***
   save me in your steadfast love.

¹⁷ Do not let me be put to shame, O LORD, for I call on you; *

    let the wicked be put to shame; let them go dumbfounded to Sheol.

¹⁸ Let the lying lips be stilled that speak insolently against the righteous *

    with pride and contempt.

Voice 1:

¹⁹ O how abundant is your goodness

  that you have laid up for those who fear you, *

    and accomplished for those who take refuge in you, in the sight of everyone!

²⁰ In the shelter of your presence you hide them from human plots; *

    you hold them safe under your shelter from contentious tongues.

²¹ Blessed be the LORD, for he has wondrously shown his steadfast love to me *

    when I was beset as a city under siege.

²² **I had said in my alarm, "I am driven far from your sight."** *

But you heard my supplications when I cried out to you for help.

Voice 2:

²³ Love the LORD, all you his saints. *

    The LORD preserves the faithful,

    but abundantly repays the one who acts haughtily.

²⁴ **Be strong, and let your heart take courage,** *

all you who wait for the LORD.

Mighty and loving God,
you protect and care for us in ways we will never understand.
Help us to love you so deeply that we will trust you,
and to trust you so completely that we will follow you now and always.
We pray this in Jesus' name. **Amen.**

Psalm 31 weaves together prayers for God's deliverance, declarations of trust in God, laments about present distress, and invitations to worship God. It aptly depicts how, in the midst of suffering, servants of God experience faith, fear, longing and testimony simultaneously. Much of the psalm conveys the sense that God is already answering the prayer (vv. 4-5, 7-8, 21-22). *Use in Worship: Good Friday or Easter Vigil (see v. 5); services in times of difficulty.*

31A I Give My Spirit

Refrain

Emp - ty, bro - ken, life - less, I give my spir - it, Lord.

Fine

1 In you, O Lord, I take ref - uge;
2 I am the scorn of all my en - e - mies,
3 My fate lies sole - ly in your hands.
4 Let your face shine on your ser - vant;

Words and Music: Shannon Cerneka (b. 1975) and Orin Johnson (b. 1973) © 2008 GIA Publications, Inc.

31B You Are My Rock

Refrain

You are my rock. My life is in your hands. You are my rock. I trust in you. You are my rock. My life is in your hands. You are my rock. I trust in you. (You are my)

Stanzas

1 Be for me a rock and a strong - hold. My
2 Help me, O God, I am in trou - ble.
3 Save me from the tongues of my en - e - mies.

life _____ is in your hands.
All _____ my strength is gone.
Shel-ter me in - side your tent.

Pull me from the net that they have
Peo - ple see me in the street and
Hear my call for help when I cry

spread for me. By you I will be saved. You are my
walk a - way, but yet in you I trust. You are my
out to you. O God, you are my rock. You are my

Harmony part for Stanzas

(you.) You are my rock. You are my rock. You are my rock. You are my

rock. You are my rock. You are my rock. You are my rock. You are my rock. You are my

Bell part for Refrain

Words: Julie Howard © 1992 Liturgical Press
Music: Julie Howard; arr. Vera Lyons © 1992 Liturgical Press

31C Psalm 31:1-5, 9-16, 19-24
A Responsorial Setting

Refrain

My times are in your hands. You strength-en me in strife.

My hope is in your Word. Your love pre-serves my life.

Refrain

1 In you, O LORD, have I taken refuge; let me never be put to shame;
  deliver me in your righteousness.

2 Incline your ear to me;
  make haste to deliver me.

3 Be my strong rock, a castle to keep me safe,
  for you are my crag and my stronghold;
    for the sake of your name, lead me and guide me.

4 Take me out of the net that they have secretly set for me,
  for you are my tower of strength.

5 Into your hands I commend my spirit,
  for you have redeemed me, O LORD, God of truth.   *Refrain*

9 Have mercy on me, O LORD, for I am in trouble;
  my eye is consumed with sorrow, and also my throat and my belly.

10 For my life is wasted with grief, and my years with sighing;
  my strength fails me because of affliction, and my bones are consumed.

11 I am the scorn of all my enemies, a disgrace to my neighbors,
  a dismay to my acquaintances;
    when they see me in the street they avoid me.

12 Like the dead I am forgotten, out of mind;
  I am as useless as a broken pot.

¹³ For I have heard the whispering of the crowd; fear is all around;

them>they put their heads together against me; they plot to take my life. *Refrain*

¹⁴ But as for me, I have trusted in you, O L<small>ORD</small>.

I have said, "You are my God.

¹⁵ My times are in your hand;

rescue me from the hand of my enemies, and from those who persecute me.

¹⁶ Let your face shine upon your servant;

save me in your steadfast love." *Refrain*

¹⁹ How great is your goodness, which you have laid up for those who fear you;

which you have done in the sight of all for those who put their trust in you.

²⁰ You hide them in the protection of your presence from those who slander them;

you keep them in your shelter from the strife of tongues.

²¹ Blessed are you, O L<small>ORD</small>!

for you have shown me the wonders of your love when I was under siege.

²² I said in my alarm, "I have been cut off from the sight of your eyes."

Nevertheless, you heard the sound of my plea when I cried out to you.

²³ Love the L<small>ORD</small>, all you saints;

the L<small>ORD</small> protects the faithful, but repays in full those who act haughtily.

²⁴ Be strong and let your heart take courage,

all you who wait for the L<small>ORD</small>. *Refrain*

Tone

Accompaniment

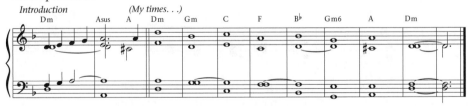

Lectionary: vv. 1-4, 15-16 Holy Saturday (A,B,C); vv. 1-5, 19-24 Eastertide (A); vv. 1-5, 19-24 Ordinary Time after Epiphany (A) and Ordinary Time after Pentecost (A); vv. 9-16 Liturgy of the Passion (A,B,C). 0

31D Haz resplandecer tu rostro / Make Your Face to Shine

Spanish Haz res - plan-de - cer tu ros-tro so-bre tu sier - vo;
English Make your face to shine up - on your ser-vant, and

sál - va - me por tu mi-se-ri - cor - dia! Haz res
in your lov - ing kind - ness save me. Make your

cor - dia! Mas yo en ti, Jeho-vá con -
save me. But as for me, I trust in

fí - o; di - go: "Tú e - res mi Dios.
you, O Lord. I have said, "You are my God. My

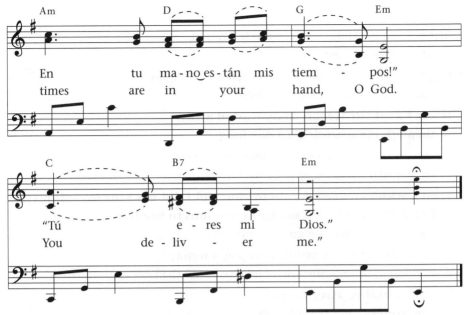

En tu ma-no_es-tán mis tiem - pos!"
times are in your hand, O God.

"Tú e - res mi Dios."
You de - liv - er me."

Words and Music: Jay Wilkey © 2002 Jay Wilkey

A Litany for Good Friday 31E

Lord God, on this day when we remember the passion and death of our Lord, Jesus Christ, we affirm, with humble gratitude, "**Since we have a great high priest who has passed through the heavens, Jesus, the Son of God, let us hold fast to our confession. For we do not have a high priest who is unable to sympathize with our weaknesses, but we have one who in every respect has been tested as we are, yet without sin. Let us therefore approach the throne of grace with boldness, so that we may receive mercy and find grace to help in time of need.**"

Hebrews 4:14-16 (NRSV)

We pray today

   ... for all who suffer [specify as appropriate], **Lord have mercy.**

   ... for all who mourn, **Lord have mercy.**

   ... for all who are victims of injustice, **Lord have mercy.**

   ... for all who are in need of healing, **Lord have mercy.**

   [other petitions may be added as appropriate]

Even as Jesus prayed, "**into your hands I commit my spirit**," so teach us to pray, "**into your hands I commit my spirit**."

Amen.

Psalm 32

Of David. A Maskil.

¹ Happy are those whose transgression is forgiven, *
   whose sin is covered.

² Happy are those to whom the LORD imputes no iniquity, *
   and in whose spirit there is no deceit.

³ **While I kept silence, my body wasted away** *
   through my groaning all day long.

⁴ For day and night your hand was heavy upon me; *
   my strength was dried up as by the heat of summer.   *Selah*

⁵ **Then I acknowledged my sin to you, and I did not hide my iniquity;** *
   I said, "I will confess my transgressions to the LORD,"
   and you forgave the guilt of my sin.   *Selah*

⁶ Therefore let all who are faithful offer prayer to you; *
   at a time of distress, the rush of mighty waters shall not reach them.

⁷ **You are a hiding place for me;** *
   you preserve me from trouble;
   you surround me with glad cries of deliverance.   *Selah*

⁸ I will instruct you and teach you the way you should go; *
   I will counsel you with my eye upon you.

⁹ Do not be like a horse or a mule, without understanding, *
   whose temper must be curbed with bit and bridle,
   else it will not stay near you.

¹⁰ **Many are the torments of the wicked,** *
   but steadfast love surrounds those who trust in the LORD.

¹¹ **Be glad in the LORD and rejoice, O righteous,** *
   and shout for joy, all you upright in heart.

God of grace,
when we keep silence in guilt or suffering, your saving love can free our hearts to sing.
Help us each day to confess our sin, receive your grace,
forgive one another, and live in peace.
We pray in the name of the Prince of Peace, Jesus Christ our Savior. **Amen.**

Psalm 32, a testimony of gratitude for God's forgiveness, is the second of the traditional seven penitential psalms. Of these, it is one of the psalms that focuses most intently on the psalmist's own sinfulness and God's abundant mercy. It concludes with a turn from testimony to moral injunction, teaching fellow worshipers to trust and rejoice in God (vv. 8-11) and exemplifying how the life of faith moves from guilt to grace and ultimately gratitude. *Use in Worship: in conjunction with the confession of sin and assurance of God's pardon.*

How Blest Are They Whose Trespass

*4 "I graciously will teach you the way that you should go,
and, with my eye upon you, help you my counsel know.
Then do not be unruly or slow to understand;
be not perverse, but willing to heed my wise command."

5 The sorrows of the wicked increase from year to year,
but those who trust the LORD God know love instead of fear.
Then in the LORD be joyful, in song lift up your voice;
be glad in God, you righteous: rejoice, O saints, rejoice!

Stanza 4 may be sung by a solo voice.

Words: *Psalter*, 1912, alt., P.D.
Music (RUTHERFORD 7.6.7.6 D): Chrétien Urhan, 1834; arr. Edward F. Rimbault, 1867, P.D.

Refrain

¹ Happy are they whose transgressions are forgiven,
   and whose sin is put away!
² Happy are they to whom the LORD imputes no guilt,
   and in whose spirit there is no guile!
³ While I held my tongue, my bones withered away,
   because of my groaning all day long.
⁴ For your hand was heavy upon me day and night;
   my moisture was dried up as in the heat of summer.   *Refrain*
⁵ Then I acknowledged my sin to you, and did not conceal my guilt.
   I said, "I will confess my transgressions to the LORD."
   Then you forgave me the guilt of my sin.
⁶ Therefore all the faithful will make their prayers to you in time of trouble;
   when the great waters overflow, they shall not reach them.   *Refrain*
⁷ You are my hiding-place; you preserve me from trouble;
   you surround me with shouts of deliverance.
⁸ "I will instruct you and teach you in the way that you should go;
   I will guide you with my eye.
⁹ Do not be like horse or mule, which have no understanding;
   who must be fitted with bit and bridle, or else they will not stay near you."
¹⁰ Great are the tribulations of the wicked;
   but mercy embraces those who trust in the LORD.
¹¹ Be glad, you righteous, and rejoice in the LORD;
   shout for joy, all who are true of heart.   *Refrain*

Tone

Lectionary: Lent (A,C); Ordinary Time after Pentecost (C); vv. 1-7 Ordinary Time after Pentecost (C).

When using as a refrain for the reading or chanting of the psalm, sing only the first half. At the conclusion of the psalm the entire refrain may be sung in canon.

Words and Music: Michael Ledner (b. 1952) © 1981 Universal Music—Brentwood-Benson Publishing/
CCCM Music, admin. Universal Music—Brentwood-Benson Publishing
Psalm Text: from *Evangelical Lutheran Worship* © 2006 Evangelical Lutheran Church in America, admin.
Augsburg Fortress Publishers
Tone: © 2011 Faith Alive Christian Resources

32C While I Keep Silence

1 While I keep si - lence, si - lence, si - lence
2 My thirst - ing spir - it, spir - it, spir - it
3 All you who wan - der, wan - der, wan - der

in my flesh, my breath and bod - y fail.
wastes a - way; I with - er in the sun.
with - out hope, who know your man - y sins,

My sins grow bit - ter, bit - ter, bit - ter
But as I'm turn - ing, turn - ing, turn - ing
seek out the Sav - ior, Sav - ior, Sav - ior

in my mouth. My bones re - turn to dust.
toward the night, you split the si - lent skies.
while he's found; he hides you in his hand.

O God, I groan both day and
O God, I stand be - neath the
O God, you hear us day and

night, be - neath your heav - y hand.
rain, be - neath the cleans - ing rain.
night; re - store us by your hand.

Accompany with soft instruments or humming voices sustaining the pitches E and B.

Words: David Wright, 2005, © 2005 David Wright
Music (SILENCE 8.6.8.6.8.6): James E. Clemens, 2005, © 2005 James E. Clemens

¹ Rejoice in the LORD, O you righteous. *
  Praise befits the upright.

² **Praise the LORD with the lyre; ***
  make melody to him with the harp of ten strings.

³ **Sing to him a new song; ***
  play skillfully on the strings, with loud shouts.

⁴ For the word of the LORD is upright, *
  and all his work is done in faithfulness.

⁵ He loves righteousness and justice; *
  the earth is full of the steadfast love of the LORD.

⁶ **By the word of the LORD the heavens were made, ***
  and all their host by the breath of his mouth.

⁷ He gathered the waters of the sea as in a bottle; *
  he put the deeps in storehouses.

⁸ Let all the earth fear the LORD; *
  let all the inhabitants of the world stand in awe of him.

⁹ **For he spoke, and it came to be; ***
  he commanded, and it stood firm.

¹⁰ The LORD brings the counsel of the nations to nothing; *
  he frustrates the plans of the peoples.

¹¹ The counsel of the LORD stands forever, *
  the thoughts of his heart to all generations.

¹² Happy is the nation whose God is the LORD, *
  the people whom he has chosen as his heritage.

¹³ **The LORD looks down from heaven; ***
  he sees all humankind.

¹⁴ **From where he sits enthroned he watches ***
  all the inhabitants of the earth—

¹⁵ **he who fashions the hearts of them all, ***
  and observes all their deeds.

¹⁶ A king is not saved by his great army; *
  a warrior is not delivered by his great strength.

¹⁷ The war horse is a vain hope for victory, *
  and by its great might it cannot save.

¹⁸ Truly the eye of the LORD is on those who fear him, *
  on those who hope in his steadfast love,

¹⁹ to deliver their soul from death, *
  and to keep them alive in famine.

(continues)

20 **Our soul waits for the Lord;** *
   he is our help and shield.

21 **Our heart is glad in him,** *
   because we trust in his holy name.

22 **Let your steadfast love, O Lord, be upon us,** *
   even as we hope in you.

Creating and redeeming God, you made our hearts to sing
and in Jesus Christ you teach us new songs.
Teach us also to wait with patience and hope for that promised victory
when all peoples return to you;
for Christ is Lord of all, and in his name we pray. **Amen.**

Psalm 33 is an enthusiastic call to praise God (vv. 1-3), especially because of the mighty acts of creation (vv. 4-9) and God's sovereign rule over all peoples (vv. 13-19). It concludes with a sturdy statement of trust in God (vv. 20-22). This psalm is comprehensive in its theology, focusing on both creation and justice, God's power and faithfulness, and God's authority and relational loyalty. It also offers a vivid reminder that God's sovereign rule must challenge reliance on human military power. *Use in Worship: services focusing on the role of civic governments or the proper response to warfare and military action.*

33A Psalm 33 | A Responsorial Setting

Refrain

Lord, let your lov - ing - kind-ness be up - on us,
as we have put our trust in you.

Refrain

1 Rejoice in the Lord, you righteous;
   praise is fitting for the upright.
2 Praise the Lord with the lyre;
   make music for God with a ten-stringed harp.

3 Sing for the LORD a new song;
   play your instrument skillfully with joyful sounds.

4 For your word, O LORD, is right,
   and faithful are all your works. *Refrain*

5 You love righteousness and justice;
   your steadfast love fills the whole earth.

6 By your word were the heavens made,
   by the breath of your mouth all the hosts of heaven.

7 You gather up the waters of the ocean as in a water-skin
   and store up the depths of the sea.

8 Let all the earth fear the LORD;
   let all who dwell in the world stand in awe. *Refrain*

9 For God spoke, and it came to pass;
   God commanded, and it stood fast.

10 The LORD brings the will of the nations to nothing
   and thwarts the designs of the peoples.

11 Your will, O LORD, stands fast forever,
   and the designs of your heart from age to age.

12 Happy is the nation whose God is the LORD!
   Happy the people chosen to be God's heritage! *Refrain*

13 The LORD looks down from heaven,
   and sees all humankind.

14 God sits firmly enthroned and watches
   all who dwell on the earth.

15 God fashions all their hearts
   and observes all their deeds. *Refrain*

16 A king is not saved by the size of the army,
   nor are warriors rescued by their great strength.

17 The horse gives vain hope for victory;
   despite its great strength it cannot save.

18 Truly, your eye is upon those who fear you, O LORD,
   upon those who wait for your steadfast love,

19 to deliver their lives from death,
   and to keep them alive in time of famine. *Refrain*

20 Our innermost being waits for you, O LORD,
   our helper and our shield.

(continues)

²¹ Surely, our heart rejoices in you,

for in your holy name we put our trust.

²² Let your lovingkindness, O LORD, be upon us,

even as we place our hope in you.   *Refrain*

Tone

Lectionary: vv. 1-12 Ordinary Time after Pentecost (A); vv. 12-22 Ordinary Time after Pentecost (C).

Words: Psalm 33:22
Music (based on the tune A LA VENUE DE NOËL): Betty Carr Pulkingham © 1991 Celebration
Psalm Text: from *Evangelical Lutheran Worship* © 2006 Evangelical Lutheran Church in America, admin.
Augsburg Fortress Publishers
Tone: © 2011 Faith Alive Christian Resources

Alternate Refrain

Words: James V. Marchionda © 1969, 1981, 1997 International Commission on English in the Liturgy Corporation
Music: James V. Marchionda, acc. Laura Kutscher © 1994 World Library Publications
Tone: © 1997 Augsburg Fortress Publishers

Rejoice, You Righteous, in the Lord 33B

1 Re-joice, you right-eous, in the Lord, in song your voic-es raise;
2 Let ev-ery na-tion, ev-ery land u-nite with one ac-cord,
3 Be-hold, God's ev-er-watch-ful eye sees through our dark de-spair;

a-wake the psal-ter-y and harp, lift up God's name in praise!
and hum-bly lay their heart-felt prayers in awe be-fore the Lord.
the arms of Grace en-cir-cle us with strong, yet ten-der care;

For by God's word the heavens were hung; God laid the sea and land,
How hap-py are God's faith-ful ones, how blest God's cho-sen heirs,
the hope of all the a-ges past, that sets at peace our fears,

and all that fills the fir-ma-ment were made at God's com-mand.
for sure-ly an in-her-i-tance of glo-ry shall be theirs!
God's mer-cy and God's stead-fast love shall fol-low all our years.

This tune in a higher key: p. 620.

Words: Michael Morgan © 1999, 2011 Michael Morgan, admin. Faith Alive Christian Resources
Music (ELLACOMBE 8.6.8.6 D): *Gesangbuch der Herzogl Wirtembergischen Kotholischen Hofkapelle*, Wittenburg, 1784, P.D.

33C The Lord God from His Throne on High

1 The Lord God from his throne on high looks down with clear and
2 God's eye is on all those who fear; to those who hope, the

search - ing eye on all that dwell be - low;
Lord is near, ac - cord - ing to his Word.

and he that fash - ioned heart and mind looks ev - er down on
Death can - not touch those in his hand, nor fam - ine con - quer

hu - man - kind, their hearts and minds to know.
in the land; we wait up - on the Lord.

Not hu-man strength or might-y hosts, not charg-ing
In God our hope is firm and sure, who makes the

steeds or war-like boasts can save from o-ver-throw;
joy-ful heart se-cure, our help-er strong and true.

but God will save from death and shame all those who fear and
Our trust is in your ho-ly name; your mer-cy, LORD, in

trust his name, and they no want shall know.
faith we claim, as we have hoped in you.

Guitar chords do not correspond with keyboard harmony.

Words: st. 1 *Psalter Hymnal*, 1934; st. 2 Marie J. Post, alt., P.D.
Music (GENEVAN 68 | 8.8.6.8.8.6 D): *Genevan Psalter*, 1539, P.D.; harm. Howard Slenk © 1987 Faith Alive
Christian Resources

Psalm 34

Of David, when he feigned madness before Abimelech, so that he drove him out, and he went away.

1 I will bless the LORD at all times; *
   his praise shall continually be in my mouth.

2 **My soul makes its boast in the LORD;** *
   let the humble hear and be glad.

3 O magnify the LORD with me, *
   and let us exalt his name together.

4 **I sought the LORD, and he answered me,** *
   and delivered me from all my fears.

5 **Look to him, and be radiant;** *
   so your faces shall never be ashamed.

6 This poor soul cried, and was heard by the LORD, *
   and was saved from every trouble.

7 The angel of the LORD encamps around those who fear him, *
   and delivers them.

8 **O taste and see that the LORD is good;** *
   happy are those who take refuge in him.

9 **O fear the LORD, you his holy ones,** *
   for those who fear him have no want.

10 The young lions suffer want and hunger, *
   but those who seek the LORD lack no good thing.

11 **Come, O children, listen to me;** *
   I will teach you the fear of the LORD.

12 Which of you desires life, *
   and covets many days to enjoy good?

13 **Keep your tongue from evil,** *
   and your lips from speaking deceit.

14 **Depart from evil, and do good;** *
   seek peace, and pursue it.

15 The eyes of the LORD are on the righteous, *
   and his ears are open to their cry.

16 The face of the LORD is against evildoers, *
   to cut off the remembrance of them from the earth.

17 **When the righteous cry for help, the LORD hears,** *
   and rescues them from all their troubles.

18 **The LORD is near to the brokenhearted,** *
   and saves the crushed in spirit.

¹⁹ Many are the afflictions of the righteous, *

    but the L ORD rescues them from them all.

²⁰ He keeps all their bones; *

    not one of them will be broken.

²¹ Evil brings death to the wicked, *

    and those who hate the righteous will be condemned.

²² **The L ORD redeems the life of his servants; ***

    none of those who take refuge in him will be condemned.

Great and loving God, you heal our broken hearts and restore our wounded spirits.
Help us to trust in your faithfulness, feast upon your goodness, and pursue your peace
as we await your kingdom's fulfillment.
We pray this in Jesus' name. **Amen.**

Psalm 34 is an acrostic psalm where each verse begins with a subsequent letter in the Hebrew alphabet. It is
a testimony of gratitude for divine deliverance, beginning with reference to a particular occasion of God's
grace (vv. 4-6) and continuing with a beautiful anthology of general reasons for praise. This psalm has been
called an "anthology of faithful spirituality" and is an address from the psalmist to the community. It is
noted for its stunning imagery: the "shining face" of those who turn toward God (v. 5), the command
to "taste" God's goodness (v. 8), and God's deliverance of those who are "crushed in spirit" (v. 18). *Use in
Worship: celebrations of the Lord's Supper; services focusing on the communion of saints.*

Psalm 34 | A Responsorial Setting 34A

Taste and see, taste and see the good-ness of the Lord.

Refrain

¹ I will bless the L ORD at all times;

    the praise of God shall ever be in my mouth.

² I will glory in the L ORD;

    let the lowly hear and rejoice.

³ Proclaim with me the greatness of the L ORD;

    let us exalt God's name together. *Refrain*

⁴ I sought the L ORD, who answered me

    and delivered me from all my terrors.

(continues)

⁵ Look upon the Lord and be radiant,
    and let not your faces be ashamed.

⁶ I called in my affliction, and the Lord heard me
    and saved me from all my troubles.

⁷ The angel of the Lord encamps around those who fear the Lord
    and delivers them.

⁸ Taste and see that the Lord is good;
    happy are they who take refuge in God!   *Refrain*

⁹ Fear the Lord, you saints of the Lord,
    for those who fear the Lord lack nothing.

¹⁰ The lions are in want and suffer hunger,
    but those who seek the Lord lack nothing that is good.

¹¹ Come, children, and listen to me;
    I will teach you reverence for the Lord.

¹² Who among you takes pleasure in life
    and desires long life to enjoy prosperity?

¹³ Keep your tongue from evil
    and your lips from lying words.

¹⁴ Turn from evil and do good;
    seek peace and pursue it.   *Refrain*

¹⁵ The eyes of the Lord are upon the righteous,
    and God's ears are open to their cry.

¹⁶ The face of the Lord is against those who do evil,
    to erase the remembrance of them from the earth.

¹⁷ The righteous cry, and the Lord hears them,
    and delivers them from all their troubles.

¹⁸ The Lord is near to the brokenhearted
    and saves those whose spirits are crushed.   *Refrain*

¹⁹ Many are the troubles of the righteous,
    but the Lord delivers them from every one.

²⁰ God will keep safe all their bones;
    not one of them shall be broken.

²¹ Evil will bring death to the wicked
    and those who hate the righteous will be punished.

²² O Lord, you redeem the life of your servants,
    and those who put their trust in you will not be punished.   *Refrain*

Tone

Lectionary: vv. 1-10, 22 All Saints' Day (A); vv. 1-8 Ordinary Time after Pentecost (B); vv. 1-8 (19-22) Ordinary Time after Pentecost (B); vv. 9-14 Ordinary Time after Pentecost (B); vv. 15-22 Ordinary Time after Pentecost (B).

Words: Psalm 34
Music: Robert E. Kreutz

Alternate Refrain

Alternate Tone

34B Taste and See

Praise shall al-ways be on my lips; my
geth-er let us all_____ praise God's name. I
You'll want for noth-ing_____ if you ask.

soul shall glo - ry_____ in the Lord; for
called the Lord, who_____ an - swered me; from
Taste and see that the Lord is good; in

To Refrain

God has been_____ so good to me.
all my trou-bles I was set free.
God we need_____ put all our trust.

Words: James E. Moore Jr. © 1983 GIA Publications, Inc.
Music (TASTE AND SEE): James E. Moore Jr. © 1983 GIA Publications, Inc.

Spanish 1 Ben - de - ci - ré   al Se - ñor en to - do tiem - po; su a - la -
2 Los que mi - ra - ron a Dios res - plan - de cie - ron   y ja -

English 1 I   will ex - tol   my God each wak - ing mo - ment, shouts of
2 All those who look   up - on the Lord are   ra - diant; they will

ban - za en mi bo - ca es - ta - rá.   En   el Se - ñor   se
más   de - frau - da - dos se ve - rán.   Dios es - cu - chó el cla -
praise for - ev - er sound - ing from my voice.   In God the Lord is my
shine with joy and nev - er blush with shame.   God hears the cries of the

glo - ria - rá   mi al - ma; lo oi - rán los man - sos   y se a - le - gra -
mor de es - te po - bre y de to - das sus an - gus - tias lo li -
on - ly cause for boast - ing; let the meek and help - less hear me and re -
poor and heals their an - guish. In thanks - giv - ing, we   ex - alt God's ho - ly

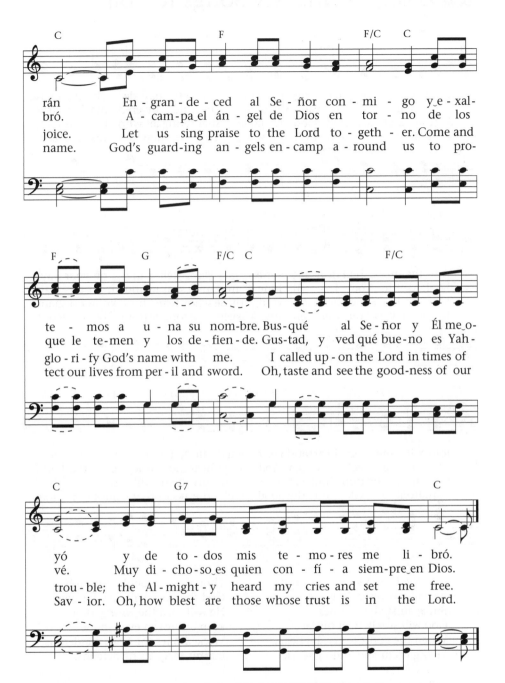

 rán En - gran - de - ced al Se - ñor con - mi - go y_e - xal-
bró. A - cam-pa_el án - gel de Dios en tor - no de los
joice. Let us sing praise to the Lord to - geth - er. Come and
name. God's guard-ing an - gels en - camp a - round us to pro-

te - mos a u - na su nom-bre. Bus-qué al Se - ñor y Él me_o-
que le te-men y los de - fien - de. Gus-tad, y ved qué bue-no es Yah-
glo - ri - fy God's name with me. I called up - on the Lord in times of
tect our lives from per - il and sword. Oh, taste and see the good-ness of our

yó y de to - dos mis te - mo - res me li - bró.
vé. Muy di - cho-so_es quien con - fí - a siem-pre_en Dios.
trou - ble; the Al - might - y heard my cries and set me free.
Sav - ior. Oh, how blest are those whose trust is in the Lord.

Words: Psalm 34:1-8; tr. Mary Louise Bringle (b. 1953) © 2011 GIA Publications, Inc.
Music (BENDECIRÉ AL SEÑOR): anonymous; arr. Felipe Blycker © 1992 Celebremos/Libros Alianza

34D LORD, I Bring My Songs to You

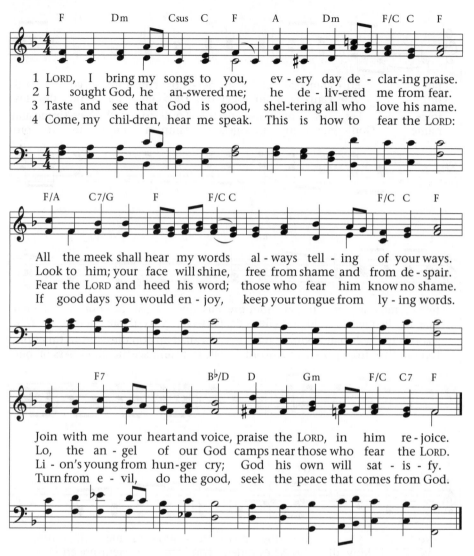

1 LORD, I bring my songs to you, ev - ery day de - clar-ing praise.
2 I sought God, he an-swered me; he de - liv-ered me from fear.
3 Taste and see that God is good, shel-tering all who love his name.
4 Come, my chil-dren, hear me speak. This is how to fear the LORD:

All the meek shall hear my words al - ways tell - ing of your ways.
Look to him; your face will shine, free from shame and from de - spair.
Fear the LORD and heed his word; those who fear him know no shame.
If good days you would en - joy, keep your tongue from ly - ing words.

Join with me your heart and voice, praise the LORD, in him re - joice.
Lo, the an - gel of our God camps near those who fear the LORD.
Li - on's young from hun-ger cry; God his own will sat - is - fy.
Turn from e - vil, do the good, seek the peace that comes from God.

5 God the LORD sees all our needs;
   he will answer us in grace.
   But against all evil ones
   God will surely turn his face.
   When the contrite cry, he hears,
   saving them and ending fears.

6 Though our troubles multiply,
   God the LORD will save his own.
   He will turn the wrong aside,
   keep unbroken every bone.
   Wicked ones the LORD condemns,
   but his servants he defends.

Guitar chords do not correspond with keyboard harmony.

Words: Marie J. Post, 1985, © 1987 Faith Alive Christian Resources
Music (LUX PRIMA 7.7.7.7.7.7): Charles F. Gounod (1818-1893), 1872, P.D.

Psalm 35

Of David.

1 Contend, O Lᴏʀᴅ, with those who contend with me; *
    fight against those who fight against me!

2 Take hold of shield and buckler, *
    and rise up to help me!

3 Draw the spear and javelin against my pursuers; *
    say to my soul, "I am your salvation."

4 **Let them be put to shame and dishonor who seek after my life.** *
    Let them be turned back and confounded
    who devise evil against me.

5 Let them be like chaff before the wind, *
    with the angel of the Lᴏʀᴅ driving them on.

6 **Let their way be dark and slippery,** *
    with the angel of the Lᴏʀᴅ pursuing them.

7 For without cause they hid their net for me; *
    without cause they dug a pit for my life.

8 Let ruin come on them unawares. *
    And let the net that they hid ensnare them; let them fall in it—to their ruin.

9 **Then my soul shall rejoice in the Lᴏʀᴅ,** *
    exulting in his deliverance.

10 **All my bones shall say, "O Lᴏʀᴅ, who is like you?** *
    You deliver the weak from those too strong for them,
    the weak and needy from those who despoil them."

11 Malicious witnesses rise up; *
    they ask me about things I do not know.

12 They repay me evil for good; *
    my soul is forlorn.

13 **But as for me, when they were sick, I wore sackcloth;** *
    I afflicted myself with fasting.
    I prayed with head bowed on my bosom,

14 **as though I grieved for a friend or a brother;** *
    I went about as one who laments for a mother,
    bowed down and in mourning.

15 But at my stumbling they gathered in glee, they gathered together against me; *
    ruffians whom I did not know tore at me without ceasing;

16 they impiously mocked more and more, *
    gnashing at me with their teeth.

(continues)

¹⁷ How long, O LORD, will you look on? *

　　Rescue me from their ravages, my life from the lions!

¹⁸ **Then I will thank you in the great congregation;** *

　　in the mighty throng I will praise you.

¹⁹ Do not let my treacherous enemies rejoice over me, *

　　or those who hate me without cause wink the eye.

²⁰ For they do not speak peace, *

　　but they conceive deceitful words against those who are quiet in the land.

²¹ They open wide their mouths against me; *

　　they say, "Aha, Aha, our eyes have seen it."

²² **You have seen, O LORD; do not be silent!** *

　　O Lord, do not be far from me!

²³ **Wake up! Bestir yourself for my defense,** *

　　for my cause, my God and my Lord!

²⁴ **Vindicate me, O LORD, my God, according to your righteousness,** *

　　and do not let them rejoice over me.

²⁵ Do not let them say to themselves, "Aha, we have our heart's desire." *

　　Do not let them say, "We have swallowed you up."

²⁶ **Let all those who rejoice at my calamity**

　be put to shame and confusion; *

　　let those who exalt themselves against me

　　be clothed with shame and dishonor.

²⁷ Let those who desire my vindication shout for joy and be glad, *

　　and say evermore, "Great is the LORD,

　　who delights in the welfare of his servant."

²⁸ **Then my tongue shall tell of your righteousness** *

　　and of your praise all day long.

The battle is yours, O Lord.
We are not strong enough to win against personal enemies or cosmic powers.
Help us to put all our trust in the mighty Savior and victorious King, our Lord Jesus,
in whose name we pray. **Amen.**

Psalm 35 is a cry to God from a victim of attack, deceit, slander, and injustice. Each of its three sections (vv. 9-10, 18, 27-28) concludes in a confession of trust in what God will do. The third section of the psalm is noteworthy for focusing on the power of human speech, lamenting the improper use of the tongue, and closing with a vow for the right use of the tongue in praise of God. The experience of the psalmist parallels those of Job and Jeremiah, among others. Jesus quotes this psalm (John 15:25) in reference to those who reject him. *Use in Worship: services focusing on being rejected by others; services focusing on the importance of truth telling (the ninth commandment); pastoral contexts with those who have experienced slander.*

Litany for the Slandered

Voice 1:

With the tongue we praise our Lord and Father, and with it we curse human beings, who have been made in God's likeness. Out of the same mouth come praise and cursing. My brothers and sisters, this should not be.

May my tongue proclaim your righteousness,
your praises all day long.

Voice 2:

Contend, LORD, with those who contend with me; arise and come to my aid. Say to me, "I am your salvation." Ruthless witnesses come forward; they question me on things I know nothing about. They repay me evil for good and leave me like one bereaved. They slandered me without ceasing. How long, Lord, will you look on?

Voice 1:

With the tongue we praise our Lord and Father, and with it we curse human beings, who have been made in God's likeness. Out of the same mouth come praise and cursing. My brothers and sisters, this should not be.

May my tongue proclaim your righteousness,
your praises all day long.

Voice 2:

LORD, you have seen this; do not be silent. Do not be far from me, Lord. Awake, and rise to my defense! Contend for me, my God and Lord. Vindicate me in your righteousness, LORD my God; do not let them gloat over me. May those who delight in my vindication shout for joy and gladness; may they always say, "The LORD be exalted, who delights in the well-being of his servant." My tongue will proclaim your righteousness, your praises all day long.

Voice 1:

With the tongue we praise our Lord and Father, and with it we curse human beings, who have been made in God's likeness. Out of the same mouth come praise and cursing. My brothers and sisters, this should not be.

May my tongue proclaim your righteousness,
your praises all day long.

The litany continues with this prayer and/or the singing of "O God, My Faithful God," as found on the next page.

Loving and faithful God, giver of every good and perfect gift,
you know our thoughts before they are formed and our words before they are spoken. Save us from our inclination to think, act or speak in crude, demeaning or vengeful ways, and heal the wounds made by the carelessness of others.
By the power of your redeeming Spirit, fill our lives with wisdom and grace,
so that we may speak truthfully, live peacefully, and bring glory and honor to your name. **Amen.**

(continues)

1 O God, my faith-ful God, true foun-tain ev-er flow-ing,
2 Give me the strength to do with read-y heart and will-ing
3 Keep me from say-ing words that lat-er need re-call-ing;
4 When dan-gers gath-er round, O keep me calm and fear-less;

with-out whom noth-ing is, all per-fect gifts be-stow-ing:
what-ev-er you com-mand, my call-ing here ful-fill-ing.
guard me lest i-dle speech may from my lips be fall-ing;
help me to bear the cross when life seems dark and cheer-less.

give me a health-y frame, and may I have with-in
Help me do what I should in all that comes my way;
but when with-in my place I must and ought to speak,
Help me, as you have taught, to love both great and small,

a con-science free from blame, a soul un-stained by sin.
I know that you are good, you bless those who o-bey.
then to my words give grace lest I of-fend the weak.
to speak the truth in love, to live at peace with all.

Text: James 3:9-10 and Psalm 35 © THE HOLY BIBLE, NEW INTERNATIONAL VERSION®, NIV® Copyright
© 1973, 1978, 1984, 2011 by Biblica, Inc.™ Used by permission. All rights reserved worldwide.
Prayer: Paul Detterman, 2011, © Creative Commons Attribution-NonCommercial-ShareAlike
Words: Johann Heermann, 1630; tr. Catherine Winkworth, 1863, alt., P.D.
Music (DARMSTADT/WAS FRAG' ICH NACH DER WELT 6.7.6.7.6.6.6.6): Ahasuerus Fritsch, 1679; harm.
Johann S. Bach (1685-1750), in *Cantata 45*, P.D.

Psalm 36

To the leader. Of David, the servant of the LORD.

¹ Transgression speaks to the wicked deep in their hearts; *
  there is no fear of God before their eyes.

² For they flatter themselves in their own eyes *
  that their iniquity cannot be found out and hated.

³ The words of their mouths are mischief and deceit; *
  they have ceased to act wisely and do good.

⁴ They plot mischief while on their beds; *
  they are set on a way that is not good; they do not reject evil.

⁵ **Your steadfast love, O LORD, extends to the heavens,** *
  your faithfulness to the clouds.

⁶ **Your righteousness is like the mighty mountains,**
  your judgments are like the great deep; *
  you save humans and animals alike, O LORD.

⁷ How precious is your steadfast love, O God! *
  All people may take refuge in the shadow of your wings.

⁸ They feast on the abundance of your house, *
  and you give them drink from the river of your delights.

⁹ For with you is the fountain of life; *
  in your light we see light.

¹⁰ **O continue your steadfast love to those who know you,** *
  and your salvation to the upright of heart!

¹¹ **Do not let the foot of the arrogant tread on me,** *
  or the hand of the wicked drive me away.

¹² **There the evildoers lie prostrate;** *
  they are thrust down, unable to rise.

Loving and faithful God, we thank you that in Jesus Christ
you have revealed the height and width, the breadth and depth of your love.
With you is the fountain of life, and in your light we see light.
May our lives reflect your goodness and by your Spirit bring healing to others,
until all creation makes its home under the shadow of your wings. **Amen.**

Psalm 36 contrasts the folly, deception, and conniving of faithless people (vv. 1-4) with the majestic goodness of God (vv. 5-9) and concludes with a prayer for continued experience of God's steadfast love rather than the influence of the godless (vv. 10-12). Rich theological themes are expressed in the middle section of the psalm, where God is praised for a quartet of characteristics: steadfast love, truthfulness, faithfulness, and sovereign authority (vv. 5-6). God is praised as the deliverer of both people and animals (v. 6), the refuge for both angels and people (v. 7), and a source of nourishing water from the fountain of life for the thirsty (vv. 8-9). *Use in Worship: during Holy Week, a context which contrasts the cruciform majesty of God with our own faithlessness; any occasion focusing on the goodness of God.*

36A Psalm 36:5-11 | A Responsorial Setting

Refrain

How pre - cious is your un - fail - ing love, O

God: the chil - dren of earth shall find ref - uge be -

neath the shad - ow of your wings.

Refrain

⁵ Your love, O LORD, reaches to the heavens,
    and your faithfulness to the clouds.

⁶ Your righteousness is like the strong mountains, your justice like the great deep;
    you save humankind and animals, O LORD.

⁷ How priceless is your love, O God!
    All people take refuge under the shadow of your wings.

⁸ They feast upon the abundance of your house;
    you give them drink from the river of your delights. *Refrain*

⁹ For with you is the well of life,
    and in your light we see light.

¹⁰ Continue your lovingkindness to those who know you,
    and your favor to those who are true of heart.

¹¹ Let not the foot of the proud come near me,
    nor the hand of the wicked push me aside. *Refrain*

Lectionary: vv. 5-10 Ordinary Time after Epiphany (C); vv. 5-11 Monday of Holy Week (A,B,C).

Words and Music: David Lee © 2010 David Lee
Psalm Text: from *Evangelical Lutheran Worship* © 2006 Evangelical Lutheran Church in America, admin. Augsburg Fortress Publishers
Tone: © 2011 Faith Alive Christian Resources

High in the Heavens, Eternal God 36B

1 High in the heavens, e - ter - nal God, your good - ness in full glo - ry shines: your truth shall break through ev - ery cloud that veils and dark - ens your de - signs.

2 For - ev - er firm your jus - tice stands, as moun - tains their foun - da - tions keep; wise are the won - ders of your hands; your judg - ments are a might - y deep.

3 From the pro - vi - sions of your house we shall be fed with sweet re - past; there mer - cy like a riv - er flows and brings sal - va - tion to our taste.

4 Life, like a foun - tain, rich and free, springs from the pres - ence of the Lord, and in your light our souls shall see the glo - ries prom - ised in your word.

Words: Isaac Watts (1674-1748), P.D.
Music (TRURO 8.8.8.8): Thomas Williams' *Psalmodia Evangelica*, 1789, P.D.

Psalm 37

Of David.

1 Do not fret because of the wicked; *
 do not be envious of wrongdoers,

2 for they will soon fade like the grass, *
 and wither like the green herb.

3 **Trust in the LORD, and do good; ***
 so you will live in the land, and enjoy security.

4 **Take delight in the LORD, ***
 and he will give you the desires of your heart.

5 Commit your way to the LORD; *
 trust in him, and he will act.

6 He will make your vindication shine like the light, *
 and the justice of your cause like the noonday.

7 **Be still before the LORD, and wait patiently for him; ***
 do not fret over those who prosper in their way,
 over those who carry out evil devices.

8 **Refrain from anger, and forsake wrath. ***
 Do not fret—it leads only to evil.

9 **For the wicked shall be cut off, ***
 but those who wait for the LORD shall inherit the land.

10 Yet a little while, and the wicked will be no more; *
 though you look diligently for their place, they will not be there.

11 But the meek shall inherit the land, *
 and delight themselves in abundant prosperity.

12 The wicked plot against the righteous, *
 and gnash their teeth at them;

13 but the LORD laughs at the wicked, *
 for he sees that their day is coming.

14 **The wicked draw the sword and bend their bows**
 to bring down the poor and needy, *
 to kill those who walk uprightly;

15 **their sword shall enter their own heart, ***
 and their bows shall be broken.

16 Better is a little that the righteous person has *
 than the abundance of many wicked.

17 For the arms of the wicked shall be broken, *
 but the LORD upholds the righteous.

¹⁸ **The LORD knows the days of the blameless, ***
   and their heritage will abide forever;

¹⁹ **they are not put to shame in evil times, ***
   in the days of famine they have abundance.

²⁰ But the wicked perish,
   and the enemies of the LORD are like the glory of the pastures; *
      they vanish—like smoke they vanish away.

²¹ **The wicked borrow, and do not pay back, ***
   but the righteous are generous and keep giving;

²² **for those blessed by the LORD shall inherit the land, ***
   but those cursed by him shall be cut off.

²³ Our steps are made firm by the LORD, *
   when he delights in our way;

²⁴ though we stumble, we shall not fall headlong, *
   for the LORD holds us by the hand.

²⁵ **I have been young, and now am old, ***
   yet I have not seen the righteous forsaken
   or their children begging bread.

²⁶ **They are ever giving liberally and lending, ***
   and their children become a blessing.

²⁷ Depart from evil, and do good; *
   so you shall abide forever.

²⁸ For the LORD loves justice; he will not forsake his faithful ones. *
   The righteous shall be kept safe forever,
   but the children of the wicked shall be cut off.

²⁹ **The righteous shall inherit the land, ***
   and live in it forever.

³⁰ The mouths of the righteous utter wisdom, *
   and their tongues speak justice.

³¹ The law of their God is in their hearts; *
   their steps do not slip.

³² **The wicked watch for the righteous, ***
   and seek to kill them.

³³ **The LORD will not abandon them to their power, ***
   or let them be condemned when they are brought to trial.

³⁴ **Wait for the LORD, and keep to his way,**
   and he will exalt you to inherit the land; *
   you will look on the destruction of the wicked.

(continues)

35 I have seen the wicked oppressing, *

   and towering like a cedar of Lebanon.

36 Again I passed by, and they were no more; *

   though I sought them, they could not be found.

37 Mark the blameless, and behold the upright, *

   for there is posterity for the peaceable.

38 But transgressors shall be altogether destroyed; *

   the posterity of the wicked shall be cut off.

39 **The salvation of the righteous is from the LORD;** *

   he is their refuge in the time of trouble.

40 **The LORD helps them and rescues them;** *

   he rescues them from the wicked,

   and saves them, because they take refuge in him.

God of eternity,
Jesus taught that the meek are blessed—they shall inherit the earth.
Help us to live each day with our eyes and hearts fixed on eternity,
trusting that in you daybreak will come, night will flee away,
and all will be made right and just.
We pray this through Christ our Lord. **Amen.**

Psalm 37, an acrostic psalm in which every second verse begins with a subsequent letter of the Hebrew alphabet, is a teaching or wisdom psalm offered as advice from an old and wise sage (v. 25). It depicts the demise of evil persons as self-inflicted (v. 15) and calls listeners to trust, wait patiently for God, and live generous and just lives. Like many other psalms (including Pss. 35 and 36), this psalm reaffirms the claims of Ps. 1 that evil is folly and goodness will be blessed, even in the face of evidence to the contrary. Verse 11 becomes one of Jesus' beatitudes (Matt. 5:5). *Use in Worship: services focusing on biblical wisdom literature (Prov., Eccl., the Beatitudes).*

Commit Your Way to God the Lord

1 Com-mit your way to God the Lord— your cause will
2 Be still be-fore the Lord and wait, and do not
3 Sal-va-tion comes from God a-lone: the faith-ful
4 Com-mit your way to God the Lord, to peace and

shine as bright as fire; de-light to do God's ho-ly
fret when wrong suc-ceeds; re-frain from an-ger, turn from
know their help is sure; to heav-en all our needs are
truth and grace as-pire; then mer-cy shall be your re-

word and you shall find what you de-sire.
hate, for God will pun-ish e-vil deeds.
known, and in God's strength we are se-cure.
ward, God's prom-is-es your heart's de-sire.

Guitar chords do not correspond with keyboard harmony.

Words: Michael Perry © 1989 The Jubilate Group, admin. Hope Publishing Company
Music (ROCKINGHAM 8.8.8.8): *Second Supplement to Psalmody in Miniature,* ca. 1780; adapt. Edward Miller (1731-1807), 1790, P.D.

37B Psalm 37:1-11, 39-40
A Responsorial Setting

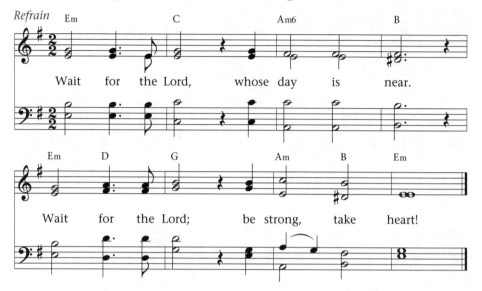

Refrain

Wait for the Lord, whose day is near.

Wait for the Lord; be strong, take heart!

Refrain

¹ Do not be provoked by evildoers;
  do not be jealous of those who do wrong.

² For they shall soon wither like the grass,
  and like the green grass fade away.

³ Put your trust in the LORD and do good;
  dwell in the land and find safe pasture.

⁴ Take delight in the LORD,
  who shall give you your heart's desire.

⁵ Commit your way to the LORD; put your trust in the LORD,
  and see what God will do.   *Refrain*

⁶ The LORD will make your vindication as clear as the light
  and the justice of your case like the noonday sun.

⁷ Be still before the LORD and wait patiently.
  Do not be provoked by the one who prospers,
  the one who succeeds in evil schemes.

⁸ Refrain from anger, leave rage alone;
  do not be provoked; it leads only to evil.

⁹ For evildoers shall be cut off,
  but those who hope in the LORD shall possess the land.   *Refrain*

¹⁰ In a little while the wicked shall be no more;
  even if you search out their place, they will not be there.

[11] But the lowly shall possess the land;
    they will delight in abundance of peace.

[39] The deliverance of the righteous comes from you, O LORD;
    you are their stronghold in time of trouble.

[40] You, O LORD, will help them and rescue them;
    you will rescue them from the wicked and deliver them,
    because in you they seek refuge.   *Refrain*

Tone

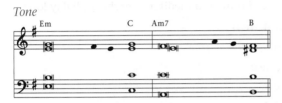

Lectionary: vv. 1-11, 39-40 Ordinary Time after Epiphany (C); vv. 1-9 Ordinary Time after Pentecost (C).

Words and Music: The Community of Taizé and Jacques Berthier (1923-1994) © 1991 Ateliers et Presses de Taizé, Taizé Community, France, GIA Publications, Inc., exclusive North American agent
Psalm Text: from *Evangelical Lutheran Worship* © 2006 Evangelical Lutheran Church in America, admin. Augsburg Fortress Publishers
Tone: © 2011 Faith Alive Christian Resources

Psalm 38

A Psalm of David, for the memorial offering.

[1] O LORD, do not rebuke me in your anger, *
    or discipline me in your wrath.

[2] For your arrows have sunk into me, *
    and your hand has come down on me.

[3] There is no soundness in my flesh because of your indignation; *
    there is no health in my bones because of my sin.

[4] **For my iniquities have gone over my head; ***
    they weigh like a burden too heavy for me.

[5] My wounds grow foul and fester *
    because of my foolishness;

[6] **I am utterly bowed down and prostrate; ***
    all day long I go around mourning.

[7] For my loins are filled with burning, *
    and there is no soundness in my flesh.

[8] **I am utterly spent and crushed; ***
    I groan because of the tumult of my heart.   (continues)

9 **O Lord, all my longing is known to you;** *
   my sighing is not hidden from you.

10 My heart throbs, my strength fails me; *
   as for the light of my eyes—it also has gone from me.

11 **My friends and companions stand aloof from my affliction,** *
   and my neighbors stand far off.

12 Those who seek my life lay their snares; *
   those who seek to hurt me speak of ruin, and meditate treachery all day long.

13 **But I am like the deaf, I do not hear;** *
   like the mute, who cannot speak.

14 Truly, I am like one who does not hear, *
   and in whose mouth is no retort.

15 **But it is for you, O LORD, that I wait;** *
   it is you, O Lord my God, who will answer.

16 For I pray, "Only do not let them rejoice over me, *
   those who boast against me when my foot slips."

17 **For I am ready to fall,** *
   and my pain is ever with me.

18 **I confess my iniquity;** *
   I am sorry for my sin.

19 Those who are my foes without cause are mighty, *
   and many are those who hate me wrongfully.

20 Those who render me evil for good *
   are my adversaries because I follow after good.

21 **Do not forsake me, O LORD;** *
   O my God, do not be far from me;

22 **make haste to help me,** *
   O Lord, my salvation.

God of hope and healing, your Son is called Jesus because he saves from sin.
In penitence we pray in that name for your saving help.
Be especially near to those who suffer today in body, mind, or spirit,
that they may know the peace of your presence and the healing power of your love. **Amen.**

Psalm 38, the third of the of seven penitential psalms, expresses lament for illness and remorse and regret for sin (vv. 1-14). It culminates in a statement of trust in God (vv. 15, 22) and confident prayer to God for salvation (vv. 21-22). The psalm includes multiple images for sin, including failure (v. 3), waywardness (v. 4), and ignorance (v. 5), and links the psalmist's sin with physical suffering (vv. 3-5), alienation from friends and neighbors (v. 11) and a sense of God's absence (vv. 15, 21). *Use in Worship: pastoral care contexts; during the season of Lent; a prayer of confession.*

Rebuke Me Not in Anger, Lord 38A

1 Re - buke me not in an - ger, Lord;
your ar - rows wound and bring de - spair.
My guilt is like a heav - y load
that is too much for me to bear.

2 My sin - ful fol - ly brought me low;
bowed down, I groan in an - guished grief.
I have no strength, for I am crushed
and spend my days with no re - lief.

3 You know my sighs and weak - ness, Lord,
my blind - ed eyes and throb - bing heart.
Friends and com - pan - ions stand far off
while oth - ers plot to seek my hurt.

4 My mouth is mute, I can - not speak;
my ear is deaf, I can - not hear.
I wait for you to an - swer, Lord,
to si - lence those who boast and jeer.

5 My pain is ever with me, Lord,
for I have sinned against your laws.
My foes are mighty—those who hate
and slander me without a cause.

6 Do not forsake me, O my Lord;
do not go far from me, my God.
Come quickly, help me now, I pray,
O Lord, my Savior and my God.

Guitar chords do not correspond with keyboard harmony.

Words: Helen Otte (b. 1931), 1985, © 1987 Faith Alive Christian Resources
Music (CHICKAHOMINY 8.8.8.8): Henry Bryan Hays, O. S. B. (b. 1920), 1981, alt. © 1981 Order of St. Benedict, Inc., admin. Liturgical Press

Psalm 39

To the leader: to Jeduthun. A Psalm of David.

1 I said, "I will guard my ways that I may not sin with my tongue; *

   I will keep a muzzle on my mouth as long as the wicked are in my presence."

2 I was silent and still; *

   I held my peace to no avail; my distress grew worse,

3 my heart became hot within me. *

   While I mused, the fire burned; then I spoke with my tongue:

4 **"Lord, let me know my end, and what is the measure of my days; ***

   let me know how fleeting my life is.

5 **You have made my days a few handbreadths,**

   and my lifetime is as nothing in your sight. *

   Surely everyone stands as a mere breath.   *Selah*

6 **Surely everyone goes about like a shadow. ***

   Surely for nothing they are in turmoil;

   they heap up, and do not know who will gather.

7 "And now, O Lord, what do I wait for? *

   My hope is in you.

8 Deliver me from all my transgressions. *

   Do not make me the scorn of the fool.

9 I am silent; I do not open my mouth, *

   for it is you who have done it.

10 Remove your stroke from me; *

   I am worn down by the blows of your hand.

11 "You chastise mortals in punishment for sin,

   consuming like a moth what is dear to them; *

   surely everyone is a mere breath.   *Selah*

12 **"Hear my prayer, O Lord, and give ear to my cry;**

   do not hold your peace at my tears. *

   For I am your passing guest, an alien, like all my forebears.

13 **Turn your gaze away from me, that I may smile again, ***

   before I depart and am no more."

O God, heavenly Father,
help us to remember that we are aliens and strangers in this world.
Do not let us be distracted by the fleeting amusements around us,
but enable us, by the power and presence of your Spirit, to keep our eyes fixed on Jesus
and our hearts set on our eternal home. **Amen.**

Psalm 39 is a bitingly ironic reflection on the brevity of life. It vents feelings of self-restraint (vv. 1-2), anger (vv. 2-3), and resignation at the punishment of God (vv. 10-11), yet also includes statements of trust and hope (v. 7). *Use in Worship: services focusing on human mortality (e.g., Ash Wednesday or services based on Eccl.); funerals (in some contexts).*

When I Sought Silence 39A

Unison

Am   **D**

1 When I sought si - lence, watched my ways,   tamed my tongue,
2 "Show me my end - ing, count my days,   let them fly—
3 What do I look for? Here and now,   once a - gain,

Am

still the wick - ed came. My heart was burn - ing,
fleet - ing like a breath. Life has no sub - stance—
God, you are my hope. My God, come save me

D   **C**   **G/B**   **Am**

full of fire, sear - ing fire, so I spoke a - gain.
work is vain, wealth is vain, death con-sumes it all.
from my sins, from the scorn. Is my pain your will?

4 Hold back your anger; still your hand.
Turn from me: I can take no more.
Are mortals nothing in your sight?
You consume; you rebuke our sins.

5 And yet I whisper: hear my prayer;
hear my cry. You will be my home.
Grant me a pardon undeserved.
Let me rest till I am no more."

Guitar chords do not correspond with keyboard harmony.

Words: Adam M. L. Tice © 2011 GIA Publications, Inc.
Music (SILENTIUM 5.3.3.5.5.3.3.5): Randall Sensmeier © 2011 GIA Publications, Inc.

39B Lord, Show Me How to Count My Days

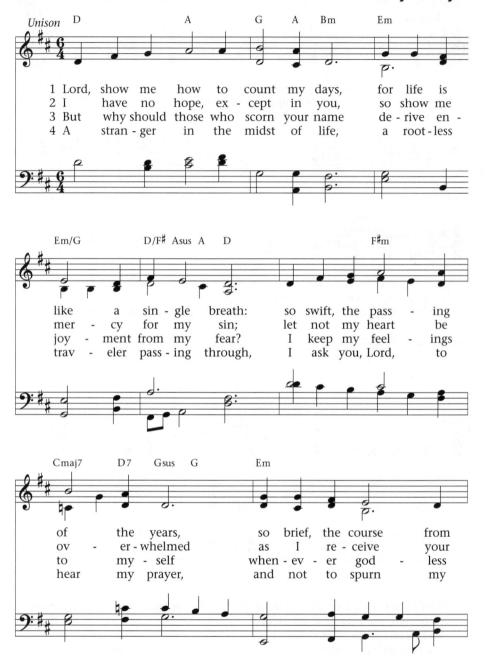

Unison

1 Lord, show me how to count my days, for life is
2 I have no hope, ex - cept in you, so show me
3 But why should those who scorn your name de - rive en -
4 A stran - ger in the midst of life, a root - less

like a sin - gle breath: so swift, the pass - ing
mer - cy for my sin; let not my heart be
joy - ment from my fear? I keep my feel - ings
trav - eler pass - ing through, I ask you, Lord, to

of the years, so brief, the course from
ov - er - whelmed as I re - ceive your
to my - self when - ev - er god - less
hear my prayer, and not to spurn my

birth to death; and all my la - bor seems in
dis - ci - pline. In hushed and ho - ly awe I
ears are near; yet how the fires with - in me
cry to you; but let me find, in - stead of

vain, how - ev - er great the wealth I gain.
stand: I feel my pain; I sense your hand.
burn un - til, at last, to you I turn.
tears, suf - fi - cient joys for all my years.

Guitar chords do not correspond with keyboard harmony.

Words: Martin Leckebusch © 2006 Kevin Mayhew Ltd.
Music (RYBURN 8.8.8.8.8.8): Norman Cocker (1889-1953) © 2011 Oxford University Press. Reproduced by permission of Oxford University Press; arr. Alfred V. Fedak (b. 1953) © 2011 Faith Alive Christian Resources

Psalm 40

To the leader. Of David. A Psalm.

1 I waited patiently for the LORD; *
    he inclined to me and heard my cry.

2 He drew me up from the desolate pit, out of the miry bog, *
    and set my feet upon a rock, making my steps secure.

3 He put a new song in my mouth, a song of praise to our God. *
    Many will see and fear, and put their trust in the LORD.

4 Happy are those who make the LORD their trust, *
    who do not turn to the proud, to those who go astray after false gods.

5 You have multiplied, O LORD my God, your wondrous deeds and your
thoughts toward us; none can compare with you. *
    Were I to proclaim and tell of them,
    they would be more than can be counted.

6 Sacrifice and offering you do not desire, but you have given me an open ear. *
    Burnt offering and sin offering you have not required.

7 Then I said, "Here I am; *
    in the scroll of the book it is written of me.

8 I delight to do your will, O my God; *
    your law is within my heart."

9 I have told the glad news of deliverance in the great congregation; *
    see, I have not restrained my lips, as you know, O LORD.

10 I have not hidden your saving help within my heart,
I have spoken of your faithfulness and your salvation; *
    I have not concealed your steadfast love and your faithfulness
    from the great congregation.

11 Do not, O LORD, withhold your mercy from me; *
    let your steadfast love and your faithfulness keep me safe forever.

12 For evils have encompassed me without number;
    my iniquities have overtaken me, until I cannot see; *
    they are more than the hairs of my head, and my heart fails me.

13 Be pleased, O LORD, to deliver me; *
    O LORD, make haste to help me.

14 Let all those be put to shame and confusion who seek to snatch away my life; *
    let those be turned back and brought to dishonor who desire my hurt.

15 Let those be appalled because of their shame *
    who say to me, "Aha, Aha!"

[16] **But may all who seek you rejoice and be glad in you;** *

> **may those who love your salvation say continually,**
> **"Great is the LORD!"**

[17] **As for me, I am poor and needy, but the Lord takes thought for me.** *

> **You are my help and my deliverer; do not delay, O my God.**

God, our help and deliverer,
we thank you for rescuing us from the miry places of our lives
and placing our feet on the firm rock of faith in Jesus Christ.
We praise you for your faithfulness in the past and your promised presence today.
In those places where we find ourselves weak,
as well as in those places where we think ourselves strong,
help us to wait for you with believing hearts, trusting in Jesus our Savior. **Amen.**

Psalm 40 begins with a testimony about a past experience of divine deliverance (vv. 1-12) and continues with a plea for continued deliverance (vv. 13-17, duplicated in Ps. 70). This psalm suggests that one way to prepare for intense petitions and even lament is to testify to God's prior redemptive actions. It has been used in some traditions in conjunction with readings about the angel's appearance to Mary. The first half of the psalm echoes themes in Mary's Magnificat and the second half is suggestive of the uncertainty and fear that Mary may have experienced. *Use in Worship: services that include testimony and petition.*

Psalm 40:1-11 | A Responsorial Setting 40A

(continues)

Refrain

1 I waited patiently upon the LORD,
  who stooped to me and heard my cry.

2 The LORD lifted me out of the desolate pit, out of the miry clay,
  and set my feet upon a high cliff, making my footing sure.

3 The LORD put a new song in my mouth, a song of praise to our God;
  many shall see, and stand in awe, and put their trust in the LORD.   *Refrain*

4 Happy are they who trust in the LORD!
  They do not turn to enemies or to those who follow lies.

5 Great are the wonders you have done, O LORD my God!
  In your plans for us, none can be compared with you!
  Oh, that I could make them known and tell them!
  But they are more than I can count.

6 Sacrifice and offering you do not desire;
  you have opened my ears:
  burnt-offering and sin-offering you have not required.

7 And so I said, "Here I am; I come.
  In the scroll of the book it is written of me:

8 'I love to do your will, O my God;
  your law is deep within me.'"   *Refrain*

9 I proclaimed righteousness in the great assembly;
  I have not restrained my lips, O LORD, you know.

10 I have not hidden your righteousness in my heart;
  I have spoken of your faithfulness and your deliverance;
  I have not concealed your steadfast love and truth from the great assembly.

11 You are the LORD; do not withhold your compassion from me;
  may your steadfast love and your truth continually keep me safe.   *Refrain*

Tone

Lectionary: Ordinary Time after Epiphany (A).

I Waited Patiently for God 40B

1 I waited patiently for God, for God
2 God raised me from a miry pit, from mud
3 And on my lips a song was put, a new
4 Great wonders you have done, O Lord, all pur -

to hear my prayer; and God bent down to where
and sinking sand, and set my feet upon
song to the Lord. Many will marvel o -
posed for our good. Unable every one

I sank and listened to me there.
a rock where I can firmly stand.
pen - eyed and put their trust in God.
to name, I bow in gratitude.

Words: The Iona Community © 1993 Wild Goose Resource Group, Iona Community, Scotland, GIA Publications, Inc., exclusive North American agent
Music (AMAZING GRACE/NEW BRITAIN 8.6.8.6): Scottish traditional; arr. The Iona Community © 1993 Wild Goose Resource Group, Iona Community, Scotland, GIA Publications, Inc., exclusive North American agent

40C I Will Wait upon the Lord

Refrain

I will wait up - on the Lord for he will hear my cry.

He has pulled me from the grave and

set me by his side. He has set my feet

up - on the sol - id ground of the Cor - ner - stone.

(last time ⌢)

1 He has put a new song on my
2 Man - y will hear the things you've done for
3 God will not re - move his mer - cy from
4 Lord, you've al - ways been my help and my

tongue. A brand new song of praise
me. And man - y more will see the
me. His good - ness and his truth have
strength, and I will trust in you to

to our God, to our God.
pow-er of your deeds, of your deeds.
set me free, set me free.
hear me a - gain, hear me a - gain.

To Refrain

Words and Music: Greg Scheer © 1993 Greg Scheer

Psalm 41

To the leader. A Psalm of David.

1 Happy are those who consider the poor; *
  the LORD delivers them in the day of trouble.

2 **The LORD protects them and keeps them alive;**
  they are called happy in the land. *
    You do not give them up to the will of their enemies.

3 The LORD sustains them on their sickbed; *
  in their illness you heal all their infirmities.

4 **As for me, I said, "O LORD, be gracious to me;** *
  heal me, for I have sinned against you."

5 **My enemies wonder in malice** *
  when I will die, and my name perish.

6 And when they come to see me, they utter empty words,
  while their hearts gather mischief; *
    when they go out, they tell it abroad.

7 **All who hate me whisper together about me;** *
  they imagine the worst for me.

8 They think that a deadly thing has fastened on me, *
  that I will not rise again from where I lie.

9 **Even my bosom friend in whom I trusted,** *
  who ate of my bread, has lifted the heel against me.

10 But you, O LORD, be gracious to me, *
  and raise me up, that I may repay them.

11 By this I know that you are pleased with me; *
  because my enemy has not triumphed over me.

12 **But you have upheld me because of my integrity,** *
  and set me in your presence forever.

13 **Blessed be the LORD, the God of Israel,** *
  from everlasting to everlasting. Amen and Amen.

Gracious God, our Lord Jesus taught us that those who imitate your mercy are blessed, and we know this to be true.
Support us in our times of chaos and despair
and help us to be alert to the needs of others
so that our lives and our lips may praise you, always and everywhere.
We pray in the name of Jesus. **Amen.**

Psalm 41, the final psalm in the first of the Psalter's five books, is a powerful sermon about living righteously before God's face. Echoing the theme of Ps. 1, it specifically lauds the goodness of those who care for the poor (v. 1). The psalm continues with a vivid testimony of a particular experience of God's deliverance from people who lack integrity (vv. 2-11) and concludes with a testimony that the psalmist's own integrity was made possible by God (v. 12). *Use in Worship: in the context of the proclamation of the Word (perhaps in conjunction with other texts that address concern for the poor or the divine initiative that makes obedience possible).*

A Prayer for Trying Times 41A

Blessed are those who consider the poor and needy; the Lord will deliver them in the time of trouble. The Lord preserves them and restores their life, that they may be happy in the land; he will not hand them over to the will of their enemies. The Lord sustains them on their sickbed; their sickness, Lord, you will remove.

Psalm 41:1-3

God who delivers, God who protects, God who sustains, God who heals: we claim your promises. In these trying times [further details may be added as appropriate], we rehearse again your goodness and ask that your Holy Spirit will work among all the peoples of this world to bring about healing and hope.

And so I said, 'Lord, be merciful to me; heal me, for I have sinned against you.' My enemies speak evil about me, asking when I shall die and my name perish. If they come to see me, they utter empty words; their heart gathers mischief; when they go out, they tell it abroad. All my enemies whisper together against me, against me they devise evil, saying that a deadly thing has laid hold on me, and that I will not rise again from where I lie. Even my bosom friend, whom I trusted, who ate of my bread, has lifted up his heel against me.

Psalm 41:4-9

We come in prayer, both as sinners and as those sinned against. We suffer, but we also cause suffering. Too often our lives are shaped by loneliness, abandonment, gossip, slander, and malice. We long for your deliverance, your protection, your sustenance, your healing.

But you, O Lord, be merciful to me and raise me up, that I may reward them. By this I know that you favor me, that my enemy does not triumph over me. Because of my integrity you uphold me and will set me before your face for ever.

Psalm 41:10-12

As we respond to these trying times, we come to you alone, the only source of true peace. By the power of your Holy Spirit, may all we do be marked by grace and truth, mercy and justice, righteousness and love. And may we dwell in your presence forever, as your adopted children who have arrived at home.

Blessed be the Lord God of Israel, from everlasting to everlasting. Amen and Amen.

Psalm 41:13

Text: Psalm 41, from *Common Worship: Daily Prayer*, Church House Publishing, alt. Reprinted by permission. Litany: John D. Witvliet, 2011, © Creative Commons Attribution-NonCommercial-ShareAlike

41B Psalm 41 | A Responsorial Setting

Refrain

Refrain What a priv - i - lege to car - ry ev-ery-thing to God in prayer!
1 What a priv - i - lege to car - ry ev-ery-thing to God in prayer!
2 Are we weak and heav - y lad - en? Take it to the Lord in prayer.
3 Have we tri - als and temp-ta - tions? Take it to the Lord in prayer.
4 Do your friends de-spise, for-sake you? Take it to the Lord in prayer.
5 Pre-cious Sav - ior, still our ref - uge! Take it to the Lord in prayer.

Refrain (or sing stanza 1)

1 Happy are they who regard the poor!
   The LORD will deliver them in the time of trouble.

2 The LORD protects and revives them, those blessed in the land,
   and does not hand them over to the power of their enemies.

3 The LORD sustains them on their sickbed
   and ministers to them in their illness.   *Refrain (or sing stanza 2)*

4 I said, "LORD, be merciful to me;
   heal me, for I have sinned against you."

5 My enemies are saying wicked things about me,
   asking when I will die, and my name perish.

6 Even if they come to see me, they speak empty words;
   their heart collects false rumors; they go outside and spread them.

7 All my enemies whisper together about me
   and devise evil against me.   *Refrain (or sing stanza 3)*

8 "A deadly thing," they say, "has fastened on him;
   he has taken to his bed and will never get up again."

9 Even my best friend, whom I trusted, who broke bread with me,
   has violently turned against me.

10 But you, O LORD, be merciful to me and raise me up,
   and I shall repay them.   *Refrain (or sing stanza 4)*

11 By this I know you are pleased with me:
   that my enemy does not triumph over me.

12 In my integrity you hold me fast,
   and shall set me before your face forever.   *Refrain (or sing stanza 5)*

13 Blessed be the LORD God of Israel,
   from age to age. Amen. Amen.

Tone

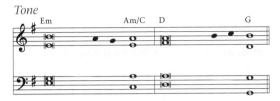

Lectionary: Ordinary Time after Epiphany (B).

Words: Joseph M. Scriven, 1855, P.D.
Music (BEACH SPRING fragment): *The Sacred Harp*, Philadelphia, 1833; harm. A. Royce Eckhardt, 1972, © 1972, 1996 Covenant Publications
Psalm Text: from *Evangelical Lutheran Worship* © 2006 Evangelical Lutheran Church in America, admin. Augsburg Fortress Publishers
Tone: © 2011 Faith Alive Christian Resources

Psalm 42

To the leader. A Maskil of the Korahites.

¹ As a deer longs for flowing streams, *
   so my soul longs for you, O God.

² **My soul thirsts for God, for the living God. ***
   When shall I come and behold the face of God?

³ My tears have been my food day and night, *
   while people say to me continually, "Where is your God?"

⁴ These things I remember, as I pour out my soul: *
   how I went with the throng, and led them in procession to the house of God,
   with glad shouts and songs of thanksgiving, a multitude keeping festival.

⁵ **Why are you cast down, O my soul,**
   and why are you disquieted within me? *
   Hope in God; for I shall again praise him, my help ⁶ and my God.

My soul is cast down within me; therefore I remember you *
   from the land of Jordan and of Hermon, from Mount Mizar.

⁷ Deep calls to deep at the thunder of your cataracts; *
   all your waves and your billows have gone over me.

⁸ **By day the Lᴏʀᴅ commands his steadfast love, ***
   and at night his song is with me, a prayer to the God of my life.

⁹ I say to God, my rock, "Why have you forgotten me? *
   Why must I walk about mournfully
   because the enemy oppresses me?"

¹⁰ As with a deadly wound in my body, my adversaries taunt me, *
   while they say to me continually, "Where is your God?"

(continues)

[11] **Why are you cast down, O my soul,**

  and why are you disquieted within me? *

    Hope in God; for I shall again praise him, my help and my God.

The psalm may continue with Psalm 43 on p. 268.

O God, our Help in past, present, and future days,
you know our deepest thoughts and needs before we can even express them.
When our world turns upside down, help us to remember happier days—
not as something lost, but as a foretaste of good things yet to come.
We pray in the name of the coming King. **Amen.**

Psalm 42, the first psalm in the second of the Psalter's five books, is an expression of profound longing for God in the midst of depression. The psalmist's hope is buoyed by two memories: a rousing procession into temple worship and the cascading waterfalls that sing God's praise as they fall from Mt. Herman. Thirst for God amidst tears is quenched with the memory of this cascading water. Its lament is answered first in Ps. 43, in which the refrain from Ps. 42 is repeated, but now in the context of greater hope and confidence. It is further answered by the visionary words of Ps. 72 (the last psalm in the second book) that portray the shalom of God's future kingdom. *Use in Worship: services of lament and healing; during the season of Advent.*

42A Como el ciervo / Like a Deer

Words: Juan Salinas; tr. Mary Louise Bringle (b. 1953), 2011
Music (LLÉNAME): Juan Salinas © 1991 CanZion Producciones; arr. Obed Valencia Lozada © 2001 Obed
Valencia Lozada

42B As the Deer Pants for the Water

1 As   the deer pants for the wa - ter
2 Day   af - ter day he sends his love, I
3 Send   me your light and truth to guide me

so   my   soul   longs for you,   my Lord.
feel His peace come   rain - ing down.
as   I   trav - el   through   this land.

When   can I come to you a - gain to
I   raise a song to him at night like
Lead   me to your ho - ly dwell - ing

praise you as be - fore?
fire____ from the ground.   Why should I
at   my   jour - ney's end.

Words and Music: Greg Scheer © 2005 Augsburg Fortress Publishers

42C Chuyŏ sasŭmi / O Lord, As a Deer

Korean Chu - yŏ sa-sŭ-mi shi-naen-mul
English O Lord, as a deer longs for cool

Chu - yŏ sa-sŭ-mi shi-naen-mul
O Lord, as a deer longs for cool

ch'at-tŭt nae nŏk-si chu-rŭl ch'at-sŭm-ni - da
wa - ter, so I am thirst-y, I long for you,

ch'at-tŭt nae nŏk-si chu - rŭl ch'at-sŭm-ni - da
wa - ter, so I am thirst - y, I long for you,

kal-kŭ-p'an nae yŏng-hon - i sa - ra - ge-shin chu -
I thirst for you, long for you, God of my life. When?

kal - kŭ-p'an nae yŏng-hon - i sa - ra - ge-shin
I thirst for you, long for you, God of my life.

ni - mŭl ŏn - che - na poe - o - ri - kka?
When, Lord, shall I be - hold you a - gain?

chu - ni - mŭl ŏn - che - na poe - o - ri - kka?
When, Lord? When shall I be - hold you a - gain?

Korean

주여 사슴이 시냇물 찾듯 내속이 주를 찾습니다
갈급한 내영혼이 살아계신 주님을 언제나 보오리까

Words: tr. I-to Loh (b. 1936) © 1990 GIA Publications, Inc.
Music: Geonyong Lee © 2000 Christian Conference of Asia, admin. GIA Publications, Inc.

As the Deer 42D

As the deer pants for the wa-ter, so my soul longs af - ter you; you a - lone are my heart's de - sire and I long to wor - ship you. You a - lone are my strength, my shield, to you a - lone may my spir - it yield; you a - lone are my heart's de-sire and I long to wor - ship you!

Words and Music: Martin Nystrom © 1984 Universal Music—Brentwood-Benson Publishing

42E As a Deer in Want of Water

1 As a deer in want of water,
so I long for you, O LORD. All
my heart and be-ing fal - ter,
thirst - ing for your liv - ing word.
When shall I be - hold your face? When shall I

2 Bit - ter tears of lam - en - ta - tion
are my food by night and day. In
my deep hu - mil - i - a - tion
"Where is now your God?" they say.
When my sor - rows weigh on me,
then I bring

Refrain O my soul, why are you griev - ing, why dis -
qui - et - ed in me? Put your hope in God, be -
liev - ing he will still your ref - uge be.
I a - gain shall praise his grace for the com -

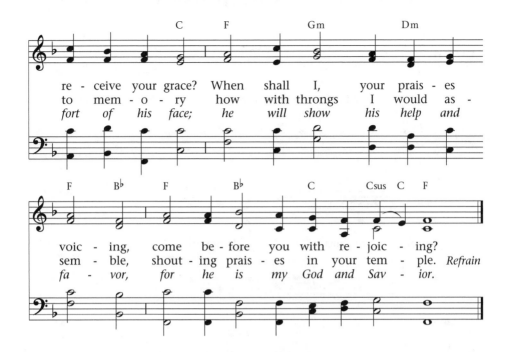

re - ceive your grace? When shall I, your prais - es
to mem - o - ry how with throngs I would as -
fort of his face; he will show his help and

voic - ing, come be - fore you with re - joic - ing?
sem - ble, shout - ing prais - es in your tem - ple. *Refrain*
fa - vor, for he is my God and Sav - ior.

Psalm 43

3 From the land beyond the Jordan
in my grief I think of you;
from the foothills of Mount Hermon
I will still remember you.
As the waters plunge and leap,
stormy troubles o'er me sweep.
Day and night God's song is with me
as a prayer to him who loves me.

4 I will say to God, my fortress,
"Why have you forgotten me?
Why must I proceed in sadness,
hounded by the enemy?"
Their rebukes and scoffing words
pierce my bones like pointed swords,
as they say with proud defiance,
"Where is God, your firm reliance?"
Refrain

5 Vindicate me, God, my Father,
come and plead my urgent cause,
for my enemies forever
threaten me and flout your laws.
I am safe with you alone;
why do you reject your own?
LORD, I need your help and blessing;
keep me safe from this oppressing.

6 Send your light and truth to lead me:
send them forth to be my guide.
To your mountain let them bring me,
to the place where you reside.
Then, O God, I will come near
and before your throne appear,
to my Savior praises bringing
with the harp and joyful singing.
Refrain

Words: *Psalter Hymnal*, 1987, © 1987 Faith Alive Christian Resources
Music (FREU DICH SEHR/GENEVAN 42 | 8.7.8.7.7.7.8.8): Louis Bourgeois (ca. 1510-1561), 1551; harm.
Johann Crüger (1598-1662), 1658, P.D.

42F Psalm 42/43 | A Responsorial Setting

Refrain

My soul thirsts for the liv-ing God. My soul needs the pre-sence of the Lord. When can I go and meet with God? When? When can I meet with God?

Refrain

^{42:1} As the deer longs for the water-brooks,
    so longs my soul for you, O God.

² I thirst for God, for the living God;
    when shall I come to appear before the presence of God?

³ My tears have been my food day and night,
    while all day long they say to me, "Where now is your God?"   *Refrain*

⁴ I pour out my soul when I think on these things;
        how I went with the multitude and led them into the house of God,
        with shouts of thanksgiving, among those keeping festival.

⁵ Why are you so full of heaviness, O my soul,
    and why are you so disquieted within me?
        Put your trust in God,
        for I will yet give thanks to the one who is my help and my God.   *Refrain*

⁶ My soul is heavy within me;

    therefore I will remember you from the land of Jordan,

    and from the peak of Mizar among the heights of Hermon.

⁷ One deep calls to another in the roar of your cascades;

    all your rapids and floods have gone over me.

⁸ The LORD grants lovingkindness in the daytime;

    in the night season the LORD's song is with me,

    a prayer to the God of my life.   *Refrain*

⁹ I will say to the God of my strength, "Why have you rejected me,

    and why do I wander in such gloom while the enemy oppresses me?"

¹⁰ While my bones are being broken, my enemies mock me to my face;

    all day long they mock me and say to me, "Where now is your God?"

¹¹ Why are you so full of heaviness, O my soul,

  and why are you so disquieted within me?

    Put your trust in God,

    for I will yet give thanks to the one who is my help and my God.   *Refrain*

⁴³:¹ Give judgment for me, O God, and defend my cause against an ungodly people;

    deliver me from the deceitful and the wicked.

² For you are the God of my strength; why have you rejected me,

    and why do I wander in such gloom while the enemy oppresses me?

³ Send out your light and your truth, that they may lead me,

    and bring me to your holy hill and to your sanctuary;

⁴ that I may go to the altar of God, to the God of my joy and gladness;

    and on the harp I will give thanks to you, O God my God.

⁵ Why are you so full of heaviness, O my soul,

  and why are you so disquieted within me?

    Put your trust in God,

    for I will yet give thanks to the one who is my help and my God.   *Refrain*

Tone

Lectionary: Easter Vigil (A,B,C); Ordinary Time after Pentecost (C).
(Pss. 42 and 43 are combined in the lectionary.)

Words and Music: Gregg DeMey © 2011 Re:Create Music; arr. Paul Detterman © 2011 Re:Create Music
Psalm Text: from *Evangelical Lutheran Worship* © 2006 Evangelical Lutheran Church in America, admin.
Augsburg Fortress Publishers
Tone: © 2011 Faith Alive Christian Resources

42G As a Hart Longs for Flowing Streams

Stanzas

1,3 As a hart longs for flow-ing streams, so my soul
2 (Day and) night, tears have been my food. Some say to

longs for you, O God. My soul thirsts for the liv-ing God.
me, "Where is your God?" My soul, why are you cast down?

When shall I come, when shall I come and be-hold the face of God?
Soon I will praise, soon I will praise, I will praise my help and God,

1, 2 *To Refrain* **3** *Fine*

When shall I come? I re-
soon I will praise,

The refrain may be sung twice after stanzas 1 and 2. The refrain is not sung after st. 3.

Words: Andrew Donaldson © 1987 Andrew Donaldson
Music (AS A HART LONGS): Andrew Donaldson © 1987 Andrew Donaldson

Psalm 43

1 Vindicate me, O God, and defend my cause against an ungodly people; *
   from those who are deceitful and unjust deliver me!

2 **For you are the God in whom I take refuge;**
   why have you cast me off? *
   Why must I walk about mournfully because of the oppression of the enemy?

3 **O send out your light and your truth; let them lead me;** *
   let them bring me to your holy hill and to your dwelling.

4 Then I will go to the altar of God, to God my exceeding joy; *
   and I will praise you with the harp, O God, my God.

5 **Why are you cast down, O my soul,**
   and why are you disquieted within me? *
   Hope in God; for I shall again praise him, my help and my God.

God, you are light and truth.
When our world seems dark and our days filled with lies,
fill our hearts with your joy and our lips with songs of praise to you,
Father, Son, and Holy Spirit—now and forever. **Amen.**

Psalm 43 is a prayer for justice in the face of injustice. The psalmist believes that God not only commands holiness but enables it by sending out light and truth to lead the people along the way. Because the psalm concludes with a refrain from Ps. 42, Pss. 42 and 43 are sometimes treated as a single unit and are often sung or prayed together. *Use in Worship: preparation for the reading and preaching of God's Word; during the season of Advent.*

For additional settings of Ps. 43 see 42B, 42E, 42F and 119K.

Send Out Your Light and Your Truth

1 Send out your light and your truth, let them lead me;
2 Lead me, O Lord, in the way ev - er - last - ing;

Oh, let them bring me to your ho - ly hill.
Oh, lead and guide me to your ho - ly hill.

Send out your light and your truth, let them lead me;
Lead me, O Lord, in the way ev - er - last - ing;

Oh, let them bring me to your ho - ly hill.
Oh, lead and guide me to your ho - ly hill.

Words: *Psalter*, 1912, P.D.
Music (LUX FIAT 11.10.11.10): Charles F. Gounod (1818-1893), P.D.

43B Send Out Your Light

Optional Introduction

1 We need you, O God, to res - cue us all.
2 We need you, O God, our souls are cast down.

When will you come?
Come, raise them up.

We need you, O God,
We need you, O God,

our ref - uge and strength.
our spir - its are dry.

Where have you gone?
Pour out your love,

Where have you gone?
pour out your love.

Bridge

You are our help,
We put our hope

you are our Sav - ior and our God.
in you, O God, so yet will we praise, —

so yet will we praise.

To Refrain

Words: Luke Hyder © 2007 Luke Hyder, admin. Faith Alive Christian Resources
Music: Luke Hyder © 2007 Luke Hyder, admin. Faith Alive Christian Resources; arr. Eelco Vos © 2011 Luke Hyder, admin. Faith Alive Christian Resources

Psalm 43 | A Responsorial Setting 43C

Refrain

Send out your light, Lord, send your truth to be my guide.

Then let them lead me to the place where you re-side.

Refrain

1 Give judgment for me, O God, and defend my cause against an ungodly people;
   deliver me from the deceitful and the wicked.

2 For you are the God of my strength; why have you rejected me,
   and why do I wander in such gloom while the enemy oppresses me?

3 Send out your light and your truth, that they may lead me,
   and bring me to your holy hill and to your sanctuary;

4 that I may go to the altar of God, to the God of my joy and gladness;
   and on the harp I will give thanks to you, O God my God. *Refrain*

5 Why are you so full of heaviness, O my soul,
   and why are you so disquieted within me?
      Put your trust in God,
      for I will yet give thanks to the one who is my help and my God. *Refrain*

Tone

Lectionary: Ordinary Time after Pentecost (A). (See also 42F.)

Words and Music: The Iona Community © 1995 Wild Goose Resource Group, Iona Community, Scotland, GIA Publications, Inc., exclusive North American agent
Psalm Text: from *Evangelical Lutheran Worship* © 2006 Evangelical Lutheran Church in America, admin. Augsburg Fortress Publishers
Tone: © 2011 Faith Alive Christian Resources

Psalm 44

To the leader. Of the Korahites. A Maskil.

Voice 1:

1 We have heard with our ears, O God, our ancestors have told us, *
   what deeds you performed in their days, in the days of old:

2 you with your own hand drove out the nations, but them you planted; *
   you afflicted the peoples, but them you set free;

3 for not by their own sword did they win the land,
   nor did their own arm give them victory; *
      but your right hand, and your arm, and the light of your countenance,
      for you delighted in them.

4 **You are my King and my God; ***
   you command victories for Jacob.

5 Through you we push down our foes; *
   through your name we tread down our assailants.

6 For not in my bow do I trust, *
   nor can my sword save me.

7 **But you have saved us from our foes, ***
   and have put to confusion those who hate us.

8 **In God we have boasted continually, ***
   and we will give thanks to your name forever.   *Selah*

Voice 2:

9 Yet you have rejected us and abased us, *
   and have not gone out with our armies.

10 **You made us turn back from the foe, ***
    and our enemies have gotten spoil.

11 **You have made us like sheep for slaughter, ***
    and have scattered us among the nations.

12 You have sold your people for a trifle, *
    demanding no high price for them.

13 **You have made us the taunt of our neighbors, ***
    the derision and scorn of those around us.

14 **You have made us a byword among the nations, ***
    a laughingstock among the peoples.

15 All day long my disgrace is before me, *
    and shame has covered my face

16 at the words of the taunters and revilers, *
    at the sight of the enemy and the avenger.

Voice 1:

¹⁷ All this has come upon us, *

    yet we have not forgotten you, or been false to your covenant.

¹⁸ **Our heart has not turned back, ***

    nor have our steps departed from your way,

¹⁹ yet you have broken us in the haunt of jackals, *

    and covered us with deep darkness.

²⁰ **If we had forgotten the name of our God, ***

    or spread out our hands to a strange god,

²¹ **would not God discover this? ***

    For he knows the secrets of the heart.

²² Because of you we are being killed all day long, *

    and accounted as sheep for the slaughter.

²³ **Rouse yourself! Why do you sleep, O Lord? ***

    Awake, do not cast us off forever!

²⁴ **Why do you hide your face? ***

    Why do you forget our affliction and oppression?

²⁵ **For we sink down to the dust; ***

    our bodies cling to the ground.

²⁶ **Rise up, come to our help. ***

    Redeem us for the sake of your steadfast love.

Ever-present God, like the disciples on a storm-tossed sea,
we sometimes ask if you still care about us.
In those times when we need you most, help us to remember
that neither death nor life, neither angels nor demons,
neither the present nor the future, nor any powers,
neither height nor depth, nor anything else in all of creation,
will be able to separate us from your love that is in Christ Jesus our Lord. **Amen.**

Psalm 44 is a communal lament offered in the context of defeat and despair. It includes several distinct sentiments: a remembrance of God's past faithfulness and deliverance (vv. 1-3), a statement of trust in God (vv. 4-8), a lament about God's judgment (vv. 9-16), a statement of righteous indignation (vv. 17-22) and an urgent prayer for divine intervention (vv. 23-26). *Use in Worship: as a way to enter into the experience of Israel's defeat (e.g., 2 Kings 15 and 18); to shape the prayers of those who experience defeat in spite of their own innocence and integrity; contemplation of the meaning of suffering and evil alongside other biblical texts (e.g., Job or Rom. 8).*

44A O God, We Have Heard

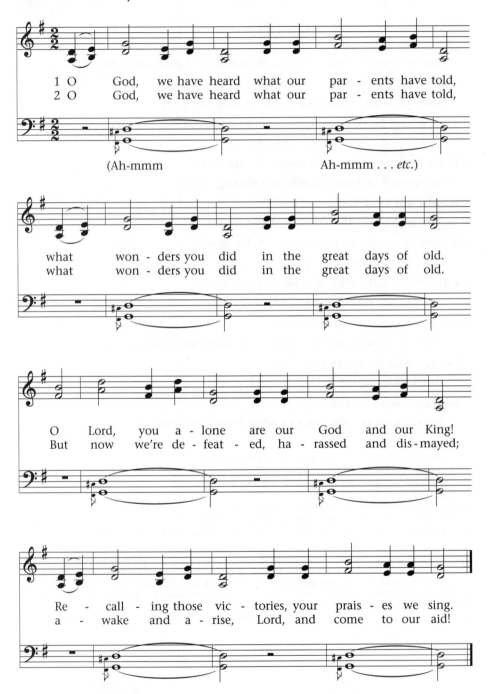

1 O God, we have heard what our par - ents have told,
2 O God, we have heard what our par - ents have told,

(Ah-mmm   Ah-mmm . . . *etc.*)

what won - ders you did in the great days of old.
what won - ders you did in the great days of old.

O Lord, you a - lone are our God and our King!
But now we're de - feat - ed, ha - rassed and dis - mayed;

Re - call - ing those vic - tories, your prais - es we sing.
a - wake and a - rise, Lord, and come to our aid!

Alternate harmonization on p. 55.

Words: Bert Polman © 1987 Faith Alive Christian Resources
Music (FOUNDATION 11.11.11.11): J. Funk's *A Compilation of Genuine Church Music*, 1832, P.D.; harm.
Martin Tel © 2011 Faith Alive Christian Resources

Psalm 45

To the leader: according to Lilies. Of the Korahites. A Maskil. A love song.

Voice 1:

1 My heart overflows with a goodly theme; I address my verses to the king; *
   my tongue is like the pen of a ready scribe.

2 You are the most handsome of men; *
   grace is poured upon your lips; therefore God has blessed you forever.

3 Gird your sword on your thigh, O mighty one, *
   in your glory and majesty.

4 **In your majesty ride on victoriously**
   for the cause of truth and to defend the right; *
   let your right hand teach you dread deeds.

5 Your arrows are sharp in the heart of the king's enemies; *
   the peoples fall under you.

6 **Your throne, O God, endures forever and ever. ***
   Your royal scepter is a scepter of equity;

7 **you love righteousness and hate wickedness. ***
   Therefore God, your God, has anointed you
   with the oil of gladness beyond your companions;

8 your robes are all fragrant with myrrh and aloes and cassia. *
   From ivory palaces stringed instruments make you glad;

9 daughters of kings are among your ladies of honor; *
   at your right hand stands the queen in gold of Ophir.

Voice 2:

10 Hear, O daughter, consider and incline your ear; *
   forget your people and your father's house,

11 and the king will desire your beauty. *
   Since he is your lord, bow to him;

12 the people of Tyre will seek your favor with gifts,
   the richest of the people 13 with all kinds of wealth. *
   The princess is decked in her chamber with gold-woven robes;

14 in many-colored robes she is led to the king; *
   behind her the virgins, her companions, follow.

15 **With joy and gladness they are led along ***
   as they enter the palace of the king.

16 In the place of ancestors you, O king, shall have sons; *
   you will make them princes in all the earth.

17 **I will cause your name to be celebrated in all generations; ***
   therefore the peoples will praise you forever and ever.   (continues)

O God, our king and our glory, set your seal upon our hearts.
Fashion our lives into a song of your justice and goodness,
so that the world may know of your righteous reign.
And when our earthly songs are spent,
bring us to the marriage supper of the Lamb, Jesus Christ, our Lord. **Amen.**

Psalm 45 is a wedding poem written to a king. It points to the power and authority of the king and the joy, beauty, and wealth of the palace. The poem depicts the polar opposite of faithless kings and queens like Ahab and Jezebel. It reminds the court of the importance of truth, faithfulness, and righteousness for the king (vv. 4, 6-7) and of commitment to the faithfulness of the royal line for the queen (vv. 10, 16), reflecting assumptions about the roles of men and women in the Ancient Near East. *Use in Worship: in conjunction with narrative texts about kings and queens in the history of Israel; as an affirmation of moral integrity; as a way of addressing the Messiah and his bride, the Church.*

45A For the Honor of Our King

1 For the hon - or of our King, ev - ery skill we have, we bring:
2 When he speaks, the truth is heard, grace and power in ev - ery word:
3 Right-eous-ness and joy are found, last - ing jus - tice will a - bound,

no - one stirs the heart to sing like our roy - al Sav - ior.
false-hood trem-bles at the sword of our roy - al Sav - ior.
all be - cause the King is crowned as our roy - al Sav - ior.

4 See the splendor of Christ's bride
led in honor to his side—
chosen, loved and beautified
by her royal Savior.

5 Now, and to eternal days,
all God's people join to raise
one unending song of praise
to our royal Savior.

Guitar chords do not correspond with keyboard harmony.

Words: Martin Leckebusch © 2002 Kevin Mayhew Ltd.
Music (MONKLAND 7.7.7.6): J. Freylinghausen's *Geistreiches Gesangbuch*, 1704; adapt. John Antes, ca. 1800; arr. John Wilkes, 1861, P.D.

Psalm 45:1-2, 6-17 45B
A Responsorial Setting

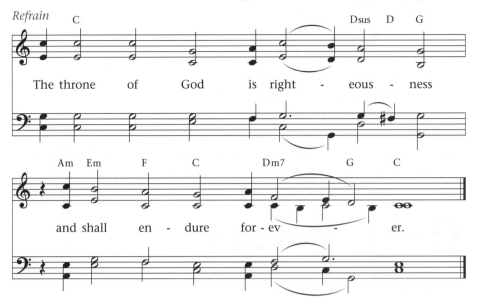

Refrain

The throne of God is right - eous - ness
and shall en - dure for - ev - er.

Refrain

1 My heart is stirring with a noble song;
  let me recite what I have fashioned for the king;
    my tongue shall be the pen of a skillful writer.

2 You are the noblest among the people;
    grace flows from your lips, because God has blessed you forever.

6 Your throne, O God, endures forever and ever,
    a scepter of righteousness is the scepter of your kingdom. *Refrain*

7 You love righteousness and hate iniquity;
    therefore God, your God, has anointed you
    with the oil of gladness above your companions.

8 All your garments are fragrant with myrrh, aloes, and cassia,
    and the music of strings from ivory palaces makes you glad.

9 Kings' daughters stand among the ladies of the court;
    on your right hand is the queen adorned with the gold of Ophir. *Refrain*

10 "Hear, O daughter; consider and listen closely;
    forget your people and your father's house.

11 The king will desire your beauty;
    he is your master, so bow before him.

12 The city of Tyre brings tribute;
    the wealthiest of the people seek your favor." *Refrain*

(continues)

¹³ All glorious is the princess as she enters;

    her gown is cloth-of-gold.

¹⁴ In embroidered apparel she is brought to the king;

    after her the bridesmaids follow in procession.

¹⁵ With joy and gladness they are brought,

    and enter the palace of the king.

¹⁶ "In place of ancestors, O king, you shall have sons;

    you shall make them princes over all the earth.

¹⁷ I will make your name to be remembered from one generation to another;

    therefore nations will praise you forever and ever."   *Refrain*

Tone

Lectionary: Annunciation (A,B,C); vv. 1-2, 6-9 Ordinary Time after Pentecost (B); vv. 10-17 Ordinary Time after Pentecost (A).

Words: Psalm 45
Music (EIN FESTE BURG fragment): Martin Luther, 1529, P.D.
Psalm Text: from *Evangelical Lutheran Worship* © 2006 Evangelical Lutheran Church in America, admin. Augsburg Fortress Publishers
Tone: © 2011 Faith Alive Christian Resources

Alternate Refrain

Alternate Tone

Words and Music: John L. Bell (b. 1949) © 1995 Wild Goose Resource Group, Iona Community, Scotland, GIA Publications, Inc., exclusive North American agent
Tone: © 2011 Faith Alive Christian Resources

Psalm 46

To the leader. Of the Korahites. According to Alamoth. A Song.

¹ God is our refuge and strength, *
    a very present help in trouble.

² **Therefore we will not fear, though the earth should change, ***
    though the mountains shake in the heart of the sea;

³ **though its waters roar and foam, ***
    though the mountains tremble with its tumult.   *Selah*

⁴ There is a river whose streams make glad the city of God, *
    the holy habitation of the Most High.

⁵ God is in the midst of the city; it shall not be moved; *
    God will help it when the morning dawns.

⁶ The nations are in an uproar, the kingdoms totter; *
    he utters his voice, the earth melts.

⁷ **The Lᴏʀᴅ of hosts is with us; ***
    the God of Jacob is our refuge.   *Selah*

⁸ Come, behold the works of the Lᴏʀᴅ; *
    see what desolations he has brought on the earth.

⁹ He makes wars cease to the end of the earth; *
    he breaks the bow, and shatters the spear; he burns the shields with fire.

¹⁰ "Be still, and know that I am God! *
    I am exalted among the nations, I am exalted in the earth."

¹¹ **The Lᴏʀᴅ of hosts is with us; ***
    the God of Jacob is our refuge.   *Selah*

(continues)

We praise and worship you, O God, because you are with your people;
powerfully and miraculously you defend your church and your Word
against all fanatic spirits, against the gates of hell,
and against the assault of flesh and sin.
All glory and praise to you, Father, Son, and Holy Spirit, now and forevermore. **Amen.**

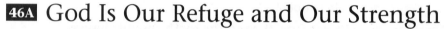

Psalm 46 is a sturdy confession of faith in God in a time of fear and upheaval. It mentions both tumult in nature (vv. 2-3) and political or military strife (vv. 6-9). Its refrain (vv. 7, 11) extols both God's presence and protection. The psalm builds up to a memorable oracle in which God commands the people to stop their ferment, to acknowledge the Lord, and to be calmed in light of divine majesty (v. 10), ending with a final refrain of trust (v. 11). *Use in Worship: celebrating the lordship of Christ over all creation; times of natural disaster or other calamities.*

46A God Is Our Refuge and Our Strength

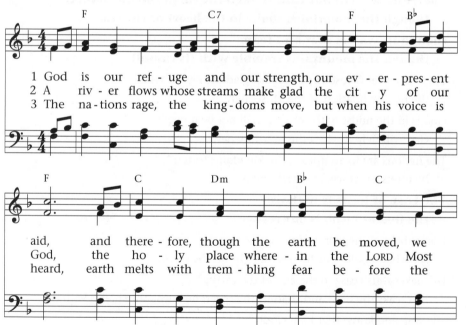

will not be a-fraid— though hills in-to the
High has his a-bode. Since God is in the
thun-der of his word. The LORD of hosts is

seas be cast, though foam-ing wa-ters roar, though
midst of her, un-moved her walls shall stand; for
on our side, our safe-ty to se-cure; the

all the might-y bil-lows shake the moun-tains on the shore.
God will has-ten to her aid when trou-ble is at hand.
God of Ja-cob is for us a ref-uge strong and sure.

4 O come and see what wondrous works the hand of God has done;
come, see what desolation great he brings beneath the sun.
In every corner of the earth he causes wars to cease;
the weapons of the strong destroyed, he makes abiding peace.

5 "Be still and know that I am God, the LORD whom all must claim;
and every nation of the earth shall magnify my name."
The LORD of hosts is on our side, our safety to secure;
the God of Jacob is for us a refuge strong and sure.

Guitar chords do not correspond with keyboard harmony.

Words: *Scottish Psalter*, 1650, alt., P.D.
Music (NOEL/GERARD 8.6.8.6 D): English; adapt. Arthur S. Sullivan, 1874, P.D.

46B Dios es nuestro amparo / God Will Be Our Refuge

Spanish
1 Dios es nues-tro_am-pa - ro, nues - tra for - ta -
2 Hay un rí - o lim - pio_de a - guas cri - sta -
3 Bra - ma - ron las na - cio - nes, rei - nos ti - tu -
4 Con - tem - plad sus o - bras, el a - so - la -

English
1 God will be our ref - uge, strength, and might - y
2 Streams of liv - ing wa - ter spar - kle bright as
3 Though na - tions rage and bel - low, kings and em - pires
4 See God's works of pow - er, fear - some deeds be -

le - za, nues - tro pron-to_au - xi - lio en la tri - bu - la - ción;
li - nas en la ciu - dad san - ta, mor - a - da_de Je - ho - vá.
bea - ron; él dio la pa - la - bra; la tie - rra de - rri - tió.
mien-to; de - ten - drá las gue - rras, las ar - mas que - bra - rá.

for - tress, ev - er - pres - ent help in our times of deep dis - tress.
crys - tal, mak - ing glad the cit - y, the dwell-ing of the Lord.
tot - ter; God speaks but a word and its thun - der melts the earth.
fore us, caus - ing wars to cease, break-ing bows and shat-tering spears.

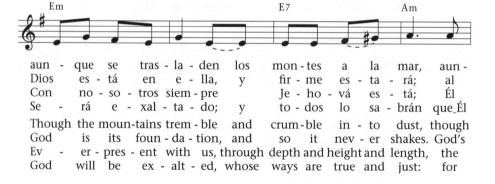

aun - que se tras - la - den los mon - tes a la mar, aun -
Dios es - tá en e - lla, y fir - me es - ta - rá; al
Con no - so - tros siem - pre Je - ho - vá es - tá; Él
Se - rá e - xal - ta - do; y to - dos lo sa - brán que_Él

Though the moun-tains trem - ble and crum-ble in - to dust, though
God is its foun - da - tion, and so it nev - er shakes. God's
Ev - er - pres - ent with us, through depth and height and length, the
God will be ex - alt - ed, whose ways are true and just: for

que	la	tie-rra	tiem-ble,	te-ne-mos	que con-fiar;	aun-
clare-ar	la	ma-ña-na	su_a-yu-da	tra-e-rá;	al
es	nues-tro	re-fu-gio,	te-ne-mos	que con-fiar;	Él
es	nues-tro	re-fu-gio,	te-ne-mos	que con-fiar;	que_Él
earth	and seas	are shak-en,	in God	we put our trust;	though
strong right arm	de-fends it	as each	new morn-ing breaks;	God's
Lord	re-mains our	ref-uge,	our strong-hold,	and our strength;	the
God	is still our	ref-uge,	in whom we	put our trust;	for

que	la	tie-rra	tiem-ble,	te-ne-mos	que con-fiar.
clare-ar	la	ma-ña-na	su_a-yu-da	tra-e-rá.
es	nues-tro	re-fu-gio,	te-ne-mos	que con-fiar.
es	nues-tro	re-fu-gio,	te-ne-mos	que con-fiar.
earth	and seas	are shak-en,	in God	we put our trust.
strong right arm	de-fends it	as each	new morn-ing breaks.
Lord	re-mains our	ref-uge,	our strong-hold,	and our strength.
God	is still our	ref-uge,	in whom we	put our trust.

Refrain

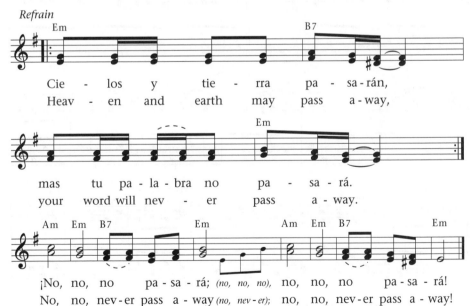

Cie - los y tie - rra pa - sa-rán,
Heav - en and earth may pass a - way,

mas tu pa - la - bra no pa - sa - rá.
your word will nev - er pass a - way.

¡No, no, no pa - sa - rá; *(no, no, no),* no, no, no pa - sa - rá!
No, no, nev-er pass a - way *(no, nev - er);* no, no, nev-er pass a - way!

Keyboard accompaniment on p. 286.

Words: traditional Latin American, based on Psalm 46; tr. Mary Louise Bringle (b. 1953) © 2011 GIA Publications, Inc.
Music (AMPARO): traditional; harm. Ronald F. Krisman (b. 1946) © 2011 GIA Publications, Inc.

Keyboard accompaniment

Music (AMPARO): traditional; harm. Ronald F. Krisman (b. 1946) © 2011 GIA Publications, Inc.

God, Our Help and Constant Refuge 46C

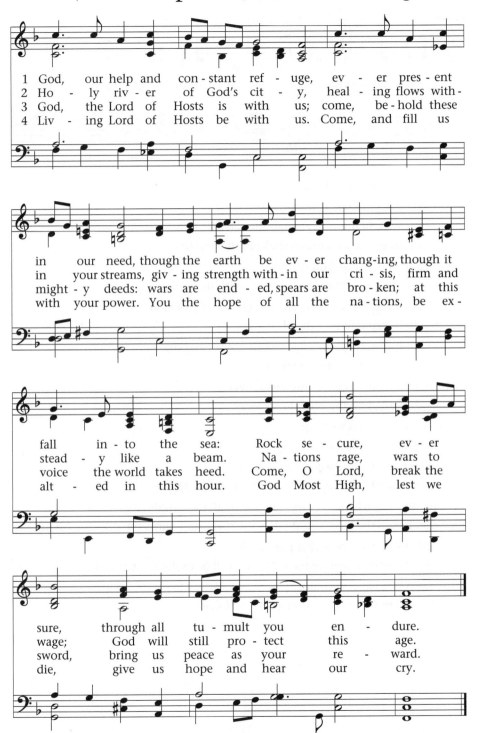

1 God, our help and con-stant ref-uge, ev-er pres-ent
2 Ho-ly riv-er of God's cit-y, heal-ing flows with-
3 God, the Lord of Hosts is with us; come, be-hold these
4 Liv-ing Lord of Hosts be with us. Come, and fill us

in our need, though the earth be ev-er chang-ing, though it
in your streams, giv-ing strength with-in our cri-sis, firm and
might-y deeds: wars are end-ed, spears are bro-ken; at this
with your power. You the hope of all the na-tions, be ex-

fall in-to the sea: Rock se-cure, ev-er
stead-y like a beam. Na-tions rage, wars to
voice the world takes heed. Come, O Lord, break the
alt-ed in this hour. God Most High, lest we

sure, through all tu-mult you en-dure.
wage; God will still pro-tect this age.
sword, bring us peace as your re-ward.
die, give us hope and hear our cry.

Words: Fred R. Anderson (b. 1941) © 1986 Fred R. Anderson
Music (MICHAEL 8.7.8.7.3.3.7): Herbert Howells (1892-1983) © 1968 Novello and Co., Ltd., admin. G.
Schirmer, Inc.

46D Psalm 46 | A Responsorial Setting

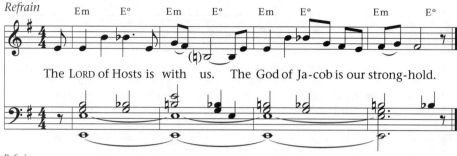

Refrain

The Lord of Hosts is with us. The God of Ja-cob is our strong-hold.

Refrain

1 God is our refuge and strength,
    a very present help in trouble.

2 Therefore we will not fear, though the earth be moved,
    and though the mountains shake in the depths of the sea;

3 though its waters rage and foam,
    and though the mountains tremble with its tumult.   *Refrain*

4 There is a river whose streams make glad the city of God,
    the holy habitation of the Most High.

5 God is in the midst of the city; it shall not be shaken;
    God shall help it at the break of day.

6 The nations rage, and the kingdoms shake;
    God speaks, and the earth melts away.

7 The Lord of hosts is with us;
    the God of Jacob is our stronghold.   *Refrain*

8 Come now, regard the works of the Lord,
    what desolations God has brought upon the earth;

9 behold the one who makes war to cease in all the world;
    who breaks the bow, and shatters the spear, and burns the shields with fire.

10 "Be still, then, and know that I am God;
    I will be exalted among the nations; I will be exalted in the earth."

11 The Lord of hosts is with us;
    the God of Jacob is our stronghold.   *Refrain*

Tone

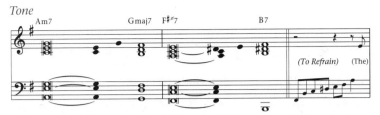

(To Refrain) (The)

Lectionary: Easter Vigil (A,B,C); Ordinary Time after Pentecost (A); Reign of Christ (C).

When using the refrain, "The Lord of Hosts Is with Us," it is not necessary to read or chant vv. 7 and 11.

Words and Music: Isaac Everett © 2009 Isaac Everett, admin. Church Pension Group/Church Publishing, Inc.
Psalm Text: from *Evangelical Lutheran Worship* © 2006 Evangelical Lutheran Church in America, admin.
Augsburg Fortress Publishers
Tone: © 2011 Faith Alive Christian Resources

Alternate Refrain 1

Echo

Be still and know that I am

Be still and know that I am God.

God. Be still and know that I am God.

Be still and know that I am God.

Alternate Tone 1

Words and Music: John L. Bell (b. 1949) © 1989 and 1998 Wild Goose Resource Group, Iona Community,
Scotland, GIA Publications, Inc., exclusive North American agent
Tone: © 2011 Faith Alive Christian Resources

(continues)

Alternate Refrain 2

Be still and know that I am God. Be still and know that I am God. Be still and know that I am God.

Alternate Tone 2

Words: Psalm 46:10
Music (BE STILL AND KNOW): anonymous; arr. Norma de Waal Malefyt, 1992, © 1994 Faith Alive Christian Resources
Tone: © 2011 Faith Alive Christian Resources

46E God Is Our Refuge and Strength

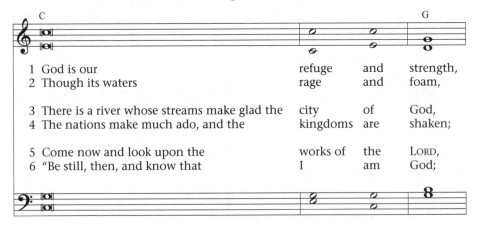

1 God is our refuge and strength,
2 Though its waters rage and foam,

3 There is a river whose streams make glad the city of God,
4 The nations make much ado, and the kingdoms are shaken;

5 Come now and look upon the works of the LORD,
6 "Be still, then, and know that I am God;

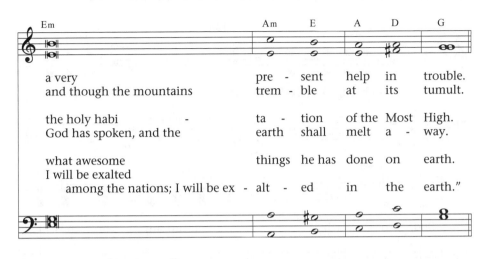

a very	pre - sent	help	in	trouble.
and though the mountains	trem - ble	at	its	tumult.

the holy habi -	ta - tion	of the	Most High.
God has spoken, and the	earth shall	melt a -	way.

what awesome	things he has	done on	earth.
I will be exalted among the nations; I will be ex - alt - ed	in	the	earth."

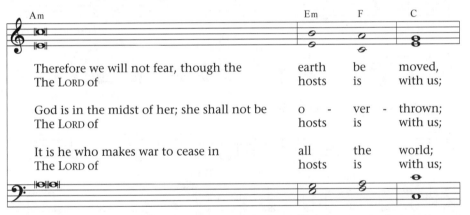

Therefore we will not fear, though the	earth	be	moved,
The LORD of	hosts	is	with us;

God is in the midst of her; she shall not be	o - ver - thrown;
The LORD of	hosts is	with us;

It is he who makes war to cease in	all	the	world;
The LORD of	hosts	is	with us;

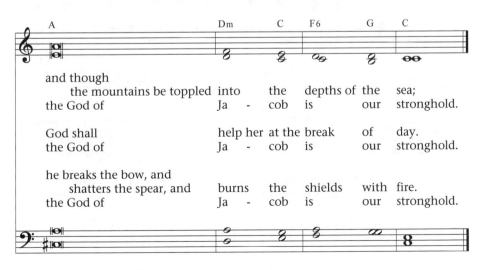

and though the mountains be toppled into	the	depths of the	sea;
the God of	Ja - cob	is	our	stronghold.

God shall	help her at the break	of	day.
the God of	Ja - cob	is	our	stronghold.

he breaks the bow, and shatters the spear, and	burns	the	shields	with	fire.
the God of	Ja - cob	is	our	stronghold.

Words: Psalm 46, *The Book of Common Prayer*
Music: Martin Luther, P.D.

Be Exalted, O God, in the Earth

God is our de-fense. Be ex-alt-ed, O God, in the earth.
spir - it is near. Be ex-alt-ed, O God, in the earth.

To Refrain

Coda

(earth.) Be ex-alt-ed, O God. Be ex-alt-ed, O

God. Yours is the pow-er; yours is the glo-ry. Be ex-

alt-ed, O God, in the earth. Be ex- earth.

Words and Music: Isaiah Jones Jr. © the Estate of Isaiah Jones Jr.

Psalm 47

To the leader. Of the Korahites. A Psalm.

1 Clap your hands, all you peoples; *
   shout to God with loud songs of joy.

2 **For the LORD, the Most High, is awesome, ***
   a great king over all the earth.

3 He subdued peoples under us, *
   and nations under our feet.

4 He chose our heritage for us, *
   the pride of Jacob whom he loves.   *Selah*

5 **God has gone up with a shout, ***
   the LORD with the sound of a trumpet.

6 **Sing praises to God, sing praises; ***
   sing praises to our King, sing praises.

7 **For God is the king of all the earth; ***
   sing praises with a psalm.

8 God is king over the nations; *
   God sits on his holy throne.

9 **The princes of the peoples gather**
   as the people of the God of Abraham. *
   For the shields of the earth belong to God; he is highly exalted.

King of all creation,
we wait for the day when, with all the hosts of heaven, we will sing:
"The kingdom of this world has become the kingdom of our Lord and of his Christ,
and he shall reign forever."
Until that day, receive the praise of our hearts and direct the pattern of our lives
so that in word and action we may exhibit your kingdom to a watching world. **Amen.**

Psalm 47 is a call to praise that focuses on God's sovereign rule. The psalm has two parallel sections: both begin with a call to praise (vv. 1, 6), a description of God's sovereign rule (vv. 2, 7), and assertions about God's rule over the nations (vv. 3-4, 8-9b), and both conclude with the image of God's ascent (vv. 5, 9b). The image of God "ascending" to a throne and "beginning to reign" (v. 8) is also found in Pss. 24, 93, and 96-99. In light of the persistent refrain throughout the Psalter that God's reign is eternal, the imagery of ascent may point to a new experience of God's lordship over human history or to a decisive moment when God reasserted authority. *Use in Worship: Ascension Day (because of the congruence between OT imagery of God's ascent and NT narratives of Jesus' ascension); celebrations of God's sovereign rule.*

Clap Your Hands, O Faithful People! 47A

1 Clap your hands, O faith-ful peo-ple! Shout to God a song of
2 With a shout and blast of trum-pet, God as-cends to reign a-

praise! The Most High our land has ran-somed, and will
bove, clothed in robes of right-eous judg-ment, crowned with

reign as Lord al-ways! Great the maj-es-ty a-
all - re-deem-ing love! Fill the world with glad re-

round us, sure the paths our feet have trod; we are
joic-ing; heaven shall sing, and earth re-ply! Let the

claimed as sons and daugh-ters, chil-dren of a gra-cious God.
na-tions rise in won-der all God's works to glo-ri-fy!

Words: Michael Morgan © 1999, 2011 Michael Morgan, admin. Faith Alive Christian Resources
Music (NETTLETON 8.7.8.7 D): J. Wyeth's *Repository of Sacred Music* Part II, 1813

47B God Has Gone Up

Refrain

God has gone up with a shout of re-joic-ing:
he has as-cend-ed in glo-ry!
O clap your hands, clap your hands all you peo-ple:
he has as-cend-ed in glo-ry!

1 Great is the Lord and how great is his king - dom,
2 All of the na - tions as - sem - ble be - fore him:
3 Praise to our Lord, O sing praise to our Sav - ior,

root - ed in heav - en and earth. Rul - er on high o - ver
all of the rich and the poor. All of the ser - vants re -
praise to our God and our King! Wor - thy the Lamb who was

all of the na - tions, Lord o - ver all of the world.
joice in his jus - tice, sing - ing his praise ev - er - more.
slain and is ris - en: glo - ry and hon - or to him.

To Refrain

47C Clap Your Hands, All Ye Nations

Refrain

Clap your hands, all ye na-tions; shout to God with a joy-ful
cry. The Lord is King o-ver all the earth; how great and awe-
-some is the Lord most high.

To stanzas
Final Ending

Stanzas

1 God has as-cend-ed a-midst shouts of joy, to the
2 God rules the na-tions in maj-es-ty, he is

sound-ing of the trum-pet and the horn;
seat-ed for all time up-on his throne;

give him the glo - ry that is due him,
princ - es and rul - ers will wor - ship him,

as you sing with all your heart, as you
for the king-doms of the earth, for the

sing with all your heart, as you sing with all
king-doms of the earth, for the king-doms of

your heart un - to the Lord.
the earth are his a - lone.

To Refrain

Words and Music: Bob Kauflin © 1986 Integrity's Praise! Music/Sovereign Grace Praise, Sovereign Grace Music, a division of Sovereign Grace Ministries, admin. EMI CMG Publishing

47D Clap Your Hands, All You Nations

1 Clap your hands!
2 Lord most high!
3 With a shout!
4 King of kings!

Come,
Our
With a
We will

1 Clap your hands, all you na-tions, shout to God.
2 Lord most high, reign-ing o - ver all the earth.
3 With a shout, God has gone up with a shout.
4 King of kings, na-tions bow be - fore his throne.

all you na - tions.
God is reign-ing.
shout of tri-umph.
bow be-fore you.

Oh,
O-ver
God
All

Clap your hands, all you na-tions, shout to God.
Lord most high, reign-ing o - ver all the earth.
With a shout, God has gone up with a shout.
King of kings, na-tions bow be - fore his throne.

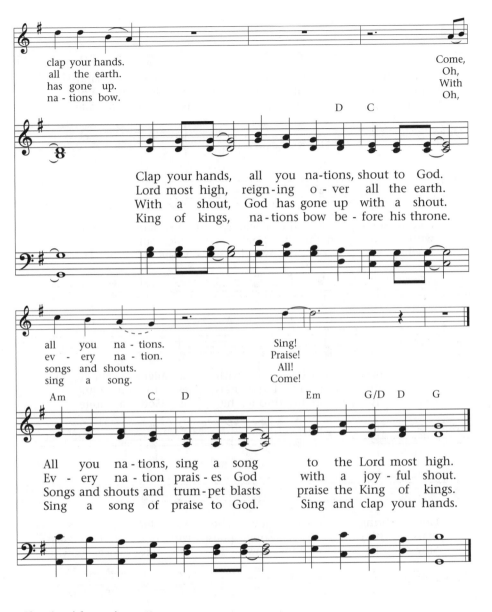

clap your hands.
all the earth.
has gone up.
na - tions bow.

Come,
Oh,
With
Oh,

D   C

Clap your hands,   all you na-tions, shout to God.
Lord most high,   reign-ing o - ver   all the earth.
With a shout,   God has gone up with a shout.
King of kings,   na - tions bow be - fore his throne.

all   you   na - tions.
ev - ery   na - tion.
songs and shouts.
sing   a   song.

Sing!
Praise!
All!
Come!

Am   C   D   Em   G/D   D   G

All   you   na - tions, sing   a   song
Ev - ery   na - tion prais - es   God
Songs and shouts and trum - pet blasts
Sing   a   song   of praise to God.

to   the Lord most high.
with   a   joy - ful shout.
praise the King of kings.
Sing and clap your hands.

Clapping / drumming pattern

simile

Words: Greg Scheer © 2009 Greg Scheer
Music: Yoruba folk song; adapt. Godwin Sadoh © 2005 Wayne Leupold Editions, Inc.; harm. Greg Scheer
© 2009 Greg Scheer

47E Nations, Clap Your Hands

1 Na - tions, clap your hands; shout with joy, you lands!
2 God goes up on high with a joy - ful cry,
3 God reigns o - ver all rul - ers great and small.

Awe - some is the Lord; spread his fame a - broad.
with a might - y shout; peo - ple, sing it out!
Lead - ers of the world, ser - vants of the Lord,

He rules ev - ery land with a might - y hand.
Let your voic - es bring prais - es to our King.
ral - ly round his throne; he is God a - lone.

God brings na - tions low; he sub - dues each foe.
Praise him with a song; praise with heart and tongue;
Sing be - fore him now, in his pres - ence bow.

From his might - y throne God pro - tects his own.
praise with ev - ery skill; praise with mind and will.
God of A - bra - ham! God of ev - ery land!

Our in - her - i - tance is our sure de - fense.
God rules all the earth; mag - ni - fy his worth.
Wor - ship and a - dore God for - ev - er - more.

Guitar chords do not correspond with keyboard harmony.

Words: *Psalter Hymnal*, 1987, alt. © 1987 Faith Alive Christian Resources
Music (GENEVAN 47 | 5.5.5.5.5.5 D): Louis Bourgeois (ca. 1510-1561), 1551; harm. Claude Goudimel (ca. 1505-1572), 1564, P.D.

Psalm 47 | A Responsorial Setting 47F

Refrain

Clap your hands all you na - tions. A-men. Hal - le - lu - jah!
Shout for joy all you peo - ple. A-men. Hal - le - lu - jah!

Refrain

¹ Clap your hands, all you peoples;
   shout to God with a joyful sound.

² For the LORD Most High is to be feared:
   a great king over all the earth,

³ who subdues the peoples under us,
   and the nations under our feet;

⁴ who chooses our inheritance for us,
   the pride of Jacob, whom God loves.   *Refrain*

⁵ God has gone up with a shout,
   the LORD with the sound of the ram's horn.

⁶ Sing praises to God, sing praises;
   sing praises to our king, sing praises.

⁷ For God is king of all the earth;
   sing praises with a song.   *Refrain*

(continues)

⁸ God reigns over the nations;

God is enthroned on high.

⁹ The nobles of the peoples have gathered as the people of the God of Abraham.

The rulers of the earth belong to God, who is highly exalted.   *Refrain*

Tone

Lectionary: Ascension of the Lord (A,B,C).

Words: The Iona Community © 1993 Wild Goose Resource Group, Iona Community, Scotland, GIA Publications, Inc., exclusive North American agent
Music: John L. Bell (b. 1949) © 1993 Wild Goose Resource Group, Iona Community, Scotland, GIA Publications, Inc., exclusive North American agent
Psalm Text: from *Evangelical Lutheran Worship* © 2006 Evangelical Lutheran Church in America, admin. Augsburg Fortress Publishers
Tone: © 2011 Faith Alive Christian Resources

Psalm 48

A Song. A Psalm of the Korahites.

¹ Great is the LORD and greatly to be praised *

in the city of our God.

His holy mountain, ² beautiful in elevation, *

is the joy of all the earth,

Mount Zion, in the far north, *

the city of the great King.

³ **Within its citadels ***

God has shown himself a sure defense.

⁴ Then the kings assembled, *

they came on together.

⁵ As soon as they saw it, they were astounded; *

they were in panic, they took to flight;

6 trembling took hold of them there, *
   pains as of a woman in labor,

7 as when an east wind shatters *
   the ships of Tarshish.

8 **As we have heard, so have we seen** *
   in the city of the LORD of hosts,

   in the city of our God, *
   which God establishes forever.   *Selah*

9 **We ponder your steadfast love, O God,** *
   in the midst of your temple.

10 **Your name, O God, like your praise,** *
   reaches to the ends of the earth.

   Your right hand is filled with victory. *
   11 **Let Mount Zion be glad,**

   let the towns of Judah rejoice *
   because of your judgments.

12 Walk about Zion, go all around it, *
   count its towers,

13 consider well its ramparts; *
   go through its citadels,

   that you may tell the next generation *
   14 **that this is God,**

   our God forever and ever. *
   He will be our guide forever.

Gracious God,
you have made us fellow citizens with the saints in the city of your eternal light.
In the times of upheaval or when the foundations shake,
teach us to wait in silence for your steadfast and transforming love,
made known to us in Jesus Christ our Lord. **Amen.**

Psalm 48 is a psalm of praise arising out of a vision of the presence of God in Zion. It is a vision of beauty and joy for the people of God (vv. 1-3, 8-13) and of terror for those opposed to God (vv. 4-7). The exclamation "We ponder your steadfast love, O God, in the midst of your temple" (v. 9) has particular resonance for Christians in light of the NT claims that the temple is now found in Jesus Christ (John 2:21) and that the body is a temple in which Holy Spirit dwells (1 Cor. 3:16, 6:19). While this poem refers to the ancient city of Jerusalem, Christians, taking care not to spiritualize the original meaning of the text, have also drawn upon this imagery in reference to the new or heavenly city of God (Gal. 4:24, Heb. 12:22, Rev. 3:12, 21:2, 10). *Use in Worship: a song of praise; services focusing on narratives of temple worship; services focusing on the heavenly city of God.*

48A Great Is the LORD Our God

1 Great is the LORD our God, and great-ly to be praised.
2 God makes his cit-y strong by liv-ing in her halls.
3 With-in your tem-ple, LORD, in your most ho-ly place,

Up-on a hill God's cit-y stands in glo-rious beau-ty raised—
When kings join forc-es and ad-vance, they mar-vel at her walls.
we on your lov-ing-kind-ness dwell, the won-ders of your grace.

his ho-ly moun-tain high, the cit-y of our King,
God scat-ters those a-round whose pride makes them so sure.
Your peo-ple sing your praise wher-e'er your name is known;

the joy of all the earth be-low. In praise to God we sing.
As we have heard, so have we seen: God's cit-y is se-cure.
by ev-ery deed your hand has done your right-eous-ness is shown.

(continues)

4 Let Zion now rejoice
   and all her people sing;
   let them with thankfulness proclaim
   the judgments of their King.
   Mount Zion's walls behold,
   about her ramparts go,
   and number all the lofty towers
   that guard her from the foe.

5 Observe her palaces,
   mark her defenses well,
   that to the children following you
   her glories you may tell.
   For God as our own God
   forever will abide,
   and till life's journey close in death
   will be our faithful guide.

Words: sts. 1-2 *Psalter Hymnal*, 1987; sts. 3-5 *Psalter*, 1887, rev., 1987, © 1987 Faith Alive Christian Resources
Music (DIADEMATA 6.6.8.6 D): George J. Elvey, 1868, P.D.

Psalm 48 | A Responsorial Setting   48B

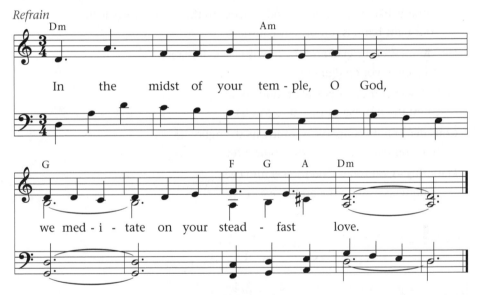

Refrain
¹ Great is the LORD, and highly to be praised,
   in the city of our God, on the LORD's holy mountain.

² Beautiful and lofty, the joy of all the earth, is Mount Zion,
   the summit of the north and city of the great king.

³ God is in the citadels of Jerusalem;
   revealed to be the sure refuge of the city.   *Refrain*

(continues)

⁴ Behold, the kings assembled
and marched forward together.

⁵ As they looked, they were astounded;
dismayed, they fled in terror.

⁶ Trembling seized them there;
they writhed like a woman in childbirth;

⁷ with an east wind you shattered them
like the ships of Tarshish.

⁸ As we have heard, so have we seen, in the city of the LORD of hosts,
in the city of our God—
may God establish it forever!   *Refrain*

⁹ In the midst of your temple, O God,
we meditate on your steadfast love.

¹⁰ Your praise, like your name, O God, reaches to the ends of the earth;
your right hand is full of righteousness.

¹¹ Let Mount Zion be glad and the towns of Judah rejoice,
because of your judgments.

¹² Make the circuit of Zion; walk round about it;
count the number of the city's towers.

¹³ Consider well its ramparts; examine its strongholds;
that you may tell those who come after.

¹⁴ Mark this—God is our God forever and ever,
guiding us even to the end.   *Refrain*

Tone

Lectionary: Ordinary Time after Pentecost (B).

Words and Music: Gregg DeMey © 2011 Re:Create Music; arr. Paul Detterman © 2011 Re:Create Music
Psalm Text: from *Evangelical Lutheran Worship* © 2006 Evangelical Lutheran Church in America, admin.
Augsburg Fortress Publishers
Tone: © 2011 Faith Alive Christian Resources

Psalm 49

To the leader. Of the Korahites. A Psalm.

1 Hear this, all you peoples; *
  give ear, all inhabitants of the world,

2 both low and high, *
  rich and poor together.

3 My mouth shall speak wisdom; *
  the meditation of my heart shall be understanding.

4 **I will incline my ear to a proverb; ***
  I will solve my riddle to the music of the harp.

5 Why should I fear in times of trouble, *
  when the iniquity of my persecutors surrounds me,

6 those who trust in their wealth *
  and boast of the abundance of their riches?

7 Truly, no ransom avails for one's life, *
  there is no price one can give to God for it.

8 For the ransom of life is costly, *
  and can never suffice

9 that one should live on forever *
  and never see the grave.

10 **When we look at the wise, they die; ***
  fool and dolt perish together and leave their wealth to others.

11 Their graves are their homes forever, their dwelling places to all generations, *
  though they named lands their own.

12 **Mortals cannot abide in their pomp; ***
  they are like the animals that perish.

13 Such is the fate of the foolhardy, *
  the end of those who are pleased with their lot.   *Selah*

14 Like sheep they are appointed for Sheol; Death shall be their shepherd; *
  straight to the grave they descend, and their form shall waste away;
  Sheol shall be their home.

15 **But God will ransom my soul from the power of Sheol, ***
  for he will receive me.   *Selah*

16 Do not be afraid when some become rich, *
  when the wealth of their houses increases.

17 For when they die they will carry nothing away; *
  their wealth will not go down after them.   (continues)

¹⁸ Though in their lifetime they count themselves happy *

    —for you are praised when you do well for yourself—

¹⁹ they will go to the company of their ancestors, *

    who will never again see the light.

²⁰ **Mortals cannot abide in their pomp; ***

    they are like the animals that perish.

God of wisdom, we do not know when our life will end.
Help us to set our hearts on things above
and not on the wealth and power of this world.
We pray this, trusting in Jesus Christ, our highest joy. **Amen.**

Psalm 49 is a wisdom or teaching psalm about the inevitability of death and the way that death levels the exalted and lowly. It specifically challenges those who trust in money (vv. 6, 16), intelligence (v. 10), and fame (vv. 12, 20). The imagery of redemption or ransom functions like a refrain (vv. 7, 8, 15), concluding with a profound statement of God's deliverance (v. 15). *Use in Worship: services focusing on human mortality (e.g., Ash Wednesday or services based on Eccl.); services focusing on the folly of trusting in money (including those that focus on Jesus' statements about trusting in money; e.g., Luke 12:16-21).*

49A Psalm 49:1-12 | A Responsorial Setting

Refrain

¹ Hear this, all you peoples;
   give ear, all you who dwell in the world,

² you of high degree and low,
   rich and poor together.

³ My mouth shall speak of wisdom,
   and my heart shall meditate on understanding.

⁴ I will incline my ear to a proverb
   and set forth my riddle upon the harp.   *Refrain*

⁵ Why should I be afraid in evil days,
   when the wickedness of those at my heels surrounds me,

⁶ the wickedness of those who trust in their own prowess,
   and boast of their great riches?

⁷ One can never redeem another,
   or give to God the ransom for another's life;

⁸ for the ransom of a life is so great
   that there would never be enough to pay it,

⁹ in order to live forever and ever
   and never see the grave.   *Refrain*

¹⁰ For we see that the wise die also; like the dull and stupid they perish
   and leave their wealth to those who come after them.

¹¹ Their graves shall be their homes forever,
   their dwelling places from generation to generation,
      though they had named lands after themselves.

¹² Even though honored, they cannot live forever;
   they are like the beasts that perish.   *Refrain*

Tone

Lectionary: Ordinary Time after Pentecost (C).

Words and Music: Gregg DeMey © 2011 Re:Create Music; arr. Paul Detterman © 2011 Re:Create Music
Psalm Text: from *Evangelical Lutheran Worship* © 2006 Evangelical Lutheran Church in America, admin.
Augsburg Fortress Publishers
Tone: © 2011 Faith Alive Christian Resources

Come, One and All, from Near and Far

Canon

1 Come, one and all, from near and far,
2 Some flaunt their gold, some trust its power—
3 Though wealth or learn - ing may be ours,
4 Be - yond this age of shame and sham
5 Why crave re - nown or o - pu - lence?

to share the in - sights I have found:
but what they cher - ish will de - cay;
or fame that spreads through-out the land,
we glimpse a bet - ter des - ti - ny:
They fade, those things we now pos - sess;

a heart which has been taught by faith
and still the ran - som for a soul
the shack - les of mor - tal - i - ty
the Lord will lift us free from death
our hope, our life are in the Lord,

in - forms the wis - dom I ex - pound.
re - mains a price too great to pay.
pre - vent so much that we have planned.
to walk with him e - ter - nal - ly.
the God we hon - or and con - fess.

Bass line is played by keyboard or xylophones. Possible rhythmic variations:

Words: Martin Leckebusch © 2006 Kevin Mayhew Ltd.
Music (KIÚ-JĪ-IT 8.8.8.8): I-to Loh (b. 1936), 1999, © 1999 I-to Loh

Let Not the Wise 49C
Glory in Their Wisdom

Refrain

Let not the wise glo-ry in their wis-dom. Let not the might-y

glo-ry in their might. Let not the rich glo-ry in their

rich-es, let those who glo-ry, glo-ry in the LORD.

Refrain

Hear this! Open your ears!
Listen, all people everywhere,
both great and small, rich and poor.
Listen to these words of wisdom!   *Refrain*

Even the wise die.
They leave all their riches to others.
Their money will not let them live forever.
Their greatness cannot keep them from death.   *Refrain*

Ostinato for Bass Xylophone (or piano down two octaves)

Hum refrain melody during the spoken verses. Verses may be read by two voices in alternation.

Words: Psalm 49
Music: Julie Howard; arr. Vera Lyons © 1992 Liturgical Press

Psalm 50

A Psalm of Asaph.

Voice 1:

1 The mighty one, God the LORD, *
   speaks and summons the earth from the rising of the sun to its setting.

2 Out of Zion, the perfection of beauty, *
   God shines forth.

3 **Our God comes and does not keep silence, ***
   before him is a devouring fire,
   and a mighty tempest all around him.

4 He calls to the heavens above *
   and to the earth, that he may judge his people:

5 "Gather to me my faithful ones, *
   who made a covenant with me by sacrifice!"

6 **The heavens declare his righteousness, ***
   for God himself is judge.   *Selah*

Voice 2:

7 "Hear, O my people, and I will speak, *
   O Israel, I will testify against you. I am God, your God.

8 Not for your sacrifices do I rebuke you; *
   your burnt offerings are continually before me.

9 I will not accept a bull from your house, *
   or goats from your folds.

10 **For every wild animal of the forest is mine, ***
    the cattle on a thousand hills.

11 **I know all the birds of the air, ***
    and all that moves in the field is mine.

12 "If I were hungry, I would not tell you, *
    for the world and all that is in it is mine.

13 Do I eat the flesh of bulls, *
    or drink the blood of goats?

14 **Offer to God a sacrifice of thanksgiving, ***
    and pay your vows to the Most High.

15 **Call on me in the day of trouble; ***
    I will deliver you, and you shall glorify me."

Voice 1:

16 But to the wicked God says: *

"What right have you to recite my statutes,

or take my covenant on your lips?

17 For you hate discipline, *

and you cast my words behind you.

18 You make friends with a thief when you see one, *

and you keep company with adulterers.

19 "You give your mouth free rein for evil, *

and your tongue frames deceit.

20 You sit and speak against your kin; *

you slander your own mother's child.

Voice 2:

21 These things you have done and I have been silent;

you thought that I was one just like yourself. *

But now I rebuke you, and lay the charge before you.

22 "Mark this, then, you who forget God, *

or I will tear you apart, and there will be no one to deliver.

23 **Those who bring thanksgiving as their sacrifice honor me; ***

to those who go the right way I will show the salvation of God."

Just and holy God,
you need nothing from us, but delight in our humble trust and thankful obedience.
We repent of our shallow rituals and empty sacrifices.
Enable us to do justice, love kindness, and humbly walk with you, our God. **Amen.**

Psalm 50 speaks of covenant faithfulness, echoing themes from the prophets about the importance of acknowledging God with faithful hearts and not merely with external acts of piety. It describes the beauty of God's advent and the initiative God takes in the covenant relationship with the people (vv. 1-6), challenges the people to offer genuine worship (vv. 7-21), and concludes with a summary of covenant faithfulness (vv. 22-23). *Use in Worship: in conjunction with celebrations of Jesus' transfiguration (in part because of the imagery of God's shining beauty [v. 2]); a call to genuine worship with integrity.*

50A The Mighty God with Power Speaks

1 The Might-y God with pow-er speaks, and
2 God comes, not with a si-lent form, but
3 The heavens de-clare your jus-tice, Lord, as

all the world o-beys; from dawn un-til the
rid-ing on the winds; be-fore God's face, the
end-less as the sky; a-gainst the taunts of

set-ting sun, God's won-der earth dis-plays.
rag-ing storm its blast of thun-der sends.
dis-be-lief, our God will tes-ti-fy.

The per-fect beau-ty all a-round from
All hail the Judge, in bold ar-ray, whose
Re-ceive my heart-felt gift of thanks as

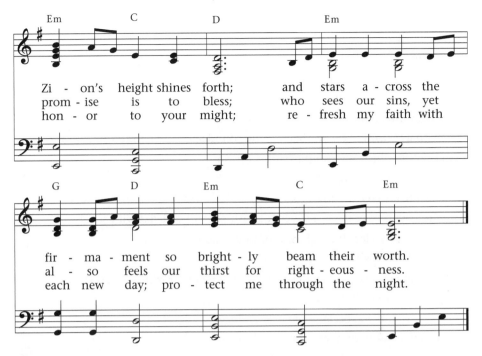

Zi - on's height shines forth; and stars a - cross the
prom - ise is to bless; who sees our sins, yet
hon - or to your might; re - fresh my faith with

fir - ma - ment so bright - ly beam their worth.
al - so feels our thirst for right - eous - ness.
each new day; pro - tect me through the night.

Words: Michael Morgan © 1999, 2011 Michael Morgan, admin. Faith Alive Christian Resources
Music (STAR OF COUNTY DOWN 8.6.8.6 D): Irish traditional; arr. Rory Cooney (b. 1952) © 1990 GIA
Publications, Inc.

Psalm 50:1-15, 22-23 **50B**
A Responsorial Setting

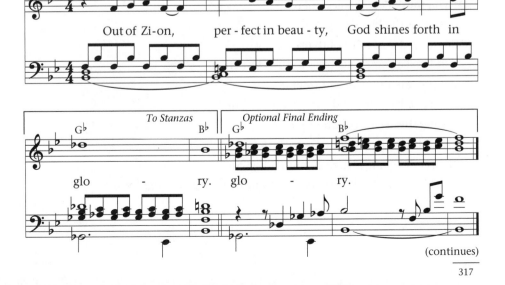

Out of Zi - on, per - fect in beau - ty, God shines forth in

glo - ry. glo - ry.

(continues)

Refrain

1 The mighty one, God the LORD, has spoken;
  calling the earth from the rising of the sun to its setting.

2 Out of Zion, perfect in its beauty,
  God shines forth in glory.

3 Our God will come and will not keep silence;
  with a consuming flame before, and round about a raging storm.

4 God calls the heavens and the earth from above
  to witness the judgment of the people.

5 "Gather before me my loyal followers,
  those who have made a covenant with me and sealed it with sacrifice."

6 The heavens declare the rightness of God's cause,
  for it is God who is judge.   *Refrain*

7 "Listen, my people, and I will speak: Israel, I will bear witness against you;
  for I am God, your God.

8 I do not accuse you because of your sacrifices;
  your burnt offerings are always before me.

9 I will not accept a calf from your stalls,
  nor goats from your pens;

10 for all the wild animals of the forest are mine,
  the cattle on a thousand hills.

11 I know every bird of the mountains,
  and the creatures of the fields are mine.

12 If I were hungry, I would not tell you,
  for the whole world is mine and all that is in it.

13 Do you think I eat the flesh of bulls,
  or drink the blood of goats?

14 Offer to God a sacrifice of thanksgiving
  and make good your vows to the Most High.   *Refrain*

15 Call upon me in the day of trouble;
  I will deliver you, and you shall honor me.

22 Consider this well, you who forget God,
  lest I tear you apart and there be none to deliver you.

23 Whoever offers me a sacrifice of thanksgiving honors me;
  I will show the salvation of God to those who go the right way."   *Refrain*

Tone

Lectionary: vv. 1-6 Transfiguration Sunday (B); vv. 1-8, 22-23 Ordinary Time after Pentecost (C); vv. 7-15 Ordinary Time after Pentecost (A).

Words: Psalm 50
Music: Robert Hobby from *Psalter for Worship, Cycle B* © 1996 Augsburg Fortress Publishers
Psalm Text: from *Evangelical Lutheran Worship* © 2006 Evangelical Lutheran Church in America, admin.
Augsburg Fortress Publishers
Tone: from *Psalter for Worship, Cycle B* © 1996 Augsburg Fortress Publishers

Alternate Refrain

Let the giv - ing of thanks be our sac - ri - fice to God.

Let the giv - ing of thanks be our sac - ri - fice to God.

Alternate Tone

Words and Music (GREYFRIARS refrain): The Iona Community © 1993 Wild Goose Resource Group, Iona Community, Scotland, GIA Publications, Inc., exclusive North American agent
Tone: © 2011 Faith Alive Christian Resources

50C Let the Giving of Thanks Be Our Sacrifice

Refrain

Let the giv - ing of thanks be our sac - ri - fice to God.

Let the giv - ing of thanks be our sac - ri - fice to God. *Fine*

1 God, the Lord, has spo - ken, God has sum - moned
2 God shines out from Zi - on, the place of
3 Fire con - sumes be - fore him and a storm is
4 "Call to me, my peo - ple, when the hour of
5 "Those who give me hon - or, whose sac - ri -

all the earth from the sun at
per - fect beau - ty. God, our God, is
rag - ing all a - round. Heaven and earth he
trou - ble strikes. I shall come to
fice is thanks - giv - ing, those who walk be -

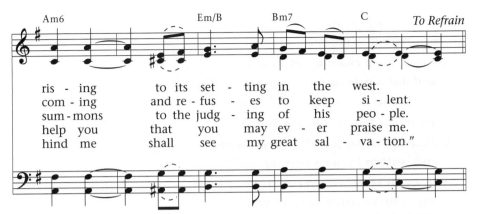

ris - ing / to its set - ting in the west.
com - ing / and re - fus - es to keep si - lent.
sum - mons / to the judg - ing of his peo - ple.
help you / that you may ev - er praise me.
hind me / shall see my great sal - va - tion."

To Refrain

Psalm 51

To the leader. A Psalm of David, when the prophet Nathan came to him, after he had gone in to Bathsheba.

1 Have mercy on me, O God, according to your steadfast love; *
   according to your abundant mercy blot out my transgressions.

2 **Wash me thoroughly from my iniquity, ***
   and cleanse me from my sin.

3 For I know my transgressions, *
   and my sin is ever before me.

4 **Against you, you alone, have I sinned,**
   and done what is evil in your sight, *
      so that you are justified in your sentence
      and blameless when you pass judgment.

5 Indeed, I was born guilty, *
   a sinner when my mother conceived me.

6 **You desire truth in the inward being; ***
   therefore teach me wisdom in my secret heart.

7 Purge me with hyssop, and I shall be clean; *
   wash me, and I shall be whiter than snow.

8 **Let me hear joy and gladness; ***
   let the bones that you have crushed rejoice.

(continues)

⁹ Hide your face from my sins, *
    and blot out all my iniquities.

¹⁰ **Create in me a clean heart, O God, ***
    and put a new and right spirit within me.

¹¹ Do not cast me away from your presence, *
    and do not take your holy spirit from me.

¹² **Restore to me the joy of your salvation, ***
    and sustain in me a willing spirit.

¹³ **Then I will teach transgressors your ways, ***
    and sinners will return to you.

¹⁴ Deliver me from bloodshed, O God, O God of my salvation, *
    and my tongue will sing aloud of your deliverance.

¹⁵ **O Lord, open my lips, ***
    and my mouth will declare your praise.

¹⁶ For you have no delight in sacrifice; *
    if I were to give a burnt offering, you would not be pleased.

¹⁷ **The sacrifice acceptable to God is a broken spirit; ***
    a broken and contrite heart, O God, you will not despise.

¹⁸ Do good to Zion in your good pleasure; *
    rebuild the walls of Jerusalem,

¹⁹ **then you will delight in right sacrifices,**
  in burnt offerings and whole burnt offerings; *
    then bulls will be offered on your altar.

Merciful God, we cannot stand before you
unless our hearts are cleansed and our spirits are made right by your redeeming.
Thank you for your merciful forgiveness,
and even more for your transforming love
made known to us in Jesus the Savior. **Amen.**

Psalm 51, one of the seven penitential psalms, is a poignant cry for divine forgiveness, appealing to God's goodness, mercy, and compassion (v. 1). It acknowledges sin in terms of three contrasting images: rebelliousness (vv. 1, 3), waywardness (v. 2), and failure (v. 3). It acknowledges the relational barrier that sin creates (v. 4), the importance of inner renewal that only God can bring (v. 10), and the way that forgiveness leads to testimony and praise (vv. 13-15). The conclusion of the psalm reprises the main theme of Ps. 50 (vv. 16-19), suggesting that Pss. 50 and 51 can helpfully be studied and prayed together: Ps. 51 is the faithful response to the prophetic word of Ps. 50. *Use in Worship: Ash Wednesday; during the season of Lent; appropriate for any occasion.*

Cámbiame, Señor / 51A
Change My Heart, O God

Spanish   Cám - bia - me, Se - ñor,   con tu gran po - der.
English   Change my heart, O God;   make it ev - er true.

Haz - me co - mo tú,   tu - yo quie - ro   ser.
Change my heart, O God;   may I be like   you.

Tú el al - fa - re - ro,   yo el ba - rro soy.
You are the Pot - ter;   I am the clay.

Só - lo a tu i - ma - gen,   quie - ro siem - pre   ser.
Mold me and make   me;   this is what I   pray.

Words and Music: Eddie Espinosa (b. 1953) © 1982 Mercy/Vineyard Publishing, admin. in North America by Music Services o/b/o Vineyard Music USA

51B Be Merciful, Be Merciful, O God

1 Be mer-ci-ful, be mer-ci-ful, O God. Ac-cord-ing to your
2 You want me truth-ful in my in-most heart; you teach me in my
3 Cre-ate in me, O God, a new, clean heart and make my spir-it

stead-fast love, have mer-cy. Blot out my sin in your a-
se-cret heart your wis-dom. To wash me clean a-gain, purge
pure and right with-in me. Oh, do not cast me help-less

bun-dant mer-cy. Wash all my sin a-way and make me clean.
me with hys-sop and make me whit-er than new-fall-en snow.
from your pres-ence. Your Ho-ly Spir-it must not go from me.

I know my sin; it will not leave my mind. A-gainst you, on-ly
Fill me with joy and glad-ness, make me sing, and let the bones you
Re-store to me the joy of be-ing yours. Up-hold me with a

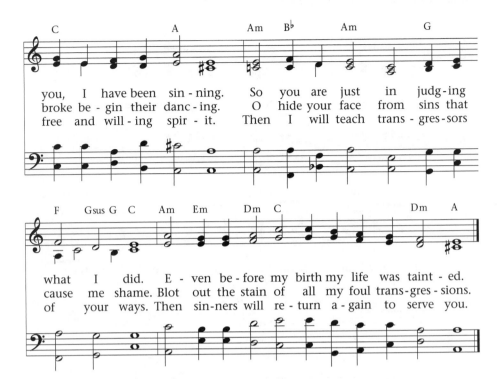

you, I have been sin - ning. So you are just in judg - ing
broke be - gin their danc - ing. O hide your face from sins that
free and will - ing spir - it. Then I will teach trans - gres - sors

what I did. E - ven be - fore my birth my life was taint - ed.
cause me shame. Blot out the stain of all my foul trans - gres - sions.
of your ways. Then sin - ners will re - turn a - gain to serve you.

4 Deliver me from guilt of blood, O God.
O God, you are the God of my salvation.
My tongue will sing then that I am delivered.
Open my lips, O Lord, to sing your praise.
For you take no delight in sacrifice.
You take no pleasure in the gifts I offer.
A broken spirit is acceptable.
You will not scorn a heart contrite and broken.

5 Be good to Zion; LORD, in mercy hear.
The walls around Jerusalem lie broken.
Rebuild the walls, LORD: help us to rebuild them.
Be good to Zion; LORD, in mercy hear.
Then you will take delight in us again,
in gifts we bring to lay upon your altar.
Then you will take delight in us again,
in proper sacrifice and righteous service.

Words: Stanley Wiersma (1930-1986), 1980, © 1987 Faith Alive Christian Resources
Music (GENEVAN 51 | 10.11.11.10.10.11.10.11): Louis Bourgeois (ca. 1510-1561), 1551; harm. Claude
Goudimel (ca. 1505-1572), 1564, P.D.

51C Give Me a Clean Heart

1 I'm not ask-ing for the rich-es of the land.
2 Some-times I am up and some-times I am down.

I'm not ask-ing for the proud to know my name.
Some-times I am al-most lev-el to the ground.

Please give me, Lord, a clean heart, so that I may fol-low thee.

To Refrain

Give me a clean heart, Lord, and I'll fol-low thee.

Words: Margaret J. Douroux (b. 1941) © 1970 Earl Pleasant Publishing
Music: Margaret J. Douroux (b. 1941) © 1970 Earl Pleasant Publishing; arr. Albert Dennis Tessier and Nolan
Williams Jr. (b. 1969) © 2000 GIA Publications, Inc.

51D Have Mercy upon Me, O God

1 Have mer - cy u - pon me, O God, ac-cord-ing
2 I hate my trans-gres-sions, O God, and I re-
3 For I have re - belled from my birth; my ve - ry
4 Cre - ate in me now a clean heart; re - new your
5 O - pen now my lips with praise and let my

to your lov - ing kind - ness, ac - cord - ing
pent my sins be - fore you. A - gainst you
bones have gone a - gainst you. O teach me
Spir - it in me whol - ly. O cast me
mouth show forth your great - ness. Do not de -

to your ten - der mer - cy. Blot out my trans-
on - ly have I sinned and done what is
all your truth in se - cret and purge me with
not a - way to dark - ness and take not your
spise my bro - ken spir - it; have mer - cy up -

gres - sions,
e - vil
hys - sop;
Spir - it
on me,

and wash me thor - ough - ly.
with - in your sight, O God.
and then I shall be clean.
from me, O Bless - ed One.
O God of hosts, I cry.

O cleanse me
Wash me and
O fill me
O Lord, re -
Cleanse me and

from
make
with
store
make

my sin.
me clean.
your joy.
my soul.
me whole.

Words: Gracia Grindal © 1993 Selah Publishing Company, Inc.
Music: Clayton J. Schmit © 1998 Clayton J. Schmit

51E Ten piedad de mí / Lord, Have Mercy on Me

Spanish 1 Ten pie-dad de mí, oh Dios, con-for-me a tu bon-dad,

English 1 Lord, have mer-cy on me, in ac-cord-ance with your grace;
2 Lord, I know my re-bel heart has wan-dered from your will,
3 Lord, re-fresh and make me like the new-ness of the spring,

tu mi-se-ri-cor-dia bo-rre mi mal-dad.

with un-fail-ing kind-ness, blot out all my sin.
and re-sis-tance with no rea-son is my path.
like a flow-er o-pening to your warm-ing rays.

Lá-va-me del mal y lím-pia-me de i-ni-qui-dad;

Cleanse me from un-right-eous-ness in thought and word and deed;
You and you a-lone have been the One to know my sin,
So my grate-ful tongue will tell the won-ders of your love,

con - tra ti no quie - ro pe - car.
in your mer - cy, heal me with - in.
and my guilt has earned me your wrath.
and my par - doned heart will sing praise.

Refrain

Vuél-ve-me, Se-ñor, a go-zar-me en ti, a sen-tir la paz de
Lord, re-store to me, Lord, re-store to me the sure-ness of sal-va-tion

tu per-dón; me sus-ten-te la no-ble-za de tu a - mor.
and its joy. Let me know for-give-ness and the peace of your love.

2 Reconozco que yo fui rebelde sin razón,
mis pecados pongo delante de ti.
Contra ti pequé y sólo a ti yo defraudé;
a tus ojos culpable soy. *Refrain*

3 Lávame, Señor y hazme más puro que una flor,
crea un nuevo corazón dentro de mí.
Cantará mi lengua tu justicia y tu perdón;
alabanza te ofreceré. *Refrain*

Words: Rafael D. Grullón, 1970; tr. Mary Louise Bringle (b. 1953), 2011
Music (TEN PIEDAD DE MÍ): Rafael D. Grullón, 1970; arr. Raquel Mora Martínez © 1996 Abingdon Press,
admin. The Copyright Company

Create in Me a Clean Heart

Cre - ate in me a clean heart, O God, and re-new a right spir-it with-in me. Cre-

me. Cast me not a - way from your pres-ence, O

Lord, and take not your Ho - ly Spir - it from me.

Re-store un-to me the joy of your sal - va-tion,

Words: Psalm 51:10, 11
Music: anonymous; arr. Sharon Bradimore (b. 1954) © 2001 Faith Alive Christian Resources

Psalm 51:1-17 | A Responsorial Setting 51G

Refrain

¹ Have mercy on me, O God, according to your steadfast love;
    in your great compassion blot out my offenses.

² Wash me through and through from my wickedness,
    and cleanse me from my sin.

³ For I know my offenses,
    and my sin is ever before me.

⁴ Against you only have I sinned and done what is evil in your sight;
    so you are justified when you speak and right in your judgment.   *Refrain*

⁵ Indeed, I was born steeped in wickedness,
    a sinner from my mother's womb.

⁶ Indeed, you delight in truth deep within me,
    and would have me know wisdom deep within.

⁷ Remove my sins with hyssop, and I shall be clean;
    wash me, and I shall be purer than snow.   *Refrain*   (continues)

8 Let me hear joy and gladness;
   that the body you have broken may rejoice.

9 Hide your face from my sins,
   and blot out all my wickedness.

10 Create in me a clean heart, O God,
   and renew a right spirit within me.   *Refrain*

11 Cast me not away from your presence,
   and take not your Holy Spirit from me.

12 Restore to me the joy of your salvation
   and sustain me with your bountiful Spirit.

13 Let me teach your ways to offenders,
   and sinners shall be restored to you.

14 Rescue me from bloodshed, O God of my salvation,
   and my tongue shall sing of your righteousness.   *Refrain*

15 O Lord, open my lips,
   and my mouth shall proclaim your praise.

16 For you take no delight in sacrifice, or I would give it.
   You are not pleased with burnt offering.

17 The sacrifice of God is a troubled spirit;
   a troubled and broken heart, O God, you will not despise.   *Refrain*

Tone

Lectionary: Ash Wednesday (A,B,C); vv. 1-12 Lent (B) and Ordinary Time after Pentecost (B); vv. 1-10 Ordinary Time after Pentecost (C).

Words: Psalm 51
Music: David Isele © 1979 GIA Publications, Inc.
Psalm Text: from *Evangelical Lutheran Worship* © 2006 Evangelical Lutheran Church in America, admin. Augsburg Fortress Publishers
Tone: © 2011 Faith Alive Christian Resources

Alternate Refrain 1

Urdhu	Khu - daa - yaa, rae-ham kar, Khu-daa - yaa, rae-ham.
English	Have mer - cy on us, Lord, have mer - cy on us.

Alternate Tone 1

Words: traditional Urdhu; trans. © 1990 GIA Publications, Inc.
Music (KHUDAAYAA fragment): traditional Urdhu; trans. © 1990 GIA Publications, Inc.
Tone: © 2011 Faith Alive Christian Resources

Alternate Refrain 2

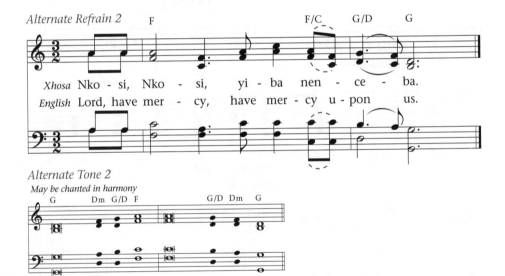

Xhosa	Nko - si, Nko - si, yi - ba nen - ce - ba.
English	Lord, have mer - cy, have mer - cy u - pon us.

Alternate Tone 2

May be chanted in harmony

Words: South African traditional
Music: © G.M. Kolisi, South Africa; US rights Walton Music; arr. Anders Nyberg © 1984 Peace of Music
Publishing AB, admin. Walton Music Corporation
Tone: © 2011 Faith Alive Christian Resources

Words and Music: Kathleen Hart Brumm (b. 1958) © 1992 Brummhart Publishing

51J Prayer of Confession 1

Prayer of Confession

Merciful God,
we confess that we have sinned
   against you
in thought, word and deed,
by what we have done,
and by what we have left
   undone.
We have not loved you
with our whole heart and mind
   and strength.

We have not loved our neighbors
   as ourselves.
In your mercy forgive what we
   have been,
help us amend what we are,
and direct what we shall be,
so that we may delight in your will
and walk in your ways,
to the glory of your holy name.

All sing:

Greek Ky - ri - e e - lei - son. Ky - ri - e e - lei - son.
English Lord, ____ have mer - cy. Lord, ____ have mer - cy.

Ky - ri - e e - lei - son.
Lord, ____ have mer - cy.

Assurance of Pardon

Who is in a position to condemn?
Only Christ, and Christ died for us, Christ rose for us,
Christ reigns in power for us, Christ prays for us.   *Romans 8:34* (NRSV)

Anyone who is in Christ is a new creation.
The old life has gone; a new life has begun.   *2 Corinthians 5:17* (NRSV)

Believe the good news of the gospel:
In Jesus Christ we are forgiven.

All sing a hymn or psalm of praise.

Prayer: *The Book of Common Prayer*, rev., P.D.
Words: early Greek liturgy
Music: Russian Orthodox Liturgy

Prayer of Confession

Gracious God,
our sins are too heavy to carry,
too real too hide,
and too deep to undo.
Forgive what our lips
   tremble to name,
what our hearts can no longer bear,
and what has become for us
a consuming fire of judgment.

Set us free from a past
that we cannot change;
open us to a future
in which we can be changed;
and grant us grace
to grow more and more
in your likeness and image;
through Jesus Christ,
the light of the world.

All sing:

Drum pattern

Assurance of Pardon

This saying is sure and worthy of full acceptance:
Christ Jesus came into the world to save sinners.   *1 Timothy 1:15* (NRSV)
He bore our sins in his body on the cross,
so that free from sins, we might live for righteousness.
By his wounds we have been healed.   *1 Peter 2:24* (NRSV)

Believe this good news and live in peace.

All sing a hymn or psalm of praise.

Prayer: *Book of Worship*, United Church of Christ © 1986, 2002 United Church of Christ, United Church Press
Words: early Greek liturgy
Music: Dinah Reindorf (b. 20th c.), Ghana © 1987 Dinah Reindorf; arr. © 2001 Faith Alive Christian Resources

51L Have Mercy on Me, O God

Refrain

Have mer-cy on me, O God, in your kind-ness.

In your com-pas-sion, blot out my of-fense.

Wash me, O God, from the stain of my guilt,

and cleanse me from my sin.

Words: Psalm 51:3-6, 12-13, 16-17
Music: Jun-G Bargayo and Junjun Delmonte © 2010 Jesuit Communication Foundation, Inc; arr. Joel
Navarro © 2011 Joel Navarro, admin. Faith Alive Christian Resources

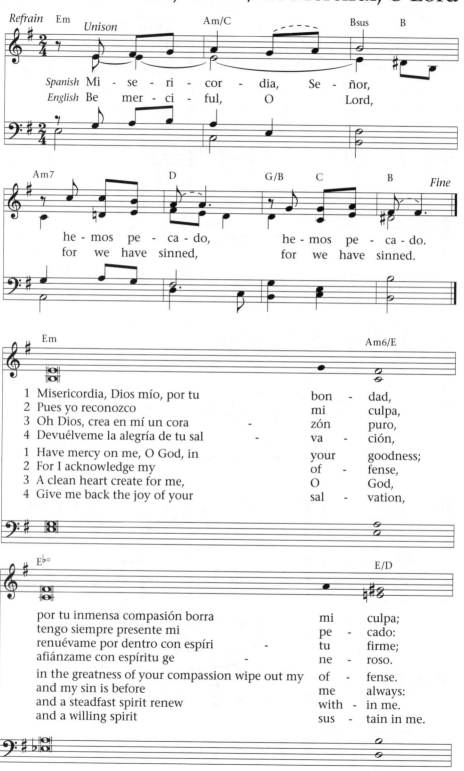

Refrain

Spanish: Mi - se - ri - cor - dia, Se - ñor,
English: Be mer - ci - ful, O Lord,

he - mos pe - ca - do, he - mos pe - ca - do.
for we have sinned, for we have sinned.

1 Misericordia, Dios mío, por tu bon - dad,
2 Pues yo reconozco mi culpa,
3 Oh Dios, crea en mí un cora - zón puro,
4 Devuélveme la alegría de tu sal - va - ción,

1 Have mercy on me, O God, in your goodness;
2 For I acknowledge my of - fense,
3 A clean heart create for me, O God,
4 Give me back the joy of your sal - vation,

por tu inmensa compasión borra mi culpa;
tengo siempre presente mi pe - cado:
renuévame por dentro con espíri - tu firme;
afiánzame con espíritu ge - ne - roso.

in the greatness of your compassion wipe out my of - fense.
and my sin is before me always:
and a steadfast spirit renew with - in me.
and a willing spirit sus - tain in me.

342

lava del todo mi de - lito,
contra ti, contra ti sólo pe - qué,
no me arrojes lejos de tu rostro,
Señor, me abrirás los labios,

Thoroughly wash me from my guilt
"Against you only have I sinned,
Cast me not out from your presence,
O Lord, open my lips,

limpia mi pe - ca - do.
cometí la maldad que a - bo - rre - ces.
no me quites tu San - to Es - spíri - tu.
y mi boca proclamará tu a - la - ban - za.

and of my sin cleanse me.
and done what is evil in your sight."
and your Holy Spirit take not from me.
and my mouth shall pro - claim your praise.

Words: Psalm 51
Music: ref. John Schiavone; sts. Michael Guimont © 1994, 1998, 2004 GIA Publications, Inc.

God, Be Merciful to Me

Optional Introduction and Interlude

1 God, be mer - ci - ful to me,
2 My trans - gres - sions I con - fess;
3 I am e - vil, born in sin;
4 Let my con - trite heart re - joice

on your grace I rest my plea;
grief and guilt my soul op - press.
you de - sire_____ truth with - in.
and in glad - ness hear your voice;

Wash me, make me pure with - in;
I have sinned a - gainst your grace
Make me pure, your mer - cy show,
from my sins, O hide your face,

cleanse, O cleanse me from my sin.
and pro - voked you to your face.
wash me whit - er than the snow.
blot them out in bound - less grace.

Refrain

God, be mer - ci - ful to me,

D.C. for Stanzas | *Final*
Last time repeat Refrain | *Ending*

on your grace I rest my plea.

Alternate tune: REDHEAD 76, p. 346.

Words: *Psalter,* 1912, alt; P.D.
Music (7.7.7.7.7.7): Christopher Miner © 1998 Christopher Miner Music; arr. Eelco Vos © 2011 Christopher Miner Music

510 Gracious God, My Heart Renew

1 Gra - cious God, my heart re - new, make my spir - it
2 So shall sin - ners be re - stored and re - turn to
3 Not the for - mal sac - ri - fice has ac - cept - ance
4 Pros - per Zi - on in your grace and her bro - ken

right and true; in your pres - ence let me stay,
you, their Lord; Sav - ior, all my guilt re - move,
in your eyes; bro - ken hearts are in your sight
walls re - place: then our right - eous sac - ri - fice

by your Spir - it show the way; your sal - va - tion's
and my tongue shall sing your love; touch my si - lent
more than sac - ri - fi - cial rite; con - trite spir - it,
shall de - light your ho - ly eyes; free - will of - ferings,

joy im - part, stead - fast make my will - ing heart.
lips, O Lord, and my mouth shall praise ac - cord.
plead - ing cries, you, O God, will not de - spise.
glad - ly made, on your al - tar shall be laid.

Guitar chords do not correspond with keyboard harmony.

For alternate tune see p. 344.

This tune in a lower key: p. 155.

Words: *Psalter*, 1912, alt., P.D.
Music (REDHEAD 76 | 7.7.7.7.7.7): Richard Redhead, 1853, P.D.

Psalm 52

To the leader. A Maskil of David, when Doeg the Edomite came to Saul and said to him, "David has come to the house of Ahimelech."

¹ Why do you boast, O mighty one, *

    of mischief done against the godly?

All day long ² you are plotting destruction. *

Your tongue is like a sharp razor, you worker of treachery.

³ You love evil more than good, *

    and lying more than speaking the truth.   *Selah*

⁴ **You love all words that devour, ***

    O deceitful tongue.

⁵ But God will break you down forever; *

    he will snatch and tear you from your tent;

    he will uproot you from the land of the living.   *Selah*

⁶ **The righteous will see, and fear, ***

    and will laugh at the evildoer, saying,

⁷ "See the one who would not take refuge in God, *

    but trusted in abundant riches, and sought refuge in wealth!"

⁸ **But I am like a green olive tree in the house of God. ***

    I trust in the steadfast love of God forever and ever.

⁹ **I will thank you forever, because of what you have done. ***

    In the presence of the faithful I will proclaim your name,

    for it is good.

Holy God, your love is both fierce and tender.
Nourish and prune us through your Word and Spirit,
so that we may grow in truth, in peace, and in joy,
bearing fruit in this world, which you dearly love. **Amen.**

Psalm 52 is about covenantal commitment, concluding with a vow to live faithfully as part of a people of covenant faithfulness (v. 9b). The psalm pivots from a prophetic injunction against a faithless, deceitful, self-sufficient warrior (vv. 1-7) to a profound statement of trust (vv. 8-9). It can be read as a response to Ps. 1, offering not only a description of the contrast between faithless and faithful living, but also a statement of commitment to choosing faithfulness. *Use in Worship: in conjunction with prayers of dedication to God; a response to the proclamation of Ps. 1.*

You Cunning Liar, Why Publicize

1 You cun-ning liar, why pub-li-cize your e-vil
2 May God rise up to pull you down, up-root and
3 God, let me like a spread-ing tree, grow as I

need to harm the good? Your slan-derous tongue is ra-zor-
sweep you far a-way. Then may the just look on a-
trust in your sure love. Where loy-al ser-vants of-fer

sharp honed to ful-fil ma-li-cious plans;
ghast and mock the one who val-ued wealth,
praise with-in your house, I'll add my voice

you love the lie and hate the truth.
who trust-ed rich-es more than God.
to glo-ri-fy your ho-ly name.

Sing slowly, softly, with a sense of weariness.

Alternate harmonization on p. 461.

Words: Doug Gay, rev. John L. Bell (b. 1949) © 2011 Wild Goose Resource Group, Iona Community,
Scotland, GIA Publications, Inc., exclusive North American agent
Music (BACA 8.8.8.8.8): William B. Bradbury (1816-1868); harm. John L. Bell (b. 1949) © 2011 Wild Goose
Resource Group, Iona Community, Scotland, GIA Publications, Inc., exclusive North American agent

Psalm 52 | A Responsorial Setting 52B

Refrain

But I am like a green ol-ive tree in the house of God.

Refrain

1 You mighty, why do you boast of wickedness
   against the godly all day long?

2 Continually you plot ruin;
   your tongue is like a sharpened razor that commits deceit.

3 You love evil more than good
   and lying more than speaking the truth.

4 You love all words that devour,
   O you deceitful tongue. *Refrain*

5 Oh, that God would demolish you utterly,
   topple you, and snatch you from your dwelling,
   and root you out of the land of the living!

6 The righteous shall see and be awestruck,
   and they shall laugh at you, saying,

7 "This is the one who did not take God for a refuge,
   but trusted in great wealth and found strength in destruction."

8 But I am like a green olive tree in the house of God;
   I trust in the steadfast love of God forever and ever.

9 I will thank you forever for what you have done;
   in the presence of the faithful I will long for your name, for it is good. *Refrain*

Tone

(To Refrain)   (But)

Lectionary: Ordinary Time after Pentecost (C).

Words: Psalm 52
Music: Aaron David Miller, from *Psalter for Worship, Year C* © 2006 Augsburg Fortress Publishers
Psalm Text: from *Evangelical Lutheran Worship* © 2006 Evangelical Lutheran Church in America, admin.
Augsburg Fortress Publishers
Tone: from *Psalter for Worship, Year C* © 2006 Augsburg Fortress Publishers

Psalm 53

To the leader: according to Mahalath. A Maskil of David.

1 Fools say in their hearts, "There is no God." *

    They are corrupt, they commit abominable acts;

    there is no one who does good.

2 **God looks down from heaven on humankind** *

    to see if there are any who are wise, who seek after God.

3 They have all fallen away, they are all alike perverse; *

    there is no one who does good, no, not one.

4 **Have they no knowledge, those evildoers,** *

    who eat up my people as they eat bread, and do not call upon God?

5 There they shall be in great terror, in terror such as has not been. *

    For God will scatter the bones of the ungodly;

    they will be put to shame, for God has rejected them.

6 **O that deliverance for Israel would come from Zion!** *

    When God restores the fortunes of his people,

    Jacob will rejoice; Israel will be glad.

Patient and loving God, so often we live as though we were God.
By your Holy Spirit show us that you alone are sovereign and holy.
Help us to see the foolishness of earthly wisdom,
and to discover the joy of knowing Jesus Christ, God's wisdom.
We pray this in Jesus' name. **Amen.**

Psalm 53, almost identical to Ps. 14, is a psalm of wisdom about the folly and pervasiveness of unbelief and faithlessness, and the link between the failure to acknowledge God and human corruption (v. 1) and oppression of others (v. 4). The psalm culminates with a strong expression of desire for God to deliver and restore the people (v. 7). It is quoted by Paul to demonstrate the universality of human sin (Rom. 3:10-12). This psalm is especially striking following the words of trust and commitment expressed in Ps. 52, suggesting that even our best expressions of integrity are flawed. *Use in Worship: call to confession.*

For additional settings of Ps. 53 see Ps. 14.

Hear the Fool 53A

1 Hear the fool say-ing loud and long, there's no God, we're
2 God looks down from his throne on high search-ing for a
3 E - vil ones who at - tack the poor steal their bread then

all a - lone. Poi - son words that pol - lute the air,
heart that's wise, an - y - one who will seek his face,
rage for more; but the Lord will de - fend his own.

spread-ing ev - ery - where.
leave their wick - ed ways. All have sinned, all have
Ev - ery - one will know.

turned a - side and there's no one right-eous. But re-demp-tion will

one day come from Zi - on, so re - joice!

Words: Bev Herrema © 2011 Pilot Point Music, admin. Music Services
Music (BLAKE 8.7.8.5 with refrain): Bev Herrema © 2011 Pilot Point Music, admin. Music Services

Psalm 54

To the leader: with stringed instruments. A Maskil of David, when the Ziphites went and told Saul, "David is in hiding among us."

¹ Save me, O God, by your name, *
and vindicate me by your might.

² **Hear my prayer, O God; ***
give ear to the words of my mouth.

³ For the insolent have risen against me, the ruthless seek my life; *
they do not set God before them.   *Selah*

⁴ **But surely, God is my helper; ***
the Lord is the upholder of my life.

⁵ He will repay my enemies for their evil. *
In your faithfulness, put an end to them.

⁶ **With a freewill offering I will sacrifice to you; ***
I will give thanks to your name, O LORD, for it is good.

⁷ **For he has delivered me from every trouble, ***
and my eye has looked in triumph on my enemies.

God who hears and answers prayer,
your Word teaches us to place our anxiety on you because you care for us.
Help us to remember this truth—not only today, but all the days of our lives.
We pray in the name of Jesus. **Amen.**

Psalm 54, similar to Ps. 13, is a condensed expression of each facet of a prayer of petition. It begins with a request for God's deliverance (vv. 1-2), continues with a lament about why deliverance is needed (v. 3), and concludes with both an expression of trust in God (vv. 4-5) and a vow to praise God (vv. 6-7). *Use in Worship: on Good Friday, perhaps to highlight the contrast between prayers against the enemy (v. 5) and Jesus' prayer for his enemies.*

Psalm 54 | A Responsorial Setting 54A

Refrain

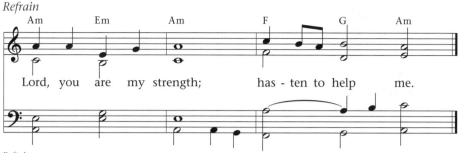

Lord, you are my strength; has-ten to help me.

Refrain

1 Save me, O God, by your name;
    in your might, defend my cause.

2 Hear my prayer, O God;
    give ear to the words of my mouth.

3 For strangers have risen up against me, and the ruthless have sought my life,
    those who have no regard for God.   *Refrain*

4 Behold, God is my helper;
    it is the Lord who sustains my life.

5 Render evil to those who spy on me;
    in your faithfulness, destroy them.

6 I will offer you a freewill sacrifice
    and praise your name, O LORD, for it is good.

7 For you have rescued me from every trouble,
    and my eye looks down on my enemies.   *Refrain*

Tone

Lectionary: Ordinary Time after Pentecost (B).

Words and Music: Hal H. Hopson © 1986 Hope Publishing Company
Psalm Text: from *Evangelical Lutheran Worship* © 2006 Evangelical Lutheran Church in America, admin.
Augsburg Fortress Publishers
Tone: © 1987 Westminster John Knox Press

Psalm 55

To the leader: with stringed instruments. A Maskil of David.

1 Give ear to my prayer, O God; *
   do not hide yourself from my supplication.
2 **Attend to me, and answer me; ***
   I am troubled in my complaint.
   I am distraught 3 by the noise of the enemy, *
   because of the clamor of the wicked.
   For they bring trouble upon me, *
   and in anger they cherish enmity against me.
4 **My heart is in anguish within me, ***
   the terrors of death have fallen upon me.
5 **Fear and trembling come upon me, ***
   and horror overwhelms me.
6 And I say, "O that I had wings like a dove! *
   I would fly away and be at rest;
7 truly, I would flee far away; *
   I would lodge in the wilderness;   *Selah*
8 I would hurry to find a shelter for myself *
   from the raging wind and tempest."
9 **Confuse, O Lord, confound their speech; ***
   for I see violence and strife in the city.
10 Day and night they go around it on its walls, *
   and iniquity and trouble are within it;
11 ruin is in its midst; *
   oppression and fraud do not depart from its marketplace.
12 **It is not enemies who taunt me—I could bear that; ***
   it is not adversaries who deal insolently with me—
   I could hide from them.
13 **But it is you, my equal, ***
   my companion, my familiar friend,
14 **with whom I kept pleasant company; ***
   we walked in the house of God with the throng.

¹⁵ Let death come upon them; let them go down alive to Sheol; *
>   for evil is in their homes and in their hearts.

¹⁶ **But I call upon God, ***
>   **and the LORD will save me.**

¹⁷ **Evening and morning and at noon ***
>   **I utter my complaint and moan, and he will hear my voice.**

¹⁸ **He will redeem me unharmed from the battle that I wage, ***
>   **for many are arrayed against me.**

¹⁹ **God, who is enthroned from of old,**   *Selah*
>   **will hear, and will humble them— ***
>   **because they do not change, and do not fear God.**

²⁰ My companion laid hands on a friend *
>   and violated a covenant with me

²¹ with speech smoother than butter, but with a heart set on war; *
>   with words that were softer than oil, but in fact were drawn swords.

²² **Cast your burden on the LORD, and he will sustain you; ***
>   **he will never permit the righteous to be moved.**

²³ **But you, O God, will cast them down into the lowest pit; ***
>   **the bloodthirsty and treacherous shall not live out half their days.**
>   **But I will trust in you.**

Loving God, help us when we have been betrayed
to look beyond hypocrisy and deceit to your throne of grace,
and there to lay our burdens down.
We trust in your covenant of unfailing love,
revealed to us in the betrayal, death, and resurrection of Jesus our Savior. **Amen.**

Psalm 55 features intertwined prayers for God to act (vv. 1-2a, 9a), descriptions of pain and brokenness (vv. 2b-8, 9b-14, 20-21), and declarations of hope (vv. 15-19, 22-23). It includes particularly poignant imagery (v. 6), the bitter recognition of betrayal (vv. 12-14), and the memorable invitation to cast (or hurl or throw) our burdens upon God (v. 22). *Use in Worship: in conjunction with narratives of betrayal (e.g., the betrayal of Jacob, Joseph, or Jesus); services expressing desperation that emerges from particularly poignant pain.*

55A I Need Your Help, O LORD My God

1 I need your help, O LORD my God; do not ig-nore my plea.
2 Long as I live and trou-bles rise, my God, on you I'll call.

For I am rest-less and dis-traught; O hear and an-swer me.
You hold the right-eous in your arms, you will not let them fall.

If I had wings, I'd fly a-way in-to the wil-der-ness
I cast my cares up-on you, LORD, you give me strength a-new.

to find a qui-et, shel-tered place where I could be at rest.
You see me through each anx-ious day; my God, I trust in you.

Guitar chords do not correspond with keyboard harmony.

Alternate tune: THIRD MODE MELODY, p. 384.

Words: st. 1 Helen Otte (b. 1931), 1984, © 1987 Faith Alive Christian Resources; st. 2 Martin Tel © 2011
Faith Alive Christian Resources
Music (RESTING PLACE 8.6.8.6 D): Henry Vander Werp (1846-1918), 1911, P.D.

Cast Your Burden upon the Lord 55B

Cast your bur-den up-on the Lord, and he shall sus - tain you;
he nev-er will suf - fer the right-eous to fall: he is at your right hand.
Your mer - cy, Lord, is great and far a - bove the heavens:
let none be made a - shamed that wait up - on you.

Words: Psalm 55:22, 16:8
Music: Felix Mendelssohn (1809-1847), from *Elijah*, P.D.

Psalm 56

To the leader: according to The Dove on Far-off Terebinths. Of David.
A Miktam, when the Philistines seized him in Gath.

1 Be gracious to me, O God, for people trample on me; *
    all day long foes oppress me;
2 my enemies trample on me all day long, *
    for many fight against me.
O Most High, 3 when I am afraid, *
I put my trust in you.
4 **In God, whose word I praise, in God I trust; ***
I am not afraid; what can flesh do to me?
5 All day long they seek to injure my cause; *
    all their thoughts are against me for evil.
6 They stir up strife, they lurk, they watch my steps. *
    As they hoped to have my life,
7 so repay them for their crime; *
    in wrath cast down the peoples, O God!
8 **You have kept count of my tossings; put my tears in your bottle. ***
Are they not in your record?
9 **Then my enemies will retreat in the day when I call. ***
This I know, that God is for me.
10 **In God, whose word I praise, ***
in the LORD, whose word I praise,
11 **in God I trust; I am not afraid. ***
What can a mere mortal do to me?
12 My vows to you I must perform, O God; *
    I will render thank offerings to you.
13 **For you have delivered my soul from death,**
and my feet from falling, *
so that I may walk before God in the light of life.

God of justice and mercy,
you count our tears and hear our prayers.
Fill us with your light, O God,
and help us to trust your promise and not be afraid.
We pray this in Jesus' name. **Amen.**

Psalm 56 depicts how fear and trust can coexist. The text alternates among descriptions of dislocation (vv. 1-2, 5-6), statements of trust in God (vv. 3-4, 9-11, 12-13), prayers for God to act (vv. 7-8), and vows of commitment (v. 12). It includes the poignant image of God holding the psalmist's "tears in a bottle" (v. 8). *Use in Worship: services focusing on narratives of the plight of various biblical characters (e.g., David's flight from the Philistines); services that explore today's experiences of hardship or hopelessness.*

In My Day of Fear 56A

Refrain

In my day of fear, I put my trust in you, God Most High.

Fine

1 All day long I am un - der at - tack, my
2 In God's Word I have put my faith, in
3 All day long they wound me with words, and
4 But you, O Lord, you have not - ed my grief and
5 I will de - clare with due grat - i - tude how

en - e - mies are al - ways near; ly - ing in wait,
you I trust, O Lord, Most High. There - fore I need no
ev - ery word is meant to harm; band - ing to - geth - er,
seen my end - less mis - er - y; keep all my tears
God has kept my soul from death; thus in God's pres - ence

To Refrain

wait - ing their chance, in - tend - ing to ha - rass and fight.
long - er fear, for what could mor - tals ev - er do?
plot - ting their worst, they sly - ly watch my ev - ery move.
stored in your flask, the tears re - cord - ed in your book.
I glad - ly walk, in pres - ence of the light of life.

Words: The Iona Community © 1993 Wild Goose Resource Group, Iona Community, Scotland, GIA Publications, Inc., exclusive North American agent
Music (DISTANT OAKS): The Iona Community © 1993 Wild Goose Resource Group, Iona Community, Scotland, GIA Publications, Inc., exclusive North American agent

56B God, I Am Beaten, Battered and Bruised

Stanzas

1 God, I am beat-en, bat - tered and bruised;
2 God, there are times when I wish you would fight;
3 Day af - ter day peo-ple plot my de - mise;

slan - dered and stepped on; hurt and a - bused. But
take up my fight; so they'll know I am right. But
look - ing at me with con - tempt in their eyes. But

I trust in you and I am not a-fraid. Let them
you hold my tears and you know all my pain. Let them
I trust in you and I am not a-fraid. Let them

do what they will. I trust in you. *To interlude, then to Stanza 2*
do what they will. I trust in you. *To interlude, then to Refrain*
do what they will. I trust in you. *To interlude, then to Refrain*

(Instrumental interlude)

Refrain

God, I am prom - ised to you. God, now my

of - fering I give. Here is my heart, my soul, my all.

Now   in your light   I will live.

(Instrumental interlude)

To Stanza 3

Now   in your light   I will live.

Now   in your light   I will live.

Keyboard Accompaniment Patterns
suggested accompaniment pattern for Stanzas

etc.

suggested accompaniment pattern for Refrain

etc.

Words and Music: Ken Medema © 2010 Ken Medema Music/Brier Patch Music

56C O God, Be Merciful to Me

1 O God, be mer-ci-ful to me; I
2 Some-times I am a-fraid, O LORD, but
3 I am sur-round-ed ev-ery day by

am dis-tressed by en-e-mies on ev-ery
I be-lieve your prom-ised word that you are
those who plot to take a-way my ver-y

side. They slan-der me in what they say, at-
near. What treach-er-y can mor-tals raise? I
life. When they con-spire to do me harm, O

tack-ing me from day to day in all their pride.
trust in God, whose word I praise. I will not fear.
LORD, lift up your might-y arm and stop their strife.

4 O LORD, take note of my lament.
Do you not list each tear I shed,
upon your scroll?
What treachery can mortals raise?
I trust in God, whose word I praise.
He guards my soul.

5 To you, O LORD, I pay my vow
as I, with thankful offerings, bow
before your face.
For you delivered me from death
and set me safely on the path
of life and grace.

Words: Helen Otte (b. 1931), 1986, © 1987 Faith Alive Christian Resources
Music (ROSALIE MCMILLAN 8.8.4 D): James Ward, 1984, © 1987 Music A. D.

Psalm 57

To the leader: Do Not Destroy. Of David. A Miktam, when he fled from Saul, in the cave.

¹ Be merciful to me, O God, be merciful to me, for in you my soul takes refuge; *

    in the shadow of your wings I will take refuge,

    until the destroying storms pass by.

² **I cry to God Most High, ***

    to God who fulfills his purpose for me.

³ **He will send from heaven and save me,**

    he will put to shame those who trample on me. * *Selah*

    God will send forth his steadfast love and his faithfulness.

⁴ I lie down among lions that greedily devour human prey; *

    their teeth are spears and arrows, their tongues sharp swords.

⁵ **Be exalted, O God, above the heavens. ***

    Let your glory be over all the earth.

⁶ They set a net for my steps; my soul was bowed down. *

    They dug a pit in my path,

    but they have fallen into it themselves.   *Selah*

⁷ **My heart is steadfast, O God, my heart is steadfast. ***

    I will sing and make melody.

⁸ **Awake, my soul! Awake, O harp and lyre! ***

    I will awake the dawn.

⁹ I will give thanks to you, O Lord, among the peoples; *

    I will sing praises to you among the nations.

¹⁰ For your steadfast love is as high as the heavens; *

    your faithfulness extends to the clouds.

¹¹ **Be exalted, O God, above the heavens. ***

    Let your glory be over all the earth.

God of love and faithfulness,
help your people to be loving, especially to those who are least loved,
and inspire your people to be faithful, especially in the most challenging times,
that with our lives as well as our voices we will sing your praise and show your glory. **Amen.**

Psalm 57 contrasts the depths of earthly pain (vv. 4, 6) with the heights of divine majesty (vv. 2, 10, and the refrain of vv. 5, 11). It includes petition (v. 1), a statement of trust (vv. 2-3), descriptions of attack (vv. 4, 6), and a vow to praise God (vv. 7-10). Among the psalms of lament and petition, this psalm features an unusual sense of buoyancy and hopefulness. *Use in Worship: a prayer for God's mercy; services of lament anticipating a future of renewed hopefulness.*

57A Be Gracious to Me, Lord

1 Be gra - cious to me, Lord, and hold my spir - it
2 Though snares are set for me, yet I will sleep in
3 My soul, a - wake and sing— such bound - less love re -

fast, that I may shel - ter by your side un -
peace, for I have asked the care of God whose
call, ex - alt God's name a - bove the skies, God's

til the storm is past, un - til the storm is past.
love shall nev - er cease, whose love shall nev - er cease.
glo - ry o - ver all, God's glo - ry o - ver all.

Words: Michael Perry © 1973 The Jubilate Group, admin. Hope Publishing Company
Music (MIKTAM 6.6.8.6.6): Larry Visser © 2011 Wayne Leupold Editions, Inc.

Psalm 57:1-3, 9-10 **57B**
A Responsorial Setting

Refrain

Optional Harmony

I rest in you, I rest in you, I rest.

G   D7   G

I rest in the shad-ow of your wings, in the shad-ow of your wings. (I)

Sing softly or hum during spoken verses

G   D7   G *Last time to Refrain*

rest   in you.   I rest.

Refrain

1. Have mercy on me, O God, have mercy! I look to you for protection.

    I will hide beneath the shadow of you wings

    until the danger passes by.   *Refrain*

2. I cry out to God Most High, to God who fulfills his purpose for me.

3. He will send help from heaven to rescue me, disgracing those who hound me.

    My God will send forth his unfailing love and faithfulness.   *Refrain*

9. I will thank you, Lord, among all the people.

    I will sing your praises among the nations.

10. For your unfailing love is as high as the heavens.

    Your faithfulness reaches to the clouds.   *Refrain*

Bell part for Refrain

Words: Psalm 57
Music: Julie Howard; arr. Vera Lyons © 1992 Liturgical Press
Text: Psalm 57, New Living Translation © 1996 Tyndale House Publishers, Inc.

Psalm 58

To the leader: Do Not Destroy. Of David. A Miktam.

¹ Do you indeed decree what is right, you gods? *

    Do you judge people fairly?

² No, in your hearts you devise wrongs; *

    your hands deal out violence on earth.

³ **The wicked go astray from the womb;** *

    they err from their birth, speaking lies.

⁴ **They have venom like the venom of a serpent,** *

    like the deaf adder that stops its ear,

⁵ **so that it does not hear the voice of charmers** *

    or of the cunning enchanter.

⁶ O God, break the teeth in their mouths; *

    tear out the fangs of the young lions, O LORD!

⁷ Let them vanish like water that runs away; ˙

    like grass let them be trodden down and wither.

⁸ Let them be like the snail that dissolves into slime; *

    like the untimely birth that never sees the sun.

⁹ Sooner than your pots can feel the heat of thorns, *

    whether green or ablaze, may he sweep them away!

¹⁰ The righteous will rejoice when they see vengeance done; *

    they will bathe their feet in the blood of the wicked.

¹¹ **People will say, "Surely there is a reward for the righteous;** *

    surely there is a God who judges on earth."

Author of all that is true and good, our world is filled with deceit,
and many would have us believe that there is no ultimate truth.
But we are your people, and by the power of your Spirit
we proclaim Jesus: the Way, the Truth, and the Life.
Write this upon our hearts and let our lives reflect our convictions. **Amen.**

Psalm 58 is a psalm of lament and vengeance offered in the context of evil and injustice. At the center is a prayer for God to act in retribution against evil (v. 6). It begins with an awareness of a supernatural cause of evil (vv. 1-2), which the OT depicts in terms of the council of the "gods" (cf. Ps. 82) and which some Christian interpreters link with "the powers and principalities" (Eph. 6:12). The psalm features some of the most arresting imagery of the entire Psalter, speaking of faithless persons as deaf snakes who refuse to hear a snake charmer (vv. 4-5) and asking God to tear the teeth out of their mouth (v. 6). When taken together with Pss. 59 and 60, this psalm is part of an unrelenting request for divine retribution against the enemy of the righteous which concludes with an expression of hope and trust in God in Ps. 61. *Use in Worship: contemplating the effects of acute evil and the kind of dramatic, divine action needed to redress it.*

For additional settings of Ps. 59 see 60A and 60B.

O When Will We See Justice Done? 58A

O when will we see justice done?
When will the righteous win?
O speed the day when we can say,
"God judges human sin!"
The venom of the wicked's lies
destroys all in their path.
Their fangs are bared; no one is spared,
and to our cries they're deaf.

These words may be sung to the tune KINGSFOLD (p. 370) and are part of the larger setting, "O When Will We See Justice Done?" (60A).

Words: Carol Bechtel © 2011 Carol Bechtel, admin. Faith Alive Christian Resources

Psalm 59

To the leader: Do Not Destroy. Of David. A Miktam, when Saul ordered his house to be watched in order to kill him.

¹ Deliver me from my enemies, O my God; *
    protect me from those who rise up against me.

² Deliver me from those who work evil; *
    from the bloodthirsty save me.

³ **Even now they lie in wait for my life;** *
    the mighty stir up strife against me.

For no transgression or sin of mine, O LORD,
⁴ **for no fault of mine, they run and make ready.** *
    Rouse yourself, come to my help and see!

⁵ **You, LORD God of hosts, are God of Israel.** *
    Awake to punish all the nations;
    spare none of those who treacherously plot evil.   *Selah*

⁶ Each evening they come back, *
    howling like dogs and prowling about the city.

⁷ There they are, bellowing with their mouths, *
    with sharp words on their lips—for "Who," they think, "will hear us?"

⁸ But you laugh at them, O LORD; *
    you hold all the nations in derision.

⁹ **O my strength, I will watch for you;** *
    for you, O God, are my fortress.

¹⁰ **My God in his steadfast love will meet me;** *
    my God will let me look in triumph on my enemies.

¹¹ Do not kill them, or my people may forget; *
    make them totter by your power, and bring them down, O Lord, our shield.

(continues)

¹² For the sin of their mouths, the words of their lips, *
  let them be trapped in their pride.

For the cursing and lies that they utter, *
  ¹³ consume them in wrath; consume them until they are no more.

Then it will be known to the ends of the earth *
  that God rules over Jacob.   *Selah*

¹⁴ Each evening they come back, *
  howling like dogs and prowling about the city.

¹⁵ They roam about for food, *
  and growl if they do not get their fill.

¹⁶ **But I will sing of your might;**
  I will sing aloud of your steadfast love in the morning. *
    For you have been a fortress for me
    and a refuge in the day of my distress.
¹⁷ **O my strength, I will sing praises to you, ***
    for you, O God, are my fortress,
    the God who shows me steadfast love.

Source of persistent hope,
when the world totters because of injustice and wickedness fills the land,
we trust that your justice will prevail.
So we will rejoice in you and find our peace in Jesus our Savior. **Amen.**

Psalm 59 is an urgent plea for divine help and retribution (vv. 1-2, 4b-5, 11-13) that alternates with descriptions of threats from the enemy (vv. 3-4, 6-7, 14-15) and statements of trust in God (vv. 8-10, 16-17). It arises from a situation of acute danger, expressing the kind of terror experienced by hostages in a prisoner-of-war camp or victims of abuse, and yet also expresses an astonishingly resilient hopefulness and confidence in God's future deliverance (vv. 12, 16) and a vow to sing praise to God in response (vv. 16-17). When taken together with Pss. 58 and 60, this psalm is part of an unrelenting request for divine retribution against the enemy of the righteous which concludes with an expression of hope and trust in a God in Ps. 61. *Use in Worship: services expressing prayers of or on behalf of others in situations of acute harm.*

For additional settings of Ps. 59 see 60A and 60B.

59A Deliver Me, O God My Strength

Deliver me, O God my strength,
from those who lie in wait,
from enemies who prowl and plot,
whose only law is hate.
But you, O Lord, could come and save,
deflating their false pride,
and show the earth your righteous worth
as in your love we hide.

These words may be sung to the tune KINGSFOLD (p. 370) and are part of the larger setting, "O When Will We See Justice Done?" (60A).

Words: Carol Bechtel © 2011 Carol Bechtel, admin. Faith Alive Christian Resources

Psalm 60

To the leader: according to the Lily of the Covenant.
A Miktam of David; for instruction; when he struggled with Aram-naharaim and with Aram-zobah,
and when Joab on his return killed twelve thousand Edomites in the Valley of Salt.

Voice 1:

1 O God, you have rejected us, broken our defenses; *
    you have been angry; now restore us!

Voice 2:

2 You have caused the land to quake; you have torn it open; *
    repair the cracks in it, for it is tottering.

Voice 1:

3 You have made your people suffer hard things; *
    you have given us wine to drink that made us reel.

Voice 2:

4 You have set up a banner for those who fear you, *
    to rally to it out of bowshot.   *Selah*

5 **Give victory with your right hand, and answer us, ***
    so that those whom you love may be rescued.

Voice 3:

6 God has promised in his sanctuary: *
    "With exultation I will divide up Shechem,
    and portion out the Vale of Succoth.

7 Gilead is mine, and Manasseh is mine; *
    Ephraim is my helmet; Judah is my scepter.

8 Moab is my washbasin; on Edom I hurl my shoe; *
    over Philistia I shout in triumph."

Voice 1:

9 Who will bring me to the fortified city? *
    Who will lead me to Edom?

Voice 2:

10 Have you not rejected us, O God? *
    You do not go out, O God, with our armies.

Voices 1 and 2:

11 O grant us help against the foe, *
    for human help is worthless.

12 **With God we shall do valiantly; ***
    it is he who will tread down our foes.   (continues)

Victorious God, your Son Jesus taught us to ask, seek, and knock
in confidence that our requests would be answered.
In the struggles we face today and in all the battles that lie ahead,
give us the strength and wisdom to trust you in all circumstances
and to rejoice in you always. **Amen.**

Psalm 60 is a communal lament following defeat and calamity. It expresses urgent prayers (vv. 5, 11) and confident hope (vv. 4, 12), set in the context of lament (v. 1-3) and divine oracle (vv. 6-8). The psalm insists that relying on human strength is folly (v. 11), and, in spite of God's apparent abandonment, it nevertheless recites God's own promise to sustain the people as a ground for future hope (v. 12). When taken together with Pss. 58 and 59, this psalm is part of an unrelenting request for divine retribution against the enemy of the righteous which concludes with an expression of hope and trust in a God in Ps. 61. *Use in Worship: services expressing prayers of or on behalf of communities that experience a sense of being abandoned by God.*

60A O When Will We See Justice Done?

(Ps. 58) 1 O when will we see jus-tice done? When will the right-eous win?
(Ps. 59) 2 De - li - ver me, O God my strength, from those who lie in wait,
(Ps. 60) 3 O God, have you re - ject - ed us, or do you on - ly sleep?

O speed the day when we can say, "God judg-es hu-man sin!"
from en - e - mies who prowl and plot, whose on - ly law is hate.
Give vic - tory with your might - y hand, your prom-is - es to keep.

The ven - om of the wick-ed's lies de - stroys all in their path.
But you, O Lord, could come and save, de - flat-ing their false pride,
For you have caused our land to quake; no step now seems se - cure.

Their fangs are bared; no one is spared, and to our cries they're deaf.
and show the earth your right-eous worth as in your love we hide.
We stag-ger in our suf-fer-ing, our faith seems less than sure.

Refrain (Ps. 61)

God, hear my cry! To you I call e-ven when my heart is faint.

To your strong tower lead me in power, and keep me ev-er safe.

Words: Carol Bechtel © 2011 Carol Bechtel, admin. Faith Alive Christian Resources
Music (KINGSFOLD 8.6.8.6 D): English; adapt. Ralph Vaughan Williams (1872-1958), 1906, P.D.

60B An Imprecation: We Are Seething in Our Fury

Unison

1 We are seeth-ing in our fu - ry, an - ger fes - ters
2 Worth-less ad - ver - sar - ies hurt us with a wrath we
3 You who set the earth's foun - da - tions, com - pre - hend - ing

in - to flame. We could kill! No judge or ju - ry
did not earn. Worth-less part - ners all des - ert us;
our dis - tress: re - con - struct our ac - cu - sa - tions

would con - vict or e - ven blame. Shep - herd, hear our
God seems dis - tant, si - lent, stern. Spir - it, hear our
and the vio - lence we pro - fess. Mas - on, hear our

cries, our fur - or; but, be - fore you
cries for ven - geance! Let our in - dig -
cries; re - build us. Through your power to

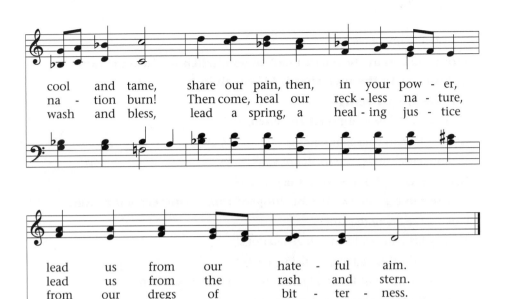

cool and tame, share our pain, then, in your pow - er,
na - tion burn! Then come, heal our reck - less na - ture,
wash and bless, lead a spring, a heal - ing jus - tice

lead us from our hate - ful aim.
lead us from the rash and stern.
from our dregs of bit - ter - ness.

Alternate tune: EBENEZER, p. 182.

Words: James Hart Brumm (b. 1962) © 2009 Wayne Leupold Editions, Inc.
Music (AUTHORITY 8.7.8.7 D): Carol Doran © 1986 Oxford University Press. Reproduced by permission of
Oxford University Press.

Psalm 61

To the leader: with stringed instruments. Of David.

¹ Hear my cry, O God; *

listen to my prayer.

² **From the end of the earth I call to you, when my heart is faint.** *

Lead me to the rock that is higher than I;

³ **for you are my refuge,** *

a strong tower against the enemy.

⁴ Let me abide in your tent forever, *

find refuge under the shelter of your wings.   *Selah*

⁵ **For you, O God, have heard my vows;** *

you have given me the heritage of those who fear your name.

⁶ Prolong the life of the king; *

may his years endure to all generations!

⁷ May he be enthroned forever before God; *

appoint steadfast love and faithfulness to watch over him!

⁸ **So I will always sing praises to your name,** *

as I pay my vows day after day.

Loving God, you hear your peoples' cry.
We turn to you for understanding, comfort, and help.
We praise and thank you for your wisdom, your strength, and your unfailing love,
made ours through Jesus Christ our Lord. **Amen.**

Psalm 61 expresses prayers for God's protection (vv. 1-3) and for blessings on the king (vv. 6-7), as well as confident trust in the protecting power of God (vv. 4-5). The expression of trust is particularly compelling, describing God as a crag, a refuge, a tower, a place of refuge, an attentive listener, and a generous provider—a remarkable multiplicity of images in the space of only a few verses. The prayer also conveys that even when we experience distance from God ("from the ends of the earth") we can be led to a place of refuge near to God. The prayer for the king can feel like an abrupt interruption to modern readers, but, given the king's representative role, the prayer is really a way of praying for both the peace and moral integrity of the entire nation. Christian appropriation of the psalm hinges in large measure on how this reference to the king is interpreted. *Use in Worship: a contemporary prayer for the peace and moral integrity of those in authority (a way of identifying with the people of Israel); a prayer for the coming of Christ's kingdom.*

For an additional setting of Ps. 61 see 60A.

Listen to My Cry, Lord

1 Lis - ten to my cry, LORD; hear my hum - ble prayer.
2 From the earth's far cor - ners you will hear my cry.
3 You are my pro - tec - tion when my foes ap - pear;
4 In your tent for - ev - er may my dwell - ing be;

When my soul is trou - bled, keep me in your care.
Set me on your rock, LORD, high - er rock than I.
keep me in your tow - er, safe from ev - ery fear.
with your wings of mer - cy gent - ly shel - ter me.

5 All my cries you've answered,
kept me safe from shame.
I am richly blest with
those who fear your name.

6 Bless with life forever
your anointed king.
Through the generations
may he always reign.

7 May your love and mercy
keep him all his days.
Then with joy forever
I will sing your praise.

Words: Henrietta Ten Harmsel, 1985, © 1987 Faith Alive Christian Resources
Music (WEM IN LEIDENSTAGEN 6.5.6.5): F. Filitz, 1847, P.D.

61B Saranam, Saranam

Tamil Sa-ra-nam, sa-ra-nam, sa-ra-nam. Ye - su raa - ja - nin thi - ru -
English Sa-ra-nam, sa-ra-nam, sa-ra-nam. Je - sus, Sav - ior, Lord, now to

ve - di - ku. Sa-ra-nam, sa-ra-nam, sa-ra-nam. Aath - me naa - dhe-
you   I come. Sa-ra-nam, sa-ra-nam, sa-ra-nam. You're my Rock, my

rin ma - le - re - di - ku. Sa-ra-nam, sa-ra-nam, sa-ra-nam. Paar
ref-uge, my heaven - ly home. Sa-ra-nam, sa-ra-nam, sa-ra-nam.

pot - trum thuu - ye thuu-ye dhee - va - nee me - i raa - jaa - vee

1 From the earth wher-ev - er I may be, out of des - per - a - tion
2 In your heart give me a hid - ing place, and be-neath your wings let
3 Then with joy to you my vows I'll pay, and give thanks for all your
4 Glo - ry to the Fa-ther and the Son, with the Ho - ly Spir - it

yeng - gell - naa - dhe-nee. Ba-yem nii - kum thun-nei yaa - vum aa - ni - ree.

and through a - go - ny, I cry in help-less-ness—O an-swer me.
me find shel-tering grace; O let me see the sun-shine of your face.
mer - cy ev - ery day. I'll hum - bly fol - low in your per-fect way.
ev - er Three - in - One; we'll sing in heav - en prais - es here be-gun.

Saranam means 'I take refuge.'

Words: D.T. Niles, rev. © 1990, 2000 Christian Conference of Asia, admin. GIA Publications, Inc.
Music (PUNJABI): Punjabi melody; arr. Geoff Weaver © 1995 Geoff Weaver, admin. The Jubilate Group/
Hope Publishing Company

61C Lord, Listen to My Cry

1 Lord, lis-ten to my cry, this faint yet ur-gent plea,
2 My Ref-uge and my Tower from foes on ev-ery side,
3 You know that all my vows were made for you to hear;

and guide me home-ward to a place of real se-cu-ri-ty.
the shel-ter you a-lone can give is where I long to hide.
the her-i-tage you gave to me is built on god-ly fear.

Ho-san-na! Ho-san-na! Lord, lis-ten to my plea.
Ho-san-na! Ho-san-na! In you I long to hide.
Ho-san-na! Ho-san-na! I bow in god-ly fear.

4 Protect your servant's life within your timeless care,
and may your perfect love become the crown and shield I bear.
Hosanna! Hosanna! Protect me in your care.

5 For then my heart's delight shall be to sing your praise:
my pledge to honor you will be my focus all my days.
Hosanna! Hosanna! I live to sing your praise.

Guitar chords do not correspond with keyboard harmony.

Hosanna is at the same time a cry for salvation ('save us now') and an expression of praise.

Words: Martin Leckebusch © 2002 Kevin Mayhew Ltd.
Music (VINEYARD HAVEN 6.6.8.6 with refrain): Richard Dirksen, 1974, © 1974, 1987 Harold Flammer, a division of Shawnee Press, Inc.; arr. © 2011 Harold Flammer, a division of Shawnee Press, Inc., reprinted by permission of Hal Leonard Corporation

Psalm 62

To the leader: according to Jeduthun. A Psalm of David.

1 For God alone my soul waits in silence; *
    from him comes my salvation.

2 **He alone is my rock and my salvation, ***
    my fortress; I shall never be shaken.

3 How long will you assail a person, *
    will you batter your victim, all of you,
    as you would a leaning wall, a tottering fence?

4 Their only plan is to bring down a person of prominence. *
    They take pleasure in falsehood;
    they bless with their mouths, but inwardly they curse.   *Selah*

5 **For God alone my soul waits in silence, ***
    for my hope is from him.

6 **He alone is my rock and my salvation, ***
    my fortress; I shall not be shaken.

7 **On God rests my deliverance and my honor; ***
    my mighty rock, my refuge is in God.

8 Trust in him at all times, O people; *
    pour out your heart before him; God is a refuge for us.   *Selah*

9 Those of low estate are but a breath, those of high estate are a delusion; *
    in the balances they go up; they are together lighter than a breath.

10 Put no confidence in extortion, and set no vain hopes on robbery; *
    if riches increase, do not set your heart on them.

11 **Once God has spoken; twice have I heard this: ***
    that power belongs to God,

12 **and steadfast love belongs to you, O Lord. ***
    For you repay to all according to their work.

God of strength and peace,
sometimes the enemies who surround us threaten everything we know and love.
But you are closer than any evil and more powerful than any threat.
Help us live today in that joy, and rest tonight in that peace.
We pray in Jesus' name. **Amen.**

Psalm 62 is a psalm of trust in God offered in the context of human relationships poisoned by attacks (v. 3), deceit (v. 4), and extortion (v. 10), as well as awareness of the brevity and fleetingness of life (v. 9). It echoes the call of Ps. 1 to choose wisdom in the face of folly. The pronouncement that God is both great and good (v. 11) has long been a central, balancing claim for Jewish and Christian theology. The psalm's call to "be still" (vv. 1, 5) is a call to poise in the midst of anxiety and a posture in which God's comforting word can be heard (v. 11). *Use in Worship: as an act of praise or testimony; services focusing on broken human relationships and obedience to the eighth and ninth commandments.*

62A In Silence My Soul Thirsts

1 In si - lence my soul thirsts for God;
(2 In) still - ness I pour out my fears,
(3 In) qui - et - ness my Lord con - ferred

for God a - lone I wait. My
the sol - i - tude builds trust. My
two truths I now de - clare: No

en - e - mies may chase me down, love shields me
ref - uge rests in God's great grace, my anx - ious
great - er love than God's is known, no pow - er

from their hate.
thoughts are hushed.
can com - pare. God is my rock,

God is my strength, God is my sal - va - tion, my ref - uge, my a - bid - ing peace.

I shall not be shak - en.

2 In
3 In

Words: Sheldon W. Sorge and Tammy Wiens © 2000 Sheldon W. Sorge
Music: Sheldon W. Sorge © 2000 Sheldon W. Sorge

My Soul Finds Rest in God Alone

1 My soul finds rest in God a-lone, my rock and my sal-va-tion;
(2 Find) rest my soul in God a-lone a-mid the world's temp-ta-tions;
(3 I'll) set my gaze on God a-lone and trust in him com-plete-ly;

a for-tress strong a-gainst my foes, and I will not be
when e-vil seeks to take a hold I'll cling to my sal-
with ev-ery day pour out my soul and he will prove his

shak-en. Though lips may bless and hearts may curse, and
va-tion. Though rich-es come and rich-es go, don't
mer-cy. Though life is but a fleet-ing breath, a

lies like ar-rows pierce me, I'll fix my heart on
set your heart up-on them; the fields of hope in
sigh too brief to mea-sure, my King has crushed the

right - eous - ness, I'll look to him who hears me.
which I sow are har - ves - ted in heav - en.
curse of death and I am his for - ev - er.

Refrain

O praise him, hal - le - lu - jah, my de - light and my re - ward;

ev - er - last - ing, nev - er fail - ing, my Re - deem - er, my

God.

2 Find
3 I'll

Words: Psalm 62:1-2, 4-8, 10, 12; Galatians 3:13
Music: Aaron Keyes and Stuart Townend © 2007 ThankYou Music, admin. worshiptogether.com songs/EMI
CMG Publishing, excl. UK and Europe, admin. Kingsway Music/www.kingswaysongs.com

62C My Soul Finds Rest in God Alone

1 My soul finds rest in God a-lone; on him my help de-pends.
2 Find rest, my soul, in God a-lone; on him my hope de-pends.
3 The great of earth are less than dust; all mor-tal strength is vain.

God is my for-tress and my rock; sal-va-tion sure he sends.
God is my for-tress and my rock; sal-va-tion sure he sends.
And fools a-lone re-ly on wealth or prize ill-got-ten gain.

My foes con-spire to bring me down; they scorn my trou-bled state.
My aid and hon-or come from God, my ref-uge strong and sure.
I know, O God, that you are strong, a faith-ful, lov-ing Lord.

Their lips are quick to sound my praise, but in their hearts they hate.
Let all God's ser-vants trust the LORD; in him we are se-cure.
Our ev-ery deed, for good or ill, you sure-ly will re-ward.

Alternate tune: RESIGNATION, p. 130.

Words: David J. Diephouse, 1986, © 1987 Faith Alive Christian Resources
Music (THIRD MODE MELODY 8.6.8.6 D): Thomas Tallis, 1561, P.D.

Psalm 62:5-12 | A Responsorial Setting **62D**

Refrain

In God a-lone my soul can find rest and peace, in God my peace and joy. On-ly in God my soul can find its rest, find its rest and peace.

Refrain

5 For God alone I wait in silence;
  truly my hope is in God.

6 God alone is my rock and my salvation,
  my stronghold, so that I shall never be shaken. *Refrain*

7 In God is my deliverance and my honor;
  God is my strong rock and my refuge.

8 Put your trust in God always, O people,
  pour out your hearts before the one who is our refuge. *Refrain*

9 Those of high degree are but a fleeting breath;
  those of low estate cannot be trusted.
    Placed on the scales together they weigh even less than a breath.

10 Put no trust in extortion; in robbery take no empty pride;
  though wealth increase, set not your heart upon it.

11 God has spoken once, twice have I heard it,
  that power belongs to God.

12 Steadfast love belongs to you, O Lord,
  for you repay all according to their deeds. *Refrain*

(continues)

Tone

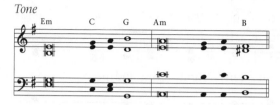

Lectionary: Ordinary Time after Epiphany (B).

Words: Psalm 62:1
Music: Jacques Berthier (1923-1994) © 1998 Ateliers et Presses de Taizé, Taizé Community, France, GIA Publications, Inc., exclusive North American agent
Psalm Text: from *Evangelical Lutheran Worship* © 2006 Evangelical Lutheran Church in America, admin. Augsburg Fortress Publishers
Tone: © 2011 Faith Alive Christian Resources

Psalm 63

A Psalm of David, when he was in the Wilderness of Judah.

1 O God, you are my God, I seek you, my soul thirsts for you; *
    my flesh faints for you, as in a dry and weary land where there is no water.

2 So I have looked upon you in the sanctuary, *
    beholding your power and glory.

3 **Because your steadfast love is better than life,** *
    my lips will praise you.

4 **So I will bless you as long as I live;** *
    I will lift up my hands and call on your name.

5 My soul is satisfied as with a rich feast, *
    and my mouth praises you with joyful lips

6 when I think of you on my bed, *
    and meditate on you in the watches of the night;

7 **for you have been my help,** *
    and in the shadow of your wings I sing for joy.

8 **My soul clings to you;** *
    your right hand upholds me.

9 But those who seek to destroy my life *
    shall go down into the depths of the earth;

10 they shall be given over to the power of the sword, *
    they shall be prey for jackals.

11 **But the king shall rejoice in God;** *
    all who swear by him shall exult,
    for the mouths of liars will be stopped.

God our Redeemer, you greet us each morning, protect us each night,
and constantly reveal your justice and mercy.
Saturate us with a desire for your presence
and then overwhelm us with the assurance of your love,
so that we can say with the apostle Paul
that "to live is Christ and to die is gain"—and mean it.
Hear us in Jesus' name. **Amen.**

Psalm 63, like Ps. 42, begins with a statement of profound longing for God. In contrast to Ps. 42, it continues with a testimony that this longing has been satisfied with a profound vision of God (vv. 2-8). It concludes with expressions of confidence in divine deliverance (vv. 9-11). *Use in Worship: morning prayer liturgies (especially v. 6 and the vow to praise in v. 3).*

Psalm 63:1-8 | A Responsorial Setting 63A

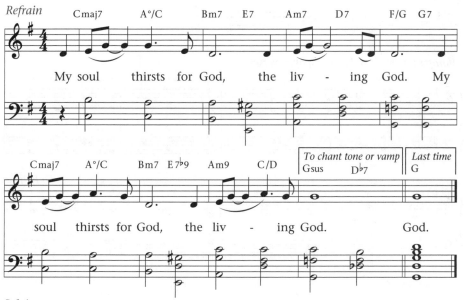

Refrain

My soul thirsts for God, the liv - ing God. My

soul thirsts for God, the liv - ing God. God.

Refrain

1. O God, you are my God; eagerly I seek you;

    my soul thirsts for you, my flesh faints for you,

    as in a dry and weary land where there is no water.

2. Therefore I have gazed upon you in your holy place,

    that I might behold your power and your glory.

3. For your steadfast love is better than life itself;

    my lips shall give you praise. *Refrain*

(continues)

4 So will I bless you as long as I live
and lift up my hands in your name.
5 My spirit is content, as with the richest of foods,
and my mouth praises you with joyful lips,
6 when I remember you upon my bed,
and meditate on you in the night watches. *Refrain*
7 For you have been my helper,
and under the shadow of your wings I will rejoice.
8 My whole being clings to you;
your right hand holds me fast. *Refrain*

Tone

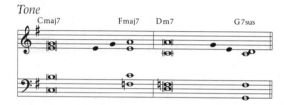

Vamp may be played under spoken verses

Lectionary: Lent (C).

Words: Psalm 63
Music: Daniel Richardson and Angel Napieralski © 2010 Daniel Richardson and Angel Napieralski, admin.
Faith Alive Christian Resources
Psalm Text: from *Evangelical Lutheran Worship* © 2006 Evangelical Lutheran Church in America, admin.
Augsburg Fortress Publishers
Tone: © 2011 Faith Alive Christian Resources

O God, You Are My God Alone

63B

Alternate tune: RESIGNATION, p. 130.

Words: The Iona Community © 1993 Wild Goose Resource Group, Iona Community, Scotland, GIA
Publications, Inc., exclusive North American agent
Music (GRATUS 8.6.8.6 D): Mary Kay Beall © 1991 Hope Publishing Company

Psalm 64

To the leader. A Psalm of David.

¹ Hear my voice, O God, in my complaint; *
   preserve my life from the dread enemy.

² **Hide me from the secret plots of the wicked, ***
   from the scheming of evildoers,

³ **who whet their tongues like swords, ***
   who aim bitter words like arrows,

⁴ **shooting from ambush at the blameless; ***
   they shoot suddenly and without fear.

⁵ They hold fast to their evil purpose; *
   they talk of laying snares secretly, thinking, "Who can see us?

⁶ Who can search out our crimes?
   We have thought out a cunningly conceived plot." *
   For the human heart and mind are deep.

⁷ **But God will shoot his arrow at them; ***
   they will be wounded suddenly.

⁸ **Because of their tongue he will bring them to ruin; ***
   all who see them will shake with horror.

⁹ Then everyone will fear; *
   they will tell what God has brought about, and ponder what he has done.

¹⁰ **Let the righteous rejoice in the Lord and take refuge in him. ***
   Let all the upright in heart glory.

Victorious God,
when we are ambushed by evil, when we feel overwhelmed by our enemies,
come and break into the darkest places of our lives
with the dazzling light of your hope and the unshakable promise of your love.
Inspire us with the power of your Spirit so we will follow wherever you may lead. **Amen.**

Psalm 64 is a prayer for deliverance in the face of threat from enemies. It is notable for its memorable reflection on the cunning and deceitful ways of human beings (vv. 3-6) and the ultimate self-destruction that evil plots cause. The psalm concludes with a remarkable statement of trust, not only in God's deliverance from enemies (vv. 7-8) but also about the coming universality of obedience to God (vv. 9-10). *Use in Worship: in conjunction with testimonies about God's deliverance; a call to repentance in Lent or other seasons.*

Hear Us, O Lord,
As We Voice Our Laments

1 Hear us, O Lord, as we voice our la - ments;
2 Heal those who have been pierced by wick - ed lies;
3 Un - do the plans that wick - ed ones de - vise;

help the op - pressed and be their sure de - fense;
shield them from e - vil lurk - ing in dis - guise,
let all their schem - ing bring their own de - mise;

guard them from plots of schem - ing en - e - mies;
and from op - pres - sors think - ing "No one sees;"
then with great fear all peo - ples will a - gree:

be a strong ref - uge for all ref - u - gees.
be a strong ref - uge for all ref - u - gees.
God is a ref - uge for all ref - u - gees.

Words: David Landegent © 2010 David Landegent
Music (LANGRAN 10.10.10.10): James Langran, 1861, P.D.

64B Better Take Shelter

Refrain

Hear me, O God, hear my shout!
Hear me out as I cry my complaint.
Hear me, hide me, rescue me
From the fear of my dread enemy.

Foes surround me, weaving their plots,
They're all around me, whetting their tongues.
Wielding their words, sharp as swords,
Keen as knives, conniving, I'm crying: *Refrain*

Fearless, shameless, from ambush they shoot,
Sudden as arrows, their cutting words fly.
From hiding they watch the innocent fall,
Blameless all, wounded and dying.

The Holy One? Far from their thoughts!
Scheming in secret, trading in hatred,
Hating the sacred, hate is their trademark.
They work the dark of the human heart.   *Refrain*

But look! A sudden arrow finds them out.
God's aim is true, straight to the heart.
Sharp tongues can't defend them;
Their own words condemn them.

Eye witnesses stand rooted to the spot,
Shaken to the core, shaking in horror.
Seeing that face unveiled: evil revealed.
Ponder what God has done, and wonder. *Refrain*

Tone

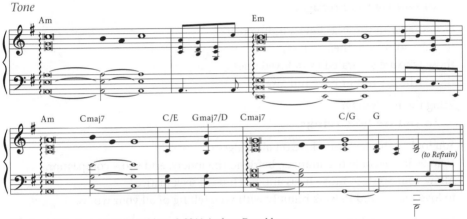

Words and Music: Andrew Donaldson © 2011 Andrew Donaldson
Text: Andrew Donaldson © 2011 Andrew Donaldson
Tone: Andrew Donaldson © 2011 Andrew Donaldson

64C A Prayer for Refugees

The litany may begin with the reading, chanting, or singing of Psalm 64.

Hear us, Lord, as we raise our voices;
> **in you we take refuge.**

Preserve those whose life is threatened by enemies
and who are the target of bitter words or evil schemes.
Remember those who are vulnerable and exposed,
those who are victims of natural disaster, war, and persecution,
those suffering anguish and sorrow.

Bring them to safety;
> **in you we take refuge.**

Give shelter to those seeking a hiding place,
to those torn from their homes,
those who are separated from loved ones,
those who are lost or have run away.

Bring them to safety;
> **in you we take refuge.**

You look with mercy and love on all refugees.
Help us to welcome the stranger, befriend the lonely, and show compassion.
Allow your Spirit to move in us and teach us to seek justice,
to love mercy, and to walk humbly with you, telling of all your works.

Let us rejoice and give praise;
> **in you we take refuge.**

Psalm 65

To the leader. A Psalm of David. A Song.

1 Praise is due to you, O God, in Zion; *
     and to you shall vows be performed,

2 **O you who answer prayer! ***
   To you all flesh shall come.

3 When deeds of iniquity overwhelm us, *
     you forgive our transgressions.

4 **Happy are those whom you choose**
   and bring near to live in your courts. *
       We shall be satisfied with the goodness of your house,
       your holy temple.

5 **By awesome deeds you answer us with deliverance,**
   O God of our salvation; *
       you are the hope of all the ends of the earth
       and of the farthest seas.

6 By your strength you established the mountains; *
     you are girded with might.

7 You silence the roaring of the seas, *
     the roaring of their waves, the tumult of the peoples.

8 **Those who live at earth's farthest bounds are awed by your signs; ***
   you make the gateways of the morning
   and the evening shout for joy.

9 You visit the earth and water it, you greatly enrich it;
   the river of God is full of water; *
       you provide the people with grain, for so you have prepared it.

10 You water its furrows abundantly, settling its ridges, *
      softening it with showers, and blessing its growth.

11 You crown the year with your bounty; *
      your wagon tracks overflow with richness.

12 **The pastures of the wilderness overflow, ***
    the hills gird themselves with joy,

13 **the meadows clothe themselves with flocks,**
    the valleys deck themselves with grain, *
        they shout and sing together for joy.   (continues)

Author of all beauty, source of all wonder,
you make the mountains sing for joy and the trees clap their hands with glee.
Inspire us to join with all creation in jubilant praise and thanksgiving
through our Lord Jesus Christ, in whom and through whom all things have their being.
Amen.

Psalm 65 is a psalm of praise and thanksgiving, celebrating God's reception of human prayers (v. 2), forgiveness of sin (v. 3), call to the people of Israel (v. 4), power in the marvels of creation (vv. 6-8), and faithfulness in the fruits of harvest (vv. 9-13). The psalm is noteworthy for celebrating the praise of God offered in Jerusalem (vv. 1, 4) and in faraway places (v. 8). *Use in Worship: traditionally sung on Thanksgiving Day or other harvest festivals (lavish references to God's provisions of crops in vv. 9-13); a response to assurance of God's pardon (see v. 3).*

65A The Earth Is Yours, O God

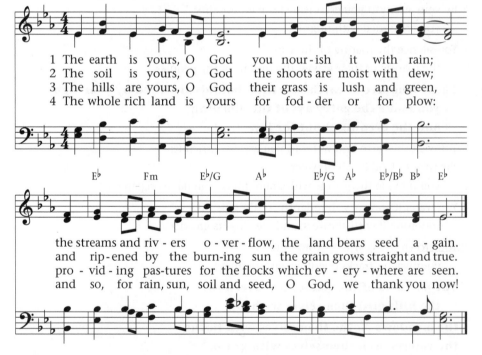

1 The earth is yours, O God
2 The soil is yours, O God
3 The hills are yours, O God
4 The whole rich land is yours

you nour-ish it with rain;
the shoots are moist with dew;
their grass is lush and green,
for fod-der or for plow:

the streams and riv-ers o-ver-flow, the land bears seed a-gain.
and rip-ened by the burn-ing sun the grain grows straight and true.
pro-vid-ing pas-tures for the flocks which ev-ery-where are seen.
and so, for rain, sun, soil and seed, O God, we thank you now!

Guitar chords do not correspond with keyboard harmony.

Words: Michael Saward © 1982 The Jubilate Group, admin. Hope Publishing Company
Music (CARLISLE 6.6.8.6): Charles Lockhart (1745-1815), 1769, P.D.

Praise Is Your Right, O God, in Zion 65B

1 Praise is your right, O God, in Zi - on. To you we
2 Your might - y acts work our sal - va - tion. All earth waits
3 You bless the earth with streams and riv - ers and with the

pay our vows. When we your peo - ple pray, you hear us.
hope - ful - ly. You have the strength to make the moun - tains,
gen - tle rain. You set - tle ridg - es, soft - en fur - rows,

All flesh to you will bow. When our trans - gres - sions o - ver -
to calm the storm - y sea. You calm the tu - mult of the
and bless the sprout - ing grain. You crown the year with am - ple

whelm us, you gra - cious - ly for - give. How sat - is - fied your
peo - ple. Such awe - some signs you do that earth, from sun - rise
har - vest; a rich a - bun - dance springs. All flocks and grains and

cho - sen ser - vants; with - in your courts they live.
to the sun - set, for joy cries out to you.
hills and mead - ows— yes, all cre - a - tion sings.

Guitar chords do not correspond with keyboard harmony.

Words: Stanley Wiersma (1930-1986), 1980, © 1987 Faith Alive Christian Resources
Music (GENEVAN 65 | 9.6.9.6 D): *Genevan Psalter*, 1543; harm. Dale Grotenhuis, 1985, © 1987 Faith Alive
Christian Resources

65C Psalm 65 | A Responsorial Setting

Refrain

1 You are to be praised, O God, in Zion;
    to you shall vows be fulfilled.

2 To you, the one who answers prayer,
    to you all flesh shall come.

3 Our sins are stronger than we are,
    but you blot out our transgressions.

4 Happy are they whom you choose and draw to your courts to dwell there!
    They will be satisfied by the beauty of your house,
    by the holiness of your temple.   *Refrain*

5 Awesome things will you show us in your righteousness, O God of our salvation,
    O hope of all the ends of the earth and of oceans far away.

6 You make firm the mountains by your power;
    you are girded about with might.

7 You still the roaring of the seas,
    the roaring of their waves, and the clamor of the peoples.

8 Those who dwell at the ends of the earth will tremble at your marvelous signs;
    you make the dawn and the dusk to sing for joy.   *Refrain*

9 You visit the earth and water it abundantly; you make it very plenteous;
    the river of God is full of water.
    You prepare the grain, for so you provide for the earth.

10 You drench the furrows and smooth out the ridges;
    with heavy rain you soften the ground and bless its increase.

11 You crown the year with your goodness,
    and your paths overflow with plenty.

12 May the fields of the wilderness be rich for grazing,
    and the hills be clothed with joy.

13 May the meadows cover themselves with flocks,
    and the valleys cloak themselves with grain;
    let them shout for joy and sing.   *Refrain*

Tone

Lectionary: Ordinary Time after Pentecost (A,C); Thanksgiving Day (A).

Words: Psalm 65
Music: Ray Makeever from *Psalter for Worship, Year C* © 2006 Augsburg Fortress Publishers
Psalm Text: from *Evangelical Lutheran Worship* © 2006 Evangelical Lutheran Church in America, admin.
Augsburg Fortress Publishers
Tone: from *Psalter for Worship, Year C* © 2006 Augsburg Fortress Publishers

Alternate Refrain

Alternate Tone

Words: Jorge A. Lockward (b. 1965) © 1996, 2000 Abingdon Press, admin. The Copyright Company
Music (LOCKWARD): Jorge A. Lockward (b. 1965) © 1996, 2000 Abingdon Press, admin. The Copyright
Company
Tone: © 2011 Faith Alive Christian Resources

65D Glory and Praise to Our God

Refrain

Glo-ry and praise to our God, who a-lone gives light to our days.

Man - y are the bless-ings he bears to those who trust in his

ways.

1 We, the daugh-ters and sons of God who
2 In his wis - dom he strength-ens us, like
3 Ev - ery mo - ment of ev - ery day our

built the val-leys and plains, praise the won-ders our
sil - ver test - ed in fire. Though the pow - er of
God is wait-ing to save, al - ways read - y to

To Refrain

God has done in ev - ery heart that sings.
sin as - sails, our God is there to save.
seek the lost, to an - swer those who pray.

4 God has wa - tered our bar - ren land and spent his mer - ci - ful rain. Now the riv - ers of life run full for an - y - one to drink.

To Refrain

Words: Daniel L. Schutte (b. 1947), based on Pss. 65 and 66 © 1976, 1979 Daniel L. Schutte, admin. OCP Publications
Music: Daniel L. Schutte (b. 1947) © 1976, 1979 Daniel L. Schutte, admin. OCP Publications

65E Every Heart Its Tribute Pays

1 Ev-ery heart its trib-ute pays, ev-ery tongue its song of praise;
2 Ev-er while his deeds en-dure our sal-va-tion stands se-cure;
3 Year by year, the sea-sons 'round sees the land with bless-ing crowned,

sin and sor-row, guilt and care, brought to him who an-swers prayer;
he whose fin-gers spun the earth, gave the seas and moun-tains birth,
where ca-ressed by sun and rain bar-ren earth gives life a-gain;

there by grace may hu-man-kind full and free for-give-ness find;
tamed the o-cean, formed the land, spread the skies with might-y hand:
sun-lit val-leys burn with gold, na-ture smiles on field and fold,

called and cho-sen, loved and blest, in his pres-ence be at rest.
far-off shores re-vere his Name, day and night his power pro-claim.
gifts of God in plen-ty poured: all things liv-ing, praise the Lord!

Words: Timothy Dudley-Smith (b. 1926) © 1984 Hope Publishing Company
Music (ST. GEORGE'S WINDSOR 7.7.7.7 D): George J. Elvey, 1858, P.D.

Psalm 66

To the leader. A Song. A Psalm.

1 Make a joyful noise to God, all the earth; *

    2 sing the glory of his name; give to him glorious praise.

3 **Say to God, "How awesome are your deeds! ***

    Because of your great power, your enemies cringe before you.

4 **All the earth worships you; ***

    they sing praises to you, sing praises to your name." *Selah*

5 **Come and see what God has done: ***

    he is awesome in his deeds among mortals.

6 He turned the sea into dry land; *

    they passed through the river on foot.

  There we rejoiced in him,

7 who rules by his might forever, *

    whose eyes keep watch on the nations—

    let the rebellious not exalt themselves. *Selah*

8 **Bless our God, O peoples, ***

    let the sound of his praise be heard,

9 **who has kept us among the living, ***

    and has not let our feet slip.

10 For you, O God, have tested us; *

    you have tried us as silver is tried.

11 You brought us into the net; *

    you laid burdens on our backs;

12 you let people ride over our heads; *

    we went through fire and through water;

    yet you have brought us out to a spacious place.

13 **I will come into your house with burnt offerings; ***

    I will pay you my vows,

14 **those that my lips uttered ***

    and my mouth promised when I was in trouble.

15 I will offer to you burnt offerings of fatlings,

  with the smoke of the sacrifice of rams; *

    I will make an offering of bulls and goats. *Selah*

16 **Come and hear, all you who fear God, ***

    and I will tell what he has done for me. (continues)

Psalm 66 (continued)

¹⁷ I cried aloud to him, *

 and he was extolled with my tongue.

¹⁸ If I had cherished iniquity in my heart, *

 the Lord would not have listened.

¹⁹ **But truly God has listened; ***

 he has given heed to the words of my prayer.

²⁰ **Blessed be God, because he has not rejected my prayer ***

 or removed his steadfast love from me.

God of life and transformation,
you have broken into the deathly silence of our sin
and restored your song of life and triumph.
By the power of your Spirit, inspire us to shout your praise with joy
and to tell of the wonderful things you have done, through Jesus Christ our Lord. **Amen.**

Psalm 66, a grand hymn of praise and thanksgiving, is noteworthy for linking praise for God's greatness and goodness to thanksgiving for particular occasions of God's deliverance and concern. It also links the praise offered by the community (vv. 1-12) with that offered by an individual (vv. 13-20), depicting God as the one who both provides deliverance for the people of Israel (vv. 6-7) and listens to an individual's prayer (vv. 19-20). Note how the psalm alternates between addressing the community (vv. 1-2, 5-9, 16-20) and addressing God (vv. 3-4, 10-15). *Use in Worship: an expression of praise for any occasion.*

For an additional setting of Ps. 66 see 65D.

66A Cry Out to God in Joy

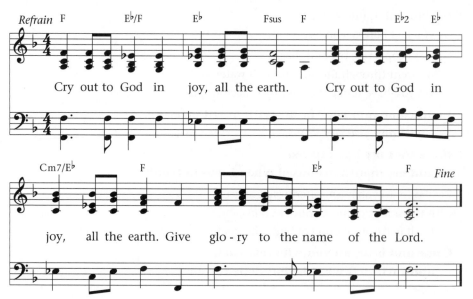

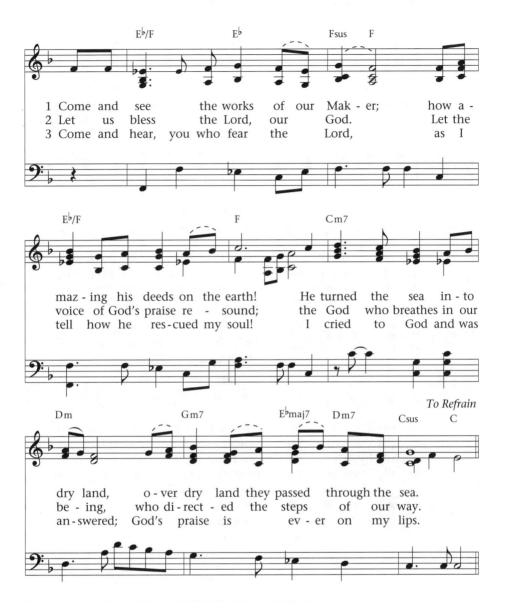

1 Come and see the works of our Mak - er; how a -
2 Let us bless the Lord, our God. Let the
3 Come and hear, you who fear the Lord, as I

maz - ing his deeds on the earth! He turned the sea in - to
voice of God's praise re - sound; the God who breathes in our
tell how he res - cued my soul! I cried to God and was

dry land, o - ver dry land they passed through the sea.
be - ing, who di - rect - ed the steps of our way.
an - swered; God's praise is ev - er on my lips.

To Refrain

Words and Music: Steven C. Warner © 2006 World Library Publications

Come, All You People

Shona U - ya - i mo - se, ti - na - ma - te Mwa - ri;
English 1 Come, all you peo - ple, come and praise your Mak - er;
2 Come, all you peo - ple, come and praise the Sav - ior;
3 Come, all you peo - ple, come and praise the Spir - it;

u - ya - i mo - se, ti - na - ma - te Mwa - ri;
come, all you peo - ple, come and praise your Mak - er;
come, all you peo - ple, come and praise the Sav - ior;
come, all you peo - ple, come and praise the Spir - it;

u - ya - i mo - se, ti - na - ma - te Mwa - ri;
come, all you peo - ple, come and praise your Mak - er;
come, all you peo - ple, come and praise the Sav - ior;
come, all you peo - ple, come and praise the Spir - it;

u - ya - i mo - se Zvi - no.
come now and wor - ship the Lord.
come now and wor - ship the Lord.
come now and wor - ship the Lord.

Words: st. 1 Alexander Gondo (20th c., Zimbabwe); tr. I-to Loh (b. 1936) © 1986 World Council of Churches; sts. 2-3 from *With One Voice*, 1995, © Augsburg Fortress Publishers
Music (UYAI MOSE 5.6.5.6.5.6.7): Alexander Gondo © 1986 World Council of Churches; arr. John L. Bell (b. 1949) © 1993 Wild Goose Resource Group, Iona Community, Scotland, GIA Publications, Inc., exclusive North American agent

Come, All You People, Praise Our God 66C

1 Come, all you peo - ple, praise our God and tell his glo - rious
2 We come with of - ferings to God's house, and here we pay the
3 Come, lis - ten, all who fear the Lord, while I with grate - ful

works a - broad, who holds our souls in life; who
sol - emn vows we ut - tered in dis - tress; to
heart re - cord what God has done for me; I

nev - er lets our feet be moved and, though our faith has
him our all we ded - i - cate, to him we whol - ly
cried to him in deep dis - tress, and now his won - drous

of - ten proved, up - holds us in the strife.
con - se - crate the lives his mer - cies bless.
grace I bless, for he has set me free.

Words: *Psalter*, 1912, P.D.
Music (ADOWA 8.8.6 D): Charles H. Gabriel (1856-1932), P.D.

66D Psalm 66 | A Responsorial Setting

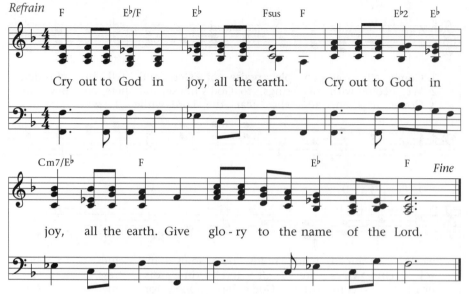

Refrain

Cry out to God in joy, all the earth. Cry out to God in joy, all the earth. Give glo-ry to the name of the Lord.

Refrain

1 Be joyful in God, all you lands;
   be joyful, all the earth.

2 Sing the glory of God's name;
   sing the glory of God's praise.

3 Say to God, "How awesome are your deeds!
   Because of your great strength your enemies cringe before you.

4 All the earth bows down before you,
   sings to you, sings out your name."   *Refrain*

5 Come now and see the works of God,
   how awesome are God's deeds toward all people.

6 God turned the sea into dry land, so that they went through the water on foot,
   and there we rejoiced in God.

7 Ruling forever in might, God keeps watch over the nations;
   let no rebels exalt themselves.   *Refrain*

8 Bless our God, you peoples;
   let the sound of praise be heard.

9 Our God has kept us among the living
   and has not allowed our feet to slip.

10 For you, O God, have tested us;
   you have tried us just as silver is tried.

11 You brought us into the net;
   you laid heavy burdens upon our backs.

[12] You let people ride over our heads; we went through fire and water,

but you brought us out into a place of refreshment. *Refrain*

[13] I will enter your house with burnt offerings

and will pay you my vows—

[14] those that I promised with my lips

and spoke with my mouth when I was in trouble.

[15] I will offer you burnt offerings of fatlings with the smoke of rams;

I will give you oxen and goats.

[16] Come and listen, all you who believe,

and I will tell you what God has done for me. *Refrain*

[17] I called out to God with my mouth,

and praised the Lord with my tongue.

[18] If I had cherished evil in my heart,

the Lord would not have heard me;

[19] but in truth God has heard me

and has attended to the sound of my prayer.

[20] Blessed be God, who has not rejected my prayer,

nor withheld unfailing love from me. *Refrain*

Tone

Lectionary: vv. 1-9 Ordinary Time after Pentecost (C); vv. 1-12 Ordinary Time after Pentecost (C); vv. 8-20 Eastertide (A).

Words and Music: Steven C. Warner © 2006 World Library Publications
Psalm Text: from *Evangelical Lutheran Worship* © 2006 Evangelical Lutheran Church in America, admin. Augsburg Fortress Publishers
Tone: © 2011 Faith Alive Christian Resources

66E Praise Our God with Shouts of Joy

1 Praise our God with shouts of joy;
  sing the glo - ry of his name:
  join to lift his prais - es high;
  through the world his love pro - claim!

2 Come and see what God has done
  by the power of his right hand;
  see the bat - tles he has won
  by his word of swift com - mand!

3 God has tamed the rag - ing seas,
  carved a high - way through the tide:
  paid the cost of our re - lease,
  come him - self to be our guide.

4 God has put us to the test,
  bringing us through flood and fire
  into freedom, peace and rest,
  for our good is his desire.

5 God has not despised my prayer,
  nor kept back his love from me;
  he has raised me from despair:
  to our God all glory be!

Guitar chords do not correspond with keyboard harmony.

Words: Christopher Idle, 1978, © 1990 The Jubilate Group, admin. Hope Publishing Company
Music (GENEVAN 136 | 7.7.7.7): *Genevan Psalter*, 1562; harm. Claude Goudimel (ca. 1505-1572), 1564, P.D.

Psalm 67

To the leader: with stringed instruments. A Psalm. A Song.

¹ May God be gracious to us and bless us *
    and make his face to shine upon us,   *Selah*

² that your way may be known upon earth, *
    your saving power among all nations.

³ **Let the peoples praise you, O God; ***
    let all the peoples praise you.

⁴ Let the nations be glad and sing for joy, *
    for you judge the peoples with equity
    and guide the nations upon earth.   *Selah*

⁵ **Let the peoples praise you, O God; ***
    let all the peoples praise you.

⁶ The earth has yielded its increase; *
    God, our God, has blessed us.

⁷ **May God continue to bless us; ***
    let all the ends of the earth revere him.

God of all,
may your lavish grace and saving power be known by all people in all places,
so that the world may resound with your praise
as all nations bow before your loving rule made known in Jesus Christ our Lord. **Amen.**

Psalm 67 is a communal expression of desire for God's blessing so that the whole world will come to acknowledge God. The psalm has a chiastic, or mirror, structure: it begins and ends with an expression of desire for God's blessing (vv. 1, 7). This frames an acknowledgement that God is the source of both deliverance and harvest (vv. 2, 6), an expression of desire that all peoples will bless God (vv. 3, 5) with a statement of confession of God's just and sovereign rule at the center (v. 4). The psalm echoes the Aaronic benediction (Num. 6:24-26) but also extends its focus by suggesting that this blessing is for the benefit of the nations. *Use in Worship: preparation for a benediction in worship; services of dedication; thanksgiving for harvest; marriage; services focusing on mission where the psalm might profitably be read in conjunction with the great commission of Matt. 28.*

67A God of Mercy, God of Grace

1 God of mer-cy, God of grace, show the bright-ness
2 Let the peo-ple praise you, Lord; be by all that
3 Let the peo-ple praise you, Lord; earth shall then its

of your face. Shine up - on us, Sav - ior, shine;
live a - dored. Let the na - tions shout and sing
fruits af - ford. Un - to us your bless-ing give;

fill your world with light di - vine; all your sav - ing
glo - ry to their gra - cious King; at your feet their
we to you de - vot - ed live, all be - low and

health ex - tend un - to earth's re - mot - est end.
trib - ute pay, and your ho - ly will o - bey.
all a - bove, one in joy and light and love.

Guitar chords do not correspond with keyboard harmony.

Words: Henry F. Lyte, 1834, alt., P.D.
Music (DIX 7.7.7.7.7.7): Conrad Kocher, 1838; adapt., P.D.

God in Mercy Grant Us Blessing

1 God in mer-cy grant us bless-ing, lift on us your ra-diant face;
2 Let them all with ju-bi-la-tion sing of your tran-scen-dent worth;
3 See the bless-ing God has grant-ed on our la-bors in the field!

may all earth, your ways con-fess-ing, know the power of sav-ing grace:
just-ly rul-ing ev-ery na-tion, sov-ereign Lord of all the earth:
May his word, in hearts im-plant-ed, world-wide har-vests du-ly yield:

let the peo-ple's voic-es raise, Lord, to you their hymns of praise.
let the peo-ple's voic-es raise, Lord, to you their hymns of praise.
so shall all the na-tions raise to our God their hymns of praise.

Guitar chords do not correspond with keyboard harmony.

Words: David G. Preston © The Jubilate Group, admin. Hope Publishing Company
Music (ZEUCH MICH, ZEUCH MICH 8.7.8.7.7.7): *Geistreiches Gesangbuch*, Darmstadt, 1698; adapt. William H. Monk, 1861, P.D.

67C Psalm 67 | A Responsorial Setting

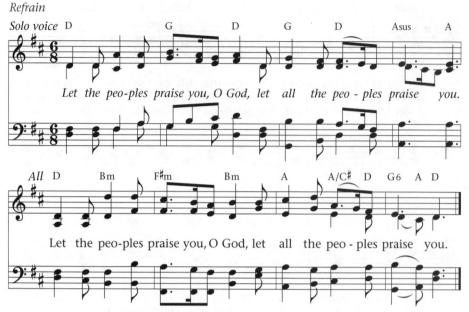

Refrain

Solo voice

Let the peo-ples praise you, O God, let all the peo - ples praise you.

All

Let the peo-ples praise you, O God, let all the peo - ples praise you.

Refrain

¹ May God be merciful to us and bless us;

may the light of God's face shine upon us.

² Let your way be known upon earth,

your saving health among all nations.

³ Let the peoples praise you, O God;

let all the peoples praise you. *Refrain*

⁴ Let the nations be glad and sing for joy,

for you judge the peoples with equity and guide all the nations on earth.

⁵ Let the peoples praise you, O God;

let all the peoples praise you. *Refrain*

⁶ The earth has brought forth its increase;

God, our God, has blessed us.

⁷ May God give us blessing,

and may all the ends of the earth stand in awe. *Refrain*

Tone

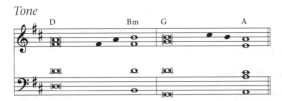

Lectionary: Eastertide (C); Ordinary Time after Pentecost (A).
When chanting the psalm text, the refrain may substitute for v. 3 and v. 5.

Words: Psalm 100 from the *Liturgical Psalter* © 1994 International Committee on English in the Liturgy Corporation
Music: John McCann © 1998, 2011 GIA Publications, Inc.
Psalm Text: from *Evangelical Lutheran Worship* © 2006 Evangelical Lutheran Church in America, admin.
Augsburg Fortress Publishers
Tone: © 2011 Faith Alive Christian Resources

Psalm 68

To the leader. Of David. A Psalm. A Song.

Voice 1:

¹ Let God rise up, let his enemies be scattered; *
    let those who hate him flee before him.

² As smoke is driven away, so drive them away; *
    as wax melts before the fire, let the wicked perish before God.

³ But let the righteous be joyful; let them exult before God; *
    let them be jubilant with joy.

⁴ **Sing to God, sing praises to his name; ***
    lift up a song to him who rides upon the clouds—
    his name is the Lord—be exultant before him.

Voice 2:

⁵ Father of orphans and protector of widows *
    is God in his holy habitation.

⁶ God gives the desolate a home to live in; *
    he leads out the prisoners to prosperity,
    but the rebellious live in a parched land.

⁷ O God, when you went out before your people, *
    when you marched through the wilderness,   *Selah*

⁸ the earth quaked, the heavens poured down rain *
    at the presence of God, the God of Sinai,
    at the presence of God, the God of Israel.

⁹ **Rain in abundance, O God, you showered abroad; ***
    you restored your heritage when it languished;

¹⁰ **your flock found a dwelling in it; ***
    in your goodness, O God, you provided for the needy. (continues)

Voice 1:

¹¹ The Lord gives the command; *
    great is the company of those who bore the tidings:
¹² "The kings of the armies, they flee, they flee!" *
    The women at home divide the spoil,
¹³ though they stay among the sheepfolds— *
    the wings of a dove covered with silver, its pinions with green gold.
¹⁴ When the Almighty scattered kings there, *
    snow fell on Zalmon.
¹⁵ O mighty mountain, mountain of Bashan; *
    O many-peaked mountain, mountain of Bashan!
¹⁶ Why do you look with envy, O many-peaked mountain, *
    at the mount that God desired for his abode,
    where the LORD will reside forever?
¹⁷ With mighty chariotry, twice ten thousand, thousands upon thousands, *
    the Lord came from Sinai into the holy place.
¹⁸ You ascended the high mount,
  leading captives in your train and receiving gifts from people, *
    even from those who rebel against the LORD God's abiding there.
¹⁹ **Blessed be the Lord, who daily bears us up;** *
    God is our salvation.   *Selah*
²⁰ **Our God is a God of salvation,** *
    and to GOD, the Lord, belongs escape from death.

Voice 2:

²¹ But God will shatter the heads of his enemies, *
    the hairy crown of those who walk in their guilty ways.
²² The Lord said, "I will bring them back from Bashan, *
    I will bring them back from the depths of the sea,
²³ so that you may bathe your feet in blood, *
    so that the tongues of your dogs may have their share from the foe."
²⁴ Your solemn processions are seen, O God, *
    the processions of my God, my King, into the sanctuary—
²⁵ the singers in front, the musicians last, *
    between them girls playing tambourines:
²⁶ "Bless God in the great congregation, *
    the LORD, O you who are of Israel's fountain!"

²⁷ There is Benjamin, the least of them, in the lead, *

    the princes of Judah in a body,

    the princes of Zebulun, the princes of Naphtali.

²⁸ **Summon your might, O God;** *

    show your strength, O God, as you have done for us before.

²⁹ **Because of your temple at Jerusalem** *

    kings bear gifts to you.

Voice 1:

³⁰ Rebuke the wild animals that live among the reeds,

    the herd of bulls with the calves of the peoples. *

        Trample under foot those who lust after tribute;

        scatter the peoples who delight in war.

³¹ Let bronze be brought from Egypt; *

    let Ethiopia hasten to stretch out its hands to God.

³² **Sing to God, O kingdoms of the earth;** *

    sing praises to the Lord,   *Selah*

³³ O rider in the heavens, the ancient heavens; *

    listen, he sends out his voice, his mighty voice.

³⁴ **Ascribe power to God, whose majesty is over Israel;** *

    and whose power is in the skies.

³⁵ **Awesome is God in his sanctuary, the God of Israel;** *

    he gives power and strength to his people.

    Blessed be God!

Mighty God, you have delivered us from sin's captivity
and freed us from the powers of death
through Jesus Christ, our risen and ascended Lord.
Inspire now our songs of extravagant praise
until all the world knows that you alone are Savior and Redeemer. **Amen.**

Psalm 68 is a complex and resplendent psalm of praise that focuses on the dynamic and powerful coming of God as warrior. The heart of the psalm is a testimony about God's action in history (vv. 7-23), framed by testimony about God's power and love (vv. 1-3, 5-6), calls to worship God (vv. 4-6, 34), a description of liturgical procession (vv. 24-27), and a prayer for God's continued action (vv. 28-30). It praises God as both powerful warrior (vv. 1, 4, 7, 21) and loving provider for orphans, widows, captives, and the needy (vv. 5-6). The psalm includes imagery that echoes Ezekiel's vision of the wheel (v. 33, see also Deut. 33:25-27) and the praise of God that will come from the corners of the earth (Ps. 87, Isa. 60). Verse 28 is a summary of the logic of much of the Psalter: God's prior actions become the ground and basis for petitions. *Use in Worship: services focusing on God's triumph over evil and the victory over the powers and principalities won through Jesus' death and resurrection.*

68A Approach Our God with Songs of Praise

The refrain and responsive reading may be used as an optional introduction to the singing of "Approach Our God with Songs of Praise"

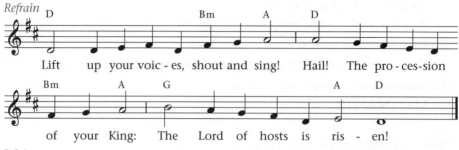

Refrain

Lift up your voic-es, shout and sing! Hail! The pro-ces-sion of your King: The Lord of hosts is ris-en!

Refrain

¹ May God arise, may his enemies be scattered;
  may his foes flee before him.

² May you blow them away like smoke—
  as wax melts before the fire, may the wicked perish before God.

³ **But may the righteous be glad and rejoice before God;**
  may they be happy and joyful.

⁴ Sing to God, sing in praise of his name,
  extol him who rides on the clouds;
  rejoice before him—his name is the LORD.   *Refrain*

⁵ A father to the fatherless, a defender of widows,
  is God in his holy dwelling.

⁶ God sets the lonely in families, he leads out the prisoners with singing;
  but the rebellious live in a sun-scorched land.

⁷ **When you, God, went out before your people,**
  when you marched through the wilderness,

⁸ **the earth shook, the heavens poured down rain,**
  before God, the One of Sinai, before God, the God of Israel.

⁹ You gave abundant showers, O God;
  you refreshed your weary inheritance.

¹⁰ Your people settled in it,
  and from your bounty, God, you provided for the poor.   *Refrain*

¹⁷ The chariots of God are tens of thousands and thousands of thousands;
  the Lord has come from Sinai into his sanctuary.

¹⁸ **When you ascended on high, you took many captives;**
  you received gifts from people,
  even from the rebellious—that you, LORD God, might dwell there.

¹⁹ Praise be to the Lord, to God our Savior,
  who daily bears our burdens.

Refrain or continue to next page for the singing of "Approach Our God with Songs of Praise."

1 Ap - proach our God with songs of praise, the Lord, and
2 We lift our voic - es, shout and sing. Hail! The pro -

light of all our days, the hope of ev - ery na - tion;
ces - sion of our King; the ris - en Lord still guides us.

from all who would our lives op - press, God will re -
The God of all in a - ges past, who reigned be -

deem by right - eous - ness, and bless us with sal - va - tion.
fore the world was cast, still comes to dwell a - mong us.

Re - joice! God calms the rag - ing sea; from bond - age
At God's right hand the hosts re - joice; earth joins the

brings us vic - to - ry; good news in an - cient sto - ry!
song in hum - bler voice, God's maj - es - ty pro - fess - ing;

By faith we know when ways con - found, God's lov - ing
strength and com - pas - sion, love and peace, from God's a -

grace is all a - round; come, now, pro - claim God's glo - ry!
bun - dance nev - er cease; a - rise, and claim God's bless - ing!

For accompaniment see p. 216.

Text: Psalm 68 © THE HOLY BIBLE, NEW INTERNATIONAL VERSION®, NIV® Copyright © 1973, 1978, 1984, 2011 by Biblica, Inc.™ Used by permission. All rights reserved worldwide.
Words: ref. Martin Tel © 2011 Martin Tel, admin. Faith Alive Christian Resources; sts. Michael Morgan © 2011 Michael Morgan, admin. Faith Alive Christian Resources
Music (GENEVAN 68 | 8.8.7.8.8.7 D): *Genevan Psalter*, 1539, P.D.

68B Psalm 68:1-10, 32-35
A Responsorial Setting

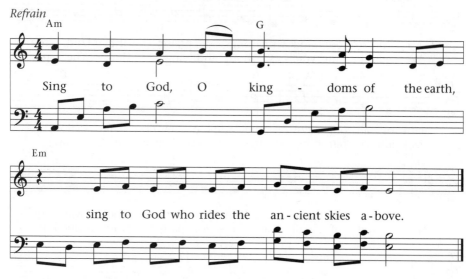

Refrain

Sing to God, O king-doms of the earth, sing to God who rides the an-cient skies a-bove.

Refrain

¹ Let God arise, and let God's enemies be scattered;
   let those who hate God flee.

² As smoke is driven away, so you should drive them away;
      as the wax melts before the fire,
      so let the wicked perish at the presence of God.

³ But let the righteous be glad and rejoice before God;
   let them also be merry and joyful.

⁴ Sing to God, sing praises to God's name; exalt the one who rides the clouds;
   I AM is that name, rejoice before God!   *Refrain*

⁵ In your holy habitation, O God,
      you are a father to orphans, defender of widows;

⁶ you give the solitary a home and bring forth prisoners into freedom;
      but the rebels shall live in desert places.

⁷ O God, when you went forth before your people,
      when you marched through the wilderness,

⁸ the earth quaked, and the skies poured down rain,
   at the presence of God, the God of Sinai,
      at the presence of God, the God of Israel.

⁹ You sent a bountiful rain, O God;
      you restored your inheritance when it languished.

¹⁰ Your people found their home in it;
      in your goodness, O God, you have made provisions for the poor.   *Refrain*

³² Sing to God, O kingdoms of the earth;

    sing praises to the Lord.

³³ You ride in the heavens, O God, in the ancient heavens;

    you send forth your voice, your mighty voice.

³⁴ Ascribe power to God,

    whose majesty is over Israel; whose strength is in the skies.

³⁵ How wonderful you are in your holy places, O God of Israel,

    giving strength and power to your people! Blessed be God!   *Refrain*

Tone

Lectionary: Eastertide (A).

Words and Music: Isaac Everett © Isaac Everett
Psalm Text: from *Evangelical Lutheran Worship* © 2006 Evangelical Lutheran Church in America, admin. Augsburg Fortress Publishers
Tone: © 2006 Augsburg Fortress Publishers

68C Let God Arise!

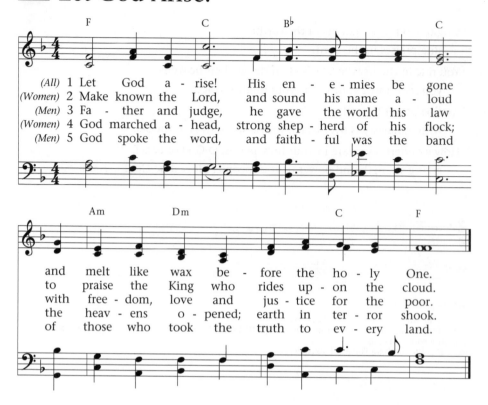

(All) 1 Let God a - rise! His en - e - mies be gone
(Women) 2 Make known the Lord, and sound his name a - loud
(Men) 3 Fa - ther and judge, he gave the world his law
(Women) 4 God marched a - head, strong shep - herd of his flock;
(Men) 5 God spoke the word, and faith - ful was the band

and melt like wax be - fore the ho - ly One.
to praise the King who rides up - on the cloud.
with free - dom, love and jus - tice for the poor.
the heav - ens o - pened; earth in ter - ror shook.
of those who took the truth to ev - ery land.

(All) 6 See God ascend,
with captives as his prize,
and gifts for all
who shall in him arise.

(Women) 7 Bless day by day
the living God who saves,
who raises up
his people from their graves.

(Men) 8 Draw near his throne:
musicians lead our song!
All nations, tribes,
and races join the throng.

(Women) 9 All strength is his!
The rebels reign no more;
he scatters all
who take delight in war.

(Men) 10 God rules on high,
and mighty is his voice:
to God be praise;
in God we shall rejoice.

(All) 11 Glory to God,
Creator, Savior, Friend,
whose greatness, love,
and wisdom never end.

Words: Christopher Idle © 1990 The Jubilate Group, admin. Hope Publishing Company
Music (SONG 46 | 10.10): Orlando Gibbons (1583-1625), P.D.

To the leader: according to Lilies. Of David.

Voice 1:

1 Save me, O God, *
> for the waters have come up to my neck.

2 **I sink in deep mire, where there is no foothold; ***
> **I have come into deep waters, and the flood sweeps over me.**

3 **I am weary with my crying; my throat is parched. ***
> **My eyes grow dim with waiting for my God.**

4 More in number than the hairs of my head are those who hate me without cause;
> many are those who would destroy me, my enemies who accuse me falsely. *
> What I did not steal must I now restore?

5 **O God, you know my folly; ***
> **the wrongs I have done are not hidden from you.**

6 **Do not let those who hope in you be put to shame because of me,**
> **O Lord GOD of hosts; ***
> **do not let those who seek you be dishonored because of me,**
> **O God of Israel.**

Voice 2:

7 It is for your sake that I have borne reproach, *
> that shame has covered my face.

8 I have become a stranger to my kindred, *
> an alien to my mother's children.

9 It is zeal for your house that has consumed me; *
> the insults of those who insult you have fallen on me.

10 When I humbled my soul with fasting, *
> they insulted me for doing so.

11 When I made sackcloth my clothing, *
> I became a byword to them.

12 I am the subject of gossip for those who sit in the gate, *
> and the drunkards make songs about me.

13 **But as for me, my prayer is to you, O LORD. ***
> **At an acceptable time, O God,**
> **in the abundance of your steadfast love, answer me.**

> **With your faithful help** 14 **rescue me from sinking in the mire; ***
> **let me be delivered from my enemies and from the deep waters.**

(continues)

Voice 1:

15 Do not let the flood sweep over me, or the deep swallow me up, *
     or the Pit close its mouth over me.

16 Answer me, O Lord, for your steadfast love is good; *
     according to your abundant mercy, turn to me.

17 Do not hide your face from your servant, *
     for I am in distress—make haste to answer me.

18 Draw near to me, redeem me, *
     set me free because of my enemies.

Voice 2:

19 You know the insults I receive, and my shame and dishonor; *
     my foes are all known to you.

20 Insults have broken my heart, so that I am in despair. *
     I looked for pity, but there was none;
     and for comforters, but I found none.

21 They gave me poison for food, *
     and for my thirst they gave me vinegar to drink.

Voice 1:

22 Let their table be a trap for them, *
     a snare for their allies.

23 Let their eyes be darkened so that they cannot see, *
     and make their loins tremble continually.

24 Pour out your indignation upon them, *
     and let your burning anger overtake them.

25 May their camp be a desolation; *
     let no one live in their tents.

26 For they persecute those whom you have struck down, *
     and those whom you have wounded, they attack still more.

27 Add guilt to their guilt; *
     may they have no acquittal from you.

28 Let them be blotted out of the book of the living; *
     let them not be enrolled among the righteous.

29 But I am lowly and in pain; *
     let your salvation, O God, protect me.

30 I will praise the name of God with a song; *
     I will magnify him with thanksgiving.

Voice 2:

³¹ This will please the LORD more than an ox *

  or a bull with horns and hoofs.

³² Let the oppressed see it and be glad; *

  you who seek God, let your hearts revive.

³³ For the LORD hears the needy, *

  and does not despise his own that are in bonds.

³⁴ **Let heaven and earth praise him, ***

  the seas and everything that moves in them.

³⁵ **For God will save Zion and rebuild the cities of Judah; ***

  and his servants shall live there and possess it;

³⁶ **the children of his servants shall inherit it, ***

  those who love his name shall live in it.

Compassionate Comforter,
pain and evil surround us and grief is twisted into the fabric of our lives.
Give us, we pray, strength equal to our need, and courage equal to any challenge.
For this we give you praise and thanks in Jesus' name. **Amen.**

Psalm 69 is a psalm of prayers for deliverance from a person who faces opposition (v. 4), alienation from family (v. 8), gossip (v. 12), and loneliness (v. 20). It includes both prayers and imprecations against the oppressor (vv. 22-28) and closes with a vow to praise and statements of truth in God (vv. 30-35). The psalm is frequently cited in the NT (John 2:17, 15:25, 19:28-29, Rom. 11:9-10, 15:3), and v. 21 is appropriated in each of the gospel narratives of Jesus' crucifixion. *Use in Worship: services focusing on the experience of unjust and oppressive opposition, where we can receive it both as an example of the honest words that a person of faith might offer and as a text that arouses horror in us as we imagine having these words prayed about our own unjust and oppressive actions; in conjunction with readings from Nehemiah, who experienced many of the concerns reflected in the psalm.*

69A Save Me, O God; I Sink in Floods

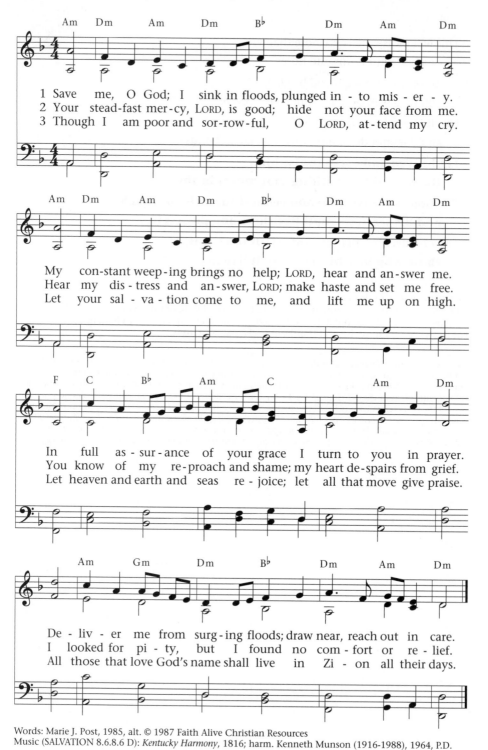

1 Save me, O God; I sink in floods, plunged in - to mis - er - y.
2 Your stead-fast mer-cy, LORD, is good; hide not your face from me.
3 Though I am poor and sor-row-ful, O LORD, at-tend my cry.

My con-stant weep-ing brings no help; LORD, hear and an-swer me.
Hear my dis-tress and an-swer, LORD; make haste and set me free.
Let your sal-va-tion come to me, and lift me up on high.

In full as-sur-ance of your grace I turn to you in prayer.
You know of my re-proach and shame; my heart de-spairs from grief.
Let heaven and earth and seas re-joice; let all that move give praise.

De-liv-er me from surg-ing floods; draw near, reach out in care.
I looked for pi-ty, but I found no com-fort or re-lief.
All those that love God's name shall live in Zi-on all their days.

Words: Marie J. Post, 1985, alt. © 1987 Faith Alive Christian Resources
Music (SALVATION 8.6.8.6 D): *Kentucky Harmony*, 1816; harm. Kenneth Munson (1916-1988), 1964, P.D.

If You Love Me 69B

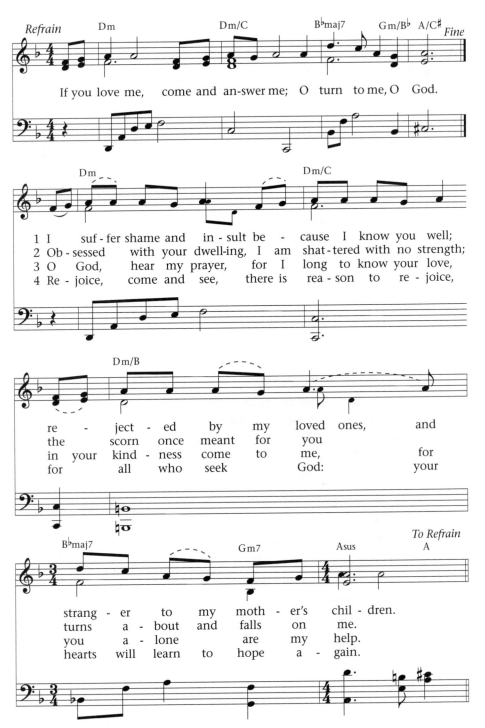

Refrain

If you love me, come and an-swer me; O turn to me, O God.

1. I suf-fer shame and in-sult be - cause I know you well;
2. Ob - sessed with your dwell-ing, I am shat-tered with no strength;
3. O God, hear my prayer, for I long to know your love,
4. Re - joice, come and see, there is rea-son to re - joice,

re - ject - ed by my loved ones, and
the scorn once meant for you
in your kind - ness come to me,
for all who seek God:

strang - er to my moth - er's chil - dren.
turns a - bout and falls on me.
you a - lone are my help.
hearts will learn to hope a - gain.

To Refrain

Words and Music: David Haas (b. 1957) © 1997 GIA Publications, Inc.

Refrain

Refrain

7 Surely, for your sake I have suffered reproach,
   and shame has covered my face.

8 I have become a stranger to my own kindred,
   an alien to my mother's children.

9 Zeal for your house has eaten me up;
   the scorn of those who scorn you has fallen upon me.   *Refrain*

10 I humbled myself with fasting,
   but that was turned to my reproach.

11 I put on sackcloth also,
   and became a byword among them.

12 Those who sit at the gate murmur against me,
   and the drunkards make songs about me.   *Refrain*

13 But as for me, this is my prayer to you, at the time you have set, O LORD:
   "In your great mercy, O God, answer me with your unfailing help.

14 Save me from the mire; do not let me sink;
   let me be rescued from those who hate me and out of the deep waters.

15 Let not the torrent of waters wash over me, neither let the deep swallow me up;
   do not let the pit shut its mouth upon me.   *Refrain*

16 Answer me, O LORD, for your love is kind;
   in your great compassion, turn to me.

17 Hide not your face from your servant;
   be swift and answer me, for I am in distress.

18 Draw near to me and redeem me;
   because of my enemies deliver me."   *Refrain*

Tone

Lectionary: Ordinary Time after Pentecost (A).

Words and Music: John L. Bell (b. 1949) © 1987 Wild Goose Resource Group, Iona Community, Scotland, GIA Publications Inc., exclusive North American agent
Psalm Text: from *Evangelical Lutheran Worship* © 2006 Evangelical Lutheran Church in America, admin. Augsburg Fortress Publishers
Tone: © 2006 Augsburg Fortress Publishers

Psalm 70

To the leader. Of David, for the memorial offering.

1 Be pleased, O God, to deliver me. *
   O LORD, make haste to help me!

2 **Let those be put to shame and confusion who seek my life. ***
   Let those be turned back and brought to dishonor
   who desire to hurt me.

3 Let those who say, "Aha, Aha!" *
   turn back because of their shame.

4 **Let all who seek you rejoice and be glad in you. ***
   Let those who love your salvation say evermore, "God is great!"

5 **But I am poor and needy; hasten to me, O God! ***
   You are my help and my deliverer; O LORD, do not delay!

Lord Jesus Christ, with saints throughout time we pray, "Come quickly!"
And we hear your promise, "I am coming soon."
With this hope in our hearts may we run the race marked out before us,
keeping our eyes, minds, and hearts fixed on you. **Amen.**

Psalm 70 picks up the themes of Ps. 69 but intensifies them in an urgent petition for God to act without delay, a theme reflected in its short, pithy lines. In contrast to psalms that call for holy patience, this prayer might be thought of as an expression of holy impatience. (See also Ps. 40, the concluding 5 verses of which resemble Ps. 70 but begin with "I waited patiently for the LORD.") The psalm begins and ends with this urgent prayer for divine action (vv. 1, 5), a prayer that frames twin expressions of desire that the psalmist's enemy may be turned back (vv. 2-3) and that the people of God may rejoice in the Lord (v. 4). *Use in Worship: traditionally used during Holy Week as a way of entering into Jesus' sorrow; the opening verse has been used as a fitting way to begin intercessory prayer.*

70A Come Quickly, LORD, to Rescue Me

1 Come quick - ly, LORD, to res - cue me, and has - ten
2 May all who seek your name re - joice, your praise in
3 Yet I am poor and need - y, LORD; be quick to

to my help, I pray. May all who seek to
grat - i - tude re - cord. May those who love your
hear my ur - gent plea. You are my help, my

take my life be put to shame with - out de - lay.
sav - ing power say ev - er - more, "Ex - alt the LORD!"
Sav - ior God! Do not de - lay; re - mem - ber me.

This tune in a lower key: p. 1030.

Words: Bert Polman, 1983, © 1987 Faith Alive Christian Resources
Music (PUER NOBIS 8.8.8.8): *Trier manuscript*, 15th c.; adapt. Michael Praetorius, 1609; harm. George Ratcliffe Woodward, 1910, P.D.

Psalm 70 | A Responsorial Setting 70B

Refrain

God, make speed to save me. Lord, make haste to help me.

Refrain

1 Be pleased, O God, to deliver me;

O LORD, make haste to help me.

2 Let those who seek my life be put to shame and confounded;

let those who take pleasure in my misfortune draw back and be disgraced.

3 Let those who say to me "Aha!" and gloat over me

turn back because of their shame. *Refrain*

4 Let all who seek you rejoice and be glad in you;

let those who love your salvation say forever, "Great is the LORD!"

5 But as for me, I am poor and needy; come to me quickly, O God.

You are my helper and my deliverer; O LORD, do not tarry. *Refrain*

Tone

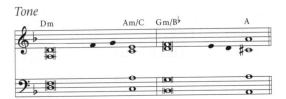

Lectionary: Wednesday of Holy Week (A,B,C); Ordinary Time after Pentecost (A).

Words and Music: David Lee © 1996, 1999 David Lee
Psalm Text: from *Evangelical Lutheran Worship* © 2006 Evangelical Lutheran Church in America, admin.
Augsburg Fortress Publishers
Tone: © 2011 Faith Alive Christian Resources

Psalm 71

1 In you, O LORD, I take refuge; *
  let me never be put to shame.

2 In your righteousness deliver me and rescue me; *
  incline your ear to me and save me.

3 Be to me a rock of refuge, a strong fortress, to save me, *
  for you are my rock and my fortress.

4 Rescue me, O my God, from the hand of the wicked, *
  from the grasp of the unjust and cruel.

5 For you, O Lord, are my hope, *
  my trust, O LORD, from my youth.

6 Upon you I have leaned from my birth;
  it was you who took me from my mother's womb. *
  My praise is continually of you.

7 I have been like a portent to many, *
  but you are my strong refuge.

8 My mouth is filled with your praise, *
  and with your glory all day long.

9 Do not cast me off in the time of old age; *
  do not forsake me when my strength is spent.

10 For my enemies speak concerning me, *
  and those who watch for my life consult together.

11 They say, "Pursue and seize that person whom God has forsaken, *
  for there is no one to deliver."

12 O God, do not be far from me; *
  O my God, make haste to help me!

13 Let my accusers be put to shame and consumed; *
  let those who seek to hurt me be covered with scorn and disgrace.

14 But I will hope continually, *
  and will praise you yet more and more.

15 My mouth will tell of your righteous acts,
  of your deeds of salvation all day long, *
  though their number is past my knowledge.

16 I will come praising the mighty deeds of the Lord GOD, *
  I will praise your righteousness, yours alone.

17 O God, from my youth you have taught me, *
  and I still proclaim your wondrous deeds.

¹⁸ **So even to old age and gray hairs, O God, do not forsake me,** *

> **until I proclaim your might to all the generations to come.**
>
> **Your power** ¹⁹ **and your righteousness, O God,**
>
> **reach the high heavens.** *
>
> **You who have done great things, O God, who is like you?**

²⁰ You who have made me see many troubles and calamities will revive me again; *

> from the depths of the earth you will bring me up again.

²¹ You will increase my honor, *

> and comfort me once again.

²² **I will also praise you with the harp for your faithfulness, O my God;** *

> **I will sing praises to you with the lyre, O Holy One of Israel.**

²³ **My lips will shout for joy when I sing praises to you;** *

> **my soul also, which you have rescued.**

²⁴ **All day long my tongue will talk of your righteous help,** *

> **for those who tried to do me harm**
>
> **have been put to shame, and disgraced.**

Faithful God, you walk with us throughout life's journey.
As our strength diminishes, may our faith increase.
As our eyes grow dim, let the light of Christ shine more brightly before us.
Help us live to the end of our years in joy, knowing that you lead us into eternal life. **Amen.**

Psalm 71 is an individual prayer of remembrance and hope that reflects and shapes an experience of the stages of life. The psalm includes sections that refer to birth and childhood (vv. 1-8, esp. 5-6), old age (vv. 9-16, esp. 9), and middle age (vv. 17-24, esp. 18). All the stages of life are marked by covenant faithfulness: God is always faithful (vv. 2, 15-16, 19, 24), and the psalmist longs to imitate this faithfulness by praising and confessing God "always" or "all day" (vv. 3, 6, 8, 14-15, 24). *Use in Worship: occasions that mark stages of life or passing of time (e.g. birth, graduation, new year); during Holy Week (reading in the voice of Christ, particularly vv. 11, 18).*

71A In You, O Lord, I Put My Trust

1 In you, O Lord, I put my trust; you are my
2 You are, O Lord, my ref - uge strong; from youth I
3 Do not re - ject me in old age; for - sake me
4 In you, O Lord, I hope once more; your love re -

rock and my de - fense. When times and tri - als
have re - lied on you. Though trou - bles rise and
not when strength has fled. For foes a - gainst me
news my trou - bled soul. From youth to age my

are un - just, you turn my foes from their in - tents.
life seems long, I speak your praise the whole day through.
plot and rage and bold - ly say, "Your God is dead."
strength re - store, and make my bat - tered spir - it whole.

5 To you I sing unending praise;
   you scorn not age and graying hair.
   Your love encompasses my days;
   all times to come will know your care.

6 I praise the Lord with harp and song;
   I sing with shouts of joy and praise.
   For you have rescued me from wrong
   and brought me hope for all my days.

This tune with guitar chords and in a lower key: p. 561.

Words: Clarence P. Walhout, 1985, © 1987 Faith Alive Christian Resources
Music (WAREHAM 8.8.8.8): William Knapp, 1783, P.D.

God, My Help and Hiding Place **71B**

Unison

1 God, my help and hid-ing place, res-cue me from shame.
2 From my youth I praised your name, trust-ing you to save.
3 Let me live to teach the young what your love can do,

Be my strength as I grow old; come and clear my name.
Now that I am turn-ing gray, lift me from the grave.
so may peo-ple yet to come place their trust in you.

False ac-cus-ers seek my life, think-ing you have left,
God, my ref-uge and my rock, hide me now. Make haste!
Show once more that you are God: raise me from de-spair!

leav-ing me with no de-fense, help-less and be-reft.
Deal with those who wish me harm; may they be dis-graced.
Then my soul will sing your name, praise your stead-fast care.

Words: Ruth C. Duck © 2011 GIA Publications, Inc.
Music (TOKYO 7.5.7.5 D): Isao Koizumi (1907-1992) © 1958 Isao Koizumi, admin. JASRAC

71C Psalm 71:1-14 | A Responsorial Setting

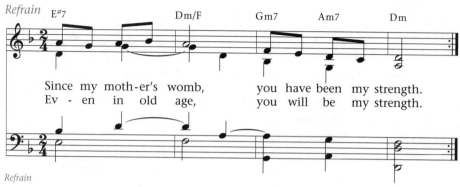

Refrain

Since my moth-er's womb, you have been my strength.
Ev - en in old age, you will be my strength.

Refrain

¹ In you, O Lᴏʀᴅ, have I taken refuge;
  let me never be put to shame.

² In your righteousness, deliver me and set me free;
  incline your ear to me and save me.

³ Be my strong rock, a castle to keep me safe;
  you are my crag and my stronghold.   *Refrain*

⁴ Deliver me, my God, from the hand of the wicked,
  from the clutches of the evildoer and the oppressor.

⁵ For you are my hope, O Lord Gᴏᴅ,
  my confidence since I was young.

⁶ I have been sustained by you ever since I was born;
  from my mother's womb you have been my strength;
  my praise shall be always of you.   *Refrain*

⁷ I have become a portent to many;
  but you are my refuge and my strength.

⁸ Let my mouth be full of your praise
  and your glory all day long.

⁹ Do not cast me off in my old age;
  forsake me not when my strength fails.

¹⁰ For my enemies are talking against me,
  and those who lie in wait for my life take counsel together.

¹¹ They say, "Pursue and seize that one whom God has forsaken;
  because there is none who will save."   *Refrain*

¹² O God, be not far from me;
  come quickly to help me, O my God.

¹³ May my accusers be put to shame and waste away;
  let those who seek my misfortune be engulfed by scorn and reproach.

¹⁴ But I shall always wait in patience,
  and shall praise you more and more.   *Refrain*

Tone

Lectionary: Tuesday of Holy Week (A,B,C); vv. 1-6 Ordinary Time after Epiphany (C) and Ordinary Time after Pentecost (C).

Words: Psalm 71
Music: Michael Guimont © 1994, 1998 GIA Publications, Inc.
Psalm Text: from *Evangelical Lutheran Worship* © 2006 Evangelical Lutheran Church in America, admin. Augsburg Fortress Publishers
Tone: © 2011 Faith Alive Christian Resources

Alternate Refrain

Alternate Tone

Words and Music: The Community of Taizé and Jacques Berthier (1923-1994) © 1998 Ateliers et Presses de Taizé, Taizé Community, France, GIA Publications, Inc., exclusive North American agent
Tone: © 2011 Faith Alive Christian Resources

Psalm 72

Of Solomon.

¹ Give the king your justice, O God, *
　　and your righteousness to a king's son.

² May he judge your people with righteousness, *
　　and your poor with justice.

³ May the mountains yield prosperity for the people, *
　　and the hills, in righteousness.

⁴ **May he defend the cause of the poor of the people, ***
　　give deliverance to the needy, and crush the oppressor.

⁵ **May he live while the sun endures, ***
　　and as long as the moon, throughout all generations.

⁶ **May he be like rain that falls on the mown grass, ***
　　like showers that water the earth.

⁷ **In his days may righteousness flourish ***
　　and peace abound, until the moon is no more.

⁸ May he have dominion from sea to sea, *
　　and from the River to the ends of the earth.

⁹ May his foes bow down before him, *
　　and his enemies lick the dust.

¹⁰ May the kings of Tarshish and of the isles render him tribute, *
　　may the kings of Sheba and Seba bring gifts.

¹¹ May all kings fall down before him, *
　　all nations give him service.

¹² **For he delivers the needy when they call, ***
　　the poor and those who have no helper.

¹³ **He has pity on the weak and the needy, ***
　　and saves the lives of the needy.

¹⁴ **From oppression and violence he redeems their life; ***
　　and precious is their blood in his sight.

¹⁵ Long may he live! May gold of Sheba be given to him. *
　　May prayer be made for him continually,
　　and blessings invoked for him all day long.

¹⁶ May there be abundance of grain in the land;

   may it wave on the tops of the mountains; *

     may its fruit be like Lebanon;

     and may people blossom in the cities like the grass of the field.

¹⁷ May his name endure forever, his fame continue as long as the sun. *

     May all nations be blessed in him; may they pronounce him happy.

¹⁸ **Blessed be the LORD, the God of Israel, ***

   who alone does wondrous things.

¹⁹ **Blessed be his glorious name forever; ***

   may his glory fill the whole earth. Amen and Amen.

²⁰ The prayers of David * son of Jesse are ended.

God of every nation, your law is right, your rule is just,
and even in this fallen world your kingdom knows no boundaries.
May the compassion, patience, and forgiveness you show us in Jesus Christ our Savior
form the ministry of reconciliation we offer to all people in Jesus' name. **Amen.**

Psalm 72, a royal psalm, prays for the king and vividly describes the shalom that arises from the king's just rule. It is the final psalm of the second of the Psalter's five books and expresses a grand conclusion to a journey that began with the psalmist's parched desire for God and continued through heights and valleys of praise and testimony (Pss. 46, 48, 66, 71), penitence (Ps. 51), lament (Ps. 59), and urgent prayer (Ps. 70). The psalm is visionary, optimistic, and future-oriented, with a vision of God's shalom that parallels the exalted language of Isa. 60-66. In this peaceable kingdom, the God-fearing king is concerned for the weak and needy but crushes those who cheat and swindle (vv. 4, 13-14), a theme echoed in the songs of Hannah and Mary. The psalm can be read both as a prayer for a specific ancient king and also as a messianic prophecy. It can also be read as a confident assurance that the psalmist's longing for a blessing that extends to the ends of the earth (Ps. 67) will be realized. The psalm concludes with a doxology that closes the entire second book of the Psalter. Many Christian traditions have interpreted this psalm Christologically. Isaac Watt's paraphrase begins "Jesus shall reign where'er the sun." *Use in Worship: during the seasons of Advent and Epiphany (because of the reference to foreign kings in vv. 10-11, 15).*

72A Hail to the Lord's Anointed

1 Hail to the Lord's a - noint - ed, great Da - vid's great-er Son!
2 You come with res - cue speed - y to those who suf - fer wrong,
3 You shall come down like show - ers up - on the fruit-ful earth;
4 Kings shall fall down be - fore you, and gold and in-cense bring;

Hail, in the time ap - point - ed, your reign on earth be - gun!
to help the poor and need - y, and bid the weak be strong;
love, joy, and hope, like flow - ers, spring in your path to birth.
all na - tions shall a - dore you, your praise all peo - ple sing.

You come to break op - pres - sion, to set the cap - tive free,
to give them songs for sigh - ing, their dark-ness turn to light,
Be - fore you on the moun - tains shall peace, the her - ald, go;
To you shall prayer un - ceas - ing and dai - ly vows as - cend;

to take a - way trans - gres - sion, and rule in eq - ui - ty.
whose souls, con-demned and dy - ing, are pre-cious in your sight.
and right-eous-ness in foun - tains from hill to val - ley flow.
your king-dom still in - creas - ing, a king-dom with-out end.

Words: James Montgomery, 1822, P.D.
Music (ES FLOG EIN KLEINS WALDVÖGELEIN 7.6.7.6 D): German; harm. George Ratcliffe Woodward, 1904, P.D.

Jesus Shall Reign Where'er the Sun 72B

1 Je - sus shall reign wher - e'er the sun does its suc -
2 To him shall end - less prayer be made, and prais - es
3 Peo - ple and realms of ev - ery tongue dwell on his

ces - sive jour - neys run, his king - dom stretch from
throng to crown his head. His name like sweet per -
love with sweet - est song, and in - fant voic - es

shore to shore, till moons shall wax and wane no more.
fume shall rise with ev - ery morn - ing sac - ri - fice.
shall pro - claim their ear - ly bless - ings on his name.

4 Blessings abound where'er he reigns:
the prisoners leap to lose their chains,
the weary find eternal rest,
and all who suffer want are blest.

5 Let every creature rise and bring
the highest honors to our King,
angels descend with songs again,
and earth repeat the loud amen.

Words: Isaac Watts (1674-1748), 1719, P.D.
Music (DUKE STREET 8.8.8.8): John Hatton, 1793, P.D.

72C Psalm 72:1-7, 10-14, 18-19
A Responsorial Setting

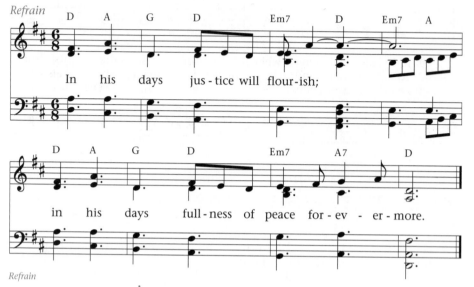

Refrain

In his days jus-tice will flour-ish;

in his days full-ness of peace for - ev - er - more.

Refrain

¹ Give the king your justice, O God,
      and your righteousness to the king's son;

² that he may rule your people righteously
      and the poor with justice;

³ that the mountains may bring prosperity to the people,
      and the hills, in righteousness.   *Refrain*

⁴ Let him defend the needy among the people,
      rescue the poor, and crush the oppressor.

⁵ May he live as long as the sun and moon endure,
      from one generation to another.

⁶ Let him come down like rain upon the mown field,
      like showers that water the earth.

⁷ In his time may the righteous flourish;
      and let there be an abundance of peace
      till the moon shall be no more.   *Refrain*

¹⁰ May the kings of Tarshish and the isles pay tribute,
      and the kings of Sheba and Seba offer gifts.

¹¹ May all kings bow down before him,
      and all the nations do him service.

¹² For the king delivers the poor who cry out in distress,
      the oppressed, and those who have no helper.

¹³ He has compassion on the lowly and poor,
      and preserves the lives of the needy.

¹⁴ From oppression and violence he redeems their lives,
　　and precious is their blood in his sight.　*Refrain*

¹⁸ Blessed are you, LORD God, the God of Israel;
　　you alone do wondrous deeds!

¹⁹ And blessed be your glorious name forever,
　　and may all the earth be filled with your glory. Amen. Amen.　*Refrain*

Tone

Lectionary: vv. 1-7, 18-19 Advent (A); vv. 1-7, 10-14 Epiphany of the Lord (A,B,C).

Words: Psalm 72:7
Music: J. Michael Joncas (b. 1951) © 1987, 1994 GIA Publications, Inc.
Psalm Text: from *Evangelical Lutheran Worship* © 2006 Evangelical Lutheran Church in America, admin.
Augsburg Fortress Publishers
Tone: © 2011 Faith Alive Christian Resources

Words: © 1969, 1981, 1997 International Commission on English in the Liturgy Corporation
Music: Val Parker © 2005 Val Parker, admin. OCP Publications
Tone: © 2011 Faith Alive Christian Resources

72D Están en tu mano / In Your Hand Alone

Refrain

Spanish: Es - tán en tu ma - no, Se - ñor el po - der y
English: In your hand a - lone, ho - ly God, are all grace and

for - ta - le - za. Y es - tá en tu ma - no el
power and gran-deur. And by your hand, you

dar - nos el po - der y la gran - de - za. *Fine*
bless us from your store of strength and splen-dor.

1 Da - le, oh Dios, al Rey tu jui - cio
1 Give the rul - ers, Lord, your wis - dom,
2 From the moun - tains, pour your bless - ing;
3 Like the sun and moon en - dur - ing,
4 Let all peo - ples bow in won - der;

y jus - ti - cia al Hi - jo del Rey.
and grant your jus - tice to their heirs,
let peace de - scend from slop - ing hills.
so long may your right - eous rul - ers live,
let Tar - sis bring trib - ute to their reign,

Ri - jan al pue - blo en jus - ti - cia;
that they may rule their lands with jus - tice,
Shield and de - fend the weak and need - y,
and like the rain on thirst - y pas - tures,
She - ba and Se - ba bear their of - ferings,

con jui - cio a los o - pri - mi - dos.
and pro - vide for the poor and hun - gry.
and shat - ter the proud op - pres - sor.
may they flou - rish from sea to sea.
and all na - tions will pay their hom - age.

2 Paz dará el mon-te al pueblo;
  dará el collado justicia,
  defensa al necesitado
  y quebrantará al opresor.

3 Mientras duren sol y luna
  eternamente vivirá
  cual lluvia regará el campo,
  regirá de mar a mar.

4 Y le adorarán los pueblos;
  Tarsis pagará tributo,
  Sheba y Seba frutos darán;
  y le servirán los reyes.

Words: Louis Olivieri; tr. Mary Louise Bringle (b. 1953), 2011, © Louis Olivieri
Music (HERMANAS JESÚS MEDIADOR): Pedro Escabí; arr. Marcus Hong © 2011 Faith Alive Christian
Resources

Psalm 73

A Psalm of Asaph.

Voice 1:

1 Truly God is good to the upright, *
> to those who are pure in heart.

2 **But as for me, my feet had almost stumbled;** *
> **my steps had nearly slipped.**

3 **For I was envious of the arrogant;** *
> **I saw the prosperity of the wicked.**

4 For they have no pain; *
> their bodies are sound and sleek.

5 They are not in trouble as others are; *
> they are not plagued like other people.

6 Therefore pride is their necklace; *
> violence covers them like a garment.

7 Their eyes swell out with fatness; *
> their hearts overflow with follies.

8 They scoff and speak with malice; *
> loftily they threaten oppression.

9 They set their mouths against heaven, *
> and their tongues range over the earth.

10 **Therefore the people turn and praise them,** *
> **and find no fault in them.**

11 **And they say, "How can God know?** *
> **Is there knowledge in the Most High?"**

12 Such are the wicked; *
> always at ease, they increase in riches.

13 All in vain I have kept my heart clean *
> and washed my hands in innocence.

14 For all day long I have been plagued, *
> and am punished every morning.

Voice 2:

15 If I had said, "I will talk on in this way," *
> I would have been untrue to the circle of your children.

16 **But when I thought how to understand this,** *
> **it seemed to me a wearisome task,**

17 **until I went into the sanctuary of God;** *
> **then I perceived their end.**

¹⁸ Truly you set them in slippery places; *
   you make them fall to ruin.

¹⁹ How they are destroyed in a moment, *
   swept away utterly by terrors!

²⁰ They are like a dream when one awakes; *
   on awaking you despise their phantoms.

²¹ When my soul was embittered, *
   when I was pricked in heart,

²² I was stupid and ignorant; *
   I was like a brute beast toward you.

²³ **Nevertheless I am continually with you;** *
   you hold my right hand.

²⁴ **You guide me with your counsel,** *
   and afterward you will receive me with honor.

²⁵ **Whom have I in heaven but you?** *
   And there is nothing on earth that I desire other than you.

²⁶ **My flesh and my heart may fail,** *
   but God is the strength of my heart and my portion forever.

²⁷ Indeed, those who are far from you will perish; *
   you put an end to those who are false to you.

²⁸ **But for me it is good to be near God;** *
   I have made the Lord GOD my refuge, to tell of all your works.

You, O Lord, have placed your hand upon us.
We need not run from you in shame.
You, O Christ, have placed your life within us.
Our lives will not end in isolation or obscurity.
You, O Holy Spirit, are nurturing your passion within us.
Turn us from vanity and reckless desire.
Father, Son, and Spirit, we give you thanks and praise. **Amen.**

Psalm 73 is testimony to God's goodness that arises out of a dramatic conversion of perspective that occurred in the sanctuary (vv. 15-17). The psalmist was converted dramatically from a perspective of embittered jealousy (v. 3) at the wealth, prestige, and ease of life of so many godless people to a perspective of contentment and trust. This opening psalm of the Psalter's third book reprises the opening theme of the entire Psalter, describing how its composer came to embrace the perspective first claimed back in Ps. 1: only the righteous will truly flourish. The intensity of the psalmist's engagement with this conversion is conveyed through the repeated use of the word *heart* (vv. 1, 7, 13, 21, 26), the place that signifies the deepest of human desires and intentions. *Use in Worship: in conjunction with testimonies; funerals (see the reference to the end of life in v. 26); services focusing on the significance of public worship for helping us perceive God's truth about the world.*

73A All My Life

1 All my life   I've sung   a jeal-ous song.
2 All my life   I've walked the way of   God.
3 All my life   I've watched the wick-ed   rule.
4 All my life   I've tried   to rea-son   why.

All my life   I've sung   a jeal-ous song.
All my life   I've walked the way of   God.
All my life   I've watched the wick-ed   rule.
All my life   I've tried   to rea-son   why.

All my life   I've sung   a jeal-ous song.   The
All my life   I've walked the way of   God.   But
All my life   I've watched the wick-ed   rule.   They
All my life   I've tried   to rea-son   why.   I

e - vil peo-ple flour-ish   and the good folks suf-fer wrong.
walk-ing got me no-where,   and I thought it nev-er would.
look down on the god-ly   and they call us sil-ly fools.
could not find the an-swers   and I lost the will to try.

Repeat 3 times

(continues)

73A (continued)

450

your be-loved I stand.

Now my song is al-to-geth-er new. Now my song is

al-to-geth-er new. Now my song is al-to-geth-er new, for

God has changed my vi-sion, as on-ly God could do.

Words and Music: Ken Medema © 2010 Ken Medema Music/Brier Patch Music

73B In Sweet Communion, Lord, with You

The following may be read before the singing of "In Sweet Communion, Lord, with You."

Voice 1:

¹ Truly God is good to Israel,
    to those whose hearts are pure.

Voice 2:

² But as for me, I almost lost my footing.
    My feet were slipping, and I was almost gone.
³ For I envied the proud
    when I saw them prosper despite their wickedness.

Voice 1:

¹² Look at these wicked people—
    enjoying a life of ease while their riches multiply.
¹³ Did I keep my heart pure for nothing?
    Did I keep myself innocent for no reason?

Voice 2:

¹⁴ I get nothing but trouble all day long;
    every morning brings me pain.
¹⁵ If I had really spoken this way to others,
    I would have been a traitor to your people.
¹⁶ So I tried to understand why the wicked prosper.
    But what a difficult task it is!
¹⁷ Then I went into your sanctuary, O God,
    and I finally understood the destiny of the wicked.

Voice 1:

²¹ Then I realized that my heart was bitter,
    and I was all torn up inside.
²² I was so foolish and ignorant—
    I must have seemed like a senseless animal to you.

Voices 1 and 2:

²³ Yet I still belong to you;
    you hold my right hand.

1 In sweet com-mu-nion, Lord, with you I
2 Your coun-sel through my earth-ly way shall
3 Whom have I, Lord, in heaven but you, to

con-stant-ly a-bide; my hand you hold with-
guide me and con-trol, and then to glo-ry
whom my thoughts as-pire? And, hav-ing you, what

in your own to keep me near your side.
af-ter-ward you will re-ceive my soul.
more on earth is there I can de-sire?

4 Though flesh and heart should faint and fail,
the Lord will ever be
the strength and portion of my heart,
my God eternally.

5 To live apart from God is death;
'tis good his face to seek.
My refuge is the living God;
his praise I long to speak.

Text: Psalm 73, New Living Translation © 1996 Tyndale House Publishers, Inc.
Words: *Psalter*, 1912, alt., P.D.
Music (PRAYER 8.6.8.6): William U. Butcher, 1860, P.D.

73C Why Do the Powerful Have It So Good?

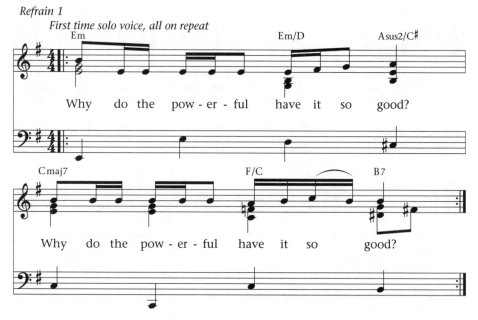

Refrain 1

First time solo voice, all on repeat

Why do the pow-er-ful have it so good?

Why do the pow-er-ful have it so good?

Text is spoken in time with Vamp A:

True, true, God is good. |
    Good to the upright, good to the just. ‖
But I—I couldn't see it, nearly missed it, |
    Feet slipping, sliding to the ditch. ‖
I couldn't take my eyes off the rich. |
    . . . ‖

"Look at them!" I said, "Sleek and slick, |
    Nothing will stain them, nothing will stick: ‖
No grime, no crime, no punishment." |
    . . . ‖

Vamp A

Refrain 1

Why do the powerful have it so good? Why do the powerful have it so good?
Why do the powerful have it so good? Why do the powerful have it so good?

Vamp A

Text is spoken in time with Vamp A:

Always in style, dressed to oppress, |
    Strings of blood-diamonds hang at their necks. ‖
People all praise them: every word they say gets |
    Scribbled, scrawled as high as heaven, ‖
Scribbled and scrawled across the earth. |
    . . . ‖

"Your God?" they scoff. "Don't make me laugh! |
    Your Most High has nothing to teach, ‖
Out of touch, out of reach, always has been, |
    From the beginning." ‖

Refrain 1

Why do the powerful have it so good? Why do the powerful have it so good?
Why do the powerful have it so good? Why do the powerful have it so good?

Text is spoken in time with Vamp A:

Why do I stand with God? |
    Why, why do I stand with God? ‖
Lord, Lord, this is my reward— |
    Agony and grief? ‖
In vain I seek relief. |
    . . . ‖

Refrain 2

Text is spoken in time with Vamp A:

Here comes the pain again, always the same again. |
    Here comes the sun—here comes someone ‖
To slap me down. |
    Grief, agony, agony, grief, ‖
In vain I seek relief. |
    . . . ‖

Refrain 2

Why do I stand with God? **Why do I stand with God?**

(continues)

Text is spoken in time with Vamp B:

Vamp B

Then I went to the holy place. |
    There I stopped. There I stood. ||
There in the temple, it became so simple; |
    There in prayer, it all came clear. ||
The wicked step on a slippery slope, |
    A slip, a slide, and they face the abyss. ||
Who mourns them? Who misses them? |
    It's as if they'd never been. ||

Refrain 2

Why do I stand with God? **Why do I stand with God?**

Text is spoken in time with Vamp B:

Thinking it through, thinking it through, |
    I turn in circles, thinking it through: ||

Refrain 2

Why do I stand with God? **Why do I stand with God?**

Text is spoken in time with Vamp B:

Vamp B

Who do I have in heaven? |
    Where can I turn on the earth? ||
I would rather cry out for God |
    Than whisper with the wicked. ||
I would rather hunger for you |
    Than feast with the proud, O God. ||
With your strong hand you lead me, |
    And at my end with honor receive me. ||
True, true: God is good. |
    God is good: It's true, it's true. ||

Congregation and/or leader may improvise repetition of the last line over Vamp C.

Vamp C

Words and Music: Andrew Donaldson © 2010 Andrew Donaldson
Text: Andrew Donaldson © 2010 Andrew Donaldson

Psalm 74

A Maskil of Asaph.

1 O God, why do you cast us off forever? *
   Why does your anger smoke against the sheep of your pasture?

2 **Remember your congregation, which you acquired long ago,**
   which you redeemed to be the tribe of your heritage. *
   Remember Mount Zion, where you came to dwell.

3 Direct your steps to the perpetual ruins; *
   the enemy has destroyed everything in the sanctuary.

4 **Your foes have roared within your holy place; ***
   they set up their emblems there.

5 At the upper entrance they hacked *
   the wooden trellis with axes.

6 And then, with hatchets and hammers, *
   they smashed all its carved work.

7 **They set your sanctuary on fire; ***
   they desecrated the dwelling place of your name,
   bringing it to the ground.

8 **They said to themselves, "We will utterly subdue them"; ***
   they burned all the meeting places of God in the land.

9 We do not see our emblems; *
   there is no longer any prophet,
   and there is no one among us who knows how long.

10 How long, O God, is the foe to scoff? *
   Is the enemy to revile your name forever?

11 Why do you hold back your hand; *
   why do you keep your hand in your bosom?

12 **Yet God my King is from of old, ***
   working salvation in the earth.

13 You divided the sea by your might; *
   you broke the heads of the dragons in the waters.

14 You crushed the heads of Leviathan; *
   you gave him as food for the creatures of the wilderness.

15 You cut openings for springs and torrents; *
   you dried up ever-flowing streams.

16 **Yours is the day, yours also the night; ***
   you established the luminaries and the sun.

17 **You have fixed all the bounds of the earth; ***
   you made summer and winter.

(continues)

¹⁸ Remember this, O LORD, how the enemy scoffs, *

and an impious people reviles your name.

¹⁹ Do not deliver the soul of your dove to the wild animals; *

do not forget the life of your poor forever.

²⁰ **Have regard for your covenant,** *

for the dark places of the land are full of the haunts of violence.

²¹ **Do not let the downtrodden be put to shame;** *

let the poor and needy praise your name.

²² Rise up, O God, plead your cause; *

remember how the impious scoff at you all day long.

²³ **Do not forget the clamor of your foes,** *

the uproar of your adversaries that goes up continually.

Faithful and compassionate God,
we know that faith is being sure of what we hope for
and certain of what we do not see.
Enable us to see with eyes of faith beyond a broken and hurting world
that you are sovereign,
and to believe with trusting hearts that you are undeniably good.
We ask in Jesus' name. **Amen.**

Psalm 74 is a psalm of communal despair at the desolation of God's sanctuary in Zion. It includes communal laments to God (vv. 1, 10-11), urgent pleas for God to act (vv. 2-3, 18-23), a description of the desolation (vv. 4-9), and recollection of the power of God demonstrated in creation (vv. 12-17). *Use in Worship: services focusing on Israel's exile; during the season of Advent, where Christians express longing for the second coming of the Messiah as the definitive answer to human folly, pain, and distress.*

74A Hymn: O Come, O Come, Emmanuel

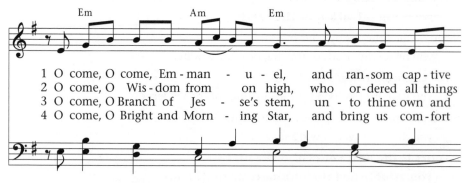

1 O come, O come, Em-man - u - el, and ran-som cap-tive
2 O come, O Wis-dom from on high, who or-dered all things
3 O come, O Branch of Jes - se's stem, un - to thine own and
4 O come, O Bright and Morn - ing Star, and bring us com-fort

Words: *Psalteriolum Cantionum Catholicarum*, Köln, 1710; tr. composite, P.D.
Music (VENI EMMANUEL 8.8.8.8 with refrain): French processional, 15th c., P.D.; arr. © 2006 Augsburg
Fortress Publishers

Psalm 75

To the leader: Do Not Destroy. A Psalm of Asaph. A Song.

¹ We give thanks to you, O God;

we give thanks; your name is near. *

People tell of your wondrous deeds.

² At the set time that I appoint *

I will judge with equity.

³ When the earth totters, with all its inhabitants, *

it is I who keep its pillars steady. *Selah*

⁴ I say to the boastful, "Do not boast," *

and to the wicked, "Do not lift up your horn;

⁵ do not lift up your horn on high, *

or speak with insolent neck."

⁶ **For not from the east or from the west** *

and not from the wilderness comes lifting up;

⁷ **but it is God who executes judgment,** *

putting down one and lifting up another.

⁸ For in the hand of the LORD there is a cup with foaming wine, well mixed; *

he will pour a draught from it, and all the wicked of the earth

shall drain it down to the dregs.

⁹ **But I will rejoice forever;** *

I will sing praises to the God of Jacob.

¹⁰ **All the horns of the wicked I will cut off,** *

but the horns of the righteous shall be exalted.

Sovereign God, in your mighty acts you revealed your justice and truth.
With Mary we sing your praise,
for you bring down the tyrant and raise the poor from the dust.
May your Son be our confidence and strength
as you judge the world in righteousness. **Amen.**

Psalm 75 is a psalm of thanksgiving and praise that confronts human assertiveness and self-reliance. It begins with a leader's report of the people's confession (vv. 1-2), continues with God's command to avoid arrogance (vv. 2-5), and concludes with the psalmist's humble assent to the providence of God and commitment to praise God (vv. 6-10). The psalm features arresting images of God as the cosmic builder (v. 3), a chemist mixing a potion (v. 8), and a judge supervising a trial (v. 7). Thus it models how worshipers can respond humbly to the sometimes inscrutable and mysterious ways of God; in exploring this theme, it is similar in content (though different in tone) to Ps. 131 and the songs of Hannah (1 Sam. 2:1-10) and Mary (Luke 1:46-55). *Use in Worship: services focusing on divine creation and providence.*

O God, Your Deeds Are Unsurpassed 75A

1 O God, your deeds are un-sur-passed; no rich-er grace can earth im-part. Your Name is near; you hold us fast. Your love en-folds each yearn-ing heart, your love en-folds each yearn-ing heart.

2 Re-move our pride lest we must taste the judg-ment cup of bit-ter gall. Let not our bold am-bi-tions take the praise from you, who gives us all, the praise from you, who gives us all.

3 Help us to know hu-mil-i-ty, to fol-low you in all your ways. From self-con-ceit, Lord, set us free to know our-selves and sing your praise, to know our-selves and sing your praise.

Alternate harmonization on p. 348.

Words: Michael Morgan © 2011 Michael Morgan, admin. Faith Alive Christian Resources
Music (BACA 8.8.8.8 with repeat): William B. Bradbury (1816-1868), P.D.

75B Canticle: My Soul Cries Out

1 My soul cries out with a joy - ful shout that the
2 Though I am small, my God, my all, you
3 From the halls of power to the for - tress tower, not a
4 Though the na - tions rage from age to age, we re -

God of my heart is great, and my spir - it sings of the
work great things in me, and your mer - cy will last from the
stone will be left on stone. Let the king be - ware for your
mem - ber who holds us fast: God's mer - cy must de -

won - drous things that you bring to the ones who wait.
depths of the past to the end of the age to be.
jus - tice tears ev - ery ty - rant from his throne.
liv - er us from the con - quer-or's crush - ing grasp.

You fixed your sight on your ser - vant's plight, and my
Your ver - y name puts the proud to shame, and to
The hun - gry poor shall weep no more, for the
This sav - ing word that our fore - bears heard is the
Refrain My heart shall sing of the day you bring. Let the

weak - ness you did not spurn, so from east to west shall my
those who would for you yearn, you will show your might, put the
food they can nev - er earn; there are ta - bles spread, ev - ery
prom - ise which holds us bound, till the spear and rod can be
fires of your jus - tice burn. Wipe a - way all tears, for the

name be blest. Could the world be a - bout to turn? *To Refrain*
strong to flight, for the world is a - bout to turn. *To Refrain*
mouth be fed, for the world is a - bout to turn. *To Refrain*
crushed by God, who is turn - ing the world a - round. *To Refrain*
dawn draws near, and the world is a - bout to turn!

Words: Rory Cooney (b. 1952), based on the Magnificat © 1990 GIA Publications, Inc.
Music (STAR OF COUNTY DOWN 8.6.8.6 D): Irish traditional; arr. Rory Cooney (b. 1952) © 1990 GIA
Publications, Inc.

Psalm 76

To the leader: with stringed instruments. A Psalm of Asaph. A Song.

¹ In Judah God is known, *
> his name is great in Israel.

² His abode has been established in Salem, *
> his dwelling place in Zion.

³ There he broke the flashing arrows, *
> the shield, the sword, and the weapons of war.   *Selah*

⁴ **Glorious are you, more majestic ***
> **than the everlasting mountains.**

⁵ The stouthearted were stripped of their spoil; they sank into sleep; *
> none of the troops was able to lift a hand.

⁶ At your rebuke, O God of Jacob, *
> both rider and horse lay stunned.

⁷ **But you indeed are awesome! ***
> **Who can stand before you when once your anger is roused?**

⁸ From the heavens you uttered judgment; *
> the earth feared and was still

⁹ when God rose up to establish judgment, *
> to save all the oppressed of the earth.   *Selah*

¹⁰ Human wrath serves only to praise you, *
> when you bind the last bit of your wrath around you.

¹¹ **Make vows to the LORD your God, and perform them; ***
> **let all who are around him bring gifts to the one who is awesome,**

¹² **who cuts off the spirit of princes, ***
> **who inspires fear in the kings of the earth.**

God of awesome majesty, silence in us each false word
and turn our lives to your obedience,
so that every word on our lips may bring honor to your name,
and our very lives may be a holy and acceptable gift to you.
In Jesus' name we pray. **Amen.**

Psalm 76 expresses fear of or reverence for God. It begins with words of awe about God (vv. 1-3), addresses God directly (vv. 4-10), and finally calls on others to make vows and render tribute to God (vv. 11-12). Psalm 76 echoes themes from Pss. 46-48 and 72-75 with its focus on God's presence in Jerusalem on Mount Zion. It includes a reference to Israel's exodus from Egypt (v. 6), pays particular attention to God's concern for the weak (v. 9), and asserts God's sovereignty over the rulers of the nations (v. 12). *Use in Worship: services focusing on the majesty of God and the life-giving experience of holy reverence toward God.*

God Is Known Among His People 76A

1 God is known a-mong his peo-ple; his name shines in
2 God, most ex-cel-lent and awe-some, more than moun-tains,
3 When from heaven your judg-ment sound-ed, all the earth in
4 Make your vows to God and keep them, pay the LORD what

Is-ra-el; for of old he has es-tab-lished
firm and high, you have stripped the val-iant-heart-ed
fear was still— when, to save the meek and low-ly,
is his own. Might-y ones come now be-fore him,

his own house on Zi-on's hill. There he broke the
who on their own strength re-ly. Who can stand be-
you worked out your right-eous will. E-ven hu-man
hum-bly kneel be-fore God's throne. Come and bring your

sword and ar-row, bade the noise of war be still.
fore your an-ger or your might-y hand de-fy?
wrath shall praise you: your de-sign it shall ful-fill.
gifts be-fore him; wor-ship God and God a-lone.

Guitar chords do not correspond with keyboard harmony.

Words: *Psalter*, 1912; *Psalter Hymnal*, 1987, rev. © 1987 Faith Alive Christian Resources
Music (LAUDA ANIMA 8.7.8.7.8.7): John Goss, 1869, P.D.

Psalm 77

To the leader: according to Jeduthun. Of Asaph. A Psalm.

1 I cry aloud to God, *
  aloud to God, that he may hear me.

**2 In the day of my trouble I seek the Lord;
  in the night my hand is stretched out without wearying; ***
  my soul refuses to be comforted.

3 I think of God, and I moan; *
  I meditate, and my spirit faints.   *Selah*

4 You keep my eyelids from closing; *
  I am so troubled that I cannot speak.

5 I consider the days of old, *
  and remember the years of long ago.

6 I commune with my heart in the night; *
  I meditate and search my spirit:

7 "Will the Lord spurn forever, *
  and never again be favorable?

8 Has his steadfast love ceased forever? *
  Are his promises at an end for all time?

9 Has God forgotten to be gracious? *
  Has he in anger shut up his compassion?"   *Selah*

10 And I say, "It is my grief *
  that the right hand of the Most High has changed."

11 I will call to mind the deeds of the LORD; *
  I will remember your wonders of old.

12 I will meditate on all your work, *
  and muse on your mighty deeds.

13 Your way, O God, is holy. *
  What god is so great as our God?

14 You are the God who works wonders; *
  you have displayed your might among the peoples.

15 With your strong arm you redeemed your people, *
  the descendants of Jacob and Joseph.   *Selah*

¹⁶ When the waters saw you, O God,

   when the waters saw you, they were afraid; *

      the very deep trembled.

¹⁷ The clouds poured out water; the skies thundered; *

   your arrows flashed on every side.

¹⁸ The crash of your thunder was in the whirlwind; *

   your lightnings lit up the world; the earth trembled and shook.

¹⁹ **Your way was through the sea,**

   your path, through the mighty waters; *

   yet your footprints were unseen.

²⁰ **You led your people like a flock ***

   by the hand of Moses and Aaron.

Covenant God,
when anguish fills our day and doubts keep us awake through the night,
help us to remember your faithfulness shown in your mighty acts of ages past,
trusting your present power and constant love, revealed in Christ our Lord. **Amen.**

Psalm 77 is a prayer of lament that centers around the recollection of God's past faithfulness in the context of despair in response to both individual (v. 6) and communal (v. 15) need. It affirms the importance of memory (vv. 5-6, 11-12) and recounts God's deliverance of the people of Israel from Egypt (vv. 15-20). Memory of these deeds is the basis for continued trust in God and also for any plea to God to be faithful to this pattern of deliverance. *Use in Worship: call to praise; celebrations of Baptism or the Lord's Supper; any occasion remembering God's past deeds.*

77A Hear My Cry, O God, and Save Me!

1 Hear my cry, O God, and save me!
2 You, O God, once walked be - side me.
3 All cre - a - tion bows be - fore you;

Trou - bles and dis - tress en - slave me.
In the night your songs re - vived me.
saints in earth and heaven a - dore you.

Day and night I seek your face,
Were your prom - is - es in vain?
Thun - der roars and tor - rents fall

yearn - ing for your light and grace.
Will you smile on me a - gain?
at your word, O God of all!

But these eyes— they can - not see you;
Long a - go you brought re - demp - tion;
In our grief you stand be - side us;

out - stretched arms— they can - not feel you.
your right hand won our sal - va - tion.
there to lift us and to guide us;

My heart breaks in deep de - spair;
I re - mem - ber deeds of old—
un - seen Sav - ior of our days,

my soul longs to hold you here.
now, re - mem - ber me, O Lord!
heir to end - less songs of praise!

Words: Michael Morgan © 2011 Michael Morgan, admin. Faith Alive Christian Resources
Music (GENEVAN 77 | 8.8.7.7 D): *Genevan Psalter*, 1551; arr. Alfred V. Fedak (b. 1953) © 2011 Faith Alive
Christian Resources

77B I Refused to Be Comforted Easily

1 In com-plete des-per-a-tion and in ut-ter frus-
2 With my eyes shut in fright and with no hope in
3 Will God al-ways re-ject me? Will he nev-er re-
4 Then, at last, I re-mem-bered all the things I'd for-

tra-tion, I called out and God lis-tened to me.
sight, I was much too dis-tract-ed to speak;
spect me? Has God's love for me failed ut-ter-ly?
got-ten, all the won-ders you, Lord, had be-gun.

Both by day and by night, with hands raised and fists
I i-ma-gined times past which I knew could-n't
Has his grace been for-got-ten, has he grudged me com-
And I saw how mis-for-tune had dis-tract-ed at-

tight, I ex-pressed and re-peat-ed my plea.
last and my heart, will, and bo-dy grew weak.
pas-sion, does his right hand not strength-en or free?
ten-tion from your faith-ful-ness in all you've done.

Refrain

1-3 I re-fused to be com-fort-ed eas-i-ly
4 Now I'm sure that your way is a ho-ly way,

and the tears of dis-tress made me blind:
for its pro-gress and path I can see;

I turned faint when my thoughts went too deep for me
and I know that your faith-ful-ness in the past

and I groaned when I called God to mind.
will be real and be pre-sent for me.

Words: John L. Bell (b. 1949) © 2011 Wild Goose Resource Group, Iona Community, admin. GIA Publications, Inc.
Music (DE JAREN 7.7.9.7.7.9.11.9.11.9): John L. Bell (b. 1949) © 2011 Wild Goose Resource Group, Iona Community, admin. GIA Publications, Inc.

77C We Will Remember

Refrain

We will re-mem-ber. We will re-mem-ber.

We will re-mem-ber the works of your hands.

We will stop and give you praise, for

To Stanzas   *Final Ending*

great is your faith - ful-ness.

Words: Tommy Walker © 2005 Universal Music—Brentwood-Benson Songs
Music: Tommy Walker © 2005 and arr. Eelco Vos © 2011 Universal Music—Brentwood-Benson Songs

77D Psalm 77:1-2, 11-20
A Responsorial Setting

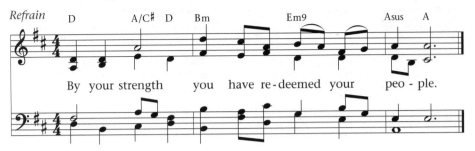

Refrain

By your strength you have re-deemed your peo - ple.

Refrain

1 I will cry aloud to God;

  I will cry aloud, and God will hear me.

2 In the day of my trouble I sought the Lord;

  my hand was stretched out by night and did not tire;

  I refused to be comforted.

11 I will remember the works of the LORD,

  and call to mind your wonders of old.

12 I will meditate on all your acts

  and ponder your mighty deeds.   *Refrain*

13 Your way, O God, is holy;

  who is so great a god as our God?

14 You are the God who works wonders

  and have declared power among the peoples.

15 By your strength you have redeemed your people,

  the descendants of Jacob and Joseph.   *Refrain*

16 The waters saw you, O God; the waters saw you and trembled;

  the very depths were shaken.

17 The clouds poured out water; the skies thundered;

  your lightning bolts flashed to and fro;

18 the sound of your thunder was in the whirlwind;

  your lightnings lit up the world;

  the earth trembled and shook.

19 Your way was in the sea, and your paths in the great waters,

  yet your footsteps were not seen.

20 You led your people like a flock

  by the hand of Moses and Aaron.   *Refrain*

Tone

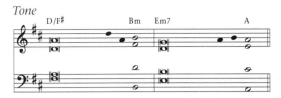

Lectionary: Ordinary Time after Pentecost (C).

Words: Psalm 77:15
Music: Walter L. Pelz from *Psalter for Worship, Year C* © 2006 Augsburg Fortress Publishers
Psalm Text: from *Evangelical Lutheran Worship* © 2006 Evangelical Lutheran Church in America, admin.
Augsburg Fortress Publishers
Tone: from *Psalter for Worship, Year C* © 2006 Augsburg Fortress Publishers

Psalm 78

A Maskil of Asaph.

Voice 1:

¹ Give ear, O my people, to my teaching; *
   incline your ears to the words of my mouth.

² I will open my mouth in a parable; *
   I will utter dark sayings from of old,

³ things that we have heard and known, *
   that our ancestors have told us.

⁴ **We will not hide them from their children; ***
   we will tell to the coming generation the glorious deeds
   of the Lᴏʀᴅ, and his might, and the wonders that he has done.

⁵ He established a decree in Jacob, and appointed a law in Israel, *
   which he commanded our ancestors to teach to their children;

⁶ **that the next generation might know them,**
   the children yet unborn, *
   and rise up and tell them to their children,

⁷ **so that they should set their hope in God,**
   and not forget the works of God, *
   but keep his commandments;

⁸ and that they should not be like their ancestors,
   a stubborn and rebellious generation, *
   a generation whose heart was not steadfast,
   whose spirit was not faithful to God.

(continues)

Voice 2:

⁹ The Ephraimites, armed with the bow, *
    turned back on the day of battle.

¹⁰ **They did not keep God's covenant, ***
    but refused to walk according to his law.

¹¹ **They forgot what he had done, ***
    and the miracles that he had shown them.

¹² In the sight of their ancestors he worked marvels *
    in the land of Egypt, in the fields of Zoan.

¹³ He divided the sea and let them pass through it, *
    and made the waters stand like a heap.

¹⁴ In the daytime he led them with a cloud, *
    and all night long with a fiery light.

¹⁵ He split rocks open in the wilderness, *
    and gave them drink abundantly as from the deep.

¹⁶ He made streams come out of the rock, *
    and caused waters to flow down like rivers.

Voice 3:

¹⁷ Yet they sinned still more against him, *
    rebelling against the Most High in the desert.

¹⁸ They tested God in their heart *
    by demanding the food they craved.

¹⁹ They spoke against God, saying, *
    "Can God spread a table in the wilderness?

²⁰ Even though he struck the rock so that water gushed out
  and torrents overflowed, *
    can he also give bread, or provide meat for his people?"

Voice 2:

²¹ Therefore, when the LORD heard, he was full of rage; *
    a fire was kindled against Jacob, his anger mounted against Israel,

²² because they had no faith in God, *
    and did not trust his saving power.

²³ **Yet he commanded the skies above, ***
    and opened the doors of heaven;

²⁴ **he rained down on them manna to eat, ***
    and gave them the grain of heaven.

²⁵ Mortals ate of the bread of angels; *
    he sent them food in abundance.

26 He caused the east wind to blow in the heavens, *
   and by his power he led out the south wind;

27 he rained flesh upon them like dust, *
   winged birds like the sand of the seas;

28 he let them fall within their camp, *
   all around their dwellings.

29 And they ate and were well filled, *
   for he gave them what they craved.

30 But before they had satisfied their craving, *
   while the food was still in their mouths,

31 the anger of God rose against them and he killed the strongest of them, *
   and laid low the flower of Israel.

Voice 3:

32 In spite of all this they still sinned; *
   they did not believe in his wonders.

33 So he made their days vanish like a breath, *
   and their years in terror.

34 When he killed them, they sought for him; *
   they repented and sought God earnestly.

35 **They remembered that God was their rock, ***
   the Most High God their redeemer.

36 But they flattered him with their mouths; *
   they lied to him with their tongues.

37 Their heart was not steadfast toward him; *
   they were not true to his covenant.

38 **Yet he, being compassionate, forgave their iniquity,**
   and did not destroy them; *
   often he restrained his anger, and did not stir up all his wrath.

39 **He remembered that they were but flesh, ***
   a wind that passes and does not come again.

40 How often they rebelled against him in the wilderness *
   and grieved him in the desert!

41 They tested God again and again, *
   and provoked the Holy One of Israel.

42 They did not keep in mind his power, *
   or the day when he redeemed them from the foe;

43 when he displayed his signs in Egypt, *
   and his miracles in the fields of Zoan.

(continues)

⁴⁴ He turned their rivers to blood, *
     so that they could not drink of their streams.
⁴⁵ He sent among them swarms of flies, which devoured them, *
     and frogs, which destroyed them.
⁴⁶ He gave their crops to the caterpillar, *
     and the fruit of their labor to the locust.
⁴⁷ He destroyed their vines with hail, *
     and their sycamores with frost.
⁴⁸ He gave over their cattle to the hail, *
     and their flocks to thunderbolts.
⁴⁹ He let loose on them his fierce anger, wrath, indignation, and distress, *
     a company of destroying angels.
⁵⁰ He made a path for his anger; *
     he did not spare them from death, but gave their lives over to the plague.
⁵¹ He struck all the firstborn in Egypt, *
     the first issue of their strength in the tents of Ham.
⁵² **Then he led out his people like sheep, ***
     and guided them in the wilderness like a flock.
⁵³ **He led them in safety, so that they were not afraid; ***
     but the sea overwhelmed their enemies.
⁵⁴ **And he brought them to his holy hill, ***
     to the mountain that his right hand had won.
⁵⁵ **He drove out nations before them; ***
     he apportioned them for a possession
     and settled the tribes of Israel in their tents.

Voice 2:
⁵⁶ Yet they tested the Most High God, and rebelled against him. *
     They did not observe his decrees,
⁵⁷ but turned away and were faithless like their ancestors; *
     they twisted like a treacherous bow.
⁵⁸ For they provoked him to anger with their high places; *
     they moved him to jealousy with their idols.
⁵⁹ When God heard, he was full of wrath, *
     and he utterly rejected Israel.
⁶⁰ He abandoned his dwelling at Shiloh, *
     the tent where he dwelt among mortals,
⁶¹ and delivered his power to captivity, *
     his glory to the hand of the foe.

⁶² He gave his people to the sword, *
    and vented his wrath on his heritage.

⁶³ Fire devoured their young men, *
    and their girls had no marriage song.

⁶⁴ Their priests fell by the sword, *
    and their widows made no lamentation.

Voice 1:

⁶⁵ Then the Lord awoke as from sleep, *
    like a warrior shouting because of wine.

⁶⁶ He put his adversaries to rout; *
    he put them to everlasting disgrace.

⁶⁷ He rejected the tent of Joseph, *
    he did not choose the tribe of Ephraim;

⁶⁸ but he chose the tribe of Judah, *
    Mount Zion, which he loves.

⁶⁹ **He built his sanctuary like the high heavens, ***
    like the earth, which he has founded forever.

⁷⁰ **He chose his servant David, ***
    and took him from the sheepfolds;

⁷¹ from tending the nursing ewes he brought him
  to be the shepherd of his people Jacob, *
    of Israel, his inheritance.

⁷² **With upright heart he tended them, ***
    and guided them with skillful hand.

O God, Beginning and Completion,
in Jesus Christ you confirmed your covenant with us
and sealed every promise in his blood.
Empower us through your Holy Spirit to teach all you have commanded,
tell all you have done, and live as those who are deeply and eternally loved,
for the glory and praise of your name. **Amen.**

Psalm 78, the second longest Psalm, is an account of the history of Israel's often rocky covenantal relationship with God and the relentless work of God to shepherd the people toward covenant faithfulness. The purpose of telling the story is to lead the next generation to trust God (vv. 6-7) and avoid the sins of rebellion (vv. 7-8). The history is told by alternating accounts of God's actions (vv. 12-16, 21-31, 38-39, 44-55, 59-72) with the peoples' faithlessness (vv. 17-20, 32-37, 40-43, 56-58). *Use in Worship: commissioning individuals involved in formative ministries with children and youth; call to confession of sin and an assurance of God's grace.*

78A People of the Lord

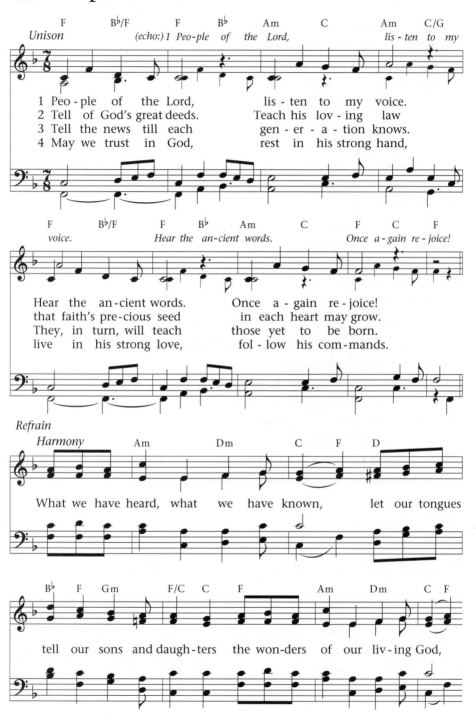

Unison

(echo:) 1 Peo-ple of the Lord, lis-ten to my

1 Peo - ple of the Lord, lis - ten to my voice.
2 Tell of God's great deeds. Teach his lov - ing law
3 Tell the news till each gen - er - a - tion knows.
4 May we trust in God, rest in his strong hand,

voice. *Hear the an-cient words.* *Once a-gain re-joice!*

Hear the an-cient words. Once a - gain re - joice!
that faith's pre-cious seed in each heart may grow.
They, in turn, will teach those yet to be born.
live in his strong love, fol - low his com-mands.

Refrain
Harmony

What we have heard, what we have known, let our tongues

tell our sons and daugh-ters the won-ders of our liv-ing God,

that they may join us in the cho-rus.

Alternate Accompaniment for Stanzas

Words: Greg Scheer © 2010 Greg Scheer
Music (JENNY VAN TSCHEGG 5.5.5.5.8.9.8.9): Greg Scheer © 2010 Greg Scheer

A Prayer for Teachers of Children 78B

Sing 78A stanzas 1 and 2, or 78C stanzas 1 and 2, or read Psalm 78:1-7

[Teachers of the youth and children may be invited to stand or come forward to be introduced to the congregation.]

God of all generations, our ears are open to hear your Word.
    We also hear your command to teach it to our children,
      so they too will praise you.
We give thanks for those who have heard your call
    to teach your Word to our children.
Send your Spirit upon them, we pray,
    so that rising generations may hope in you, love your ways,
    and live according to your will.
    In Jesus' name. Amen.

Sing 78A stanzas 3 and 4, or 78C stanza 3

78C Open Your Ears, O Faithful People

Unison

1 O - pen your ears, O faith - ful peo - ple, o - pen your
2 They who have ears to hear the mes - sage, they who have
3 What we have heard we'll teach our chil - dren; may they have

ears and hear God's Word. O - pen your hearts, O
ears, now let them hear. They who would learn the
ears to hear God's Word. Let us through ev - ery

roy - al priest - hood, God has come to you.
way of wis - dom, let them hear God's Word.
gen - er - a - tion make God's won - ders known.

Refrain

To - rah o - ra, To - rah o - ra, hal - le - lu - jah!
God has spo - ken to the peo - ple, hal - le - lu - jah!

To - rah o - ra, To - rah o - ra, hal-le - lu - jah!
God has spo-ken words of wis-dom, hal-le - lu - jah!

To - rah o - ra, To - rah o - ra, hal - le - lu - jah!
God has spo-ken to the peo-ple, hal-le - lu - jah!

To - rah o - ra, To - rah o - ra, hal - le - lu - jah!
God has spo-ken words of wis-dom, hal - le - lu - jah!

Words: Hasidic traditional; tr. Willard F. Jabusch © 1966, 1982 Willard F. Jabusch, admin. OCP Publications; st. 3 Martin Tel © 2011 Martin Tel, admin. Faith Alive Christian Resources
Music (YISRAEL V'ORAITA 9.8.9.5 with refrain): Hasidic traditional; arr. Robert Buckley Farlee © 2006 Augsburg Fortress Publishers

78D Psalm 78:1-7, 12-16, 23-29
A Responsorial Setting

Refrain

O- pen your ears, O faith-ful peo-ple, o- pen your ears and hear God's Word.

O - pen your hearts, O roy - al priest-hood, God has come to you.

Refrain

1 Hear my teaching, O my people;
   incline your ears to the words of my mouth.

2 I will open my mouth in a parable;
   I will declare the mysteries of ancient times—

3 that which we have heard and known, and what our forebears have told us,
   we will not hide from their children.

4 We will recount to generations to come the praiseworthy deeds
   and the power of the LORD,
      and the wonderful works God has done.   *Refrain*

5 The LORD gave a decree in Jacob and established a law in Israel,
   commanding our ancestors to teach it to their children;

6 that the generations to come might know, and the children yet unborn;
   that they in their turn might tell it to their children;

7 so that they might put their trust in God,
   and not forget the deeds of God, but keep God's commandments.   *Refrain*

12 God worked marvels in the sight of their ancestors,
   in the land of Egypt, in the field of Zoan,

13 splitting open the sea and letting them pass through;
   making the waters stand up like walls;

14 leading them with a cloud by day,
   and all the night with a glow of fire;

15 splitting the rocks in the wilderness
   and giving them drink as from the deep;

16 bringing streams out of a rock,
   making them flow down like a river.   *Refrain*

²³ So God commanded the clouds above
　　and opened the doors of heaven,

²⁴ raining down manna upon them to eat
　　and giving them grain from heaven.

²⁵ So mortals ate the bread of angels;
　　God provided for them food enough.

²⁶ The LORD caused the east wind to blow in the heavens
　　and powerfully led out the south wind,

²⁷ raining down flesh upon them like dust
　　and flying birds like the sand of the seas,

²⁸ letting them fall in the midst of the camp
　　and round about the dwellings.

²⁹ So the people ate and were well filled,
　　for God gave them what they craved.　　*Refrain*

Tone

Lectionary: vv. 1-4, 12-16 Ordinary Time after Pentecost (A); vv. 1-7 Ordinary Time after Pentecost (A); vv. 23-29 Ordinary Time after Pentecost (B).

For accompaniment see p. 482.

Words: Hasidic traditional; tr. Willard F. Jabusch © 1966, 1982 Willard F. Jabusch, admin. OCP Publications
Music (YISRAEL V'ORAITA fragment): Hasidic traditional
Psalm Text: from *Evangelical Lutheran Worship* © 2006 Evangelical Lutheran Church in America, admin. Augsburg Fortress Publishers
Tone: © 2011 Faith Alive Christian Resources

78E We Will Tell Each Generation

1 We will tell each gen-er-a-tion all that
2 Tell the time of our re-bel-ling— how we
3 Tell how once, when spite and ter-ror threat-ened

you, our God, have done; how you called and
wan-dered from your way, how your law our
to en-gulf our land, you de-fend-ed

led your peo-ple, chose us out to be your own.
love com-pel-ling taught us hum-bly to o-bey.
us with vig-or, saved us by a might-y hand.

4 Tell the grace that falls from heaven,
angels' food as faith's reward;
tell how sins may be forgiven
through the mercy of the Lord.

5 We will tell each generation
all that you, our God, have done.
As a shepherd you have led us;
by your hand still lead your own.

Words: sts. 1-4 Michael Perry; st. 5 Michael Perry, alt. Martin Tel © 1989 The Jubilate Group, admin. Hope Publishing Company
Music (ARISE/RESTORATION 8.7.8.7): W. Walker's *Southern Harmony*, 1835; harm. Charles H. Webb (b. 1933), P.D.

Psalm 79

A Psalm of Asaph.

¹ O God, the nations have come into your inheritance; *

    they have defiled your holy temple; they have laid Jerusalem in ruins.

² They have given the bodies of your servants to the birds of the air for food, *

    the flesh of your faithful to the wild animals of the earth.

³ They have poured out their blood like water all around Jerusalem, *

    and there was no one to bury them.

⁴ **We have become a taunt to our neighbors, ***

    mocked and derided by those around us.

⁵ **How long, O LORD? Will you be angry forever? ***

    Will your jealous wrath burn like fire?

⁶ **Pour out your anger on the nations that do not know you, ***

    and on the kingdoms that do not call on your name.

⁷ For they have devoured Jacob *

    and laid waste his habitation.

⁸ **Do not remember against us the iniquities of our ancestors; ***

    let your compassion come speedily to meet us,

    for we are brought very low.

⁹ **Help us, O God of our salvation, for the glory of your name; ***

    deliver us, and forgive our sins, for your name's sake.

¹⁰ Why should the nations say, "Where is their God?" *

    Let the avenging of the outpoured blood of your servants

    be known among the nations before our eyes.

¹¹ **Let the groans of the prisoners come before you; ***

    according to your great power preserve those doomed to die.

¹² Return sevenfold into the bosom of our neighbors *

    the taunts with which they taunted you, O Lord!

¹³ **Then we your people, the flock of your pasture,**

  will give thanks to you forever; *

    from generation to generation we will recount your praise.

O God, through your Son, the Man of Sorrows, you are acquainted with our grief.
We pray for your church, especially in places of persecution and distress.
When hope grows dim, kindle within us patience in prayer
and persistence in the struggle for justice and peace.
We ask this in the name of Jesus. **Amen.**

Psalm 79, like Ps. 74, voices bitter communal reflection on the conquest of Jerusalem (vv. 1-4), a cry for deliverance (vv. 5-10), a prayer for justice for the enemy (vv. 10b-12), and a vow to offer praise to God for God's justice and faithfulness (v. 13). It is graphic in its depiction of violence and vivid in its depiction of human shame, grief, fear, and longing. The psalm asks for divine retribution against the enemy (v. 12) but hands over this vengeance to God rather than taking it into human hands. It is also unique in daring to pray for divine retribution while acknowledging the human faithlessness that led to divine judgment (vv. 8- 9). Used with great care, it may be appropriate in places where the vitality of God's covenant people has been decimated through (their own) unfaithfulness and the violent forces of culture. *Use in Worship: in conjunction with OT narratives of judgment and exile; services focusing on situations of extreme persecution.*

Refrain

¹ O God, the nations have come into your inheritance;
　they have profaned your holy temple;
　　they have made Jerusalem a heap of rubble.

² They have given the bodies of your servants as food for the birds of the air,
　　and the flesh of your faithful ones to the beasts of the field.

³ They have shed their blood like water on every side of Jerusalem,
　　and there was no one to bury them.

⁴ We have become a reproach to our neighbors,
　　an object of scorn and derision to those around us.　　*Refrain*

⁵ How long will you be angry, O LORD?
　　Will your fury blaze like fire forever?

⁶ Pour out your wrath upon the nations who have not known you
　　and upon the kingdoms that have not called upon your name.

⁷ For they have devoured Jacob
　　and made his dwelling a ruin.　　*Refrain*

⁸ Remember not our past sins; let your compassion be swift to meet us;

for we have been brought very low.

⁹ Help us, O God our Savior, for the glory of your name;

deliver us and forgive us our sins, for your name's sake.   *Refrain*

Tone

Lectionary: Ordinary Time After Pentecost (C).

Words: Marvin V. Frey © 1977 Marvin V. Frey
Music (KUM BA YAH 8.8.8.5): Marvin V. Frey © 1977 and arr. Bethany Vrieland © 2011 Marvin V. Frey
Psalm Text: from *Evangelical Lutheran Worship* © 2006 Evangelical Lutheran Church in America, admin.
Augsburg Fortress Publishers
Tone: © 2011 Faith Alive Christian Resources

Remember Not, O God   79B

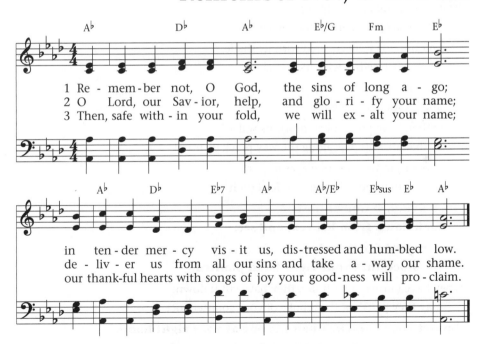

1 Re - mem - ber not, O   God,   the sins of long a - go;
2 O   Lord, our Sav - ior, help,   and glo - ri - fy your name;
3 Then, safe with - in your   fold,   we will ex - alt your name;

in ten - der mer - cy vis - it us, dis - tressed and hum - bled low.
de - liv - er us from all our sins and take a - way our shame.
our thank-ful hearts with songs of joy your good-ness will pro - claim.

This tune in a higher key: p. 702.

Words: *Psalter*, 1912, P.D.
Music (GORTON 6.6.8.6): Ludwig van Beethoven (1770-1827), 1807, adapt., P.D.

Psalm 80

To the leader: on Lilies, a Covenant. Of Asaph. A Psalm.

1 Give ear, O Shepherd of Israel, you who lead Joseph like a flock! *
  You who are enthroned upon the cherubim, shine forth

2 before Ephraim and Benjamin and Manasseh. *
  Stir up your might, and come to save us!

3 **Restore us, O God; ***
  let your face shine, that we may be saved.

4 O LORD God of hosts, *
  how long will you be angry with your people's prayers?

5 You have fed them with the bread of tears, *
  and given them tears to drink in full measure.

6 You make us the scorn of our neighbors; *
  our enemies laugh among themselves.

7 **Restore us, O God of hosts; ***
  let your face shine, that we may be saved.

8 You brought a vine out of Egypt; *
  you drove out the nations and planted it.

9 You cleared the ground for it; *
  it took deep root and filled the land.

10 The mountains were covered with its shade, *
  the mighty cedars with its branches;

11 it sent out its branches to the sea, *
  and its shoots to the River.

12 Why then have you broken down its walls, *
  so that all who pass along the way pluck its fruit?

13 The boar from the forest ravages it, *
  and all that move in the field feed on it.

14 **Turn again, O God of hosts; ***
  look down from heaven, and see;
  have regard for this vine, *
    15 **the stock that your right hand planted.**

16 They have burned it with fire, they have cut it down; *
  may they perish at the rebuke of your countenance.

17 **But let your hand be upon the one at your right hand, ***
  the one whom you made strong for yourself.

18 **Then we will never turn back from you; ***
  give us life, and we will call on your name.

¹⁹ **Restore us, O Lᴏʀᴅ God of hosts;** *
let your face shine, that we may be saved.

Shepherd of your flock, restore your wayward people;
lead us again to green pastures and renew us beside the waters of comfort.
Because of your faithful care we worship and praise your holy name. **Amen.**

Psalm 80 is a prayer for God's intervention to restore the people and is especially poignant after the desolation and violence depicted in Ps. 79. The theme is clearly established by the cry for restoration and salvation repeated throughout the psalm (vv. 3, 7, 19), ending with a vow to faithful obedience (v. 18) before the last refrain. *Use in Worship: intercessory prayer during the season of Advent; services focusing on the image of God as shepherd; in conjunction with OT narratives of judgment and exile.*

Psalm 80 | A Responsorial Setting 80A

Refrain

¹ Hear, O Shepherd of Israel, leading Joseph like a flock;
shine forth, you that are enthroned upon the cherubim.

² In the presence of Ephraim, Benjamin, and Manasseh,
stir up your strength and come to help us.

³ Restore us, O God;
let your face shine upon us, and we shall be saved.   *Refrain*

⁴ O Lᴏʀᴅ God of hosts,
how long will your anger fume when your people pray?

⁵ You have fed them with the bread of tears;
you have given them bowls of tears to drink.   (continues)

⁶ You have made us the derision of our neighbors,
  and our enemies laugh us to scorn.

⁷ Restore us, O God of hosts;
  let your face shine upon us, and we shall be saved.   *Refrain*

⁸ You have brought a vine out of Egypt;
  you cast out the nations and planted it.

⁹ You cleared the ground for it;
  it took root and filled the land.

¹⁰ The mountains were covered by its shadow
  and the towering cedar trees by its boughs.

¹¹ You stretched out its tendrils to the sea
  and its branches to the river.   *Refrain*

¹² Why have you broken down its wall,
  so that all who pass by pluck off its grapes?

¹³ The wild boar of the forest has ravaged it,
  and the beasts of the field have grazed upon it.

¹⁴ Turn now, O God of hosts,
  look down from heaven;

¹⁵ behold and tend this vine;
  preserve what your right hand has planted.

¹⁶ They burn it with fire like rubbish;
  at the rebuke of your countenance let them perish.   *Refrain*

¹⁷ Let your hand be upon the one at your right hand,
  the one you have made so strong for yourself.

¹⁸ And so will we never turn away from you;
  give us life, that we may call upon your name.

¹⁹ Restore us, O Lord God of hosts;
  let your face shine upon us, and we shall be saved.   *Refrain*

Tone

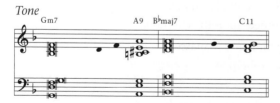

*Lectionary: vv. 1-7, 17-19, Advent (A,B); vv. 1-7 Advent (C); vv. 1-2, 8-19 Ordinary Time after Pentecost (C);
vv. 7-15 Ordinary Time after Pentecost (C).*

Words and Music: David Lee © 1996 David Lee
Psalm Text: from *Evangelical Lutheran Worship* © 2006 Evangelical Lutheran Church in America, admin.
Augsburg Fortress Publishers
Tone: © 2011 Faith Alive Christian Resources

O Hear Our Cry, O Lord 80B

Guitar chords do not correspond with keyboard harmony.

Words: Fred R. Anderson (b. 1941), 1986, © 1986 Fred R. Anderson
Music (VINEYARD HAVEN 6.6.8.6 with refrain): Richard Dirksen, 1974, © 1974, 1987 Harold Flammer,
a division of Shawnee Press; arr. © 2011 Harold Flammer, a division of Shawnee Press, Inc., reprinted by
permission of Hal Leonard Corporation

80C O Shepherd, Hear and Lead Your Flock

1 O Shep-herd, hear and lead your flock, as lambs we crave your care;
2 Our self - ish prayers de-serve God's wrath, our pride, a sud - den burst;
3 God's lin - eage, like a vine, once spread and flour-ished in the land;

what strength on earth ap-proach-es yours, what mer - cies can com-pare?
we have but stones to serve as bread, and tears to quell our thirst.
but now the vine-yard fails, the fruit lies with-ered in the sand.

Re - store, O God, your fav - or, the ra - diance of your face
Re - store, O God Al - might - y, the ra - diance of your face
Re - store, LORD God Al - might - y, the ra - diance of your face

to light-en and re - veal the gift of your re - deem - ing grace.
to light-en and re - veal the gift of your re - deem - ing grace.
to light-en and re - veal the gift of your re - deem - ing grace.

Guitar chords do not correspond with keyboard harmony.

Words: Michael Morgan © 1999, 2011 Michael Morgan, admin. Faith Alive Christian Resources
Music (ST. LOUIS 8.6.8.6.7.6.8.6): Lewis H. Redner (1831-1908), P.D.

Psalm 81

To the leader: according to The Gittith. Of Asaph.

1 Sing aloud to God our strength; *
  shout for joy to the God of Jacob.

2 **Raise a song, sound the tambourine, ***
  the sweet lyre with the harp.

3 Blow the trumpet at the new moon, *
  at the full moon, on our festal day.

4 **For it is a statute for Israel, ***
  an ordinance of the God of Jacob.

5 **He made it a decree in Joseph,**
  when he went out over the land of Egypt. *
  I hear a voice I had not known:

6 "I relieved your shoulder of the burden; *
  your hands were freed from the basket.

7 In distress you called, and I rescued you; *
  I answered you in the secret place of thunder;
  I tested you at the waters of Meribah.   *Selah*

8 **Hear, O my people, while I admonish you; ***
  O Israel, if you would but listen to me!

9 There shall be no strange god among you; *
  you shall not bow down to a foreign god.

10 **I am the Lord your God,**
  who brought you up out of the land of Egypt. *
  Open your mouth wide and I will fill it.

11 "But my people did not listen to my voice; *
  Israel would not submit to me.

12 So I gave them over to their stubborn hearts, *
  to follow their own counsels.

13 **O that my people would listen to me, ***
  that Israel would walk in my ways!

14 **Then I would quickly subdue their enemies, ***
  and turn my hand against their foes.

15 Those who hate the Lord would cringe before him, *
  and their doom would last forever.

16 **I would feed you with the finest of the wheat, ***
  and with honey from the rock I would satisfy you."   (continues)

Pour out your Spirit's power upon your people, O God,
until we humble ourselves, seek your face, and turn from wicked ways.
Revive your church and heal our land.
We pray in Jesus' name. **Amen.**

Psalm 81 is a song of praise composed for use at a solemn religious festival (v. 3). It begins with an exuberant call to praise and concludes with an extended oracle that retells God's history with the people of Israel. (See Ps. 50 for another example of an extended record of God's speech.) Following several psalms that explore the predicament of God's exiled people and plead with God for restoration (esp. Pss. 74, 79, 80), this divine speech answers with an especially poignant rejoinder: "If only my people would listen to me..., then I would act" (see vv. 13-14). The psalm also includes the vivid metaphor of divine nourishment (vv. 10, 16) and repeated desire that God's people would listen or hear (vv. 8, 11, 13). *Use in Worship: call to worship (opening verses); celebrations of the Lord's Supper (image of divine nourishment, remembrance of God's actions in history, a call to exuberant praise and to covenantal faithfulness); preparation for the reading and preaching of God's Word (pivot from the call to make music in vv. 1-3 to the call to listen in vv. 8-13).*

81A Psalm 81 | A Responsorial Setting

Refrain

O be joy - ful, O be joy - ful in your hearts,
and give thanks to God our Sav - ior.
For God's mer - cy, for God's mer - cy's ev - er - last - ing.

Refrain

1. Sing with joy to God our strength
   and raise a loud shout to the God of Jacob.

2. Raise a song and sound the timbrel,
   the merry harp, and the lyre.

3. Blow the ram's horn at the new moon,
   and at the full moon, the day of our feast;

4. for this is a statute for Israel,
   a law of the God of Jacob. *Refrain*

5. God laid it as a solemn charge upon Joseph, going out over the land of Egypt,
   where I heard a voice I did not know:

⁶ "I eased your shoulder from the burden;
    your hands were set free from the gravedigger's basket.

⁷ You called on me in trouble, and I delivered you;
    I answered you from the secret place of thunder
    and tested you at the waters of Meribah.

⁸ Hear, O my people, and I will admonish you:
    O Israel, if you would but listen to me!

⁹ There shall be no strange god among you;
    you shall not worship a foreign god.

¹⁰ I am the LORD your God, who brought you out of the land of Egypt.
    Open your mouth wide, and I will fill it.   *Refrain*

¹¹ Yet my people did not hear my voice,
    and Israel would not obey me.

¹² So I gave them over to the stubbornness of their hearts,
    to follow their own devices.

¹³ Oh, that my people would listen to me,
    that Israel would walk in my ways!

¹⁴ I would quickly subdue their enemies
    and turn my hand against their foes.

¹⁵ Those who hate the LORD would cringe in fear,
    and their punishment would last forever.

¹⁶ But I would feed you with the finest wheat
    and satisfy you with honey from the rock."   *Refrain*

Tone

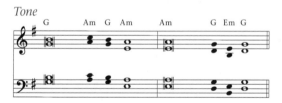

Claves   *Maracas*

Lectionary: vv. 1-10 Ordinary Time after Epiphany (B) and Ordinary Time after Pentecost (B); vv. 1, 10-16 Ordinary Time after Pentecost (C).

(continues)

Alternate Refrain: Gift of Finest Wheat

Words: Omer Westendorf, 1976, © 1977 Archdiocese of Philadelphia, published by International Liturgy Publications
Music (BICENTENNIAL refrain 8.6.8.6): Robert E. Kreutz, 1976, © 1977 Archdiocese of Philadelphia, published by International Liturgy Publications
A full version of Gift of Finest Wheat *with verses is available from the publisher.*
Tone: © 2011 International Liturgy Publications

Strike Up the Music! 81B

Sing softly or hum during spoken verses

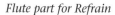

Flute part for Refrain

Bell part for Refrain

May be used as a refrain with 81A when verses are spoken.

Words: Psalm 81
Music: Julie Howard; arr. Vera Lyons © 1992 Liturgical Press

81C Sing a Psalm of Joy!

1 Sing a psalm of joy! Shout in cel - e - bra - tion.
2 Sound the fes - tal horn, your thanks - giv - ing voic - ing.

[The exhortation of the LORD (Psalm 81:6-10) or a reading of the law may be spoken here.]

*3 Tune our hearts to praise; turn our ears to hear you.

Let the tam - bou - rine and the trum - pet bring
Praise the LORD your God, as he did com - mand
Then in thank - ful - ness may we walk your way

prais - es to our King for his great sal - va - tion.
when from E - gypt's land you came forth re - joic - ing.
and from day to day hon - or and a - dore you.

To sing the entire psalm, skip this stanza and continue with the optional stanzas 3-7 on facing page.

A Reading of the Law

Hear the Word of the Lord:
"I am the LORD your God, who brought you out of Egypt,
  out of the land of slavery.
You shall have no other gods before me.
You shall not make for yourself an image in the form of anything
  in heaven above or on the earth beneath or in the waters below.
You shall not bow down to them or worship them.
You shall not misuse the name of the LORD your God.

Remember the Sabbath day by keeping it holy.

Honor your father and your mother.

You shall not murder.

You shall not commit adultery.

You shall not steal.

You shall not give false testimony against your neighbor.

You shall not covet anything that belongs to your neighbor." *Exodus 20:1-7* (NIV)

Alternate stanzas for use when the exhortation or a reading of the Law is not spoken

3 When in need you cried,
  I was near and saved you.
  From the cloud I spoke,
  answered your request—
  Meribah the test—
  I did not forsake you.

4 O my people, hear;
  when I call you, listen.
  Choose no foreign god—
  listen to my plea.
  Have no god but me;
  come and be forgiven.

5 I, the LORD your God,
  brought you out of Egypt.
  I removed your yoke,
  all your needs supplied.
  Open your mouth wide:
  surely I will fill it.

6 Oh, that Israel
  would but hear my pleading!
  Oh, that they would turn,
  walk upon my path;
  I would pour my wrath
  on their foes unheeding.

7 With the finest wheat
  I, your LORD, would feed you.
  Honey from the rock
  I would gladly give
  that you all might live.
  Hear me, O my people.

Guitar chords do not correspond with keyboard harmony.

Words: Marie J. Post, 1984, © 1987 Faith Alive Christian Resources, *st. 3 Martin Tel © 2011 Martin Tel, admin. Faith Alive Christian Resources
Music (GENEVAN 81 | 5.6.5.5.5.6): *Genevan Psalter*, 1562; harm. Dale Grotenhuis, 1985, © 1987 Faith Alive Christian Resources
Text: Exodus 20 © THE HOLY BIBLE, NEW INTERNATIONAL VERSION®, NIV® Copyright © 1973, 1978, 1984, 2011 by Biblica, Inc.™ Used by permission. All rights reserved worldwide.

Psalm 82

A Psalm of Asaph.

Voice 1:

¹ God has taken his place in the divine council; *

    in the midst of the gods he holds judgment:

Voice 2:

² "How long will you judge unjustly *

    and show partiality to the wicked?   *Selah*

³ Give justice to the weak and the orphan; *

    maintain the right of the lowly and the destitute.

⁴ Rescue the weak and the needy; *

    deliver them from the hand of the wicked."

⁵ **They have neither knowledge nor understanding,**

  they walk around in darkness; *

  all the foundations of the earth are shaken.

⁶ I say, "You are gods, *

    children of the Most High, all of you;

⁷ nevertheless, you shall die like mortals, *

    and fall like any prince."

⁸ **Rise up, O God, judge the earth;** *

  for all the nations belong to you!

Sovereign Lord,
your justice and your mercy surpass what we can know or imagine.
Open our eyes so that as we feed the hungry, welcome the stranger,
tend the sick, visit the prisoner, and defend the weak,
we may see your Son, Jesus Christ,
and be welcomed into the kingdom he has prepared for us. **Amen.**

Psalm 82 is rooted in profound concern for the weak, the orphaned, the lowly, and the poor (vv. 3-4), along with the conviction that sovereign authority is properly exercised on their behalf rather than on behalf of the faithless (v. 2). This theme is dramatized by depicting God in an assembly of deities, bringing charges of unfaithfulness against them—a vision that resembles other prophetic critiques of false gods (e.g., Isa. 41:21-29). The nature of these lesser deities is unclear: are these lesser deities merely a part of an ancient world view which the Bible ends up rejecting in its claim that they are ultimately nonexistent, or are they lesser members of the divine council, "heavenly powers" that misuse their God-given authority (like the powers which were created through Christ (Col. 1:15-16) but which Christ had to conquer (Col. 2:15) and which we still face and pray against (1 Cor. 15:24, 25, Eph. 6:12)? In any case, faithful usage of this psalm requires rehearsal of a countercultural concern for justice and confident, but urgent, prayer for God as the ultimate agent of justice. Psalms 82 and 83 offer two complementary perspectives on international terror: Ps. 82 from the perspective of heavenly forces and Ps. 83 from the perspective of conspiring authorities. *Use in Worship: services focusing on themes of idolatry or injustice.*

There Where the Judges Gather

82A

1 There where the judg-es gath-er, a great-er takes his seat;
2 "Deal just-ly with the need-y, pro-tect the par-ent-less,
3 God speaks: "I named you rul-ers, to serve the Most High God;

"How long," he asks the judg-es, "will you pro-nounce de-ceit?
de-liv-er the af-flict-ed from those who would op-press.
but you shall die as mor-tals and per-ish by my rod."

How long show spe-cial fa-vor to those of ill re-pute?
But you are whol-ly blind-ed, you do not un-der-stand;
A-rise, O God, in judg-ment, your sov-ereign-ty make known;

How long ne-glect the or-phaned, the poor and des-ti-tute?
there-fore foun-da-tions tot-ter, in-jus-tice rocks the land."
for yours are all the na-tions, the peo-ples are your own.

Guitar chords do not correspond with keyboard harmony.

Words: Henry Zylstra, 1953, alt., P.D.
Music (MEIRIONYDD 7.6.7.6 D): William Lloyd, 1840, P.D.

503

82B Psalm 82 | A Responsorial Setting

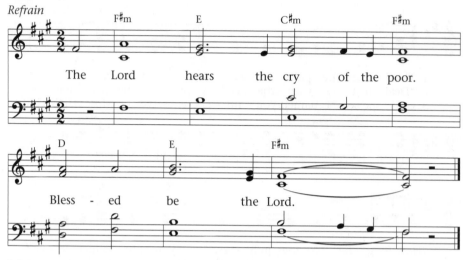

Refrain

The Lord hears the cry of the poor.

Bless - ed be the Lord.

Refrain

¹ God stands to charge the divine council assembled,
  giving judgment in the midst of the gods;

² "How long will you judge unjustly,
  and show favor to the wicked?

³ Save the weak and the orphan;
  defend the humble and needy;

⁴ rescue the weak and the poor;
  deliver them from the power of the wicked.

⁵ They do not know, neither do they understand; they wander about in darkness;
  all the foundations of the earth are shaken.   *Refrain*

⁶ Now I say to you, 'You are gods,
  and all of you children of the Most High;

⁷ nevertheless, you shall die like mortals,
  and fall like any prince.'"

⁸ Arise, O God, and rule the earth,
  for you shall take all nations for your own.   *Refrain*

Tone

Lectionary: Ordinary Time after Pentecost (C).

Words and Music: John B. Foley, S. J. © 1978, 1991 John B. Foley, S. J., admin. OCP Publications
Psalm Text: from *Evangelical Lutheran Worship* © 2006 Evangelical Lutheran Church in America, admin.
Augsburg Fortress Publishers
Tone: © 2011 Faith Alive Christian Resources

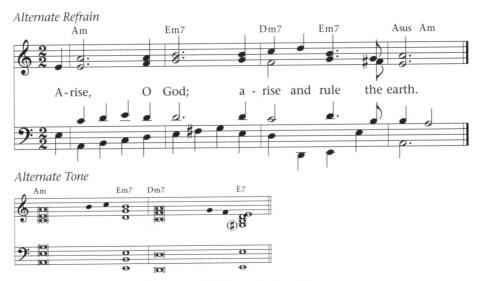

Alternate Refrain

A-rise, O God; a - rise and rule the earth.

Alternate Tone

Words and Music: Howard Hughes, S. M. © 1991 Howard Hughes, S. M.
Tone: © 2011 Faith Alive Christian Resources

Psalm 83

A Song. A Psalm of Asaph.

Voice 1:

1 O God, do not keep silence; *
  do not hold your peace or be still, O God!

2 **Even now your enemies are in tumult; ***
  those who hate you have raised their heads.

3 **They lay crafty plans against your people; ***
  they consult together against those you protect.

4 **They say, "Come, let us wipe them out as a nation; ***
  let the name of Israel be remembered no more."

5 They conspire with one accord; *
  against you they make a covenant—

6 the tents of Edom and the Ishmaelites, *
  Moab and the Hagrites,

7 Gebal and Ammon and Amalek, *
  Philistia with the inhabitants of Tyre;

8 Assyria also has joined them; *
  they are the strong arm of the children of Lot. *Selah*

(continues)

Voice 2:

⁹ Do to them as you did to Midian, *
  as to Sisera and Jabin at the Wadi Kishon,

¹⁰ who were destroyed at En-dor, *
  who became dung for the ground.

¹¹ Make their nobles like Oreb and Zeeb, *
  all their princes like Zebah and Zalmunna,

¹² who said, "Let us take the pastures of God *
  for our own possession."

Voice 1:

¹³ O my God, make them like whirling dust, *
  like chaff before the wind.

¹⁴ As fire consumes the forest, *
  as the flame sets the mountains ablaze,

¹⁵ so pursue them with your tempest *
  and terrify them with your hurricane.

¹⁶ **Fill their faces with shame, ***
  so that they may seek your name, O LORD.

¹⁷ **Let them be put to shame and dismayed forever; ***
  let them perish in disgrace.

¹⁸ **Let them know that you alone, whose name is the LORD, ***
  are the Most High over all the earth.

Sovereign God, the nations seek no glory but their own.
Reveal to all the mystery of your will from before the foundations of the world.
In the fullness of time, unite all things in heaven and on earth,
in Jesus Christ your Son. **Amen.**

Psalm 83 is a communal lament that asks God to do whatever is necessary to enable all of God's enemies to acknowledge God (vv. 16, 18). It catalogs a list of the nations that conspire against God (vv. 5-11, echoing the concern of Ps. 2) and then, remarkably, turns images of divine violence (vv. 13-15) into missionary images, suggesting the outcome of the hoped for divine violence is that "every knee shall bow." Paradoxically, the psalm prays for the conspiring nations to experience humiliation, shame, terror, and disgrace in such a way that they confess God, the very activity that heals shame and terror. *Use in Worship: in conjunction with OT narratives of judgment; in juxtaposition with OT and NT texts about the peoples of the earth learning to praise God (e.g., Ps. 65, Isa. 60, Rev. 19).*

Do Not Keep Silent, O God 83A

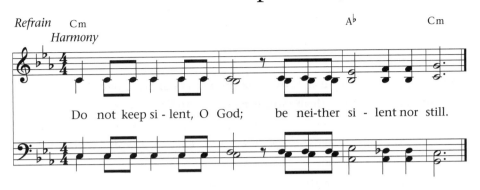

Refrain — Harmony

Do not keep si - lent, O God; be nei-ther si - lent nor still.

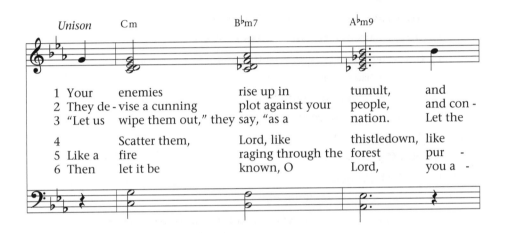

Unison

1 Your enemies rise up in tumult, and
2 They de-vise a cunning plot against your people, and con -
3 "Let us wipe them out," they say, "as a nation. Let the

4 Scatter them, Lord, like thistledown, like
5 Like a fire raging through the forest pur -
6 Then let it be known, O Lord, you a -

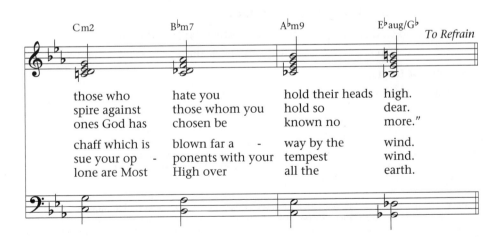

To Refrain

those who hate you hold their heads high.
spire against those whom you hold so dear.
ones God has chosen be known no more."

chaff which is blown far a - way by the wind.
sue your op - ponents with your tempest wind.
lone are Most High over all the earth.

Sung angrily. Keep the half-note pulse steady from the refrain to the verses.

Psalm 84

To the leader: according to The Gittith. Of the Korahites. A Psalm.

¹ How lovely is your dwelling place, *
   O LORD of hosts!

² **My soul longs, indeed it faints for the courts of the LORD; ***
   my heart and my flesh sing for joy to the living God.

³ Even the sparrow finds a home, and the swallow a nest for herself, *
   where she may lay her young, at your altars, O LORD of hosts,
   my King and my God.

⁴ **Happy are those who live in your house, ***
   ever singing your praise.   *Selah*

⁵ **Happy are those whose strength is in you, ***
   in whose heart are the highways to Zion.

⁶ As they go through the valley of Baca they make it a place of springs; *
   the early rain also covers it with pools.

⁷ They go from strength to strength; *
   the God of gods will be seen in Zion.

⁸ **O LORD God of hosts, hear my prayer; ***
   give ear, O God of Jacob!   *Selah*

⁹ Behold our shield, O God; *
   look on the face of your anointed.

¹⁰ **For a day in your courts is better than a thousand elsewhere. ***
   I would rather be a doorkeeper in the house of my God
   than live in the tents of wickedness.

¹¹ For the LORD God is a sun and shield; he bestows favor and honor. *
   No good thing does the LORD withhold from those who walk uprightly.

¹² **O LORD of hosts, ***
   happy is everyone who trusts in you.

God of all loveliness and beauty,
even the humblest of creatures finds its home close to you.
May your church be a place of safety to every wanderer who seeks you,
every believer who trusts you, and every disciple who follows you.
We pray this in Jesus' name. **Amen.**

Psalm 84 is a psalm of trust and praise that expresses radiant joy and repose in communing with the living God, a dramatic relief after a grueling series of psalms that focus on disobedience, exile, evil, and violence. It evokes the importance of temple worship (vv. 1, 4, 10) with which the third book of the Psalter began (73:15-16) and provides a perfect complement to Ps. 42: the parched longing for God has now been fulfilled in the temple, ultimately the place where God is encountered. *Use in Worship: services focusing on the presentation of Jesus in the temple; funerals; dedications of worship spaces or churches; services focusing on the joy, peace, and repose that come from encounters with Christ, the true temple of God (see John 2:21), from experiences of the Holy Spirit who dwells in God's people as the temple (1 Cor. 3:16, 6:19), and from anticipating the day when the temple will not be needed because of the unmediated experience of God's presence (Rev. 3:12, 21:2, 10).*

How Lovely Is Your Dwelling 84A

1 How love - ly is your dwell-ing, O Lord of hosts, to me;
2 Be - neath your care the spar-row finds place for peace - ful rest;
3 Blest they who love and serve you, whose joy and strength you are.

my soul is long-ing, faint - ing, the courts of God to see.
to keep her young in safe - ty the swal-low finds a nest.
For - ev - er they will praise you, your ways are in their heart.

The beau - ty of your dwell - ing will bring me joy a - new.
So, Lord, my King Al - might - y, your love will shel - ter me;
Though tried, their tears like show - ers shall fill the springs of peace;

My heart and flesh are cry - ing, O liv - ing God, for you.
be - neath your wings of mer - cy my dwell - ing place will be.
and all the way to Zi - on their strength shall still in - crease.

Words: *Psalter*, 1912, alt., P.D.
Music (ST. EDITH 7.6.7.6 D): Justin H. Krecht, 1799; rev. Edward Husband, 1871, P.D.

84B Better Is One Day

1 How love-ly is your dwell-ing place, O Lord Al-might-y.
(2 One) thing I ask and I would seek: to see your beau-ty,

For my soul longs and ev - en faints for you.
to find you in the place your glo - ry dwells.

For here my heart is sat - is - fied, with-in your pres-
One thing I ask and I would seek: to see your beau-

- ence. I sing be-neath the shad - ow of your wings.
- ty, to find you in the place your glo - ry dwells.

(continues)

Bridge

My heart and flesh cry out for you, the liv-ing God; your Spir-it's wa-ter to my soul. I've tast-ed and I've seen, come once a-gain to me; I will draw near to you, I will draw near to you. *(to you.)* Bet-ter is

Words: Psalm 84 and Psalm 27:4; Matt Redman © 1996 Kingsway's Thankyou Music, admin. EMI CMG Publishing
Music: Matt Redman © 1996 Kingsway's Thankyou Music, admin. EMI CMG Publishing

84C How Lovely, Lord, How Lovely

1 How love-ly, Lord, how love-ly is your a-bid-ing place;
2 In your blest courts to wor-ship, O God, a sin-gle day
3 A sun and shield for-ev-er are you, O Lord Most High;

my soul is long-ing, faint-ing, to feast up-on your grace.
is bet-ter than a thou-sand if I from you should stray.
you show-er us with bless-ings; no good will you de-ny.

The spar-row finds a shel-ter, a place to build her nest,
I'd rath-er keep the en-trance and claim you as my Lord
The saints, your grace re-ceiv-ing, from strength to strength shall go,

and so your tem-ple calls us with-in its walls to rest.
than rev-el in the rich-es the ways of sin af-ford.
and from their life shall riv-ers of bless-ing o-ver-flow.

Guitar chords do not correspond with keyboard harmony.

Words: Arlo D. Duba © 1986 Hope Publishing Company
Music (MERLE'S TUNE 7.6.7.6 D): Hal H. Hopson © 1983 Hope Publishing Company; harm. Hal H. Hopson
© 2011 Hope Publishing Company

Almighty Lord, 84D
How Lovely Is That Place

Unison

1 Al - might - y Lord, how love - ly is that place
2 At times we sigh, are slow to sing your praise,
3 From strength to strength we live each pass - ing year,
4 Lord, hear my prayer, with fa - vor look on me;
5 *Glo - ry to God, the Fa - ther and the Son*

where you are dwell - ing, robed in light and grace!
yet find in you the strength for all our days,
led by your love, which casts a - way all fear,
there is no place that I would rath - er be
and Ho - ly Spir - it, ev - er three in one;

Oh, how we long to see you, face to face!
as des - ert paths are flood - ed by your grace!
till we in Zi - on sure - ly shall ap - pear!
than in your courts, to dwell e - ter - nal - ly!
ev - er the same, while end - less a - ges run!

Al - le - lu - ia! Al - le - lu - ia!

Guitar chords do not correspond with keyboard harmony.
Words: Stephen P. Starke © 1991 Stephen P. Starke, admin. Concordia Publishing House
Music (SINE NOMINE 10.10.10 with alleluias): Ralph Vaughan Williams (1872-1958), P.D.

515

84E How Lovely Is Thy Dwelling Place

1 How love-ly is thy dwell-ing place, O Lord of hosts, to
2 Be-side thine al-tars, gra-cious Lord, the swal-lows find a
3 They who go through the des-ert vale will find it filled with
4 One day with-in thy courts ex-cels a thou-sand spent a-

me! My thirst-y soul de-sires and longs with-
nest; how hap-py they who dwell with thee and
springs, and they shall climb from height to height till
way; how hap-py they who keep thy laws nor

in thy courts to be; my ver-y heart and
praise thee with-out rest, and hap-py they whose
Zi-on's tem-ple rings with praise to thee, in
from thy pre-cepts stray, for thou shalt sure-ly

flesh cry out, O liv-ing God, for thee.
hearts are set up-on the pil-grims' quest.
glo-ry throned, Lord God, great King of kings.
bless all those who live the words they pray.

(continues)

Optional stanza from Psalm 23
> Goodness and mercy all my life
> shall surely follow me,
> and in God's house forevermore
> my dwelling place shall be;
> and in God's house forevermore
> my dwelling place shall be.

Words: sts. 1, 2, and opt. st. *Scottish Psalter*, 1650; sts. 3 and 4 Carl P. Daw Jr. (b. 1944) © 1982 Hope Publishing Company
Music (BROTHER JAMES' AIR 8.6.8.6.8.6): J. L. Macbeth Bain (1840-1925), harm. Gordon Jacob (1895-1984). Reproduced by permission of Oxford University Press.

Psalm 84 | A Responsorial Setting 84F

How dear to me is your dwell - ing place, O LORD.

Refrain

1 How dear to me is your dwelling,
   O LORD of hosts!

2 My soul has a desire and longing for the courts of the LORD;
   my heart and my flesh rejoice in the living God.

3 Even the sparrow has found a home,
   and the swallow a nest where she may lay her young,
   by the side of your altars, O LORD of hosts, my King and my God. *Refrain*

4 Happy are they who dwell in your house!
   They will always be praising you.

5 Happy are the people whose strength is in you,
   whose hearts are set on the pilgrims' way.

6 Those who go through the balsam valley will find it a place of springs,
   for the early rains have covered it with pools of water.

7 They will climb from height to height,
   and the God of gods will be seen in Zion. *Refrain*

(continues)

8 LORD God of hosts, hear my prayer;
   give ear, O God of Jacob.

9 Behold our defender, O God;
   and look upon the face of your anointed.

10 For one day in your courts is better than a thousand elsewhere.
   I would rather stand at the threshold of the house of my God
   than dwell in the tents of the wicked.

11 For the LORD God is both sun and shield, bestowing grace and glory;
   no good thing will the LORD withhold from those who walk with integrity.

12 O LORD of hosts,
   happy are they who put their trust in you!   *Refrain*

Tone

Lectionary: Ordinary Time after Pentecost (B); vv. 1-7 Ordinary Time after Pentecost (C).

Words: Psalm 84
Music: Thomas Pavlechko, based on music by Johannes Brahms, from *Psalter for Worship, Cycle C* © 1997
Augsburg Fortress Publishers
Psalm Text: from *Evangelical Lutheran Worship* © 2006 Evangelical Lutheran Church in America, admin.
Augsburg Fortress Publishers
Tone: from *Psalter for Worship, Cycle C* © 1996 Augsburg Fortress Publishers

Psalm 85

To the leader. Of the Korahites. A Psalm.

1 LORD, you were favorable to your land; *
    you restored the fortunes of Jacob.

2 You forgave the iniquity of your people; *
    you pardoned all their sin.   *Selah*

3 You withdrew all your wrath; *
    you turned from your hot anger.

4 **Restore us again, O God of our salvation, ***
    and put away your indignation toward us.

5 **Will you be angry with us forever? ***
    Will you prolong your anger to all generations?

6 **Will you not revive us again, ***
    so that your people may rejoice in you?

7 **Show us your steadfast love, O LORD, ***
    and grant us your salvation.

8 Let me hear what God the LORD will speak, *
    for he will speak peace to his people,
    to his faithful, to those who turn to him in their hearts.

9 Surely his salvation is at hand for those who fear him, *
    that his glory may dwell in our land.

10 **Steadfast love and faithfulness will meet; ***
    righteousness and peace will kiss each other.

11 **Faithfulness will spring up from the ground, ***
    and righteousness will look down from the sky.

12 **The LORD will give what is good, ***
    and our land will yield its increase.

13 **Righteousness will go before him, ***
    and will make a path for his steps.

Provider of righteousness and peace,
through the death and resurrection of Jesus Christ you reunited heaven and earth.
When sin disrupts the harmony of creation,
pour out your Holy Spirit upon your waiting people
so that we would trust you, love you, and become your agents of reconciliation
in a cruel and hurting world. **Amen.**

Psalm 85 moves from the past to the present to the future. It begins with remembrance of God's forgiveness and restoration (vv. 1-3), continues with a prayer for God's restoration (vv. 4-7), and culminates with expressions of confident hope in God's future salvation (vv. 8-13). The psalm depicts God's deliverance in terms of a cluster of the loftiest of ideals, variously translated as covenant commitment, truthfulness, faithfulness, justice, peace, righteousness, loving-kindness, and mercy (vv. 10-11, see also Ps. 36:5-6). *Use in Worship: during the season of Advent; celebrations of the Lord's Supper.*

85A Lord, You Have Lavished on Your Land

1 Lord, you have lav-ished on your land a - maz-ing bless-ings
2 Lord, bring us back to grace a - gain; blot out your an - ger
3 To all his saints, the Lord speaks peace; his faith-ful love and
4 Then love will meet with faith - ful - ness; God's right-eous-ness and

from your hand, re - stored us from cap - tiv - i - ty
at our sin. Re - vive us, Lord, that we may raise
care in - crease. He shares his grace with o - pen hand
peace will kiss. As right - eous-ness smiles down from heaven,

and par - doned our in - iq - ui - ty. In grace you caused
our thank - ful hymns and psalms of praise. In mer - cy, Lord,
to spread his glo - ry through our land. Sal - va - tion from
great har - vests to our land are given. With God all right -

your wrath to turn; you did not let your an - ger burn.
your peo - ple bless with sav - ing love and faith - ful - ness.
the Lord is near to all who trust the Lord in fear.
eous - ness a - bides; his truth and jus - tice are our guides.

Guitar chords do not correspond with keyboard harmony.

Words: Marie J. Post, 1985, © 1987 Faith Alive Christian Resources
Music (MELITA 8.8.8.8.8.8): John B. Dykes (1823-1876), 1861, P.D.

Dona nobis pacem 85B

Dona nobis pacem means 'grant us your peace.'

Words: traditional
Music: The Community of Taizé © 1982, 1983, 1984 Ateliers et Presses de Taizé, Taizé Community, France, GIA Publications, Inc., exclusive North American agent

85C Psalm 85 | A Responsorial Setting

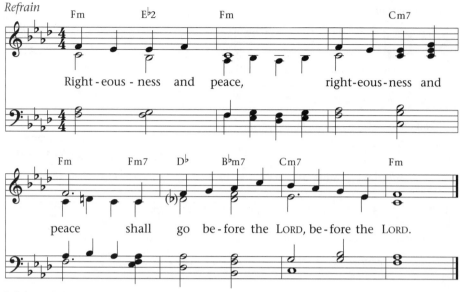

Refrain

Right-eous-ness and peace, right-eous-ness and peace shall go be-fore the LORD, be-fore the LORD.

Refrain

¹ You have been gracious to your land, O LORD;
   you have restored the good fortune of Jacob.

² You have forgiven the iniquity of your people
   and blotted out all their sins.

³ You have withdrawn all your fury
   and turned yourself from your wrathful indignation.

⁴ Restore us then, O God our Savior;
   let your anger depart from us. *Refrain*

⁵ Will you be displeased with us forever?
   Will you prolong your anger from age to age?

⁶ Will you not give us life again,
   that your people may rejoice in you?

⁷ Show us your steadfast love, O LORD,
   and grant us your salvation. *Refrain*

⁸ I will listen to what the LORD God is saying;
   for you speak peace to your faithful people
   and to those who turn their hearts to you.

⁹ Truly, your salvation is very near to those who fear you,
   that your glory may dwell in our land. *Refrain*

¹⁰ Steadfast love and faithfulness have met together;
   righteousness and peace have kissed each other.

¹¹ Faithfulness shall spring up from the earth,
   and righteousness shall look down from heaven.

¹² The LORD will indeed grant prosperity,
    and our land will yield its increase.

¹³ Righteousness shall go before the LORD
    and shall prepare for God a pathway.   *Refrain*

Tone

Lectionary: Ordinary Time after Pentecost (C); vv. 1-2, 8-13 Advent (B); vv. 8-13 Ordinary Time after Pentecost (A,B).

Words: Psalm 85
Music: Mary David Callahan, O. S. B. from *Psalter for Worship, Cycle B* © 1996 Augsburg Fortress Publishers
Psalm Text: from *Evangelical Lutheran Worship* © 2006 Evangelical Lutheran Church in America, admin.
Augsburg Fortress Publishers
Tone: from *Psalter for Worship, Cycle B* © 1996 Augsburg Fortress Publishers

Psalm 86

A Prayer of David.

¹ Incline your ear, O LORD, and answer me, *
    for I am poor and needy.

² Preserve my life, for I am devoted to you; *
    save your servant who trusts in you.

  You are my God; ³ **be gracious to me, O Lord,** *
    for to you do I cry all day long.

⁴ **Gladden the soul of your servant,** *
    for to you, O Lord, I lift up my soul.

⁵ For you, O Lord, are good and forgiving, *
    abounding in steadfast love to all who call on you.

⁶ Give ear, O LORD, to my prayer; *
    listen to my cry of supplication.

⁷ In the day of my trouble I call on you, *
    for you will answer me.

⁸ **There is none like you among the gods, O Lord,** *
    nor are there any works like yours.

⁹ **All the nations you have made shall come**
  and bow down before you, O Lord, *
    and shall glorify your name.

(continues)

¹⁰ **For you are great and do wondrous things; ***
   you alone are God.

¹¹ Teach me your way, O LORD, that I may walk in your truth; *
   give me an undivided heart to revere your name.

¹² **I give thanks to you, O Lord my God, with my whole heart, ***
   and I will glorify your name forever.

¹³ For great is your steadfast love toward me; *
   you have delivered my soul from the depths of Sheol.

¹⁴ O God, the insolent rise up against me; *
   a band of ruffians seeks my life, and they do not set you before them.

¹⁵ **But you, O Lord, are a God merciful and gracious, ***
   slow to anger and abounding in steadfast love and faithfulness.

¹⁶ **Turn to me and be gracious to me;**
  give your strength to your servant; *
  save the child of your serving girl.

¹⁷ **Show me a sign of your favor,**
  so that those who hate me may see it and be put to shame, *
  because you, LORD, have helped me and comforted me.

Merciful God, whose very name is Love,
you never turn away from anyone who seeks you.
Like the tax collector who cried for mercy, keep us honest and humble in our prayer,
receiving your forgiveness in our broken lives and proclaiming your salvation,
available to all the world through Jesus Christ. **Amen.**

Psalm 86 is an expression of deep trust and fervent prayer in times of trouble. It has a mirror-like structure in which prayers for deliverance (vv. 1-7, 14-17) frame statements of confident trust and commitment to God (vv. 8-13). This psalm echoes Ps. 85 in its confidence in the compassion, graciousness, covenant faithfulness, and truthfulness of God (v. 15). It expresses longing to see God's face (v. 16), an echo of Ps. 67's desire for God's blessing. *Use in Worship: as a model of intercession during troubling experiences.*

LORD, My Petition Heed 86A

1 LORD, my petition heed, now help me in my need,
2 Comfort your servant now, while at your throne I bow
3 LORD, hear me when I pray; in every troubled day
4 By nations you have made, your praise will be displayed
5 Lead me to do your will, in me your truth instill,

or else I die. I am your servant, LORD; my trust is
and call to you. Your pardoning grace is free; sinners who
I seek your face. O Lord, you far outshine the gods of
through earth abroad. Your name be glorified, your greatness
teach me your word. I will give thanks to you, your praise I

in your word. Mercy to me accord; to you I cry.
raise their plea your love and mercy see; they are made new.
our design; most bright your glories shine, O God of grace.
magnified; matchless your works abide, for you are God!
will pursue; all glory be to you, O Lord my God!

6 Great is your love to me;
   from death you set me free
      when foes alarm.
   Your grace I surely know,
   your anger, Lord, is slow;
   your loving-kindness show,
      save me from harm.

7 Show me your mercy true,
   your servant's strength renew,
      salvation send.
   A sign of favor show,
   your comfort, LORD, bestow;
   let those who hate me know
      you are my friend.

Words: *Psalter*, 1912; rev. Bert Polman, 1983, © 1987 Faith Alive Christian Resources
Music (MASON 6.6.4.6.6.6.4): William F. Sherwin (1826-1888); harm. Dale Grotenhuis, 1985, © 1987 Faith Alive Christian Resources

86B Psalm 86 | A Responsorial Setting

Refrain

1. Bow down your ear, O LORD, and answer me,
   for I am poor and in misery.

2. Keep watch over my life, for I am faithful;
   save your servant who trusts in you.

3. Be merciful to me, O Lord, for you are my God;
   I call upon you all the day long.

4. Gladden the soul of your servant,
   for to you, O Lord, I lift up my soul. *Refrain*

5. For you, O Lord, are good and forgiving,
   and abundant in mercy to all who call upon you.

⁶ Give ear, O LORD, to my prayer,
 and attend to the voice of my supplications.

⁷ In the time of my trouble I will call upon you,
 for you will answer me.

⁸ Among the gods there is none like you, O Lord,
 nor anything like your works.

⁹ All the nations you have made will come and worship you, O Lord,
 and glorify your name.

¹⁰ For you are great; you do wondrous things;
 and you alone are God.   *Refrain*

¹¹ Teach me your way, O LORD, and I will walk in your truth;
 give me an undivided heart to revere your name.

¹² I will thank you, O Lord my God, with all my heart,
 and glorify your name forevermore.

¹³ For great is your love toward me;
 you have delivered me from the pit of death.

¹⁴ The arrogant rise up against me, O God,
 and a band of violent people seeks my life;
 they have not set you before their eyes.

¹⁵ But you, O Lord, are gracious and full of compassion,
 slow to anger, and full of kindness and truth.   *Refrain*

¹⁶ Turn to me and have mercy on me;
 give your strength to your servant, and save the child of your handmaid.

¹⁷ Show me a sign of your favor,
 so that those who hate me may see it and be put to shame;
 because you, LORD, have helped me and comforted me.   *Refrain*

Tone

Lectionary: vv. 1-10, 16-17 Ordinary Time after Pentecost (A); vv. 11-17 Ordinary Time after Pentecost (A).

For harmony setting and for simplified guitar chords see p. 566.

Words: © 1969, 1981, 1997 International Commission on English in the Liturgy Corporation
Music: Val Parker © 2005 Val Parker, admin. OCP Publications
Psalm Text: from *Evangelical Lutheran Worship* © 2006 Evangelical Lutheran Church in America, admin. Augsburg Fortress Publishers
Tone: © 2011 Faith Alive Christian Resources

Psalm 87

Of the Korahites. A Psalm. A Song.

¹ On the holy mount stands the city he founded; *
   ² the LORD loves the gates of Zion
   more than all the dwellings of Jacob.

³ **Glorious things are spoken of you,** *
   O city of God.   *Selah*

⁴ Among those who know me I mention Rahab and Babylon; *
   Philistia too, and Tyre, with Ethiopia—
   "This one was born there," they say.

⁵ And of Zion it shall be said, "This one and that one were born in it"; *
   for the Most High himself will establish it.

⁶ The LORD records, as he registers the peoples, *
   "This one was born there."   *Selah*

⁷ **Singers and dancers alike say,** *
   "All my springs are in you."

Fount of every blessing,
all we have or ever hope to possess,
all we accomplish or ever hope to achieve, comes from you.
In the assurance of your salvation and the joy of your unfailing care,
help us call all peoples and nations back to you.
We pray in Jesus' name. **Amen.**

Psalm 87 extols the virtues of Zion, the city of Jerusalem, which is emblematic of God's presence with the people. It is noteworthy for its global vision of ethnic diversity in the people of God (v. 4) and is a natural complement to Ps. 86: both celebrate that all nations will honor God. Psalm 86 confesses this in the context of trouble, while Ps. 87 provides a confident reassurance that the confession is true. *Use in Worship: in conjunction with OT narratives about Israel's longing for Jerusalem; services focusing on the beauty and glory of the New Jerusalem, especially as a gathering place for the gifts of all nations and cultures (Isa. 2:2-4, Isa. 60, Rev. 20).*

Zion, Founded on the Mountain 87A

1 Zi - on, found - ed on the moun - tain, God, your
2 Glo - rious things of you are spo - ken, Zi - on,
3 When the LORD shall count the na - tions, sons and

Mak - er, loves you well; God has cho - sen
cit - y of our LORD: peo - ple of all
daugh - ters shall be - long, born to end - less

you most pre - cious, he de - lights in you to dwell;
tribes and na - tions know sal - va - tion from the Word.
life in Zi - on; God him - self will keep them strong.

God's own cit - y, who can all your glo - ry tell?
God Al - might - y shall him - self their names re - cord.
"All my foun - tains are in you!" shall be their song.

Words: st. 1 *Psalter*, 1912; sts. 2-3 *Psalter Hymnal*, 1987, © 1987 Faith Alive Christian Resources
Music (WORCHESTER 8.7.8.7.4.7): Walter G. Whinfield (1865-1919); harm. Paul Bunjes (1914-1998) © 1982
Concordia Publishing House

87B Built upon God's Holy Mountain

1 Built up-on God's ho - ly moun-tain: proph-ets cel - e - brate and sing
2 Out of ev - ery tribe and na - tion come the cit - i - zens of heaven;

of your worth be - yond re-count-ing, cit - y of the e-ter - nal King!
God has made them heirs to-geth - er and to each a birth-right given.

Home of peace! The Lord es-teems you more than an - y oth-er place,
In his reg - is - ter is list - ed ev - ery-one who's born a-new.

choos-ing here to make his dwell - ing with his fam - i - ly of grace.
Hear the joy-ful songs as-cend-ing—"All my life flows out from you!"

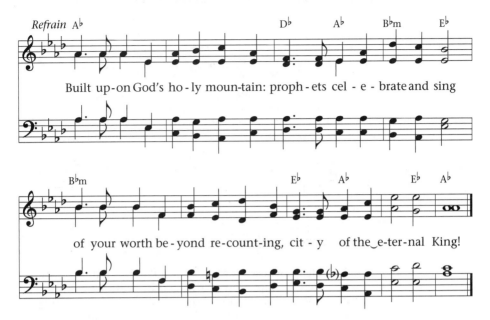

Built up-on God's ho-ly moun-tain: proph-ets cel - e - brate and sing

of your worth be - yond re-count-ing, cit - y of the eternal King!

Guitar chords do not correspond with keyboard harmony.

Words: Emma Turl © 2009 The Jubilate Group, admin. Hope Publishing Company
Music (MORGENLIED 8.7.8.7 D with refrain): Frederick Charles Maker (1844-1927), P.D.

A Prayer for the Nations 87C

The prayer may end with, or be framed by, the singing of 87F, "You Are the Source."

Glorious things are spoken of you, God, the source of all springs.
> **Our names are known by you and recorded in your book.**

Your blessing was pronounced on all families through your servant Abraham,
> **and you have established a home for all of us.**

We pray, O God, for all the nations of the earth,
> lands physically separated by geography—
> peoples divided by language, culture, custom, and color—
> **yet united as your children.**

As of old you claimed your people from all lands and nations—
> from Egypt and Babylon, Philistia and Ethiopia—
> even so, look with mercy upon your church in this land and in every nation.
> [Other nations may be added.]
> Guide us in your ways of justice and peace.

We call upon you—from every tribe and every nation,
in every tongue and language, joining our voices together in song proclaiming,
> **all our springs are in you.**

87D Glorious Things of Thee Are Spoken

1 Glo - rious things of thee are spo - ken, Zi - on, cit - y
2 See, the streams of liv - ing wa - ters, spring - ing from e -
3 Round each hab - i - ta - tion hov - ering, see the cloud and
4 Sav - ior, if of Zi - on's cit - y I through grace a

of our God; He, whose word can - not be bro - ken,
ter - nal love, well sup - ply thy sons and daugh - ters
fire ap - pear for a glo - ry and a cov - ering,
mem - ber am, let the world de - ride or pit - y,

formed thee for his own a - bode. On the Rock of
and all fear of want re - move. Who can faint while
show - ing that the Lord is near. Thus de - riv - ing
I will glo - ry in thy name. Fad - ing are the

A - ges found - ed, what can shake thy sure re - pose?
such a riv - er ev - er flows their thirst to as-suage?
from their ban - ner light by night and shade by day,
world-lings' plea - sures, all their boast - ed pomp and show;

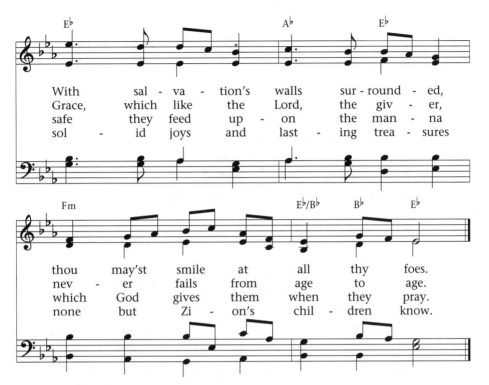

With sal - va - tion's walls sur - round - ed,
Grace, which like the Lord, the giv - er,
safe they feed up - on the man - na
sol - id joys and last - ing trea - sures

thou may'st smile at all thy foes.
nev - er fails from age to age.
which God gives them when they pray.
none but Zi - on's chil - dren know.

Guitar chords do not correspond with keyboard harmony.

Alternate tune: JEFFERSON, p. 534.

Words: John Newton, 1779, alt., P.D.
Music (AUSTRIAN HYMN 8.7.8.7 D): Franz Joseph Haydn (1732-1809), 1797, P.D.

87E Glorious Things of You Are Spoken

Unison

1 Glo - rious things of   you are spo - ken,   Zi - on,   cit - y
2 See,   the streams of   liv - ing wa - ters, spring-ing   from e -
3 Round each hab - i -   ta - tion hov-ering, see the   cloud and
4 Sav - ior,   since of   Zi - on's cit - y   I through grace a

of   our God!   He whose word can - not be   bro - ken
ter - nal love,   well sup - ply your   sons and daugh - ters,
fire ap - pear   for a   glo - ry   and a   cov - ering,
mem-ber am,   let the   world de - ride or   pit - y,

formed   you   for   his   own   a - bode.
and   all   fear   of   want   re - move.
show - ing   that   the   Lord   is   near.
I   will   glo - ry   in   your   name.

On the Rock of A - ges found - ed, what can shake your
Who can faint, while such a riv - er ev - er will their
Thus de - riv - ing from their ban - ner light by night and
Fad - ing are the world's vain plea - sures, all their boast - ed

sure re - pose? With sal - va - tion's walls sur - round - ed,
thirst as - suage? Grace which, like the Lord, the giv - er,
shade by day, safe they feed up - on the man - na
pomp and show; sol - id joys and last - ing trea - sures

you may smile at all your foes.
nev - er fails from age to age.
which God gives them on their way.
none but Zi - on's chil - dren know.

Guitar chords do not correspond with keyboard harmony.

Alternate tune: AUSTRIAN HYMN, p. 532.

Words: John Newton, 1779, alt., P.D.
Music (JEFFERSON 8.7.8.7 D): W. Walker's *Southern Harmony*, 1835; harm. Alfred V. Fedak (b. 1953) © 2011
Faith Alive Christian Resources

87F You Are the Source

You are the source, cre - a - ting wa - ter.
You are the source, you sav - ing stream. You are the source, sus -
tain-ing riv - er. All my springs are in you!

Maracas

Claves

Words and Music: Nathan Crabtree © 2011 Nathan Crabtree, admin. Faith Alive Christian Resources

Psalm 88

A Song. A Psalm of the Korahites. To the leader: according to Mahalath Leannoth. A Maskil of Heman the Ezrahite.

¹ O LORD, God of my salvation, *

    when, at night, I cry out in your presence,

² let my prayer come before you; *

    incline your ear to my cry.

³ **For my soul is full of troubles, ***

    and my life draws near to Sheol.

⁴ I am counted among those who go down to the Pit; *

    I am like those who have no help,

⁵ like those forsaken among the dead, like the slain that lie in the grave, *

    like those whom you remember no more, for they are cut off from your hand.

⁶ **You have put me in the depths of the Pit, ***

    in the regions dark and deep.

⁷ **Your wrath lies heavy upon me, ***

    and you overwhelm me with all your waves.   *Selah*

⁸ **You have caused my companions to shun me;**

    you have made me a thing of horror to them. *

    I am shut in so that I cannot escape;

⁹ my eye grows dim through sorrow. *

    Every day I call on you, O LORD; I spread out my hands to you.

¹⁰ Do you work wonders for the dead? *

    Do the shades rise up to praise you?   *Selah*

¹¹ Is your steadfast love declared in the grave, *

    or your faithfulness in Abaddon?

¹² Are your wonders known in the darkness, *

    or your saving help in the land of forgetfulness?

¹³ **But I, O LORD, cry out to you; ***

    in the morning my prayer comes before you.

¹⁴ **O LORD, why do you cast me off? ***

    Why do you hide your face from me?

¹⁵ Wretched and close to death from my youth up, *

    I suffer your terrors; I am desperate.

¹⁶ **Your wrath has swept over me; ***

    your dread assaults destroy me.

¹⁷ **They surround me like a flood all day long; ***

    from all sides they close in on me.

¹⁸ **You have caused friend and neighbor to shun me; ***

    my companions are in darkness.

(continues)

God of honesty and hope, you know our moments of pain and despair.
Redeem the time, O Lord;
fill endless days with purpose and sleepless nights with peace,
until the groaning in our hearts becomes an offering of praise too deep for words,
through Jesus Christ our Savior. **Amen.**

Psalm 88 is a poignant lament of unrelenting darkness. It is the only lament psalm that does not include a statement of hope or a vow to praise. Yet even in this persistent darkness the psalmist confesses that God is the "God of my salvation" (v. 1). The psalmist describes not only weakness (vv. 4, 15) and loneliness (vv. 7, 18) but also a sense of separation from or abandonment by God (vv. 5, 14). The Hebrew text of the last verse trails off with a sense of halting incompleteness or gasping exhaustion. The psalm also appeals to God's commitment, truthfulness, and faithfulness (vv. 11-12), echoing Pss. 33, 85, and 86. *Use in Worship: times and places of utter distress (e.g., in the face of a humanitarian crisis, in a prison or an Alzheimer unit); pastoral care settings or prayers with those facing death or unrelenting difficulties; Good Friday (reading in the voice of Christ).*

88A Dans nos obscurités / Within Our Darkest Night

The following may be read with the singing of "Dans nos obscurités" / "Within Our Darkest Night."

God, you're my last chance of the day.
    I spend the night on my knees before you.
Put me on your salvation agenda;
    take notes on the trouble I'm in.
I've had my fill of trouble;
    I'm camped on the edge of hell.
You've dropped me into a bottomless pit,
    sunk me in a pitch-black abyss.

You turned my friends against me,
    made me horrible to them.
I'm caught in a maze and can't find my way out,
    blinded by tears of pain and frustration.

I'm standing my ground, God, shouting for help,
    at my prayers every morning, on my knees each daybreak.
Why, God, do you turn a deaf ear?
    Why do you make yourself scarce?
For as long as I remember I've been hurting;
    I've taken the worst you can hand out, and I've had it.
You made lover and neighbor alike dump me;
    the only friend I have left is Darkness.

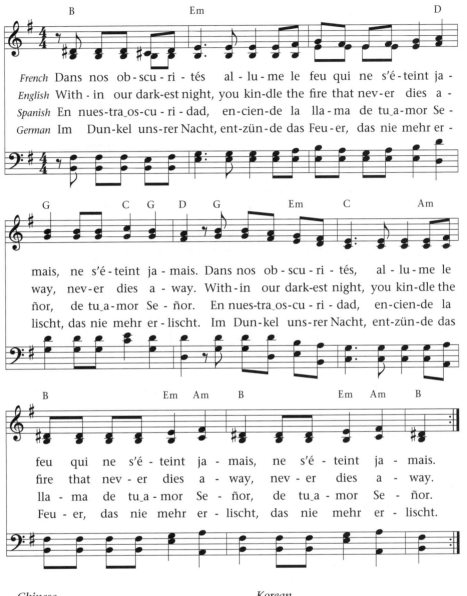

French Dans nos ob-scu-ri-tés al-lu-me le feu qui ne s'é-teint ja-
English With-in our dark-est night, you kin-dle the fire that nev-er dies a-
Spanish En nues-tra_os-cu-ri-dad, en-cien-de la lla-ma de tu_a-mor Se-
German Im Dun-kel uns-rer Nacht, ent-zün-de das Feu-er, das nie mehr er-

mais, ne s'é-teint ja-mais. Dans nos ob-scu-ri-tés, al-lu-me le
way, nev-er dies a-way. With-in our dark-est night, you kin-dle the
ñor, de tu_a-mor Se-ñor. En nues-tra_os-cu-ri-dad, en-cien-de la
lischt, das nie mehr er-lischt. Im Dun-kel uns-rer Nacht, ent-zün-de das

feu qui ne s'é-teint ja-mais, ne s'é-teint ja-mais.
fire that nev-er dies a-way, nev-er dies a-way.
lla-ma de tu_a-mor Se-ñor, de tu_a-mor Se-ñor.
Feu-er, das nie mehr er-lischt, das nie mehr er-lischt.

Chinese

在幽暗黑夜中，祢所點燃之火
永遠不熄滅，永遠永遠不滅。

Korean

어두운 밤속에 주여
영원히 꺼지지 않는 불 밝혀 주소서

Hungarian

Gyújts éjszakánkba fényt,
hadd égjen a soha ki new alvó tűz.

Swahili

Katika giza letu,
washa mo-oto isiozimika, isiozimika.

88B Spiritual: Sometimes I Feel Like a Motherless Child

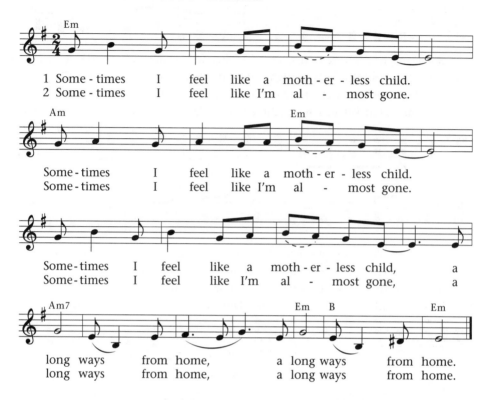

1 Some - times I feel like a moth - er - less child.
2 Some - times I feel like I'm al - most gone.

Some - times I feel like a moth - er - less child.
Some - times I feel like I'm al - most gone.

Some - times I feel like a moth - er - less child, a
Some - times I feel like I'm al - most gone, a

long ways from home, a long ways from home.
long ways from home, a long ways from home.

Words: Afro-American spiritual
Music (MOTHERLESS CHILD): Afro-American spiritual

Psalm 89

A Maskil of Ethan the Ezrahite.

Voice 1:

¹ I will sing of your steadfast love, O LORD, forever; *
   with my mouth I will proclaim your faithfulness to all generations.

² **I declare that your steadfast love is established forever;** *
   your faithfulness is as firm as the heavens.

³ You said, "I have made a covenant with my chosen one,*
   I have sworn to my servant David:

⁴ 'I will establish your descendants forever, *
   and build your throne for all generations.' "   *Selah*

⁵ **Let the heavens praise your wonders, O LORD,** *
   your faithfulness in the assembly of the holy ones.

6 **For who in the skies can be compared to the Lord?** *
   Who among the heavenly beings is like the Lord,

7 **a God feared in the council of the holy ones,** *
   great and awesome above all that are around him?

8 O Lord God of hosts, who is as mighty as you, O Lord? *
   Your faithfulness surrounds you.

9 **You rule the raging of the sea;** *
   when its waves rise, you still them.

10 You crushed Rahab like a carcass; *
   you scattered your enemies with your mighty arm.

11 **The heavens are yours, the earth also is yours;** *
   the world and all that is in it—you have founded them.

12 The north and the south—you created them; *
   Tabor and Hermon joyously praise your name.

13 **You have a mighty arm;** *
   strong is your hand, high your right hand.

14 Righteousness and justice are the foundation of your throne; *
   steadfast love and faithfulness go before you.

15 **Happy are the people who know the festal shout,** *
   who walk, O Lord, in the light of your countenance;

16 **they exult in your name all day long,** *
   and extol your righteousness.

17 **For you are the glory of their strength;** *
   by your favor our horn is exalted.

18 **For our shield belongs to the Lord,** *
   our king to the Holy One of Israel.

Voice 2:

19 Then you spoke in a vision to your faithful one, and said: *
   "I have set the crown on one who is mighty,
   I have exalted one chosen from the people.

20 I have found my servant David; *
   with my holy oil I have anointed him;

21 my hand shall always remain with him; *
   my arm also shall strengthen him.

22 The enemy shall not outwit him, *
   the wicked shall not humble him.

23 I will crush his foes before him *
   and strike down those who hate him.

(continues)

24 **My faithfulness and steadfast love shall be with him; ***
   and in my name his horn shall be exalted.

25 I will set his hand on the sea *
   and his right hand on the rivers.

26 **He shall cry to me, 'You are my Father, ***
   my God, and the Rock of my salvation!'

27 I will make him the firstborn, *
   the highest of the kings of the earth.

28 **Forever I will keep my steadfast love for him, ***
   and my covenant with him will stand firm.

29 I will establish his line forever, *
   and his throne as long as the heavens endure.

30 If his children forsake my law *
   and do not walk according to my ordinances,

31 if they violate my statutes *
   and do not keep my commandments,

32 then I will punish their transgression with the rod *
   and their iniquity with scourges;

33 but I will not remove from him my steadfast love, *
   or be false to my faithfulness.

34 **I will not violate my covenant, ***
   or alter the word that went forth from my lips.

35 **Once and for all I have sworn by my holiness; ***
   I will not lie to David.

36 **His line shall continue forever, ***
   and his throne endure before me like the sun.

37 **It shall be established forever like the moon, ***
   an enduring witness in the skies."   *Selah*

Voice 3:

38 But now you have spurned and rejected him; *
   you are full of wrath against your anointed.

39 You have renounced the covenant with your servant; *
   you have defiled his crown in the dust.

40 You have broken through all his walls; *
   you have laid his strongholds in ruins.

41 All who pass by plunder him; *
   he has become the scorn of his neighbors.

⁴² You have exalted the right hand of his foes; *

   you have made all his enemies rejoice.

⁴³ Moreover, you have turned back the edge of his sword, *

   and you have not supported him in battle.

⁴⁴ You have removed the scepter from his hand, *

   and hurled his throne to the ground.

⁴⁵ You have cut short the days of his youth; *

   you have covered him with shame.   *Selah*

⁴⁶ How long, O Lᴏʀᴅ? Will you hide yourself forever? *

   How long will your wrath burn like fire?

⁴⁷ Remember how short my time is— *

   for what vanity you have created all mortals!

⁴⁸ Who can live and never see death? *

   Who can escape the power of Sheol?   *Selah*

⁴⁹ Lord, where is your steadfast love of old, *

   which by your faithfulness you swore to David?

⁵⁰ Remember, O Lord, how your servant is taunted; *

   how I bear in my bosom the insults of the peoples,

⁵¹ with which your enemies taunt, O Lᴏʀᴅ, *

   with which they taunted the footsteps of your anointed.

⁵² Blessed be the Lᴏʀᴅ forever. *

   Amen and Amen.

Faithful God, you are the same yesterday, today, and forever.
Your Word remains true, your love remains constant;
your plan and purpose stand unaltered.
Remember us in our present distress.
By the power of your Holy Spirit make us ready and willing to live this day for you.
We pray this through the power of Jesus' name. **Amen.**

Psalm 89, the final psalm in the third of the Psalter's five books, features two contrasting sentiments. The opening verses offer praise for God's covenantal faithfulness (vv. 1-17), after which the psalm pivots dramatically into a sustained lament about the demise of the monarchy and an experience of God's abandonment (vv. 38-51). In light of the foibles of human kings, it is significant that many of the psalms that follow focus more on God's sovereign rule than on human kings. *Use in Worship: call to worship or acclamation of praise (v. 1); services focusing on accounts in the OT about covenant unfaithfulness; services focusing on the gap between our praise and the full experience of God's covenantal intent for us.*

89A I Will Sing of the Mercies of the LORD

1 I will sing of the mer-cies of the LORD for - ev-er, I will
2 All the hosts of the an - gels sing God's praise for - ev-er for the

sing, I will sing. I will sing of the mer-cies of the
things he has done. All the hosts of the an - gels sing God's

LORD for - ev - er, I will sing of the mer-cies of the LORD.
praise for - ev - er, all the hosts of the an - gels sing God's praise.

With my mouth will I make known your faith-ful-ness, your
Who can be com-pared to God in faith-ful-ness, in

faith - ful - ness; with my mouth will I make known your
faith - ful - ness? Who can be com-pared to God in

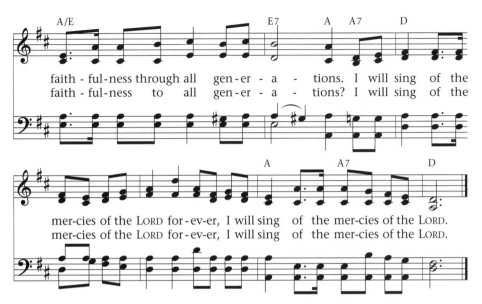

faith - ful-ness through all gen-er - a - tions. I will sing of the
faith - ful-ness to all gen-er - a - tions? I will sing of the

mer-cies of the LORD for - ev-er, I will sing of the mer-cies of the LORD.
mer-cies of the LORD for - ev-er, I will sing of the mer-cies of the LORD.

Words: st. 1 James H. Fillmore (1849-1936); st. 2 Marie J. Post, 1983, © 1987 Faith Alive Christian Resources
Music (FILLMORE): James H. Fillmore (1849-1936), P.D.

Psalm 89:1-4, 15-37 89B
A Responsorial Setting

For - ev - er I will sing the good - ness of the

Lord, the good - ness of the Lord.

(continues)

Refrain

¹ Your love, O Lᴏʀᴅ, forever will I sing;

   from age to age my mouth will proclaim your faithfulness.

² For I am persuaded that your steadfast love is established forever;

   you have set your faithfulness firmly in the heavens.

³ "I have made a covenant with my chosen one;

   I have sworn an oath to David my servant:

⁴ 'I will establish your line forever,

   and preserve your throne for all generations.'"   *Refrain*

¹⁵ Happy are the people who know the festal shout!

   They walk, O Lᴏʀᴅ, in the light of your presence.

¹⁶ They rejoice daily in your name;

   they are jubilant in your righteousness.

¹⁷ For you are the glory of their strength,

   and by your favor our might is exalted.

¹⁸ Truly, our shield belongs to the Lᴏʀᴅ;

   our king to the Holy One of Israel.   *Refrain*

¹⁹ You spoke once in a vision and said to your faithful people:

   "I have set the crown upon a warrior

   and have exalted one chosen out of the people.

²⁰ I have found David my servant;

   with my holy oil I have anointed him.

²¹ My hand will hold him fast

   and my arm will make him strong.

²² No enemy shall deceive him,

   nor shall the wicked bring him down.

²³ I will crush his foes before him

   and strike down those who hate him.

²⁴ My faithfulness and steadfast love are with him,

   and he shall be victorious through my name.

²⁵ I will set his hand on the sea,

   and his right hand on the rivers.

²⁶ He will say to me, 'You are my father,

   my God, and the rock of my salvation.'   *Refrain*

²⁷ I will make him my firstborn

   and higher than the kings of the earth.

²⁸ I will keep my love for him forever,

   and my covenant will stand firm for him.

²⁹ I will establish his line forever
  and his throne as the days of heaven.

³⁰ If his children forsake my teaching
  and do not walk according to my judgments;

³¹ if they break my statutes
  and do not keep my commandments;

³² I will punish their transgressions with a rod
  and their iniquities with the lash;

³³ but I will not take my love from him,
  nor let my faithfulness prove false.

³⁴ I will not break my covenant,
  nor change what has gone out of my lips.   *Refrain*

³⁵ Once for all I have sworn by my holiness:
  I will not lie to David.

³⁶ His line shall endure forever
  and his throne as the sun before me;

³⁷ it shall stand fast forevermore like the moon,
  the abiding witness in the sky."   *Refrain*

Tone

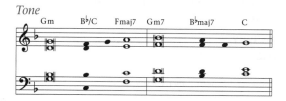

Lectionary: vv. 1-4, 19-26 Advent (B); vv. 1-4, 15-18 Ordinary Time after Pentecost (A); vv. 20-37 Ordinary Time after Pentecost (B).

89C A Prayer of Remembrance and Hope

We remember your people, O Lord, the people of the promise.
We hear their songs of praise, and our hearts rise up as we join our voices with
theirs. We too will sing of your steadfast love forever.

Read selections from Psalm 89:1-37 or sing stanzas 1-2 on facing page.

We remember your people, O Lord, the people of the promise.
We also hear and echo their lament. We attempt to grasp their despair.

Read selections from Psalm 89:38-51 or sing stanza 3 on facing page.

We remember your people, the people of your covenant.
We tremble at their persistent praise. Even in the face of hardship, they said:
"Blessed be the name of the Lord."

Read Psalm 89:52 or sing stanza 4 on facing page.

We remember your people, O Lord, the people of the promise.
And we also know that even in times of trouble, you were with them.
You were with them,

> sending prophets to announce your covenant faithfulness
> and to call your people to obedience.

You were with them,

> preparing the way for the coming of the Anointed One,
> our Messiah and Christ.

Truly, we say: "Blessed be the name of the Lord."

When we despair, we remember your faithfulness and we proclaim:
"Blessed be the name of the Lord.
The Lord gives, the Lord takes away.
Blessed be the name of the Lord."

John D. Witvliet, 2011, © Creative Commons Attribution-NonCommercial-ShareAlike

Forever We Will Sing 89D

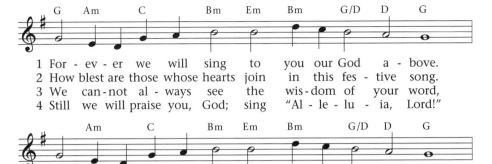

1 For - ev - er we will sing to you our God a - bove.
2 How blest are those whose hearts join in this fes - tive song.
3 We can-not al - ways see the wis-dom of your word,
4 Still we will praise you, God; sing "Al - le - lu - ia, Lord!"

With psalms we cel - e - brate your faith - ful - ness and love.
De - liv-ered from the foe, your fa - vor makes them strong.
the ten - der voice you speak so of - ten goes un - heard.
E - ven in death's cold night, your name must be a - dored.

Your grace is ev - er sure, we trust in your sal - va - tion;
Your hand that stretched the heavens, that laid the earth's foun - da - tion,
You swore to break the chains, but still op - pres - sion binds us;
We may not see your face in trou-bles that con-found us,

your cov - e - nant ex - tends to ev - ery gen - er - a - tion.
will bear your peo - ple up through ev - ery trib - u - la - tion.
you vowed to us your care, yet con - dem - na - tion finds us.
but we will trust your grace and know your arms sur - round us.

The u - ni-verse re-sounds with praise for mer - cies giv - en;
From the be - gin-ning, God, you shaped cre - a-tion's sto - ry;
How long, O God, how long shall we in dark-ness fal - ter?
"A - men, a - gain A - men!" to God whose love a - maz - es!

your right-eous - ness and truth still e - cho through the heav - ens.
now grant us peace, O Lord, and we will sing your glo - ry!
Will we with shat - tered hopes find com-fort at your al - tar?
To you, the Lord of all, we bring our end - less prais - es!

Keyboard accompaniment on p. 550.

Words: Michael Morgan and Martin Tel © 2011 Michael Morgan and Martin Tel, admin. Faith Alive Christian Resources
Music (GENEVAN 89 | 12.12.13.13.13.13): *Genevan Psalter*, 1562

Keyboard accompaniment

Music (GENEVAN 89 | 12.12.13.13.13.13): *Genevan Psalter*, 1562; harm. Alfred V. Fedak (b. 1953) © 2011
Faith Alive Christian Resources

My Song Forever Shall Record

89E

1 My song for-ev-er shall re-cord the ten-der
2 I sing of mer-cies that en-dure, for-ev-er
3 Al-might-y God, your loft-y throne has jus-tice

mer-cies of the Lord; your faith-ful-ness will
build-ed firm and sure, of faith-ful-ness that
for its cor-ner-stone, and shin-ing bright be-

I pro-claim, and ev-ery age shall know your name.
nev-er dies, es-tab-lished change-less in the skies.
fore your face are truth and love and bound-less grace.

4 With blessing is the nation crowned
   whose people know the joyful sound;
   they in the light, O Lord, shall live,
   the light your face and favor give.

5 All glory unto God we yield,
   who is our constant help and shield;
   all praise and honor we will bring
   to you, the Holy One, our King.

Words: *Psalter*, 1912, alt., P.D.
Music (WINCHESTER NEW 8.8.8.8): *Musikalisches Hand-buch*, Hamburg, 1690, P.D.

Psalm 90

A Prayer of Moses, the man of God.

¹ Lord, you have been our dwelling place *
 in all generations.

² Before the mountains were brought forth,
 or ever you had formed the earth and the world, *
 from everlasting to everlasting you are God.

³ **You turn us back to dust, ***
 and say, "Turn back, you mortals."

⁴ **For a thousand years in your sight are like yesterday when it is past, ***
 or like a watch in the night.

⁵ You sweep them away; they are like a dream, *
 like grass that is renewed in the morning;

⁶ in the morning it flourishes and is renewed; *
 in the evening it fades and withers.

⁷ For we are consumed by your anger; *
 by your wrath we are overwhelmed.

⁸ **You have set our iniquities before you, ***
 our secret sins in the light of your countenance.

⁹ **For all our days pass away under your wrath; ***
 our years come to an end like a sigh.

¹⁰ The days of our life are seventy years, or perhaps eighty, if we are strong; *
 even then their span is only toil and trouble;
 they are soon gone, and we fly away.

¹¹ **Who considers the power of your anger? ***
 Your wrath is as great as the fear that is due you.

¹² **So teach us to count our days ***
 that we may gain a wise heart.

¹³ Turn, O LORD! How long? *
 Have compassion on your servants!

¹⁴ **Satisfy us in the morning with your steadfast love, ***
 so that we may rejoice and be glad all our days.

¹⁵ **Make us glad as many days as you have afflicted us, ***
 and as many years as we have seen evil.

¹⁶ Let your work be manifest to your servants, *
 and your glorious power to their children.

¹⁷ **Let the favor of the Lord our God be upon us,**
 and prosper for us the work of our hands— *
 O prosper the work of our hands!

God of every time and place,
apart from you, our life is brief and meaningless.
In you we experience endless abundance.
Reveal to us all we can comprehend of our place in your design for eternity.
Help us to receive each new day as a gift, and to use your gift wisely and well,
so that we may live in joy and bring glory to Christ your Son, our Lord. **Amen.**

Psalm 90, the first psalm in the fourth book of the Psalter, is a meditation on the everlastingness of God and the brevity of human life. It lauds the everlasting love of God (vv. 1-5), laments the current conditions of life (vv. 6-12), and concludes with a plea for God's blessing (vv. 13-17). The psalm seeks both wisdom in the face of human limitation (v. 12) and the kind of divine blessing that offers both delight and prosperity of the fruit of human labor (v. 14-17). *Use in Worship: funerals; services marking the passing of time; gatherings in times of crisis or tragedy.*

God Everlasting, at Your Word 90A

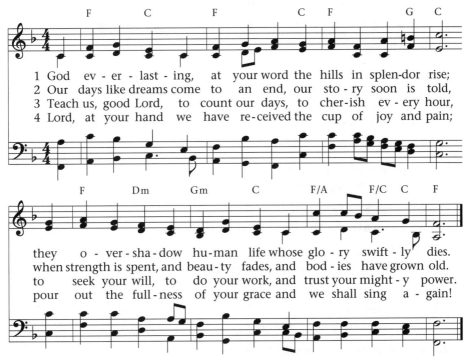

1 God ev - er - last - ing, at your word the hills in splen-dor rise;
2 Our days like dreams come to an end, our sto - ry soon is told,
3 Teach us, good Lord, to count our days, to cher-ish ev - ery hour,
4 Lord, at your hand we have re-ceived the cup of joy and pain;

they o - ver-sha-dow hu-man life whose glo - ry swift - ly dies.
when strength is spent, and beau - ty fades, and bod - ies have grown old.
to seek your will, to do your work, and trust your might - y power.
pour out the full-ness of your grace and we shall sing a - gain!

Guitar chords do not correspond with keyboard harmony.

Words: David Mowbray © 1990 The Jubilate Group, admin. Hope Publishing Company
Music (ST. MAGNUS 8.6.8.6): Jeremiah Clarke (1660-1707), P.D.

90B O God, Our Help in Ages Past

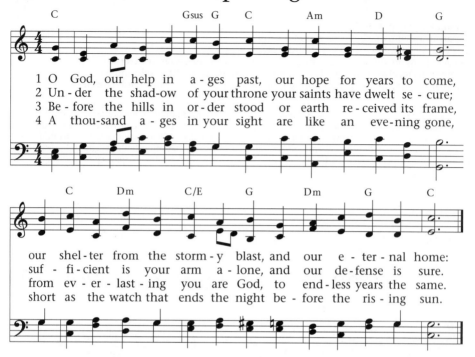

1 O God, our help in a-ges past, our hope for years to come,
2 Un-der the shad-ow of your throne your saints have dwelt se-cure;
3 Be-fore the hills in or-der stood or earth re-ceived its frame,
4 A thou-sand a-ges in your sight are like an eve-ning gone,

our shel-ter from the storm-y blast, and our e-ter-nal home:
suf-fi-cient is your arm a-lone, and our de-fense is sure.
from ev-er-last-ing you are God, to end-less years the same.
short as the watch that ends the night be-fore the ris-ing sun.

5 Time, like an ever-rolling stream,
   soon bears us all away;
   we fly forgotten, as a dream
   dies at the opening day.

6 O God, our help in ages past,
   our hope for years to come,
   still be our guard while troubles last,
   and our eternal home!

Sing stanzas 1-3

We are consumed by your anger
   and terrified by your indignation.

**You have set our iniquities before you,
   our secret sins in the light of your presence.**

If we only knew the power of your anger!
   Your wrath is as great as the fear that is your due.

Sing stanzas 4-5

Teach us to number our days,
   that we may gain a heart of wisdom.

**Relent, Lord! How long will it be?
   Have compassion on your servants.**

Satisfy us in the morning with your unfailing love,
   that we may sing for joy and be glad all our days.

**Make us glad for as many days as you have afflicted us,
   for as many years as we have seen trouble.**

May your deeds be shown to your servants,
  your splendor to their children.

May the favor of the Lord our God rest on us;
  establish the work of our hands for us—
  yes, establish the work of our hands.

Sing stanza 6

Guitar chords do not correspond with keyboard harmony.

Words: Isaac Watts (1674-1748), 1719, alt., P.D.
Music (ST. ANNE 8.6.8.6): William Croft, 1708, P.D.
Text: Psalm 90 © THE HOLY BIBLE, NEW INTERNATIONAL VERSION®, NIV® Copyright © 1973, 1978, 1984, 2011 by Biblica, Inc.™ Used by permission. All rights reserved worldwide.

Psalm 90 | A Responsorial Setting 90C

Refrain

1 Lord, you have been our refuge
    from one generation to another.

2 Before the mountains were brought forth, or the land and the earth were born,
    from age to age you are God.

3 You turn us back to the dust and say,
    "Turn back, O children of earth."

4 For a thousand years in your sight are like yesterday when it is past
    and like a watch in the night;

(continues)

⁵ you sweep them away like a dream,
   they fade away suddenly like the grass:

⁶ in the morning it is green and flourishes;
   in the evening it is dried up and withered.   *Refrain*

⁷ For we are consumed by your anger;
   we are afraid because of your wrath.

⁸ Our iniquities you have set before you,
   and our secret sins in the light of your countenance.

⁹ When you are angry, all our days are gone;
   we bring our years to an end like a sigh.   *Refrain*

¹⁰ The span of our life is seventy years, perhaps in strength even eighty;
   yet the sum of them is but labor and sorrow,
   for they pass away quickly and we are gone.

¹¹ Who regards the power of your wrath?
   Who rightly fears your indignation?

¹² So teach us to number our days
   that we may apply our hearts to wisdom.   *Refrain*

¹³ Return, O LORD; how long will you tarry?
   Be gracious to your servants.

¹⁴ Satisfy us by your steadfast love in the morning;
   so shall we rejoice and be glad all our days.

¹⁵ Make us glad as many days as you afflicted us
   and as many years as we suffered adversity.

¹⁶ Show your servants your works,
   and your splendor to their children.

¹⁷ May the graciousness of the Lord our God be upon us;
   prosper the works of our hands; prosper our handiwork.   *Refrain*

Tone

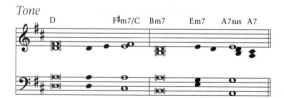

Lectionary: vv. 1-6, 13-17 Ordinary Time after Pentecost (A); vv. 1-12 Ordinary Time after Pentecost (A); vv. 12-17 Ordinary Time after Pentecost (B).

Words and Music: Hal H. Hopson © 1988 Hope Publishing Company
Psalm Text: from *Evangelical Lutheran Worship* © 2006 Evangelical Lutheran Church in America, admin. Augsburg Fortress Publishers
Tone: © 2011 Faith Alive Christian Resources

Wildflowers Bloom and Fade 90D

1 Wild-flow-ers bloom and fade, soon come and gone,
2 Your love will nev - er end; our days are brief.
3 Our lives are like the rose that quick - ly dies.
4 Fill us with faith - ful love as morn - ing wakes.

but God, from age to age you still live on.
Our years are full of sin, lab - or, and grief.
Teach us to count our days; God, make us wise.
Let us re - joice in you as each day breaks.

Old - er than time and space, you are our dwell-ing place.
You turn us back to dust, yet all your ways are just,
Though time flies swift - ly past, God, let our good work last.
May your great work be known, your power on earth be shown.

Keep us in your em-brace, O God, our home.
so we will live in trust, O God, our home.
Your strong arms hold us fast, O God, our home.
Do not for - get your own, O God, our home.

Words: Ruth C. Duck, 1995, © 1996 The Pilgrim Press
Music (INCARNATION 6.4.6.4.6.6.6.4): John L. Bell (b. 1949), 1987, © 1987 Wild Goose Resource Group,
Iona Community (Scotland), GIA Publications, Inc., exclusive North American agent

90E May the Gracious Care

Refrain

May the gra-cious care of the Lord be ours;
Alt. Ref. May the love of God fill us all our days;

may he al-ways be our ref-uge and help. *Fine*
let us sing for joy as morn-ing fills the sky.

Unison

1 O Lord, you have been our ref-uge from one_____ age
2 Our sin____ is al-ways be-fore you, our faults in the truth
3 ⅜ Fill us, O Lord, with your love__ as the prom-ise of dawn

to the next. Be-fore____ the birth of the moun-tains, be-
of your light. Our days are con-sumed by your an-ger, our
is ful-filled. Give joy____ to soft-en our sor-rows, to

To Refrain

Gm7 Cm2 Fm B♭sus B♭

fore the world came to be, you are God___ for - ev - er - more.
life is spent like a sigh. We are drawn to the end of our days.
soothe our years of pain. Lord, pros - per the work of our hands!

Words and Music: Steven C. Warner © 2006 World Library Publications

Psalm 91

¹ You who live in the shelter of the Most High, *
    who abide in the shadow of the Almighty,

² will say to the LORD, "My refuge and my fortress; *
    my God, in whom I trust."

³ **For he will deliver you from the snare of the fowler ***
    and from the deadly pestilence;

⁴ **he will cover you with his pinions,**
    and under his wings you will find refuge; *
    his faithfulness is a shield and buckler.

⁵ You will not fear the terror of the night, *
    or the arrow that flies by day,

⁶ or the pestilence that stalks in darkness, *
    or the destruction that wastes at noonday.

⁷ **A thousand may fall at your side, ten thousand at your right hand, ***
    but it will not come near you.

⁸ You will only look with your eyes *
    and see the punishment of the wicked.

⁹ **Because you have made the LORD your refuge, ***
    the Most High your dwelling place,

¹⁰ **no evil shall befall you, ***
    no scourge come near your tent.

(continues)

¹¹ For he will command his angels concerning you *
    to guard you in all your ways.
¹² On their hands they will bear you up, *
    so that you will not dash your foot against a stone.
¹³ You will tread on the lion and the adder, *
    the young lion and the serpent you will trample under foot.
¹⁴ **Those who love me, I will deliver; ***
    I will protect those who know my name.
¹⁵ **When they call to me, I will answer them; ***
    I will be with them in trouble, I will rescue them and honor them.
¹⁶ **With long life I will satisfy them, ***
    and show them my salvation.

God of endless love,
you have promised to protect your people in times of danger
and to hear us when we pray.
May your promises overcome any doubt or fear
so that we may live confidently and praise you joyfully
no matter what this day may bring.
We pray in Jesus' name. **Amen.**

Psalm 91 is comprised of a series of testimonies about how God serves as a refuge and protector. A concluding word from God (vv. 14-16) affirms the truth of these testimonies and serves as a promise of future redemption. In the face of human tragedy, the psalm seems audacious. Throughout history, Christian interpreters have seen this as a statement of ultimate protection like that of Rom. 8:38-39 ("nothing shall separate us from the love of Christ"). *Use in Worship: funerals; times of danger or tragedy.*

Whoever Shelters with the LORD 91A

1 Who - ev - er shel - ters with the LORD and lives with-
2 The faith - ful LORD will spare you death. God's wings will
3 Though thou - sands per - ish at your side, such pun - ish-

in the Al-might - y's shade can say, "My God, in
cov - er you from harm. No ter - ror, sick - ness,
ment shall not touch you. Be - cause the LORD serves

whom I trust, your ref - uge makes me un - a - fraid!"
night or day, will ev - er cause you grave a - larm.
as your home, God's grace will al - ways see you through.

4 God gives his angels charge of you
to guard from those who persecute.
You shall not trip against a stone,
but trample serpents underfoot.

5 "Because you cleave to me in love
and know my name to call in need,
I shall protect and keep you safe
with blessing, glory, life indeed."

Alternate harmonization on p. 434.

Words: Calvin Seerveld © 1985 Calvin Seerveld
Music (WAREHAM 8.8.8.8): William Knapp, 1738; harm. Emily R. Brink (b. 1940), 1994, © 1994 Faith Alive
Christian Resources

91B Within the Shelter of the Lord

1 With - in the shel - ter of the Lord, at
2 Though bru - tal con - flicts scar the day, though
3 God an - swers ev - ery cry for help; his

home in his un - fail - ing care, we
name - less per - ils fill the night, God's
love is ours till jour - ney's end— how -

trust in his e - ter - nal strength to
pres - ence calms our trou - bled minds and
ev - er long our lives may be, on

res - cue us from ev - ery snare:
puts our pri - mal fears to flight.
God's firm prom - ise we de - pend.

how safe it is, this hid - ing - place be -
When sin per - sists and judg - ment falls the
Who knows what dan - gers we are spared since

neath his ev - er - last - ing wings; how
true se - cur - i - ty is ours: pro -
an - gels guard the way we take? And

strong a for - tress is our God, the
tect - ed by the Lord, we stand, be -
all who trust and love the Lord he

Might - y One, the King of kings.
yond the grasp of e - vil powers.
pledg - es nev - er to for - sake.

El que habita al abrigo de Dios / Those Who Dwell in the Shelter of God

Spanish 1 El que ha-bi - ta_al a-bri - go de Dios
English 1 Those who dwell in the shel - ter of God
2 Those who dwell in the shel - ter of God
3 Those who dwell in the shel - ter of God

mo - ra - rá ba - jo som - bras de_a-mor;
find their home in love's rest - giv-ing shade.
from de - struc - tion and death live se - cure.
are the peo - ple most fa - vored of all:

con - fi - a - do_y se - gu - ro_es-ta - rá
Safe from harm, from temp - ta - tions and snares,
Though a thou - sand may fall at their side,
for God's an - gels keep watch on their paths,

de los la - zos del vil ten - ta - dor.
they will trust and will not be a - fraid.
they are saved by a grace that is sure.
that their feet nei-ther stum - ble nor fall.

Refrain

Oh yo quie - ro ha - bi - tar al a - bri - go de Dios;
How my heart longs to dwell in the shel - ter of God.

só - lo a - llí en - cuen - tro paz y pro - fun - do a - mor.
There a - lone can I find deep - est love and peace.

Mi de - li - cia es con Él co - mu - nión dis - fru -
I re - joice and de - light to com - mune there with

tar y por siem - pre su nom - bre a - la - bar.
God, where my songs filled with praise nev - er cease!

2 El que habita al abrigo de Dios
para siempre seguro estará;
caerán miles en derredor,
mas a él no vendrá mortandad. *Refrain*

3 El que habita al abrigo de Dios
muy feliz ciertamente será;
ángeles guardarán su salud
y su pie nunca resbalará. *Refrain*

Words: Robert Savage © 1954; vers. Luz Ester Rios de Cuna, alt.; tr. Mary Louise Bringle © 2011 New Spring Publishing, admin. Music Services
Music (ABRIGO DE DIOS): Robert Savage © 1954; harm. Louis Olivieri © 1996 New Spring Publishing, admin. Music Services

91D Psalm 91:1-6, 9-16
A Responsorial Setting

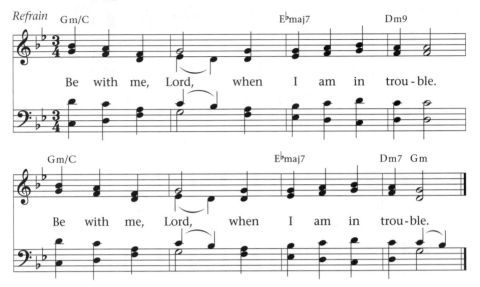

Refrain

Be with me, Lord, when I am in trou-ble.

Be with me, Lord, when I am in trou-ble.

Refrain

1 You who dwell in the shelter of the Most High,
   who abide in the shadow of the Almighty—

2 you will say to the Lord, "My refuge and my stronghold,
   my God in whom I put my trust."

3 For God will rescue you from the snare of the hunter
   and from the deadly plague.

4 God's wings will cover you, and you will find refuge beneath them;
   God's faithfulness will be your shield and defense.

5 You shall not fear any terror in the night,
   nor the arrow that flies by day;

6 nor the plague that stalks in the darkness,
   nor the sickness that lays waste at noon.   *Refrain*

9 Because you have made the Lord your refuge,
   and the Most High your habitation,

10 no evil will befall you,
   nor shall affliction come near your dwelling.

11 For God will give the angels charge over you,
   to guard you in all your ways.

12 Upon their hands they will bear you up,
   lest you strike your foot against a stone.

13 You will tread upon the lion cub and viper;
   you will trample down the lion and the serpent.   *Refrain*

¹⁴ I will deliver those who cling to me;

I will behold them, because they know my name.

¹⁵ They will call me, and I will answer them;

I will be with them in trouble; I will rescue and honor them.

¹⁶ With long life will I satisfy them,

and show them my salvation.   *Refrain*

Tone

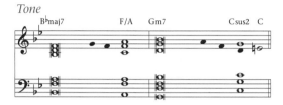

Lectionary: vv. 1-2, 9-16 Lent (C); vv. 1-6, 14-16 Ordinary Time after Pentecost (C); vv. 9-16 Ordinary Time after Pentecost (B).

Guitar chords do not correspond with keyboard harmony. For unison setting with keyboard accompaniment see p. 526.

Alternate Refrain

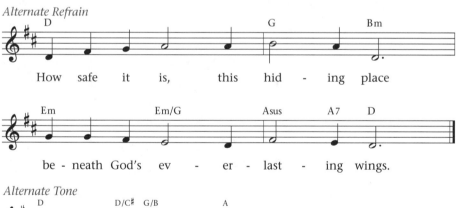

Alternate Tone

For accompaniment see p. 244.

91E On Eagle's Wings

1 You who dwell in the shel-ter of the Lord, who a-
bide in his shad-ow for life, say to the Lord: "My
ref-uge, my rock in whom I trust!"

Refrain
And he will raise you up on ea-gle's wings, bear you on the
breath of dawn, make you to shine like the sun, and
hold you in the palm of his hand.

2 The snare of the fowl-er will nev-er cap-ture you, and fam-ine will bring you no fear: un-der his wings your ref-uge, his faith-ful-ness your shield.

3 You need not fear the ter-ror of the night, nor the ar-row that flies by day; though thou-sands fall a-bout you, near you it shall not come.

4 For to his an-gels is giv-en a com-mand to guard you in all of your ways; up-on their hands they will bear you up, lest you dash your foot a-gainst a stone.

Keyboard accompaniment on p. 570.

Words and Music: J. Michael Joncas (b. 1951) © 1979 J. Michael Joncas, admin. OCP Publications

Accompaniment

Music: J. Michael Joncas (b. 1951) © 1979 J. Michael Joncas, admin. OCP Publications

Psalm 92

A Psalm. A Song for the Sabbath Day.

1 It is good to give thanks to the LORD, *
> to sing praises to your name, O Most High;

2 to declare your steadfast love in the morning, *
> and your faithfulness by night,

3 to the music of the lute and the harp, *
> to the melody of the lyre.

4 **For you, O LORD, have made me glad by your work; ***
> **at the works of your hands I sing for joy.**

5 **How great are your works, O LORD! ***
> **Your thoughts are very deep!**

6 The dullard cannot know, *
> the stupid cannot understand this:

7 though the wicked sprout like grass and all evildoers flourish, *
> they are doomed to destruction forever,

8 but you, O LORD, *
> are on high forever.

9 For your enemies, O LORD, for your enemies shall perish; *
> all evildoers shall be scattered.

10 **But you have exalted my horn like that of the wild ox; ***
> **you have poured over me fresh oil.**

11 My eyes have seen the downfall of my enemies; *
> my ears have heard the doom of my evil assailants.

12 **The righteous flourish like the palm tree, ***
> **and grow like a cedar in Lebanon.**

13 **They are planted in the house of the LORD; ***
> **they flourish in the courts of our God.**

14 **In old age they still produce fruit; ***
> **they are always green and full of sap,**

15 showing that the LORD is upright; *
> **he is my rock, and there is no unrighteousness in him.**

Holy and loving God, you spoke creation out of chaos
and brought your people out of darkness into the marvelous light of your love.
May the music of your creation and the praises sung by your people bring joy to you
and comfort to a tormented world.
We pray in Jesus' name. **Amen.**

Psalm 92, long associated with the Sabbath, is a psalm of praise and testimony about the goodness, faithfulness, and truthfulness of the Lord. It offers a Sabbath perspective on the world in which the apparent joys of faithless people are seen for what they are (v. 7) and the way of faithful service to God leads to a life of flourishing (vv. 12-19). The psalm speaks frankly about perennial exhaustion or burn-out (v. 10) and the kind of refreshment and joy that God offers, in part through the joy of Sabbath worship (vv. 1-4). *Use in Worship: an act of preparation or reflection on worship; preparation for Sabbath or Sunday.*

92A It Is Good to Sing Your Praises

1 It is good to sing your prais - es and to thank you,
O Most High, show - ing forth your lov - ing-kind - ness
when the morn - ing lights the sky. It is good when
night is fall - ing of your faith - ful - ness to tell,

2 You have filled my heart with glad - ness through the works your
hands have wrought; you have made my life vic - to - rious;
great your works and deep your thought. You, O Lord, on
high ex - alt - ed, reign for - ev - er - more in might;

3 But the good shall live be - fore you, plant - ed in your
dwell - ing place, fruit - ful trees and ev - er ver - dant,
nour - ished by your bound - less grace. In his good - ness
to the right - eous God his right-eous - ness dis - plays;

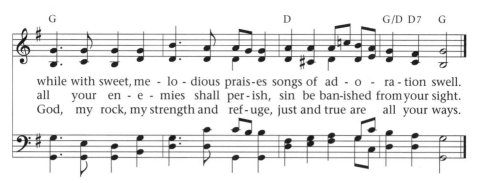

while with sweet, me - lo - dious prais-es songs of ad - o - ra - tion swell.
all   your en - e - mies shall per - ish, sin be ban-ished from your sight.
God,   my rock, my strength and ref - uge, just and true are   all your ways.

Words: *Psalter*, 1912, P.D.
Music (ELLESDIE 8.7.8.7 D): J. Leavitt's *Christian Lyre*, 1831, P.D.

Mah Gadlu / 92B
Oh, How Great Are Your Works

Hebrew Mah gad - lu   ma - a - se - cha   Yah,
English Oh, how great   are your works, O   LORD,

m'   - od am - ku mach-sh' - vo - te - cha.
your   thoughts, they are   ver - y   deep.

(echo): *Hal - le - lu - jah.*   *Hal - le - lu - jah.*

Ha - l' - lu - yah.   Ha - l' - lu - yah.
Hal - le - lu - jah.   Hal - le - lu - jah.

Hal - le - lu - jah.   *Hal - le - lu - jah.*

Ha - l' - lu - yah.   Ha - l' - lu - yah.
Hal - le - lu - jah.   Hal - le - lu - jah.

Words: Psalm 92:5
Music: Shefa Gold © 1994 Shefa Gold

92C It's Good to Give Thanks

Refrain

It's good to give thanks, give thanks to the Lord.

By day and by night with the harp and the lute.

You make me glad. Your works make me re - joice.

Yes, it is good, good to give thanks, thanks to the Lord. *Fine*

1 Fools don't get it. They nev-er will.

Set for de - struc - tion, they will be stilled.

The god - ly are root - ed deep in God's will.

To Refrain

Yes, it is good, good to give thanks, thanks to the Lord.

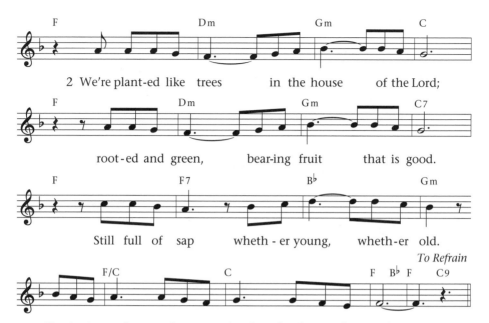

2 We're plant-ed like trees   in the house   of the Lord;

root-ed and green,   bear-ing fruit   that is good.

Still full of sap   wheth - er young,   wheth-er old.

To Refrain

Yes, it is good,   good to give thanks, thanks to the Lord.

Optional Keyboard Accompaniment

Words and Music: Ken Medema and Friends © 2010 Ken Medema Music/Brier Patch Music

92D Psalm 92:1-4, 12-15
A Responsorial Setting

Refrain

It's good to give thanks, give thanks to the Lord.
By day and by night with the harp and the lute.

You make me glad. Your works make me re - joice.

Yes, it is good, good to give thanks, thanks to the Lord.

Refrain

1 It is a good thing to give thanks to the LORD,
   to sing praise to your name, O Most High;

2 to herald your love in the morning
   and your faithfulness at night;

3 on the psaltery, and on the lyre,
   and to the melody of the harp.

4 For you have made me glad by your acts, O LORD;
   and I shout for joy because of the works of your hands. *Refrain*

12 The righteous shall flourish like a palm tree,
   and shall spread abroad like a cedar of Lebanon.

13 Those who are planted in the house of the LORD
   shall flourish in the courts of our God;

14 they shall still bear fruit in old age;
   they shall be green and succulent;

15 that they may show how upright the LORD is,
   my rock, in whom there is no injustice. *Refrain*

Tone

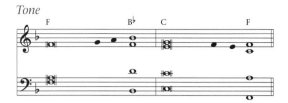

Lectionary: Ordinary Time after Epiphany (C); Ordinary Time after Pentecost (B,C).

Words and Music: Ken Medema and Friends © 2010 Ken Medema Music/Brier Patch Music
Psalm Text: from *Evangelical Lutheran Worship* © 2006 Evangelical Lutheran Church in America, admin. Augsburg Fortress Publishers
Tone: © 2011 Faith Alive Christian Resources

Psalm 93

¹ The LORD is king, he is robed in majesty; *

    the LORD is robed, he is girded with strength.

He has established the world; it shall never be moved; *

    ² **your throne is established from of old; you are from everlasting.**

³ The floods have lifted up, O LORD, *

    the floods have lifted up their voice; the floods lift up their roaring.

⁴ **More majestic than the thunders of mighty waters, ***

    more majestic than the waves of the sea,

    majestic on high is the LORD!

⁵ **Your decrees are very sure; ***

    holiness befits your house, O LORD, forevermore.

God of all time and all glory: Father, Son, and Spirit,
inspire our praise,
perfect our praise,
receive our praise,
now and forever. **Amen.**

Psalm 93 is a hymn of praise about the reign of God over all creation. *Use in Worship: services focusing on creation; services focusing on the reign of God including, from a NT perspective, the reign of Christ; Ascension Day; other celebrations of the lordship of Christ.*

93A Robed in Majesty

1 Robed in maj-es-ty, he reigns, sov-ereign from e-ter-ni-ty;
2 Surg-ing seas and pound-ing waves: might-ier is the Lord than these;

praise the Lord, the God of strength, robed in awe-some maj-es-ty.
might-ier than the break-er's roar, might-ier than those surg-ing seas.

Firm and sure the world will stand: here the Mak-er's power is shown—
Ho-li-ness a-dorns his house; age on age will hear his law;

yet, pre-dat-ing e-ven time, firm-er, sur-er stands his throne.
praise the Lord, whose reign up-holds ho-li-ness for ev-er-more.

Guitar chords do not correspond with keyboard harmony.

Words: Martin Leckebusch © 2003 Kevin Mayhew Ltd.
Music (SALZBURG 7.7.7.7 D): Jakob Hintze; harm. Johann S. Bach (1685-1750), P.D.

Psalm 93 | A Responsorial Setting 93B

Refrain

Ev - er since the world be - gan, your throne has been es - tab-lished.

Refrain

¹ The LORD is king, robed in majesty;

the LORD is robed in majesty and armed with strength.

The LORD has made the world so sure that it cannot be moved.

² Ever since the world began, your throne has been established;

you are from everlasting. *Refrain*

³ The waters have lifted up, O LORD, the waters have lifted up their voice;

the waters have lifted up their pounding waves.

⁴ Mightier than the sound of many waters, mightier than the breakers of the sea,

mightier is the LORD who dwells on high.

⁵ Your testimonies are very sure,

and holiness befits your house, O LORD, forever and forevermore. *Refrain*

Tone

Lectionary: Ascension Day (A,B,C); Reign of Christ (B).

Words: Psalm 93
Music: William Beckstrand from *Psalter for Worship, Cycle B* © 1996 Augsburg Fortress Publishers
Psalm Text: from *Evangelical Lutheran Worship* © 2006 Evangelical Lutheran Church in America, admin.
Augsburg Fortress Publishers
Tone: from *Psalter for Worship, Cycle B* © 1996 Augsburg Fortress Publishers

Psalm 94

¹ O L<small>ORD</small>, you God of vengeance,*
  you God of vengeance, shine forth!

² **Rise up, O judge of the earth;***
  give to the proud what they deserve!

³ O L<small>ORD</small>, how long shall the wicked,*
  how long shall the wicked exult?

⁴ They pour out their arrogant words;*
  all the evildoers boast.

⁵ They crush your people, O L<small>ORD</small>,*
  and afflict your heritage.

⁶ They kill the widow and the stranger,*
  they murder the orphan,

⁷ and they say, "The L<small>ORD</small> does not see;*
  the God of Jacob does not perceive."

⁸ **Understand, O dullest of the people;***
  fools, when will you be wise?

⁹ **He who planted the ear, does he not hear?***
  He who formed the eye, does he not see?

¹⁰ **He who disciplines the nations,***
  he who teaches knowledge to humankind, does he not chastise?

¹¹ **The L<small>ORD</small> knows our thoughts,***
  that they are but an empty breath.

¹² Happy are those whom you discipline, O L<small>ORD</small>,*
  and whom you teach out of your law,

¹³ giving them respite from days of trouble,*
  until a pit is dug for the wicked.

¹⁴ **For the L<small>ORD</small> will not forsake his people;***
  he will not abandon his heritage;

¹⁵ **for justice will return to the righteous,***
  and all the upright in heart will follow it.

¹⁶ Who rises up for me against the wicked?*
  Who stands up for me against evildoers?

¹⁷ **If the L<small>ORD</small> had not been my help,***
  my soul would soon have lived in the land of silence.

¹⁸ When I thought, "My foot is slipping," *
  your steadfast love, O Lord, held me up.

¹⁹ **When the cares of my heart are many, ***
  your consolations cheer my soul.

²⁰ Can wicked rulers be allied with you, *
  those who contrive mischief by statute?

²¹ They band together against the life of the righteous, *
  and condemn the innocent to death.

²² **But the Lord has become my stronghold, ***
  and my God the rock of my refuge.

²³ **He will repay them for their iniquity**
 and wipe them out for their wickedness; *
  the Lord our God will wipe them out.

God of justice,
wicked people rejoice in their sin, believing you neither see nor care.
Help your people to rejoice in your justice,
and even more in the gift of Jesus Christ, your Son,
who paid the price for our wickedness and restores us to fellowship with you. **Amen.**

Psalm 94 is a lament offered out of despair at the injustice suffered by widows, migrants, and orphans (vv. 5-6) that ultimately concludes with a strong assertion of the ways in which God serves as a haven and source of justice (vv. 22-23). This psalm speaks to perennial issues of social injustice; it is a lament in which we may have to identify not only with the victims but also with the victimizers. *Use in Worship: services focusing on social injustices.*

94A O Great God and Lord of the Earth

1 O great God and Lord of the earth,
2 Those who crush your peo - ple de - light,
3 God the Lord will not stay a - way
4 Should the wrong change plac - es with right

rouse your - self and de - mon-strate jus - tice; give the
claim-ing God a - bove takes no no - tice; they pro -
nor for - sake his well - be - loved peo - ple; heav - en's
and the courts play host to cor - rup - tion; should the

ar - ro-gant what they de - serve, si - lence all ma -
claim that heav - en is blind, that the God of
jus - tice soon will ap - pear and the pure in
in - no-cent fear for their lives while the guilt - y

le - vo - lent boast - ing. See how some you love are
Ja - cob is si - lent. Stu - pid fools, when will you
heart will em - brace it. Yes, the ones whom God in -
smile at their schem - ing; still the Lord will be your

bro - ken, for they know the weight of op - pres - sion;
lis - ten? Now take heed, you ig - nor - ant peo - ple.
struc - ted, who re - vere and stu - dy God's Word
ref - uge, be your strength and cour - age and tow - er.

e - ven wi - dows and or - phans are mur - dered, and poor
God who gave us sight and hear - ing has ob -
will be saved from all that harms them while a
Though your foot should verge on slip - ping, God will

strang-ers are in - no - cent vic - tims.
served and no - ted what hap - pened.
pit is dug for the wick - ed.
cher - ish, keep, and pro - tect you.

(last time)

Words: Psalm 94; para. and arr. John L. Bell (b. 1949) © 2002 Wild Goose Resource Group, Iona Community, Scotland, GIA Publications, Inc., exclusive North American agent
Music (VOS SOS EL DESTAZADO 8.9.8.9.8.9.8.9): Guillermo Cuellar © 1986, 1996 GIA Publications, Inc.; arr. Marcus Hong © 2011 GIA Publications, Inc.

Psalm 95

¹ O come, let us sing to the LORD; *
   let us make a joyful noise to the rock of our salvation!

² **Let us come into his presence with thanksgiving; ***
   let us make a joyful noise to him with songs of praise!

³ For the LORD is a great God, *
   and a great King above all gods.

⁴ **In his hand are the depths of the earth; ***
   the heights of the mountains are his also.

⁵ The sea is his, for he made it, *
   and the dry land, which his hands have formed.

⁶ **O come, let us worship and bow down, ***
   let us kneel before the LORD, our Maker!

⁷ **For he is our God,**
   and we are the people of his pasture, and the sheep of his hand. *
   O that today you would listen to his voice!

⁸ Do not harden your hearts, as at Meribah, *
   as on the day at Massah in the wilderness,

⁹ when your ancestors tested me, *
   and put me to the proof, though they had seen my work.

¹⁰ For forty years I loathed that generation *
   and said, "They are a people whose hearts go astray,
   and they do not regard my ways."

¹¹ Therefore in my anger I swore, *
   "They shall not enter my rest."

Holy God—Father, Son, and Spirit,
it is too easy for your people to talk about you without worshiping you,
to worship you without obeying you, and to obey you without joy.
Infuse us with such passion for you that our words become worship,
our desires become obedience,
and our lives reveal the joy that can be found only in you. **Amen.**

Psalm 95, a psalm of praise in three parts, calls worshipers to three essential actions: exuberant praise (vv. 1-5); humble submission, pictured graphically as an act of prostration (vv. 6-7a); and attentive listening (vv. 7b-11). Like Pss. 50, 81, 132, 134, and several others, this psalm assumes that faithful covenant worship includes both praise directed toward God and faithful listening to the word that comes from God. *Use in Worship: a call to worship; a call to listen to God's Word. Consider using this psalm in two parts, with vv. 1-7a at the beginning of worship and vv. 7b-11 prior to the reading and preaching of God's Word.*

Come, Let Us Praise the Lord 95A

1 Come, let us praise the Lord, with joy our God ac - claim,
2 Our God of match - less worth, our King be - yond com - pare,
3 In wor - ship bow the knee, our glo - rious God con - fess;
4 Come, hear his voice to - day, re - ceive what love im - parts;

his great - ness tell a - broad and bless his sav - ing name.
the deep - est bounds of earth, the hills, are in his care.
the great Cre - a - tor, he, the Lord of Right - eous - ness.
his ho - ly will o - bey and hard - en not your hearts.

Lift high your songs be - fore his throne to
He all de - crees, who by his hand pre -
He reigns un - seen: his flock he feeds and
His ways are best and lead at last, all

whom a - lone all praise be - longs.
pared the land and formed the seas.
gent - ly leads in pas - tures green.
trou - bles past, to per - fect rest.

Guitar chords do not correspond with keyboard harmony.

Words: Timothy Dudley-Smith (b. 1926) © 1984 Hope Publishing Company
Music (DARWALL'S 148TH 6.6.6.6.4.4.4.4): John Darwall (1731-1789), 1770, P.D.

95B Come, Let Us Worship and Bow Down

Come, let us wor-ship and bow down, let us kneel be-fore the Lord, our God, our Mak - er. Mak - er. For he is our God, and we are the peo-ple of his pas - ture, and the sheep of his hand, just the sheep of his hand.

Words: Psalm 95:6-7
Music: Dave Doherty © 1980 Universal Music—Brentwood-Benson Publishing; arr. © 1997 Universal Music—Brentwood-Benson Publishing

Come, Let Us Sing 95C

1 Come, let us sing for joy to the LORD;
2 For the LORD is the great God,
3 The sea is his, for he made it;
4 For he is our God
5 *Glory be the Father, and to the Son,*

let us shout aloud to the Rock of our sal - vation.
the great King a - bove all gods.
and his hands formed the dry land.
and we are the peo - ple of his pasture,
and to the Ho - ly Spirit;

Let us come before him with thanks - giving;
In his hand are the depths of the earth;
Come, let us bow down in worship,
the flock under his care.
as it was in the beginning, is now, and ev - er shall be;

and extol him with music and song.
and the mountain peaks be - long to him.
let us kneel be - fore the LORD our Maker;
O that today you would lis - ten to his voice!
world without end. A - men!

95D Now with Joyful Exultation

1 Now with joy-ful ex-ul-ta-tion let us sing to
2 For how great a God, and glo-rious, is the LORD of
3 To the LORD, such might re-veal-ing, let us come with
4 While he of-fers peace and par-don let us hear his

God our praise; to the Rock of our sal-va-tion
whom we sing; o-ver i-dol gods vic-to-rious,
rev-erence meet, and, be-fore our Mak-er kneel-ing,
voice to-day, lest, if we our hearts should hard-en,

loud ho-san-nas let us raise. Thank-ful trib-ute
great is he, our God and King. In his hand are
let us wor-ship at his feet. He is our own
we should per-ish in the way— lest to us, so

glad-ly bring-ing, let us come be-fore him now, and, with
earth's deep plac-es, al-so his are all the hills; his the
God who leads us, we the peo-ple of his care; with a
un-be-liev-ing, he in judg-ment should de-clare: "You, so

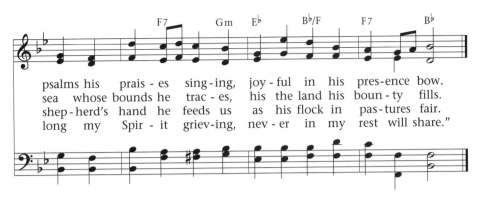

			psalms his	prais-es	sing-ing,	joy-ful	in	his	pres-ence bow.
sea	whose bounds he	trac-es,	his	the land his	boun-ty	fills.
shep-herd's	hand	he	feeds us	as	his flock in	pas-tures fair.
long	my	Spir-it	griev-ing,	nev-er	in	my	rest will share."

Words: *Psalter*, 1912, alt., P.D.
Music (BEECHER 8.7.8.7 D): John Zundel, 1870, P.D.

Psalm 95 | A Responsorial Setting **95E**

Refrain

Oh, that to-day you would lis-ten to God's voice, "Hard-en not your hearts."

Refrain

1 Come, let us sing to the LORD;

let us shout for joy to the rock of our salvation.

2 Let us come before God's presence with thanksgiving

and raise a loud shout to the LORD with psalms. *Refrain*

3 For you, LORD, are a great God,

and a great ruler above all gods.

4 In your hand are the caverns of the earth;

the heights of the hills are also yours.

5 The sea is yours, for you made it,

and your hands have molded the dry land.

6 Come, let us worship and bow down,

let us kneel before the LORD our maker. *Refrain*   (continues)

⁷ For the Lᴏʀᴅ is our God, and we are the people of God's pasture
  and the sheep of God's hand.

    Oh, that today you would hear God's voice!

⁸ "Harden not your hearts,
  as at Meribah, as on that day at Massah in the desert.

⁹ There your ancestors tested me,
  they put me to the test, though they had seen my works.

¹⁰ Forty years I loathed that generation, saying,
  'The heart of this people goes astray; they do not know my ways.'

¹¹ Indeed I swore in my anger,
  'They shall never come to my rest.'" *Refrain*

Tone

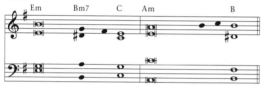

Lectionary: Lent (A); vv. 1-7a Reign of Christ (A).

Words: Susan Sayers (b. 1946) © 1989 Kevin Mayhew Ltd.
Music: Andrew Moore (b. 1954) © 1995 Kevin Mayhew Ltd.
Psalm Text: from *Evangelical Lutheran Worship* © 2006 Evangelical Lutheran Church in America, admin.
Augsburg Fortress Publishers
Tone: © 2011 Faith Alive Christian Resources

Alternate Tone

The alternate tone may be used with the refrain of 95F on facing page.

Tone: © 2011 Faith Alive Christian Resources

Come Now, and Lift Up Your Hearts [95F]

Leader

1 Come now, and lift   up   your hearts and sing,   en - ter the courts   of   the
2 Know that the Lord   is   a   might - y   God,   rul - er su - preme   in   the
3 He   has cre - at - ed   the depths be - low;   his own   hands made the
4 Come, let   us bow down and   wor - ship him;   kneel in the   pres - ence of

All

King   of   kings.   Come now, and lift   up   your hearts and   sing,
realms a - bove;   Know   that the Lord   is   a   might - y   God,
beau - teous land;   He   has cre - at - ed   the depths be - low;
God   the Lord.   Come,   let   us bow down and   wor - ship him;

en - ter the courts   of   the King   of   kings. *Come and re - joice in his*
rul - er su - preme   in   the realms a - bove;   *he   is   the Lord of the*
his own   hands made the beau - teous land;   *gen - tle and kind, the good*
kneel in the   pres - ence of   God   the Lord.   *If   you will heark - en and*

Leader

won - drous works; thank him and praise him with   joy - ous psalm.
depths be   low;   he   is   the strength of   the moun - tains high.
shep - herd   he;   we   are   the sheep of   his   pas - ture land.
heed   his word,   you   shall be   glad and your hearts   re - joice.

Refrain

All

Come   now, and lift   up   your hearts   and   sing,

en - ter the courts   of   the King   of   kings.

Optional ostinato accompaniment

Words: anonymous; alt. James Minchin
Music (SWEINDIA 9.9.9.9 with refrain): Karnatic hymn melody; arr. I-to Loh (b. 1936) © 1990, 2000 Christian
Conference of Asia, admin. GIA Publications, Inc.

95G Come, Worship God

1 Come, wor-ship God, who is wor-thy of hon-or;
en - ter God's pres - ence with thanks and a song!
You are the rock of your peo - ple's sal - va - tion,
to whom our ju - bi-lant prais - es be - long.

2 Ruled by your might are the heights of the moun-tains;
held in your hands are the depths of the earth.
Yours is the sea, yours the land, for you made them,
God a - bove all gods, who gave us our birth.

3 We are your peo - ple, the sheep of your pas - ture;
you are our Mak - er, and to you we pray.
Glad - ly we kneel in o - be - dience be - fore you;
great is the one whom we wor - ship this day!

4 Now let us lis - ten, for you speak a - mong us;
o - pen our hearts to re - ceive what you say.
Peace be to all who re - mem - ber your good-ness,
trust in your word, and re - joice in your way!

Words: Michael Perry © 1980 The Jubilate Group, admin. Hope Publishing Company
Music (O QUANTA QUALIA 11.10.11.10): *Antiphoner*, Paris, 1681; harm. John B. Dykes (1823-1876), P.D.

Come with All Joy to Sing to God

95H

1 Come with all joy to sing to God our sav - ing
2 In ho - li - ness and light ar - rayed a - bove all
3 The earth is his from east to west, from o - cean
4 Come near to wor - ship! Come with faith, bow down to

rock, the liv - ing Lord; in glad thanks-giv - ing seek
gods that we have made, he is the one al - might -
floor to moun - tain crest; he made the sea and formed
God who gives us breath: God is our shep - herd, God

his face with songs of vic - to - ry and grace.
y King, and his the glo - ry that we sing.
the lands, he shaped the is - lands by his hands.
a - lone; we are his peo - ple, all his own.

5 But if you hear his voice today
do not reject what he will say;
when Israel wandered from God's path
they suffered forty years of wrath.

6 That generation went astray;
they did not want to know his way:
they put their Savior to the test,
and saw his power, but lost their rest.

Guitar chords do not correspond with keyboard harmony.

This tune in a lower key: p. 707.

Words: Christopher Idle © 1982 The Jubilate Group, admin. Hope Publishing Company
Music (GERMANY 8.8.8.8): W. Gardiner's *Sacred Melodies*, 1815, P.D.

951 Let Not Your Hearts Be Hardened

Refrain Oboe

D Em/D D C/D D D9 C

Let not your hearts be hard-ened, if to-day you hear God's

Fine

D2 D C6/E Em G6/D Bm7 C2 Am Dsus D

voice, if to-day you hear God's voice.

D D9

1 Come, ring out your joy to the Lord; hail the
2 Come, let us bow and bend low; kneel - ing be -
3 Oh, that to - day you would heark-en! Hard-en not your
4 *Praise to the Source of our be - ing, praise to the*

To Refrain

rock who saves us. Let us come be-fore him giv-ing
fore our Cre - a - tor. For the Lord is our God, we his
hearts as at Mer-i-bah, as on that day at Mas-sah in the
Son, our Re-deem-er, *to the Ad-vo-cate* *dwell - ing with-*

thanks, with songs let us hail the Lord.
peo - ple, the flock that is led by his hand.
des - ert, when your an - ces-tors test - ed me.
in us, *both* *now* *and for-ev - er - more.*

Psalm 96

1 O sing to the LORD a new song; *
    sing to the LORD, all the earth.

2 **Sing to the LORD, bless his name; ***
    tell of his salvation from day to day.

3 **Declare his glory among the nations, ***
    his marvelous works among all the peoples.

4 For great is the LORD, and greatly to be praised; *
    he is to be revered above all gods.

5 For all the gods of the peoples are idols, *
    but the LORD made the heavens.

6 **Honor and majesty are before him; ***
    strength and beauty are in his sanctuary.

7 Ascribe to the LORD, O families of the peoples, *
    ascribe to the LORD glory and strength.

8 Ascribe to the LORD the glory due his name; *
    bring an offering, and come into his courts.

9 **Worship the LORD in holy splendor; ***
    tremble before him, all the earth.

10 Say among the nations, "The LORD is king! *
    The world is firmly established; it shall never be moved.
    He will judge the peoples with equity."

11 **Let the heavens be glad, and let the earth rejoice; ***
    let the sea roar, and all that fills it;
    12 **let the field exult, and everything in it.**

Then shall all the trees of the forest sing for joy *
    13 **before the LORD; for he is coming,**
    for he is coming to judge the earth.

He will judge the world with righteousness, *
    and the peoples with his truth.

Great and wondrous God, your love and your mercy are new every morning.
Do not let your people be content with the repetition of threadbare praise.
Inspire us to join with all of your creation in fresh songs of hope and blessing
offered to you each new day, through Jesus Christ our Lord. **Amen.**

Psalm 96 is a call to worship addressed to all of creation and all peoples. It extols God's work of creation
(v. 4); God's honor, majesty, might, and glory (vv. 5-6); and God's righteous, faithful, and truthful rule
(vv. 10, 13). The praise of God is to be expressed not only by people but also by the heavens, the earth, the
sea, rural landscapes, and trees (vv. 11-12). *Use in Worship: Advent and Christmas celebrations (along with Pss.
97 and 98); services focusing on both the first and second comings of Jesus, a link suggested by the emphasis on the
advent or "coming" of God to rule in righteousness (v. 13).*

Come and Sing a New Song 96A

1 Come and sing a new song, a song of cel - e - bra - tion.
2 Sing to God and bless his name in ev - ery con - gre - ga - tion.
3 All his works are mar - vel - ous—make bold your pro - cla - ma - tion.
4 Bow be - fore his maj - es - ty in ho - ly con - tem - pla - tion.

Lift to God your voic - es in joy - ful a - do - ra - tion.
Day by day ex - tol him, and tell of his sal - va - tion.
Tell - ing of his glo - ry to ev - ery race and na - tion.
Wor - ship and a - dore him with hum - ble ded - i - ca - tion.

Refrain

Come and sing a new song.

Alternate ostinato accompaniment
for Orff instruments or xylophones

Use the alternate accompaniment for unison singing.

Words: Punjabi; tr. Alison Blenkinsop © Alison Blenkinsop
Music: Punjabi; arr. Geoff Weaver © The Royal School of Church Music; ostinato acc. Martin Tel © 2011 Faith
Alive Christian Resources

96B Sing to the LORD, Sing His Praise

1 Sing to the LORD, sing his praise, all you peo-ples;
2 Tell of his won-drous works, tell of his glo-ry
3 Vain are the i-dols and gods of the na-tions;
4 Give un-to God Most High glo-ry and hon-or;

new be your song as new hon-ors you pay.
till through the na-tions his name is re-vered.
God made the heavens, and his glo-ry they tell.
come with your of-ferings and hum-bly draw near.

Sing of his maj-es-ty, praise him for-ev-er,
Praise and ex-alt him, for he is al-might-y;
Splen-dor and maj-es-ty shine out be-fore him;
Wor-ship the LORD in all beau-ty and splen-dor;

show his sal-va-tion from day to day.
God o-ver all, let the LORD be feared.
glo-ry and strength in his tem-ple dwell.
trem-ble be-fore him with god-ly fear.

(continues)

5 Say to the nations, "The LORD reigns forever."
　　Earth is established as he did decree.
　　Righteous and just is the King of the nations,
　　judging the peoples with equity.

6 Let heaven and earth be glad; oceans, be joyful;
　　forest and field, exultation express.
　　For God is coming, the judge of the nations,
　　coming to judge in his righteousness.

Words: *Psalter*, 1912, alt., P.D.
Music (WESLEY 11.10.11.9): Lowell Mason (1792-1872), 1830, P.D.

Psalm 96 | A Responsorial Setting 96C

Refrain

Refrain

¹ Sing to the LORD a new song;
　　sing to the LORD, all the earth.

² Sing to the LORD, bless the name of the LORD;
　　proclaim God's salvation from day to day.

³ Declare God's glory among the nations
　　and God's wonders among all peoples.

⁴ For great is the LORD and greatly to be praised,
　　more to be feared than all gods.　*Refrain*

⁵ As for all the gods of the nations, they are but idols;
　　but you, O LORD, have made the heavens.

⁶ Majesty and magnificence are in your presence;
　　power and splendor are in your sanctuary.

(continues)

7 Ascribe to the LORD, you families of the peoples,
    ascribe to the LORD honor and power.

8 Ascribe to the LORD the honor due the holy name;
    bring offerings and enter the courts of the LORD.

9 Worship the LORD in the beauty of holiness;
    tremble before the LORD, all the earth.   *Refrain*

10 Tell it out among the nations: "The LORD is king!
    The one who made the world so firm that it cannot be moved
    will judge the peoples with equity."

11 Let the heavens rejoice, and let the earth be glad;
    let the sea thunder and all that is in it;
    let the field be joyful and all that is therein.

12 Then shall all the trees of the wood shout for joy at your coming, O LORD,
    for you come to judge the earth.

13 You will judge the world with righteousness
    and the peoples with your truth.   *Refrain*

Tone

Lectionary: Christmas (A,B,C); Ordinary Time after Pentecost (A,C); vv. 1-9 Ordinary Time after Epiphany (C) and Ordinary Time after Pentecost (C).

Words: Psalm 96
Music: Tim TenClay © 2010 Tim TenClay, admin. Faith Alive Christian Resources
Psalm Text: from *Evangelical Lutheran Worship* © 2006 Evangelical Lutheran Church in America, admin. Augsburg Fortress Publishers
Tone: © 2011 Faith Alive Christian Resources

96D Sing, Sing, Sing to the Lord

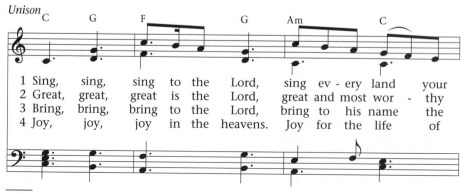

Unison

1 Sing, sing, sing to the Lord, sing ev - ery land your
2 Great, great, great is the Lord, great and most wor - thy
3 Bring, bring, bring to the Lord, bring to his name the
4 Joy, joy, joy in the heavens. Joy for the life of

own new song: sing ev-ery day that he saves!
of our love, great a-bove all oth-er gods.
wor-ship due. Bring your best gift to his throne:
sea and earth. Joy in the field and the wood!

Let all the na-tions hear of his glo-ry, vic-to-ries, won-ders,
They are but noth-ings, God is all glo-rious, splen-did, maj-es-tic,
God is all ho-ly, trem-ble be-fore him: clothed in his beau-ty,
Wel-come his king-dom, praise his sal-va-tion; now he is com-ing,

tell them the sto-ry, prais-ing the Lord with heart and tongue,
strong, and vic-to-rious, mak-er of earth and heaven a-bove,
come to a-dore him. Tell what the Lord has done for you,
Lord of cre-a-tion, judg-ing the peo-ples with his truth,

prais-ing the Lord with heart and tongue.
mak-er of earth and heaven a-bove.
tell what the Lord has done for you.
judg-ing the peo-ples with his truth.

Words: Christopher Idle © 1992 The Jubilate Group, admin. Hope Publishing Company
Music (SING 6.8.7.5.5.5.5.8.8): Iteke Prins © 2011 Iteke Prins, admin. Faith Alive Christian Resources

96E Sing a Song to God

1 Sing a song, sing a song to God,
2 Great is God, wor - thy of all praise,
3 Tribes on earth, bow, con - fess God's might,
4 Tell the na - tions God reigns as King,

all the world sing and bless God's Name,
wor - ship God high a - bove all things,
bow down and give all glo - ry due,
judg - ing with truth and right - eous - ness,

ay, ay, sa - li - dum - may, ay, ay, sa - li - dum - may.

Dai - ly sing of the sav - ing power,
Who with might made the u - ni - verse,
Come to God, bring your gifts most rare;
Sing a song, sing a song to God,

tell all lands of the won - drous works;
hon - or give to God's maj - es - ty,
fill heavens' hall with your joy - ful sound,
all the world sing and bless God's name,

ay, ay, sa - li - dum - may, ay, ay, sa - li - dum - may.

Optional hand clapping or percussion

Group 1

Group 2   *simile*

Optional xylophone ostinato

simile

The meaning of Salidummay has long been forgotten, but for Christians in the Philippines the word is used as an expression of joy.

Words: Francisco F. Feliciano © Francisco F. Feliciano
Music (SALIDUMMAY 8.8.8.8 with refrain): Ben Pangosban © 1990, 2000 Christian Conference of Asia, admin. GIA Publications, Inc.; arr. I-to Loh (b. 1936) © 2011 Christian Conference of Asia, admin. GIA Publications, Inc.

Sing to the Lord a New Song 96F

1 Sing to the Lord a new song; sing to God, all you
2 Let earth and heav - en glo - ry; let o - cean depths re -

lands. Sing of sal - va - tion al - ways; God's
joice. Let hills and plains and for - ests sing

glo - ry now at hand. God's love shall nev - er cease.
prais - es with one voice. God's love shall nev - er cease.

God comes to rule with jus - tice; God comes to rule with peace.
God comes to rule with jus - tice; God comes to rule with peace.

Guitar chords do not correspond with keyboard harmony.

Words: Scott Soper © 2005 World Library Publications
Music (ES IST EIN' ROS' ENTSPRUNGEN 7.6.7.6.6.7.6): from *Alte Catholische Geistliche Kirchengesäng,*
Cologne, 1599; harm. Michael Praetorius, 1609, P.D.

96G Sing to the Lord No Threadbare Song

Unison

1 Sing to the Lord no thread-bare song, no time-worn, tooth-less hymn,
2 Let earth's di-verse, me - lo - dic tongues de-clare in tell - ing phrase
3 Heav-ens re-joice, and earth be glad! Ex - ult, you roar - ing seas!

no sen - ti - ment-al plat - i - tude, no emp - ty pi - ous whim;
the glo - ry of the on - ly God who mer - its thanks and praise.
Let fields and plains re-sound with joy that ech - oes from the trees!

but raise a song just off the loom, fresh - wov - en, strong, and dense,
All oth - er hopes will dis - ap-point, their brit - tle lus - ter fade,
As na - ture sings, let peo - ple join and hu - man dis - cord cease,

as new as God's e - ter - nal now tran-scend - ing time and sense.
but sure and strong re-mains the Lord by whom all things were made.
for God shall come to rule the world with jus - tice, love, and peace.

Words: Carl P. Daw Jr. (b. 1944) © 1995 Hope Publishing Company
Music (CANTICUM NOVUM 8.6.8.6 D): Alfred V. Fedak (b. 1953), 1995, © 1995 Selah Publishing
Company, Inc.

O Sing a New Song

Refrain

O sing a new song to the Lord, sing to the Lord, sing all the earth.

1 O sing a new song to the Lord,
2 Proclaim God's salvation day by day,
3 The Lord is great and worthy of all praise,
4 For the Lord made the heavens!
5 Let the heavens be glad, let the earth rejoice,
6 Shout for joy, all trees of the woods,

sing to the Lord, all the earth!
tell of God's glory among the nations,
to be feared more than all gods;
Oh, the splendor and majesty of God's presence!
let the sea roar, and all its creatures;
at the presence of God, who now comes

Sing to God and praise the Name.
and God's marvels to all the people. *To Refrain*
all other gods are merely idols.
Oh, the power and beauty of God's temple. *To Refrain*
be glad, you fields, and all your fruit.
to judge the earth with right and the people with truth. *To Refrain*

Words: Helen L. Wright, 1983, © 1986 Helen L. Wright; ref. Hal H. Hopson © 1986 Hope Publishing Company
Music: Hal H. Hopson © 1986 Hope Publishing Company

Psalm 97

1 The LORD is king! Let the earth rejoice; *
   let the many coastlands be glad!

2 **Clouds and thick darkness are all around him;** *
   righteousness and justice are the foundation of his throne.

3 Fire goes before him, *
   and consumes his adversaries on every side.

4 His lightnings light up the world; *
   the earth sees and trembles.

5 The mountains melt like wax before the LORD, *
   before the Lord of all the earth.

6 **The heavens proclaim his righteousness;** *
   and all the peoples behold his glory.

7 **All worshipers of images are put to shame,**
   those who make their boast in worthless idols; *
   all gods bow down before him.

8 Zion hears and is glad, and the towns of Judah rejoice, *
   because of your judgments, O God.

9 **For you, O LORD, are most high over all the earth;** *
   you are exalted far above all gods.

10 The LORD loves those who hate evil; *
    he guards the lives of his faithful;
    he rescues them from the hand of the wicked.

11 **Light dawns for the righteous,** *
    and joy for the upright in heart.

12 **Rejoice in the LORD, O you righteous,** *
    and give thanks to his holy name!

O God, our God, awesome and righteous, sovereign of all,
we have seen your power, justice, and love revealed in your Son, our Redeemer.
In him we joyfully praise you this day and eagerly await the day that is yet to come
when all the earth will see your glory. **Amen.**

Psalm 97 proclaims the Lord's reign, beginning and ending with a call to praise God (vv. 1, 12). It continues by evoking a memory of God leading the people by fire and cloud in the wilderness, drawing on vivid natural images of fire, cloud, and darkness to convey the majesty of God (vv. 2-6). The psalm goes on to celebrate God's attentive response and gift of illumination to the people (vv. 8, 11), contrasting the inaction of idols and other gods. *Use in Worship: Advent and Christmas celebrations (along with Pss. 96 and 98).*

God Reigns! Earth Rejoices! 97A

1 God reigns! Earth re - joic - es! O - ceans shout God's might!
2 Fires will blaze the path - way; stars will mark the place,
3 E - vil walks be - side us, crush - es with its grief;
4 Light dawns for the right - eous, joy for God's own heirs;

Clad in truth and joy, God's throne is our de - light.
when God comes in glo - ry, meets us face to face.
yet in God the faith - ful find their sure re - lief.
love all loves ex - cel - ling; grace be - yond com - pare.

Clouds roll a - side, and night be - comes as day.
Moun - tains will shake, and worth - less i - dols fall;
Shack - les will break, and chains of bon - dage cease;
Daugh - ters and sons, God's maj - es - ty pro - claim!

God will dwell a - mong us; God will show the way!
Zi - on will re - joice, for God is Lord of all!
for - mer lam - en - ta - tions now are songs of peace.
Let your hearts de - clare the Lord's most ho - ly name!

Words: Michael Morgan © 2011 Michael Morgan, admin. Faith Alive Christian Resources
Music (NOËL NOUVELET 11.11.10.11): Medieval French carol, P.D.

97B God Reigns: Let Earth Rejoice!

1 God reigns: let earth re-joice! Sing praise with one great voice.
2 Fire goes be-fore his path, con-sum-ing in his wrath
3 Those wor-ship-ers, un-wise, who bow to cults and lies
4 God sends de-liv-er-ance to res-cue all his saints;

All shores, with sea sur-round - ing, praise with your
all those who seek out e - vil. Storms flash and
pro - voke God's in-dig-na - tion. They can-not
he keeps them safe from e - vil. God tru-ly

voice re-sound - ing. Dark clouds of mys-ter-y
shake and rum - ble. Great moun-tains melt like wax
gain sal-va - tion. Now all in Ju - dah praise
loves be-liev - ers. Light dawns for all his own;

pro - claim his maj-es-ty. Firm found-ed is God's
be - fore the LORD's at-tacks. His heav-ens, stretched a-
their LORD's most right-eous ways, and Zi-on prais-es
true joy is theirs a-lone. Re-deemed, with heart and

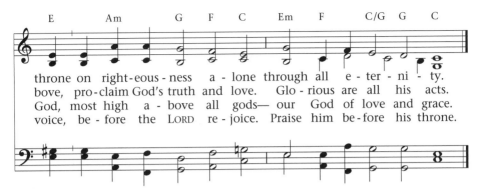

throne on right-eous - ness a - lone through all e - ter - ni - ty.
bove, pro-claim God's truth and love. Glo - rious are all his acts.
God, most high a - bove all gods— our God of love and grace.
voice, be - fore the LORD re - joice. Praise him be-fore his throne.

Guitar chords do not correspond with keyboard harmony.

Words: Marie J. Post, 1981, © 1987 Faith Alive Christian Resources
Music (GENEVAN 97 | 6.6.7.7.6.6.6.6.6.6): *Genevan Psalter*, 1562; harm. Dale Grotenhuis, 1985, © 1987 Faith Alive Christian Resources

Psalm 97 | A Responsorial Setting 97C

Light dawns for the right - eous, and joy for the hon-est of heart.

Refrain

¹ The LORD reigns; let the earth rejoice;
   let the multitude of the isles be glad.

² Clouds and darkness surround the LORD,
   righteousness and justice are the foundations of God's throne.

³ Fire goes before the LORD,
   burning up enemies on every side.

⁴ Lightnings light up the world;
   the earth sees and trembles.

⁵ The mountains melt like wax
   before the Lord of all the earth.

⁶ The heavens declare your righteousness, O LORD,
   and all the peoples see your glory. *Refrain*

(continues)

⁷ Confounded be all who worship carved images and delight in false gods!
  Bow down before the Lord, all you gods.

⁸ Zion hears and is glad, and the cities of Judah rejoice,
  because of your judgments, O Lord.

⁹ For you are the Lord, most high over all the earth;
  you are exalted far above all gods.   *Refrain*

¹⁰ You who love the Lord, hate evil!
  God guards the lives of the saints
  and rescues them from the hand of the wicked.

¹¹ Light dawns for the righteous,
  and joy for the honest of heart.

¹² Rejoice in the Lord, you righteous,
  and give thanks to God's holy name.   *Refrain*

Tone

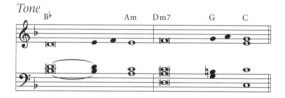

Lectionary: Christmas (A,B,C); Eastertide (C).

Words: Psalm 97:11
Music: George A. Black (b. 1931), 1995, © 2001 Selah Publishing Company, Inc.
Psalm Text: from *Evangelical Lutheran Worship* © 2006 Evangelical Lutheran Church in America, admin.
Augsburg Fortress Publishers
Tone: © 2011 Faith Alive Christian Resources

97D A Christmas Prayer of Praise

Almighty and loving God,
  on this day when we celebrate the birth of your Son, we testify with joy:
  "the Lord is King, let the earth rejoice."
As we rehearse again the stories of signs in the stars and choir of angels in the
  heaven, we echo the ancient words of the psalm:
  **"the heavens proclaim your righteousness and all the peoples
  behold your glory."**
As we glimpse the "perfect image of the invisible God," we see again that
  "all who make their boast in worthless idols are put to shame."
As we receive the gift of a savior, we announce with grateful hearts:
  "light dawns for the righteous, and joy for the upright in heart."
Alleluia! **Amen.**

The prayer may conclude with the singing of 97A or another psalm or hymn of praise.

John D. Witvliet, 2011, © Creative Commons Attribution-NonCommercial-ShareAlike

Psalm 98

1 O sing to the LORD a new song, for he has done marvelous things. *
    His right hand and his holy arm have gotten him victory.

2 The LORD has made known his victory; *
    he has revealed his vindication in the sight of the nations.

3 He has remembered his steadfast love and faithfulness to the house of Israel. *
    All the ends of the earth have seen the victory of our God.

4 **Make a joyful noise to the LORD, all the earth; ***
    break forth into joyous song and sing praises.

5 **Sing praises to the LORD with the lyre, ***
    with the lyre and the sound of melody.

6 **With trumpets and the sound of the horn ***
    make a joyful noise before the King, the LORD.

7 Let the sea roar, and all that fills it; *
    the world and those who live in it.

8 **Let the floods clap their hands; ***
    let the hills sing together for joy

9 **at the presence of the LORD, for he is coming ***
    to judge the earth. *

He will judge the world with righteousness, *
    and the peoples with equity.

Victorious God, all creation lifts its voice in a cacophony of joyful praise.
In your Son, Jesus Christ our Lord,
you have come to judge the world in truth and equity.
We await his return to make all things new,
joining creation's chorus with our new songs of praise. **Amen.**

Psalm 98 calls all of creation to praise God. It emphasizes that God is the God not only of Israel (v. 3) but also of the whole world (v. 9), and that God's enthronement is for the purpose of sovereign governance, a rule that will reveal, in the words of Isaac Watts, "the wonders of his love." *Use in Worship: Advent and Christmas celebrations (along with Pss. 96 and 97).*

98A Sing to the Lord a New Song

Words and Music: Greg Scheer © 1995 Greg Scheer

98B Psalm 98 | A Responsorial Setting

Refrain

Sing a new song to the Lord, he to whom won-ders be-long; re-joice in his tri-umph and tell of his power, O sing to the Lord a new song!

Refrain

1 Sing a new song to the LORD, who has done marvelous things,
   whose right hand and holy arm have won the victory,

2 O LORD, you have made known your victory,
   you have revealed your righteousness in the sight of the nations.

3 You remember your steadfast love and faithfulness to the house of Israel;
   all the ends of the earth have seen the victory of our God.   *Refrain*

4 Shout with joy to the LORD, all you lands;
   lift up your voice, rejoice, and sing.

5 Sing to the LORD with the harp,
   with the harp and the voice of song.

6 With trumpets and the sound of the horn
   shout with joy before the king, the LORD.   *Refrain*

7 Let the sea roar, and all that fills it,
   the world and those who dwell therein.
8 Let the rivers clap their hands,
   and let the hills ring out with joy before the LORD,
   who comes to judge the earth.
9 The LORD will judge the world with righteousness
   and the peoples with equity. *Refrain*

Tone

Lectionary: Christmas (A,B,C); Easter Vigil (A,B,C); Eastertide (B); Ordinary Time after Pentecost (C).

Words: Timothy Dudley-Smith (b. 1926) © 1973 Hope Publishing Company
Music (ONSLOW SQUARE 7.7.11.8): David G. Wilson © 1973 The Jubilate Group, admin. Hope Publishing Company
Psalm Text: from *Evangelical Lutheran Worship* © 2006 Evangelical Lutheran Church in America, admin. Augsburg Fortress Publishers
Tone: © 2011 Faith Alive Christian Resources

Alternate Refrain

All the ends of the earth have seen the vic-to-ry of our God.

Alternate Tone

Words: Psalm 98:3b
Music: Robert Hobby from *Psalter for Worship, Cycle B* © 1996 Augsburg Fortress Publishers
Tone: from *Psalter for Worship, Cycle B* © 1996 Augsburg Fortress Publishers

98C Sing, Sing a New Song to the Lord God

1 Sing, sing a new song to the Lord God for all the
2 Shout, make a joy-ful noise be-fore him, O all the
3 Let all the streams in joy-ous u-nion now clap their

won-ders he has wrought; his right hand and his
earth, his prais-es sing; with harp and trum-pet
hands and praise ac-cord; let moun-tains sing in

arm most ho-ly the vic-to-ry to him have brought.
sound a-dore him, make mu-sic to the Lord, the King.
glad com-mu-nion and skip for joy be-fore the Lord.

The Lord has shown his great sal-va-tion, to Is-ra-el his
Let o-ceans roar with all their full-ness, the world and all who
He comes, he comes to judge the peo-ple, ar-rayed in truth and

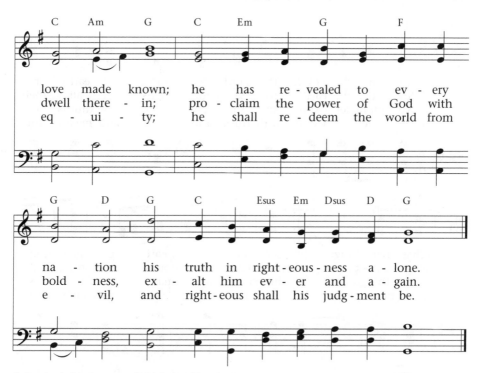

love made known; he has re - vealed to ev - ery
dwell there - in; pro - claim the power of God with
eq - ui - ty; he shall re - deem the world from

na - tion his truth in right - eous - ness a - lone.
bold - ness, ex - alt him ev - er and a - gain.
e - vil, and right - eous shall his judg - ment be.

Guitar chords do not correspond with keyboard harmony.

Alternate harmonization on p. 756.

Words: Dewey Westra, 1931; rev. *Psalter Hymnal*, 1987, © 1987 Faith Alive Christian Resources
Music (RENDEZ À DIEU/GENEVAN 98/118 | 9.8.9.8 D): *Genevan Psalter*, 1551; harm. Dale Grotenhuis, 1985, © 1987 Faith Alive Christian Resources

98D Joy to the World!

1 Joy to the world! the Lord is come: let earth re-
2 Joy to the earth! the Sav-ior reigns: let all their
3 No more let sin and sor-row grow nor thorns in-
4 He rules the world with truth and grace, and makes the

ceive her King. Let ev-ery heart pre-pare him
songs em-ploy, while fields and floods, rocks, hills, and
fest the ground; he comes to make his bless-ings
na-tions prove the glo-ries of his right-eous-

room, and heaven and na-ture sing, and heaven and na-ture
plains re-peat the sound-ing joy, re-peat the sound-ing
flow far as the curse is found, far as the curse is
ness and won-ders of his love, and won-ders of his

and heaven and na-ture sing,

sing, and heaven, and heaven and na-ture sing.
joy, re-peat, re-peat the sound-ing joy.
found, far as, far as the curse is found.
love, and won-ders, won-ders of his love.

heaven and na-ture sing,

Words: Isaac Watts (1674-1748), 1719, P.D.
Music (ANTIOCH 8.6.8.6 with repeat): Lowell Mason (1792-1872), 1848, P.D.

Psalm 99

1 The LORD is king; let the peoples tremble! *
  He sits enthroned upon the cherubim; let the earth quake!

2 The LORD is great in Zion; *
  he is exalted over all the peoples.

3 Let them praise your great and awesome name. *
  Holy is he!

4 Mighty King, lover of justice, you have established equity; *
  you have executed justice and righteousness in Jacob.

5 Extol the LORD our God; worship at his footstool. *
  Holy is he!

6 Moses and Aaron were among his priests,
  Samuel also was among those who called on his name. *
  They cried to the LORD, and he answered them.

7 He spoke to them in the pillar of cloud; *
  they kept his decrees, and the statutes that he gave them.

8 O LORD our God, you answered them; *
  you were a forgiving God to them,
  but an avenger of their wrongdoings.

9 Extol the LORD our God, and worship at his holy mountain; *
  for the LORD our God is holy.

Holy are you, the Lord Almighty, God who was, and is, and is to come.
Grant us strength and conviction to worship you with our actions as well as our lips,
that at every opportunity we may bring glory to your name,
through Jesus Christ our Lord. **Amen.**

Psalm 99 offers praise for the reign of God, with a particular focus on God's holiness (a recurring theme in vv. 3, 5, 9). It focuses on a variety of God's excellencies, including power and authority (vv. 1-3), righteousness and faithfulness (vv. 4-5), and responsiveness to the people (vv. 6-9). *Use in Worship: services calling attention to the theme of holiness (both God's holiness and the call for God's people to be holy; see also Pss. 15 and 24); services focusing on the transfiguration of Jesus.*

99A The LORD Is King, Enthroned in Might

1 The LORD is king en-throned in might on wings of cher-u-bim;
2 Of old to priests and proph-ets known with trem-bling, fear and awe,
3 O mag-ni-fy the God of grace who hears his peo-ple's cry,

he reigns in hol-i-ness and light, bow down to wor-ship him!
he gave his peo-ple, set in stone, his stat-utes and his law.
and come with songs be-fore his face, ex-alt his name on high!

Be-yond all maj-es-ty and praise his ho-ly name con-fess;
By those who called up-on his name the voice of God was heard,
To see at last, by grace re-stored from sin and all its stains,

the king of ev-er-last-ing days, who rules in right-eous-ness.
his pres-ence shown in cloud and flame when they o-beyed his word.
the ho-ly moun-tain of the Lord where God in glo-ry reigns.

This tune in a lower key: p. 215.

Words: Timothy Dudley-Smith (b. 1926) © Timothy Dudley-Smith in Europe and Africa, reproduced with permission of Oxford University Press; © 2007 Hope Publishing Company in the United States of America and the rest of the world
Music (ELLACOMBE 8.6.8.6 D): *Gesangbuch der Herzogl, Würtemburg,* 1784, P.D.

Psalm 99 | A Responsorial Setting 99B

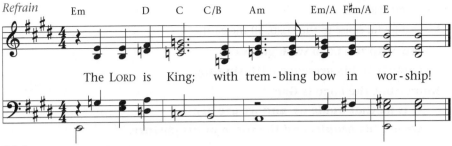

The LORD is King; with trem-bling bow in wor-ship!

Refrain

¹ The LORD is king; let the people tremble.
   The LORD is enthroned upon the cherubim; let the earth shake.

² The LORD, great in Zion,
   is high above all peoples.

³ Let them confess God's name, which is great and awesome;
   God is the Holy One.   *Refrain*

⁴ O mighty king, lover of justice, you have established equity;
   you have executed justice and righteousness in Jacob.

⁵ Proclaim the greatness of the LORD and fall down before God's footstool;
   God is the Holy One.   *Refrain*

⁶ Moses and Aaron among your priests,
   and Samuel among those who call upon your name, O LORD;
      they called upon you, and you answered them,

⁷ you spoke to them out of the pillar of cloud;
   they kept your testimonies and the decree that you gave them.

⁸ O LORD our God, you answered them indeed;
   you were a God who forgave them, yet punished them for their evil deeds.

⁹ Proclaim the greatness of the LORD and worship upon God's holy hill;
   for the LORD our God is the Holy One.   *Refrain*

Tone

Lectionary: Transfiguration Sunday (A,C); Ordinary Time after Pentecost (C).

Words: Martin Tel © 2011 Martin Tel, admin. Faith Alive Christian Resources
Music: Robert Wetzler from *Psalter for Worship, Cycle A* © 1998 Augsburg Fortress Publishers
Psalm Text: from *Evangelical Lutheran Worship* © 2006 Evangelical Lutheran Church in America, admin.
Augsburg Fortress Publishers
Tone: © 2011 Faith Alive Christian Resources

Psalm 100

A Psalm of thanksgiving.

¹ Make a joyful noise to the LORD, all the earth. *

> ² **Worship the LORD with gladness;**
> **come into his presence with singing.**

³ **Know that the LORD is God.** *

> **It is he that made us, and we are his;**
> **we are his people, and the sheep of his pasture.**

⁴ Enter his gates with thanksgiving, and his courts with praise. *

> Give thanks to him, bless his name.

⁵ **For the LORD is good;** *

> **his steadfast love endures forever,**
> **and his faithfulness to all generations.**

We thank you and we praise you, faithful God.
By your power at work within us, may we cheerfully proclaim your goodness,
selflessly show your love, and joyfully come into your presence.
You are our God. We are your people, now and always.
Hallelujah! **Amen.**

Psalm 100 is a call to praise and serve God. It is noteworthy for depicting obedience to God's kingly rule as an experience of joy (v. 2), for celebrating not only that God made us but also that we belong to God (v. 3), and for celebrating the enduring quality of God's covenant love to all generations (v. 5). *Use in Worship: Thanksgiving Day; other harvest festivals; celebrations of the lordship of Christ.*

All People That on Earth Do Dwell 100A

English All peo-ple that on earth do dwell, sing to the
French Vous, qui sur la terre ha-bi-tez, chan-tez à
Dutch Juicht Go-de toe, ba-zuint en zingt, Treedt na-der

Hungarian E föl-dön ti min-den né-pek, az Is-ten-

Lord with cheer-ful voice; him serve with mirth, his
plei-ne voix, chan-tez, ré-jou-is-sez-vous
tot gij Hem om-ringt, gij aard' al-om, zijn
nek ör-vend-je-tek, e-lüt-te szép é-

praise forth tell, come ye be-fore him and re-joice.
au Sei-gneur, é-ga-yez-vous à son hon-neur.
rijks-do-mein, zult voor den HEER dienst-vaar-dig zijn.
ne-kek-kel szol-gál já-tok ût víg szív-vel.

(continues)

Guitar chords do not correspond with keyboard harmony.

Alternate tunes: GENEVAN 100, p. 628; NEW DOXOLOGY, p. 626.

Words: English William Kethe, 1561, alt., P.D.; French tr. Roger Chapal 1970, after Théodore de Bèze, 1562 © Fédération Musique et Chant de la Réforme, c/o Editions Olivétan; Chinese tr. Timothy Ting Fang Lew, rev. Ernest Yang © Chinese Christian Literature Council, Ltd.; Dutch tr. Willem Barnard, 1967, © Interkerkelijke Stichting voor het Kerklied, Leidschendam; German tr. after Cornelius Becker; Hungarian tr. Albert Szenczi Molnár, 1607; Indonesian tr. H. A. Pandopo © 1989 Yamuger, Indonesian Institute for Sacred Music; Japanese tr. from The 150 Genevan Psalm Songs in Japanese (The General Assembly of Reformed Church in Japan Publishing Committee, 2006); Korean tr. The United Methodist Korean Hymnal Committee © 2001 The United Methodist Publishing House, admin. The Copyright Company; Spanish tr. Federico J. Pagura, 1960, © Federico J. Pagura; Swahili tr. *Nyimbo Standard*
Music (GENEVAN 134/OLD HUNDREDTH 8.8.8.8): Louis Bourgeois (ca. 1510-1561), 1551, P.D.

English

2 The Lord, ye know, is God indeed;
  without our aid he did us make;
  we are his folk, he doth us feed,
  and for his sheep he doth us take.

3 O enter then his gates with praise;
  approach with joy his courts unto;
  praise, laud, and bless his name always,
  for it is seemly so to do.

4 For why? the Lord our God is good;
  his mercy is for ever sure;
  his truth at all times firmly stood,
  and shall from age to age endure.

Dutch

2 Roept uit met blijdschap: "God is Hij.
  Hij schiep ons, Hem behoren wij,
  zijn volk, de schapen die Hij hoedt
  en als beminden weidt en voedt."

3 Treedt statig binnen door de poort.
  Hier staat zijn troon, hier woont zijn Woord.
  Heft hier voor God uw lofzang aan:
  Gebenedijd zijn grote naam.

4 Want God is overstelpend goed,
  die ons in vrede wonen doet.
  Zijn goedheid is als morgendauw:
  elk nieuw geslacht ervaart zijn trouw.

German

1 Nun jauchzt dem Herren, alle Welt!
  Kommt her, zu seinem Dienst euch stellt,
  kommt mit Frohlocken, säumet nicht,
  kommt vor sein heilig Angesicht.

2 Erkennt, dass Gott ist unser Herr,
  der uns erschaffen ihm zur Ehr.
  Als guter Hirt ist er bereit,
  zu führen uns auf seine Weid.

3 Die ihr nun wollet bei ihn sein,
  kommt, geht zu seinen Toren ein
  mit Loben durch der Psalmen Klang,
  zu seinem Hause mit Gesang.

4 Er ist voll Güt und Freundlichkeit,
  voll Lieb und Treu zu jeder Zeit.
  Sein Gnad währt immer dort und hier
  und seine Wahrheit für und für.

French

2 Lui seul est notre souverain,
  c'est lui qui nous fit de sa main:
  nous le peuple qu'il mènera,
  le troupeau qu'il rassemblera.

3 Présentez-vous tous devant lui,
  dans sa maison dès aujourd'hui;
  célébrez son nom glorieux,
  exaltez-le jusques aux cieux.

4 Pour toi, Seigneur, que notre amour
  se renouvelle chaque jour:
  ta bonté, ta fidélité,
  demeurent pour l'éternité.

Hungarian

2 Tudjátok, hogy ez az Isten,
  ki minket teremtett bölcsen,
  és mi vagyunk õ népei,
  és õ nyájának juhai.

3 Õ kapuin menjetek be,
  hálát adván szívetekbe'!
  Jer, menjünk be tornácába,
  néki nagy hálákat adva!

4 Mert nagy az õ kegyessége,
  és megmarad mindörökre,
  és õ hûsége mindenha
  megáll és el nem fogy soha.

Indonesian

1 Hai bumi, bergembiralah
  dan pada TUHAN menyembah!
  Mari menghadap Yang Kudus;
  bersukacitalah terus!

2 Akuilah dengan teguh:
  TUHANlah saja Allahmu!
  Pencipta kita Dialah;
  kita kawanan dombaNya.

3 Masukilah gapuraNya,
  bawa syukurmu naik serta:
  nyanyikan sukacitamu
  di pelataran Bait Kudus!

4 Abadi TUHAN mahabaik,
  kasih setiaNya ajaib
  dan perjanjianNya teguh
  turun temurun bagimu!

Spanish

1 Oh pueblos todos alabad
en alta voz a Dios cantad,
regocijaos en su‿honor
servid alegres al Señor.

2 El soberano Creador
de nuestra vida‿es el autor;
el pueblo suyo somos ya,
rebaño que‿Él pastoreará.

3 A su santuario pues entrad,
y vuestras vidas ofrendad;
al nombre augusto dad loor,
que‿al mundo llena de‿esplendor.

4 Incomparable‿es su bondad,
y para siempre su verdad;
de bienes colma nuestro ser
su gracia no‿ha de fenecer.

Swahili

1 Enyi mkaao nchi,
mwimbieni Mungu sana,
msifuni kwa sauti kuu,
mbele zake mwakutana.

2 Mungu mwamjua, kwani
aliyetuumba ndiye,
atuchunga malishani,
na tu kundi lake Yeye.

3 Haya! malangoni mwake,
hata nyuani, imbeni;
mulikuze Jina lake,
Jina la Bwana si duni.

4 Kwani, Jehova ni mwema
ana rehema milele;
kweli yake yasimama
leo na kesho vivile.

Chinese

1 普天之下萬族萬邦，
皆當向主歡呼頌揚，
樂意事奉，虔誠頌讚，
主前崇拜，高聲歌唱。

2 當知主是獨一真神，
不藉人力創造萬人，
賜人身心，賜人糧食，
招集萬民進祂羊群。

3 大家踴躍踏進主門，
歡欣快樂入主院庭，
同心一意感謝真神，
高歌頌揚讚美主名。

4 我主、我神、祂本善良，
我主憐憫、慈愛永存，
我主真理亙古不變，
我主恩德萬世永恆。

Japanese

1 地はみな声あげ
主をたたえまつれ。
歌いつつ来たり
喜び仕えよ。

2 われら造りたもう
主こそ神と知れ。
われらはその民
その牧の羊。

3 歌もてほめつつ
大前に進め。
主の宮に入りて
御名を賛美せよ。

4 主は恵み深く
憐れみは尽きず、
変わらぬまことは
よろず代におよぶ。

Korean

1 온 땅의 모든 사람들
흥겨운 소리 높여서
기쁘게 주를 섬기며
주 앞에 나와 찬양해

2 우리를 친히 만드신
주 하나님을 경배해
우리는 모두 주의 것
그 기르시는 양일세

3 찬송함으로 그 문에
기뻐함으로 그 전에
주 이름 찬양하면서
온전한 경배 드리세

4 선하신 우리 하나님
그 자비 영원하시고
그 진리 변치 않으며
영원히 함께 하시리

100B All People That on Earth Do Dwell

1 All peo - ple that on earth do dwell,
2 Know that the LORD is God in - deed;
3 O en - ter then his gates with joy,
4 Be - cause the LORD our God is good,
5 *Praise God from whom all bless - ings flow;*

sing to the Lord with cheer - ful voice.
he formed us all with - out our aid.
with - in his courts his praise pro - claim.
his mer - cy is for - ev - er sure.
praise him, all crea - tures here be - low;

Serve him with joy, his prais - es tell,
We are the flock he comes to feed,
Let thank-ful songs your tongues em - ploy,
His faith - ful - ness at all times stood
praise him a - bove, ye heaven - ly host;

C   F   Dm   C/G   G   C   *To Stanzas 2 - 5*

come now be - fore him and re - joice!
the sheep who by his hand were made.
O bless and mag - ni - fy his name.
and shall from age to age en - dure.
praise Fa - ther, Son, and Ho - ly Ghost.

Final Ending after Stanza 5

F   Fm   C   F   Fm   C

A - men.   A - men.

Alternate tunes: GENEVAN 134/OLD HUNDREDTH, p. 623; GENEVAN 100, p. 628.

Words: sts. 1-4 William Kethe, 1561, alt.; st. 5 Thomas Ken, 1709; P.D.
Music (NEW DOXOLOGY [DUKE STREET variant] 8.8.8.8 with amens): traditional Black gospel

100C Let Every Voice on Earth Resound

1 Let ev - ery voice on earth re - sound, and joy - ful
2 You are the Lord; by whose de - sign all we in
3 Be - fore the Lord bring thanks and praise, un - fath - omed

hearts hold God a - dored; in glad - ness may God's
na - ture claim our place; your flock, we bind our
mer - cies wait in store; God's good - ness bless - es

courts a - bound with songs of praise un - to the Lord.
lives to you, and rest se - cure be - neath your grace.
all our days, God's truth en - dures for - ev - er - more!

Alternate tunes: GENEVAN 134/OLD HUNDREDTH, p. 623; NEW DOXOLOGY, p. 626.

Words: Michael Morgan © 2011 Michael Morgan, admin. Faith Alive Christian Resources
Music (GENEVAN 100 | 8.8.8.8): Louis Bourgeois (ca. 1510-1561), 1551; harm. Dale Grotenhuis, 1985,
© 1987 Faith Alive Christian Resources

With Shouts of Joy 100D
Come Praise the LORD

*Finger cymbals**

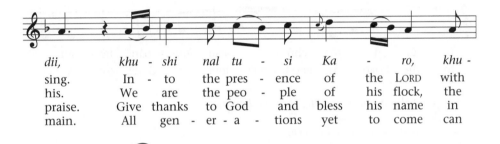

Punjabi	1 Ae	sab	Za - miin - de	lo - ko,	ta - riif	Ka - ro	rab
English	1 With shouts of	joy,	come praise the LORD;	all earth your prais - es			
	2 Ac - knowl-edge that the	LORD is God;	he made us, we	are			
	3 His gates are o - pen—	en - ter in	to wor - ship God with				
	4 The LORD is good, his	love is sure	and al - ways will	re -			

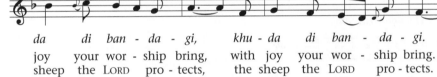

dii,   khu - shi   nal tu - si   Ka - ro,   khu -
sing.   In - to   the pres - ence   of   the LORD with
his.   We are   the peo - ple   of   his flock, the
praise.   Give thanks   to God   and   bless   his name in
main.   All   gen - er - a - tions   yet   to come can

da   di ban - da - gi,   khu - da   di ban - da - gi.
joy   your wor - ship bring,   with joy   your wor - ship bring.
sheep   the LORD pro - tects,   the sheep   the LORD pro - tects.
wor - ship   all your days,   in wor - ship   all your days.
trust   his faith - ful name,   can trust   his faith - ful name.

Ostinato pattern
Bells or Orff instruments or pitched percussion instruments

simile

simile

* o = open (strong)
+ = closed (weak)

Words: Punjabi; English tr. Emily R. Brink (b. 1940) © 2011 Faith Alive Christian Resources
Music (KHUSHI RAHO 8.6.8.6.6): traditional melody, Pakistan; trans. I-to Loh (b. 1936) © 1990, 2000
Christian Conference of Asia, admin. GIA Publications, Inc.; arr. I-to Loh (b. 1936) © 2011 Christian
Conference of Asia, admin. GIA Publications, Inc.

100E Lán tióh kèng-pài Chú Siōng-tè / Let Us Come to Worship God

Taiwanese Lán tióh kèng-pài Chú Siōng-tè, Lán tióh kèng-pài Chú Siōng-tè,
English Let us come to wor-ship God, let us come to wor-ship God,

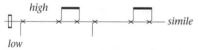

I sèng-miâ chì-tōa; Tióh ēng khiân-sèng kám-siā jip sèng-tian,
bless the ho-ly name; en-ter God's house with thanks and rev-erence,

In - ūi I tōa chû - ài kàu èng - oán bô - soah.
for the LORD is good, God's love en - dures for - ev - er.

Drum (may also be played on jingles or tambourine)

high

low

simile

Bass Xylophone ostinato

simile

Words: I-to Loh (b. 1936), Taiwan © 1990, 2000 Christian Conference of Asia, admin. GIA Publications, Inc.
Music (HA-A-O-HO-I-AN): traditional tribal melody, Taiwan; trans. © 1990, 2000 Christian Conference of Asia, admin. GIA Publications, Inc.

100F Psalm 100 | A Responsorial Setting

Refrain

May be sung in a round

Make a joy-ful noise to the LORD, al-le-lu-ia, a - men!

Refrain

¹ Make a joyful noise to the LORD, all you lands!

  ² Serve the LORD with gladness; come into God's presence with a song.

³ Know that the LORD is God, our maker to whom we belong;

  we are God's people and the sheep of God's pasture.   *Refrain*

⁴ Enter the gates of the LORD with thanksgiving and the courts with praise;

  give thanks and bless God's holy name.

⁵ Good indeed is the LORD, whose steadfast love is everlasting,

  whose faithfulness endures from age to age.   *Refrain*

Tone

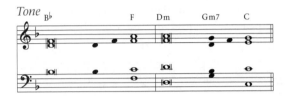

Al - le - lu - ia!   Al - le - lu - ia! Al - le - lu - ia!   Al - le - lu - ia!

Lectionary: Ordinary Time after Pentecost (A); Reign of Christ (A); Thanksgiving Day (C).

Words and Music: Hal H. Hopson © 1988 Hope Publishing Company
Psalm Text: from *Evangelical Lutheran Worship* © 2006 Evangelical Lutheran Church in America, admin.
Augsburg Fortress Publishers
Tone: © 2011 Faith Alive Christian Resources

100G Jubilate Deo omnis terra / Raise a Song of Gladness

May be sung in canon

Translation of Latin text: Be joyful in the Lord, all the earth; serve the Lord with gladness.

Words and Music: Jacques Berthier (1923-1994) © 1979 Ateliers et Presses de Taizé, Taizé Community, France, admin. GIA Publications, Inc., exclusive North American agent

All the Earth, Proclaim the Lord 100H

Refrain

All the earth, pro-claim the LORD, sing your praise to God.

1 Serve you the LORD, heart filled with glad - ness;
2 Know that the LORD is our Cre - a - tor.
3 We are the sheep of his green pas - ture,
4 En - ter his gates, bring - ing thanks - giv - ing;

come in - to his pres - ence, sing - ing for joy!
Yes, he is our Fa - ther; we are his own.
for we are his peo - ple; he is our God.
O en - ter his courts while sing - ing his praise.

To Refrain

5 Our LORD is good,
his love is lasting;
his word is abiding
now and always. *To Refrain*

6 *Honor and praise*
be to the Father,
the Son, and the Spirit,
world without end. *To Refrain*

Words: Lucien Deiss (1921-2007) © 1965 World Library Publications
Music (DEISS 100 | 4.5.6.4 with refrain): Lucien Deiss (1921-2007) © 1965 World Library Publications

Psalm 101

Of David. A Psalm.

¹ I will sing of loyalty and of justice; *
   to you, O LORD, I will sing.

² **I will study the way that is blameless. When shall I attain it? ***
   I will walk with integrity of heart within my house;

³ **I will not set before my eyes anything that is base. ***
   I hate the work of those who fall away; it shall not cling to me.

⁴ Perverseness of heart shall be far from me; *
   I will know nothing of evil.

⁵ One who secretly slanders a neighbor I will destroy. *
   A haughty look and an arrogant heart I will not tolerate.

⁶ **I will look with favor on the faithful in the land,**
   so that they may live with me; *
   whoever walks in the way that is blameless shall minister to me.

⁷ No one who practices deceit shall remain in my house; *
   no one who utters lies shall continue in my presence.

⁸ **Morning by morning I will destroy all the wicked in the land, ***
   cutting off all evildoers from the city of the LORD.

God of love and justice, help us to live with integrity.
When tempted to boast or slander, tune our hearts and voices to sing your praise.
Guide us by your Spirit so that we may grow in grace
and in the knowledge of our Lord and Savior, Jesus Christ.
To him be glory both now and evermore. **Amen.**

Psalm 101 represents a positive answer to the challenge posed in Ps. 1: to choose integrity and faithfulness over evil and deceit. It is a resolute affirmation of the intent to follow God's law with integrity. The psalm goes further than Ps. 1 in resolving not only to avoid evil but also to actively resist and prosecute it. Throughout history this psalm has been used at the coronations of kings. Christian appropriations of this psalm have tended to see it in light of Pss. 14 and 53, which declare the sinfulness of all human persons and resist the sense that the world is broken into two tidy groups of people. Christian appropriations of this text have also tended to treat the strong and confident statements of the psalmist as something to which we both aspire and that we say in order to discover the gaps in our obedience. Each of these moves resists the idea that the psalm is a claim to an arrogant self-righteousness; rather, it is a means of growth in grace and obedience. Further, it is important to receive the psalm as something that a community or even a nation (as opposed to just an individual) would consider saying. In a communal context, the text is both a prophetic call to resist corruption and an expression of resolve to restore justice and integrity. *Use in Worship: prayer of dedication.*

Psalm 101 | A Responsorial Setting

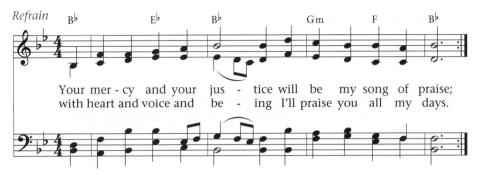

Refrain

Your mer-cy and your jus-tice will be my song of praise;
with heart and voice and be-ing I'll praise you all my days.

Refrain

What does God forbid in the ninth commandment?
That I should ever give false testimony against anyone,
twist anyone's words, gossip or slander,
or join in condemning anyone rashly or without a hearing. *Refrain*

¹ I will sing of your love and justice, LORD.
I will praise you with songs.

² I will be careful to live a blameless life—when will you come to help me?
I will lead a life of integrity in my own home.

³ I will refuse to look at anything vile and vulgar.
I hate all who deal crookedly; I will have nothing to do with them.

⁴ I will reject perverse ideas
and stay away from every evil.

⁵ I will not tolerate people who slander their neighbors.
I will not endure conceit and pride.

⁶ I will search for faithful people to be my companions.
Only those who are above reproach will be allowed to serve me.

⁷ I will not allow deceivers to serve in my house,
and liars will not stay in my presence.

⁸ My daily task will be to ferret out the wicked
and free the city of the LORD from their grip. *Refrain*

What does God require in the ninth commandment?
That I love the truth,
speak it candidly, and openly acknowledge it.
And that I do what I can
to guard and advance my neighbor's good name. *Refrain*

Words: Martin Tel © 2011 Martin Tel, admin. Faith Alive Christian Resources
Music (ST. THEODULPH/VALET WILL ICH DIR GEBEN fragment): Melchior Teschner, 1615, P.D.
Text: *Heidelberg Catechism*, 1563, © 2011 Faith Alive Christian Resources; Psalm 101, New Living
Translation © 1996 Tyndale House Publishers, Inc.

Psalm 102

*A prayer of one afflicted, when faint and pleading before the L*ORD.

Voice 1:

¹ Hear my prayer, O LORD; *
    let my cry come to you.

² **Do not hide your face from me in the day of my distress. ***
    Incline your ear to me; answer me speedily in the day when I call.

³ **For my days pass away like smoke, ***
    and my bones burn like a furnace.

⁴ My heart is stricken and withered like grass; *
    I am too wasted to eat my bread.

⁵ Because of my loud groaning *
    my bones cling to my skin.

⁶ **I am like an owl of the wilderness, ***
    like a little owl of the waste places.

⁷ **I lie awake; ***
    I am like a lonely bird on the housetop.

⁸ All day long my enemies taunt me; *
    those who deride me use my name for a curse.

⁹ For I eat ashes like bread, *
    and mingle tears with my drink,

¹⁰ because of your indignation and anger; *
    for you have lifted me up and thrown me aside.

¹¹ **My days are like an evening shadow; ***
    I wither away like grass.

Voice 2:

¹² But you, O LORD, are enthroned forever; *
    your name endures to all generations.

¹³ You will rise up and have compassion on Zion, *
    for it is time to favor it; the appointed time has come.

¹⁴ **For your servants hold its stones dear, ***
    and have pity on its dust.

¹⁵ **The nations will fear the name of the LORD, ***
    and all the kings of the earth your glory.

¹⁶ **For the LORD will build up Zion; ***
    he will appear in his glory.

¹⁷ **He will regard the prayer of the destitute, ***
    and will not despise their prayer.

[18] Let this be recorded for a generation to come, *
    so that a people yet unborn may praise the LORD:

[19] that he looked down from his holy height, *
    from heaven the LORD looked at the earth,

[20] to hear the groans of the prisoners, *
    to set free those who were doomed to die;

[21] so that the name of the LORD may be declared in Zion, *
    and his praise in Jerusalem,

[22] when peoples gather together, *
    and kingdoms, to worship the LORD.

Voice 1:

[23] He has broken my strength in midcourse; *
    he has shortened my days.

[24] "O my God," I say, "do not take me away at the mid-point of my life, *
    you whose years endure throughout all generations."

Voice 2:

[25] Long ago you laid the foundation of the earth, *
    and the heavens are the work of your hands.

[26] **They will perish, but you endure;** *
    they will all wear out like a garment.

You change them like clothing, and they pass away; *
    [27] but you are the same, and your years have no end.

[28] **The children of your servants shall live secure;** *
    their offspring shall be established in your presence.

God of eternity,
you sent your Son Jesus to proclaim good news to the poor,
release for the captives, sight to the blind, and freedom for the oppressed.
Meet us today, no matter where we are,
speaking your saving health into whatever darkness and fear surrounds us.
We pray with confidence in Jesus' name. **Amen.**

Psalm 102, one of seven penitential psalms, is a poignant cry to God by a person weakened by old age (vv. 3, 23), illness (v. 5), and persecution (v. 8). Like Ps. 103, it draws a sharp distinction between the brevity of life (vv. 1-11) and the enduring reign of God (vv. 12-28). The psalm both speaks of the value of writing down a testimony of God's love as a legacy to future generations (v. 18) and serves as a prayer that future generations would respond faithfully to God (v. 28). *Use in Worship: a prayer on behalf of those facing death; pastoral care settings (especially hospice units and nursing homes); a prayer in worship services on behalf of those without the strength or health to participate themselves.*

102A O Lord, Hear My Prayer

1 O Lord, hear my prayer, O Lord, hear my prayer;
2 The Lord is my song, the Lord is my praise.

when I call answer me. O Lord, hear my prayer, O
All my hope comes from God. The Lord is my song, the

Lord, hear my prayer; come and lis-ten to me.
Lord is my praise. God, the well-spring of life.

Words: Psalm 102:1-2; adapt. The Community of Taizé © 1991 Ateliers et Presses de Taizé, Taizé
Community, France, GIA Publications, Inc., exclusive North American agent
Music: Jacques Berthier (1923-1994) © 1991 Ateliers et Presses de Taizé, Taizé Community, France, GIA
Publications, Inc., exclusive North American agent

A Litany for the Sick or Dying 102B

Sing stanza 1 of 102A

Voice 1:

Hear my prayer, LORD; let my cry for help come to you.
Do not hide your face from me when I am in distress.
Turn your ear to me; when I call, answer me quickly.

Voice 2:

For my days vanish like smoke, my bones burn like glowing embers.
My heart is blighted and withered like grass; I forget to eat my food.

> *For those struck down or dying at a younger age:*
>
> *Voice 2:*
>
> In the course of my life he broke my strength; he cut short my days. So I said:
> "Do not take me away, my God, in the midst of my days; your years go
> on through all generations.
>
> **In the beginning you laid the foundation of the earth, and the**
> **heavens are the work of your hands. They will perish, but you**
> **remain; they will all wear out like a garment. Like clothing you**
> **will change them and they will be discarded. But you remain the**
> **same, and your years will never end.**"

Sing stanza 1 of 102A

Voice 1:

Hear my prayer, LORD; let my cry for help come to you.
Do not hide your face from me when I am in distress.
Turn your ear to me; when I call, answer me quickly.

This or other prayers may be spoken

Almighty God,
by your power Jesus Christ was raised from death.
Watch over [name].
Fill his/her eyes with your vision
to see, beyond human sight, a home within your love,
where pain is gone and frail flesh turns to glory.
Banish fear.
Brush tears away.
Let death be gentle as nightfall,
promising a day when songs of joy
shall make us glad to be together with Jesus Christ,
who lives in triumph,
the Lord of life eternal. Amen.

After a period of silence, sing stanza 1 of 102A

(continues)

The psalm continues:

Voice 2:

My days are like the evening shadow; I wither away like grass.
But you, Lord, sit enthroned forever; your renown endures through
all generations. You will arise and have compassion on Zion, for it is
time to show favor to her; the appointed time has come.

Voice 1:

The nations will fear the name of the Lord,
all the kings of the earth will revere your glory.
For the Lord will rebuild Zion and appear in his glory. He will
respond to the prayer of the destitute; he will not despise their plea.

Voice 2:

Let this be written for a future generation,
that a people not yet created may praise the Lord.

"The Lord looked down from his sanctuary on high, from heaven he
viewed the earth, to hear the groans of the prisoners and release
those condemned to death." So the name of the Lord will be
declared in Zion and his praise in Jerusalem when the peoples and
the kingdoms assemble to worship the Lord.
Amen.

Sing stanza 2 of 102A

Of David.

1 Bless the LORD, O my soul, *
   and all that is within me, bless his holy name.

2 **Bless the LORD, O my soul, ***
   and do not forget all his benefits—

3 who forgives all your iniquity, *
   who heals all your diseases,

4 **who redeems your life from the Pit, ***
   who crowns you with steadfast love and mercy,

5 who satisfies you with good as long as you live *
   so that your youth is renewed like the eagle's.

6 **The LORD works vindication ***
   and justice for all who are oppressed.

7 He made known his ways to Moses, *
   his acts to the people of Israel.

8 **The LORD is merciful and gracious, ***
   slow to anger and abounding in steadfast love.

9 **He will not always accuse, ***
   nor will he keep his anger forever.

10 **He does not deal with us according to our sins, ***
   nor repay us according to our iniquities.

11 For as the heavens are high above the earth, *
   so great is his steadfast love toward those who fear him;

12 as far as the east is from the west, *
   so far he removes our transgressions from us.

13 **As a father has compassion for his children, ***
   so the LORD has compassion for those who fear him.

14 **For he knows how we were made; ***
   he remembers that we are dust.

15 As for mortals, their days are like grass; *
   they flourish like a flower of the field;

16 for the wind passes over it, and it is gone, *
   and its place knows it no more.

17 **But the steadfast love of the LORD is from everlasting to everlasting**
   on those who fear him, *
   and his righteousness to children's children,

18 **to those who keep his covenant ***
   and remember to do his commandments.

(continues)

¹⁹ The LORD has established his throne in the heavens, *

and his kingdom rules over all.

²⁰ **Bless the LORD, O you his angels,** *

you mighty ones who do his bidding, obedient to his spoken word.

²¹ **Bless the LORD, all his hosts,** *

his ministers that do his will.

²² **Bless the LORD, all his works, in all places of his dominion.** *

Bless the LORD, O my soul.

Creator of all, you formed us in your image and filled us with life-giving breath.
We bless you: even your name is holy.
Redeemer of all, you have ransomed and healed us, restored and forgiven us.
We remember your blessings with thankful praise.
Sustainer of all, tune the very fiber of our being to resonate with the songs of angels.
We join the hymn of all creation, praising you,
Father, Son, and Holy Spirit—one God forever. **Amen.**

Psalm 103 is like an entire worship service condensed into a poem. It begins with a call to the self to praise God (vv. 1-2) and continues in remembrance of God's saving work (vv. 3-14), extolling God's role as one who pardons, heals, and accomplishes justice—ministering at once to the wayward, the ill, the fatigued, and the oppressed. The psalm continues with a proverb-like sermon on how the everlasting, generation-to-generation love of God overcomes our frank acknowledgement of the frailty of human life (vv. 15-19) and concludes with another call to worship, this time challenging all the heavenly hosts to join in praise. It is closely linked with Ps. 102, especially in its reflection on the fleetingness of life and the everlasting love of God, and Ps. 104, which also begins and ends with a call to worship. Praying Pss. 102, 103, and 104 in sequence leads us on a journey in which the awareness of the frailty of humanity is increasingly displaced by an overwhelming awareness of the grandeur of God. *Use in Worship: call to worship; assurance of God's pardon; response to the Lord's Supper.*

Bless the Lord, O My Soul 103A

Bless the Lord, O my soul, and all that is within me, bless his ho - ly name.

Fine

He has done great things, he has done great things,

D.C al Fine

he has done great things: bless his ho - ly name.

Words: Andraé Crouch (b. 1945), 1973, © 2000 Bud John Songs, admin. EMI CMG Publishing
Music (BLESS THE LORD): Andraé Crouch (b. 1945), 1973; arr. Richard Smallwood (b. 1948), 1981, © 2000 Bud John Songs, admin. EMI CMG Publishing

103B O Come, My Soul, Sing Praise to God

1 O come, my soul, sing praise to God your Mak - er,
2 Good is the Lord and full of kind com - pas - sion,
3 His love is like a fa - ther's to his chil - dren,

and all with - in me, praise his ho - ly name.
most slow to an - ger, plen - te - ous in love.
ten - der and kind to all who fear his name;

Sing praise to God, for - get not all his mer - cies;
Rich is his grace to all who hum - bly seek him,
for well he knows our weak - ness and our frail - ty;

his par - doning grace and sav - ing love pro - claim.
bound - less and end - less as the heavens a - bove.
he knows that we are dust, he knows our frame.

Refrain

Praise him, you an - gels, won - drous in might;
praise him, you ser - vants who in his will de - light.

4 We fade and die like flowers that grow in beauty,
like tender grass that soon will disappear;
but evermore the love of God is changeless,
still shown to those who look to him in fear. *Refrain*

5 High in the heavens his throne is fixed forever;
his kingdom rules o'er all from pole to pole.
Praise to the Lord through all his wide dominion;
forever praise his holy name, my soul. *Refrain*

Words: *Psalter*, 1912, alt., P.D.
Music (TIDINGS 11.10.11.10 with refrain): James Walch, 1875, P.D.

103C Bless the Lord, My Soul

Ostinato Refrain

Bless the Lord, my soul, and bless God's ho-ly name.

Bless the Lord, my soul, who leads me in-to life.

Solo Voice (sung over ostinato refrain)

1 It is God who for-gives all your guilt, who heals ev-ery one of your ills,

who re-deems your life from the grave, who crowns you with love and com-pas-sion.

2 The Lord is com-pas-sion and love, slow to an-ger and rich in mer-cy.

God does not treat us ac-cord-ing to our sins nor re-pay us ac-cord-ing to our faults.

3 As a fa-ther has com-pas-sion on his chil-dren, the Lord has pit-y on those who

fear him, for God knows of what we are made, God re-mem-bers that we are dust.

Words: Robert Batastini (b. 1942) and The Community of Taizé © 1991, 1998 Ateliers et Presses de Taizé, Taizé Community, France, GIA Publications, Inc., exclusive North American agent
Music: Jacques Berthier (1923-1994) © 1991, 1998 Ateliers et Presses de Taizé, Taizé Community, France, GIA Publications, Inc., exclusive North American agent

The Tender Love a Father Has 103D

1 The ten-der love a fa-ther has for
2 The Lord re-mem-bers we are dust, and
3 The flower is with-ered by the wind that

all his chil-dren dear— such love the Lord beall our frail-ty knows; our life is like the
smites with blight-ing breath; so we are quick-ly

stows on those who wor-ship him in fear.
ten-der grass, and as the flower it grows.
swept a-way be-fore the blast of death.

4 Unchanging is the love of God,
from age to age the same,
displayed to all who do his will
and reverence his name.

5 Those who his gracious covenant keep
the Lord will ever bless;
their children's children shall rejoice
to see his righteousness.

Words: *Psalter*, 1912, alt., P.D.
Music (TALLIS ORDINAL 8.6.8.6): Thomas Tallis, ca. 1567, P.D.

103E My Soul Will Sing

Unison

1 My soul will sing with all the strength I have in me;
2 Our King de-lights to show com-pas-sion to the weak;
3 Though we are dust, a mom-ent in e-ter-ni-ty,

I will re-joice with ev-ery day he gives. I will re-
their deep-est needs he loves to sat-is-fy. Through-out the
as flow-ers bloom to-day and then are gone, he crowns our

call the won-ders he has shown to me, his power to heal,
earth his jus-tice and his mer-cy speak, and he will run
lives with beau-ty and with dig-ni-ty; his pa-tience smiles

his mer-cy to for-give. We join with an-gels
to meet the vic-tim's cry. From ev-er-last-ing
on all who turn to him. From gen-er-a-tion

Words and Music: Kristyn Getty and Stuart Townend © 2007 Thankyou Music, admin. EMI CMG Publishing, excl. UK and Europe, admin. by Kingsway Music/www.kingswaysongs.com

Praise, My Soul, the King of Heaven

1 Praise, my soul, the King of heav - en; to his feet your
2 Praise him for his grace and fa - vor to his peo - ple
3 Fa - ther - like he tends and spares us; well our fee - ble

trib - ute bring. Ran - somed, healed, re - stored, for - giv - en,
in dis - tress. Praise him, still the same as ev - er,
frame he knows. In his hand he gent - ly bears us,

ev - er - more his prais - es sing. Al - le - lu - ia,
slow to chide, and swift to bless. Al - le - lu - ia,
res - cues us from all our foes. Al - le - lu - ia,

al - le - lu - ia! Praise the ev - er - last - ing King!
al - le - lu - ia! Glo - rious in his faith - ful - ness!
al - le - lu - ia! Wide - ly yet his mer - cy flows!

(continues)

4 Frail as summer's <u>flower</u> we flourish,
blows the wind and it is gone;
but while mortals rise and perish
God endures unchanging on.
Alleluia, alleluia!
Praise the High, Eternal One.

5 Angels, help us to adore him;
you behold him face to face.
Sun and moon, bow down before him,
dwellers all in time and space.
Alleluia, alleluia!
Praise with us the God of grace!

Guitar chords do not correspond with keyboard harmony.

Words: Henry F. Lyte, 1834, alt., P.D.
Music (LAUDA ANIMA 8.7.8.7.8.7): John Goss, 1869, P.D.

Psalm 103:1-13, 22 **103G**
A Responsorial Setting

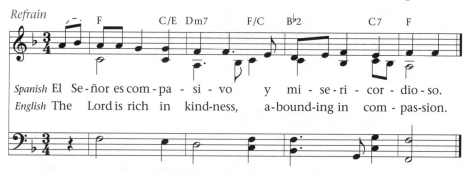

Refrain

¹ Bless the LORD, O my soul,

   and all that is within me, bless God's holy name.

² Bless the LORD, O my soul,

   and forget not all God's benefits—

³ who forgives all your sins

   and heals all your diseases;

⁴ who redeems your life from the grave

   and crowns you with steadfast love and mercy;

⁵ who satisfies your desires with good things

   so that your youth is renewed like an eagle's.   *Refrain*

⁶ O LORD, you provide vindication

   and justice for all who are oppressed.

⁷ You made known your ways to Moses

   and your works to the children of Israel.

⁸ LORD, you are full of compassion and mercy,

   slow to anger and abounding in steadfast love;   *Refrain*   (continues)

[9] you will not always accuse us,
   nor will you keep your anger forever.

[10] You have not dealt with us according to our sins,
   nor repaid us according to our iniquities.

[11] For as the heavens are high above the earth,
   so great is your steadfast love for those who fear you.

[12] As far as the east is from the west,
   so far have you removed our transgressions from us.

[13] As a father has compassion for his children,
   so you have compassion for those who fear you, O LORD.

[22] Bless the LORD, all you works of God, in all places where God rules;
   bless the LORD, O my soul.   *Refrain*

Tone

Lectionary: Ordinary Time after Epiphany (B); Ordinary Time after Pentecost (B); vv. 1-13 Ordinary Time after Pentecost (A); vv. 1-8 Ordinary Time after Pentecost (C).

Words: Spanish © 1970 Conferencia Episcopal Española; English Peter M. Kolar © 1998 World Library Publications
Music: Peter M. Kolar © 1998 World Library Publications
Psalm Text: from *Evangelical Lutheran Worship* © 2006 Evangelical Lutheran Church in America, admin. Augsburg Fortress Publishers
Tone: © 2011 Faith Alive Christian Resources

Psalm 104

Voice 1:

¹ Bless the LORD, O my soul. *
   O LORD my God, you are very great.

You are clothed with honor and majesty, *
   ² **wrapped in light as with a garment.**

You stretch out the heavens like a tent, *
   ³ **you set the beams of your chambers on the waters,**

you make the clouds your chariot, *
   you ride on the wings of the wind,

⁴ **you make the winds your messengers, ***
   fire and flame your ministers.

Voice 2:

⁵ You set the earth on its foundations, *
   so that it shall never be shaken.

⁶ You cover it with the deep as with a garment; *
   the waters stood above the mountains.

⁷ At your rebuke they flee; *
   at the sound of your thunder they take to flight.

⁸ They rose up to the mountains, ran down to the valleys *
   to the place that you appointed for them.

⁹ **You set a boundary that they may not pass, ***
   so that they might not again cover the earth.

Voice 3:

¹⁰ You make springs gush forth in the valleys; *
   they flow between the hills,

¹¹ giving drink to every wild animal; *
   the wild asses quench their thirst.

¹² **By the streams the birds of the air have their habitation; ***
   they sing among the branches.

¹³ **From your lofty abode you water the mountains; ***
   the earth is satisfied with the fruit of your work.

Voice 2:

¹⁴ You cause the grass to grow for the cattle,
   and plants for people to use, *
      to bring forth food from the earth,

¹⁵ and wine to gladden the human heart, oil to make the face shine, *
   and bread to strengthen the human heart.

(continues)

¹⁶ **The trees of the L**ORD** are watered abundantly,** *
    the cedars of Lebanon that he planted.

¹⁷ **In them the birds build their nests;** *
    the stork has its home in the fir trees.

¹⁸ The high mountains are for the wild goats; *
    the rocks are a refuge for the coneys.

¹⁹ **You have made the moon to mark the seasons;** *
    the sun knows its time for setting.

²⁰ You make darkness, and it is night, *
    when all the animals of the forest come creeping out.

²¹ **The young lions roar for their prey,** *
    seeking their food from God.

²² When the sun rises, they withdraw *
    and lie down in their dens.

²³ **People go out to their work** *
    and to their labor until the evening.

Voice 3:

²⁴ O L ORD, how manifold are your works! *
    In wisdom you have made them all; the earth is full of your creatures.

²⁵ **Yonder is the sea, great and wide,**
  creeping things innumerable are there, *
    living things both small and great.

²⁶ There go the ships, *
    and Leviathan that you formed to sport in it.

²⁷ **These all look to you** *
    to give them their food in due season;

²⁸ **when you give to them, they gather it up;** *
    when you open your hand, they are filled with good things.

²⁹ When you hide your face, they are dismayed; *
    when you take away their breath, they die and return to their dust.

³⁰ **When you send forth your spirit, they are created;** *
    and you renew the face of the ground.

Voice 1:

³¹ May the glory of the L ORD endure forever; *
    may the L ORD rejoice in his works—

³² who looks on the earth and it trembles, *
    who touches the mountains and they smoke.

[33] **I will sing to the LORD as long as I live; ***
 I will sing praise to my God while I have being.

[34] **May my meditation be pleasing to him, ***
 for I rejoice in the LORD.

[35] **Let sinners be consumed from the earth,**
 and let the wicked be no more. *
 Bless the LORD, O my soul. Praise the LORD!

God who spoke creation into being,
astonishing the angels with galaxies and sunsets,
all your creatures proclaim your majestic power and playful wisdom.
Send forth your renewing Spirit, that we might discover your purpose for us
and live for your glory and delight. **Amen.**

Psalm 104, a psalm of praise, focuses on God's creative work. Complementing descriptions of creation in Gen. 1 and Job 38-39, this text stresses God's ongoing involvement with creation. It is especially noteworthy for its luminous description of God "wrapped in light as with a garment" (v. 2), for stressing God's ongoing involvement with creation as one who "grows grass for cattle" (v. 14) and "brings forth wine to gladden the human heart" (v. 15), for renewing creation by the breath of the spirit (v. 30), and for taking delight in all of creation (v. 31). Like Ps. 103, it begins and ends by calling the self to praise. *Use in Worship: evening prayer (especially Eastern Orthodox Christian liturgies); on Pentecost (serving as an important text for establishing how God's Spirit works to renew not only the human heart but also all of creation; see v. 30).*

A Litany of Praise   104A

Lord our God, you are very great.

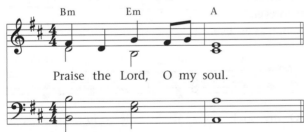

You are clothed with splendor and majesty,
and wrapped in light as with a garment.

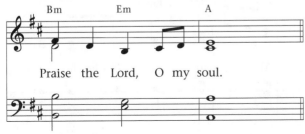

(continues)

You have made the winds your messengers and flames of fire your servants.

Praise the Lord, O my soul.

You water the fields and shelter the birds;
you bring forth bread and wine to fill our hearts.

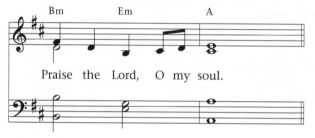

Praise the Lord, O my soul.

How many are your works, O Lord!

In wisdom you made them all; the earth is full of your creatures.

You open your hand and give us all good things.

Send us your Spirit, create in us a new heart,

and renew the face of the earth.

Lord, may your glory endure forever.

We will sing praise to you as long as we live.

Praise the Lord, O my soul. Al - le - lu - ia.
Al - le - lu - ia. Al - le - lu - ia. Al - le - lu - ia.

Litany and Music: Coni Huisman © 2011 Coni Huisman, admin. Faith Alive Christian Resources

The Mountains Stand in Awe 104B

1 The moun-tains stand in awe. The thun-der speaks your name.
2 The might-y rains pour down as bless-ings from a-bove.
3 Al-might-y, Sov-ereign Lord, I wait at your com-mand.

Cre-a-tion waits to serve its God with wind and flame.
The storms that seem to howl and rage are storms of love.
I live and move and breathe with-in your might-y hand.

The heav-ens know your power. None ques-tion what you do.
They wa-ter all the earth. Your riv-ers full-er flow.
With earth and sea and sky, with all your love has made,

The o-ceans ri-ot un-re-strained but bow to you.
They bring the faith-ful care that all your crea-tures know.
with ev-ery thought and breath I rise to give you praise!

Guitar chords do not correspond with keyboard harmony.

Words: Ken Bible © 2007 LNWhymns.com, admin. Music Services
Music (LEONI/YIGDAL 6.6.8.4 D): Hebrew melody; adapt. Meyer Lyon (1751-1797), P.D.

104C We Worship You, Whose Splendor Dwarfs the Cosmos

1 We wor-ship you, whose splen-dor dwarfs the cos-mos,
2 You made the earth, de-ter-min-ing its or-bit:
3 The wa-ters flow, till plain and pas-ture flour-ish;
4 You formed the moon to mark the pass-ing sea-sons;

whose ver-y clothes are robes of daz-zling light;
prim-e-val cha-os fled at your com-mand.
the for-est thrives— there birds may free-ly nest;
you gave the sun, whose ra-diance lights the day;

on wind and cloud you ride a-cross the heav-ens;
You send the streams from moun-tain peak to val-ley,
the thirst-y crea-tures drink and find re-fresh-ment;
as each new morn-ing calls us to your ser-vice,

your word bids fi-ery an-gels soar in flight. *To Stanza 2*
and yet pre-vent them flood-ing all the land. *To Refrain*
and hu-man hearts with wine and grain are blessed. *To Stanza 4*
the wild-life of the night-time steals a-way. *To Refrain*

Refrain

Lord God, our voic - es glad - ly we raise,
join - ing cre - a - tion's un - end - ing hymn of praise.

5 Unnumbered marvels emphasize your wisdom:
who knows what mysteries lie beneath the sea?
Yet every mouth relies on your provision:
without your care, how brief our lives would be.
To Stanza 6

6 May you rejoice in all you have created,
though just your glance could set the earth ablaze;
may we direct our lives to bring you pleasure,
and praise you with the song of all our days.
To Refrain

Words: Martin Leckebusch © 2006 Kevin Mayhew Ltd.
Music (TIDINGS 11.10.11.10 with refrain): James Walch, 1875, P.D.

104D Send Forth Your Spirit, O Lord

Refrain

Send forth your Spir-it, O Lord, and re-new the
face of the earth. Send forth your Spir-it, O
Lord, and re-new the face of the earth.

1 Bless the Lord, O my soul! Lord God, how
2 Lord, my God, great are your works! In wis-dom you
3 All of your crea-tures look to you to give them their

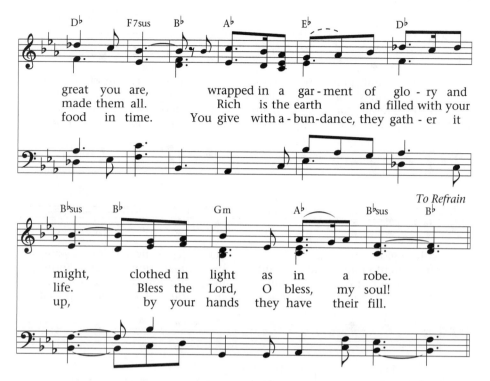

great you are, wrapped in a gar-ment of glo-ry and
made them all. Rich is the earth and filled with your
food in time. You give with a-bun-dance, they gath-er it

To Refrain

might, clothed in light as in a robe.
life. Bless the Lord, O bless, my soul!
up, by your hands they have their fill.

Words: Steven C. Warner © 1996 World Library Publications
Music: Steven C. Warner; arr. Steven C. Warner and Shirley Luttio © 1996 World Library Publications

104E My Soul, Praise the Lord!

1 My soul, praise the Lord! The Lord is most great,
2 He rides on the clouds and wings of the storm.
3 On moun-tains and plains the dark wa-ters lay.
Refrain *Your Spir - it, O Lord, makes life to a - bound.*

with glo - ry ar - rayed, ma - jes - tic in state.
The light-ning and wind his mis - sion per - form.
They heard his re - buke and hur - ried a - way.
The earth is re - newed, and fruit - ful the ground.

The light is his gar - ment, the skies form a tent,
Foun - da - tions of earth he for - ev - er has stayed;
He lift - ed the moun-tains, to val - leys gave birth,
To God be all glo - ry and wis - dom and might.

and o - ver the wa - ters his cou - riers are sent.
to cov - er it, o - ceans like gar - ments were laid.
set bound-aries for seas that once cov - ered the earth. *Refrain*
May God in his crea - tures for - ev - er de - light.

4 God causes the springs of water to flow
in streams from the hills to valleys below.
The LORD gives the streams for all living things there,
while birds with their singing enrapture the air.

5 Down mountains and hills your showers are sent.
With fruit of your work the earth is content.
You give grass for cattle and food for our toil,
enriching our labors with bread, wine, and oil.

6 The trees that the LORD has planted are fed,
and over the earth their branches are spread.
They keep in their shelter the birds of the air.
The life of each creature God keeps in his care.   *Refrain*

7 The seasons are fixed by wisdom divine.
The slow-changing moon shows forth God's design.
The sun in its circuit its Maker obeys
and, running its journey, hastes not nor delays.

8 The LORD makes the night, when, leaving their lair,
the lions go forth, God's bounty to share.
The LORD makes the morning, when beasts steal away,
when we are beginning the work of the day.

9 How many and wise the works of the LORD!
The earth with its wealth of creatures is stored.
The sea bears in safety the ships to and fro;
Leviathan plays in the waters below.

10 Your creatures all look to you for their food.
Your hand opens wide, they gather the good.
When you hide your face, LORD, in anguish they yearn;
when you stop their breathing, to dust they return.   *Refrain*

11 Before the LORD's might earth trembles and quakes.
The mountains are rent, and smoke from them breaks.
I promise to worship the LORD all my days.
Yes, while I have being, my God will I praise.

12 Rejoicing in God, my thought shall be sweet.
May sinners depart in ruin complete.
My soul, praise the LORD God—his name be adored.
Come, praise him, all people, and worship the LORD.

Guitar chords do not correspond with keyboard harmony.

Words: *Psalter*, 1912, alt., P.D.
Music (HANOVER 10.10.11.11): attr. William Croft, 1708, P.D.

104F O Worship the King

1 O wor-ship the King all-glo-rious a-bove,
2 O tell of his might and sing of his grace,
3 Your boun-ti-ful care, what tongue can re-cite?

O grate-ful-ly sing his power and his love:
whose robe is the light, whose can-o-py space.
It breathes in the air, it shines in the light;

our shield and de-fend-er, the An-cient of Days,
His char-iots of wrath the deep thun-der-clouds form,
it streams from the hills, it de-scends to the plain,

pa-vil-ioned in splen-dor and gird-ed with praise.
and dark is his path on the wings of the storm.
and sweet-ly dis-tills in the dew and the rain.

(continues)

4 Frail children of dust, and feeble as frail,
  in you do we trust, nor find you to fail.
  Your mercies, how tender, how firm to the end,
  our Maker, Defender, Redeemer, and Friend!

5 O measureless Might, unchangeable Love,
  whom angels delight to worship above!
  Your ransomed creation, with glory ablaze,
  in true adoration shall sing to your praise!

Words: Robert Grant, 1833, alt., P.D.
Music (LYONS 10.10.11.11): W. Gardiner's *Sacred Melodies*, 1815; attr. Johann Michael Haydn, P.D.

Psalm 104:1-9, 24-34, 35b 104G
A Responsorial Setting

Refrain

Lord, send out your Spir - it and re - new the face of the earth.

Refrain

¹ Bless the LORD, O my soul; O LORD my God, you are very great!
  You are clothed with majesty and splendor.

² You wrap yourself with light as with a cloak
  and stretch out the heavens like a tent.

³ You lay the beams of your chambers in the waters above;
  you make the clouds your chariot; you ride on the wings of the wind.

⁴ You make the winds your messengers
  and flames of fire your servants.   *Refrain*

(continues)

5 You set the earth upon its foundations,
so that from now until forever it shall never be moved.

6 You covered it with the deep as with a garment;
the waters stood above the mountains.

7 At your rebuke the waters fled,
scattered by your voice of thunder.

8 They went up into the mountains and descended down to the valleys,
to the place where you assigned them.

9 You set the limits that they should not pass;
never shall they return to cover the earth again.

24 How manifold are your works, O LORD!
In wisdom you have made them all;
the earth is full of your creatures. *[Hallelujah!]   †*Refrain*

25 Yonder is the sea, great and wide, with its swarms too many to number,
living things both small and great.

26 There go the ships to and fro,
and Leviathan, which you made for the sport of it.

27 All of them look to you
to give them their food in due season.

28 You give it to them; they gather it;
you open your hand, and they are filled with good things.

29 When you hide your face, they are terrified;
when you take away their breath, they die and return to their dust.   *Refrain*

30 You send forth your Spirit, and they are created;
and so you renew the face of the earth.

31 May the glory of the LORD endure forever;
O LORD, rejoice in all your works.

32 You look at the earth and it trembles;
you touch the mountains and they smoke.

33 I will sing to the LORD as long as I live;
I will praise my God while I have my being.

34 May these words of mine please God.
I will rejoice in the LORD.

35b Bless the LORD, O my soul.
Hallelujah!   *Refrain*

Tone

Lectionary: vv. 1-9, 24 with 'Hallelujah' Ordinary Time after Pentecost (B); vv. 24-34, 35b Day of Pentecost (A,B,C).

*Hallelujah is sung when the lection ends at this verse.

†Disregard this refrain indication when the lection begins with this verse.

Words: Arlo D. Duba © 1980 Arlo D. Duba
Music: Richard T. Proulx © 1981 Richard T. Proulx
Psalm Text: from *Evangelical Lutheran Worship* © 2006 Evangelical Lutheran Church in America, admin. Augsburg Fortress Publishers
Tone: © 2011 Faith Alive Christian Resources

Alternate Refrain

Cre-a - tor Spir - it, come we pray, come re-new the face of the earth.

AlternateTone

Words: Rhabanus Maurus (776-856); tr. composite, P.D.
Music (VENI CREATOR SPIRITUS fragment): Sarum plainsong, mode VIII; arr. Martin Tel © 2011 Faith Alive Christian Resources
Tone: © 2011 Faith Alive Christian Resources

Psalm 105

Voice 1:

¹ O give thanks to the LORD, call on his name, *
    make known his deeds among the peoples.

² **Sing to him, sing praises to him; ***
    tell of all his wonderful works.

³ Glory in his holy name; *
    let the hearts of those who seek the LORD rejoice.

⁴ **Seek the LORD and his strength; ***
    seek his presence continually.

⁵ Remember the wonderful works he has done, *
    his miracles, and the judgments he uttered,

⁶ O offspring of his servant Abraham, *
    children of Jacob, his chosen ones.

⁷ He is the LORD our God; *
    his judgments are in all the earth.

⁸ **He is mindful of his covenant forever, ***
    of the word that he commanded, for a thousand generations,

⁹ **the covenant that he made with Abraham, ***
    his sworn promise to Isaac,

¹⁰ **which he confirmed to Jacob as a statute, ***
    to Israel as an everlasting covenant,

¹¹ **saying, "To you I will give the land of Canaan ***
    as your portion for an inheritance."

Voice 2:

¹² When they were few in number, *
    of little account, and strangers in it,

¹³ wandering from nation to nation, *
    from one kingdom to another people,

¹⁴ he allowed no one to oppress them; *
    he rebuked kings on their account,

¹⁵ saying, "Do not touch my anointed ones; *
    do my prophets no harm."

¹⁶ When he summoned famine against the land, *
    and broke every staff of bread,

¹⁷ he had sent a man ahead of them, *
    Joseph, who was sold as a slave.

¹⁸ His feet were hurt with fetters, *
    his neck was put in a collar of iron;

¹⁹ until what he had said came to pass, *
    the word of the L<small>ORD</small> kept testing him.

²⁰ The king sent and released him; *
    the ruler of the peoples set him free.

²¹ **He made him lord of his house, ***
    and ruler of all his possessions,

²² **to instruct his officials at his pleasure, ***
    and to teach his elders wisdom.

Voice 1:

²³ Then Israel came to Egypt; *
    Jacob lived as an alien in the land of Ham.

²⁴ And the L<small>ORD</small> made his people very fruitful, *
    and made them stronger than their foes,

²⁵ whose hearts he then turned to hate his people, *
    to deal craftily with his servants.

²⁶ He sent his servant Moses, *
    and Aaron whom he had chosen.

²⁷ They performed his signs among them, *
    and miracles in the land of Ham.

²⁸ He sent darkness, and made the land dark; *
    they rebelled against his words.

²⁹ **He turned their waters into blood, ***
    and caused their fish to die.

³⁰ Their land swarmed with frogs, *
    even in the chambers of their kings.

³¹ **He spoke, and there came swarms of flies, ***
    and gnats throughout their country.

³² He gave them hail for rain, *
    and lightning that flashed through their land.

³³ **He struck their vines and fig trees, ***
    and shattered the trees of their country.

³⁴ He spoke, and the locusts came, *
    and young locusts without number;

³⁵ they devoured all the vegetation in their land, *
    and ate up the fruit of their ground.

³⁶ **He struck down all the firstborn in their land, ***
    the first issue of all their strength.

(continues)

Voice 2:

37 Then he brought Israel out with silver and gold, *
> and there was no one among their tribes who stumbled.

38 Egypt was glad when they departed, *
> for dread of them had fallen upon it.

39 **He spread a cloud for a covering,** *
> **and fire to give light by night.**

40 They asked, and he brought quails, *
> and gave them food from heaven in abundance.

41 **He opened the rock, and water gushed out;** *
> **it flowed through the desert like a river.**

42 For he remembered his holy promise, *
> and Abraham, his servant.

43 **So he brought his people out with joy,** *
> **his chosen ones with singing.**

44 **He gave them the lands of the nations,** *
> **and they took possession of the wealth of the peoples,**

45 **that they might keep his statutes and observe his laws.** *
> **Praise the LORD!**

O God of our salvation, through Jesus Christ you bring freedom,
fulfilling every promise you made to our ancestors in the faith.
So nourish us at your table with the bread of life and the cup of salvation,
that we may endure our wilderness journeys and come at last to your eternal feast. **Amen.**

Psalm 105 is a psalm of praise that, like Pss. 78, 106, 107, and 136, offers a sweeping account of God's history with Israel. It is a prime example of narrative remembrance as a means of praise—an approach to prayer echoed in many Christian Lord's Supper prayers. This historical narrative emphasizes God's promise of the land and God's repeated actions of deliverance by summarizing the Bible's first six books (all in contrast with Ps. 106, which emphasizes the history of Israel's unfaithfulness). *Use in Worship: baptisms; celebrations of the Lord's Supper; a model for contemporary narrative prayers (recounting an even larger sweep of God's actions, as depicted and predicted in all 66 books of the Bible).*

Recalling God's Faithfulness: A Litany 105A

Give praise to the LORD, proclaim his name;
   make known among the nations what he has done.
Sing to him, sing praise to him;
   tell of all his wonderful acts.
Glory in his holy name; let the hearts of those who seek the LORD rejoice.
   Look to the LORD and his strength; seek his face always.
Remember the wonders he has done,
   his miracles, and the judgments he pronounced.   *Psalm 105:1-5* (NIV)

On this day, we remember with gratitude and joy God's faithfulness:
   in the life of Abraham and Sarah, Isaac, Jacob, and Joseph,
   in the lives of Moses, Miriam, and Aaron,
   in the lives of Ruth and David, Isaiah and Jeremiah,
   in the lives of Mary and Martha, Peter and John,
   in the lives of Paul, Barnabas, and Lydia,
   in the lives of an Ethiopian eunuch and Roman centurion,
   in our own congregational life.
   Truly, God is faithful.

For God remembered his holy promise.
God brought out his people with rejoicing,
his chosen ones with shouts of joy;
that they might keep his precepts and observe his laws.
Praise the LORD!

105B Psalm 105:1-11, 16-26, 37-45
A Responsorial Setting

Refrain

1 Give thanks to the LORD and call upon God's name;
> make known the deeds of the LORD among the peoples.

2 Sing to the LORD, sing praises,
> and speak of all God's marvelous works.

3 Glory in God's holy name;
> let the hearts of those who seek the LORD rejoice.

4 Search for the strength of the LORD;
> continually seek God's face.

5 Remember the marvels God has done,
> the wonders and the judgments of God's mouth,

6 O offspring of Abraham, God's servant,
> O children of Jacob, God's chosen ones.   *Refrain*

7 The LORD is our God,
> whose judgments prevail in all the world,

8 who has always been mindful of the covenant,
> the promise made for a thousand generations:

9 the covenant made with Abraham,
> the oath sworn to Isaac,

10 which God established as a statute for Jacob,
> an everlasting covenant for Israel,

11 saying, "To you will I give the land of Canaan
> to be your allotted inheritance." *[Hallelujah!]   *Refrain*

16 Then God called for a famine in the land
> and destroyed the supply of bread.

17 The LORD sent a man before them,
> Joseph, who was sold as a slave.

18 They bruised his feet in fetters;
> his neck they put in an iron collar.

19 Until his prediction came to pass,
> the word of the LORD tested him.

20 The king sent and released him;
> the ruler of the peoples set him free,

21 setting him as a master over his household,
> as a ruler over all his possessions,

22 to instruct his princes according to his will
> and to teach his elders wisdom. *[Hallelujah!]   *Refrain*

(continues)

²³ Israel came into Egypt,

and Jacob became a sojourner in the land of Ham.

²⁴ The LORD made the people of Israel very fruitful,

more numerous than their enemies,

²⁵ whose hearts God turned, so that they hated God's people,

and dealt unjustly with the servants of God.

²⁶ O LORD, you sent Moses your servant,

and Aaron, your chosen one. *[Hallelujah!]   *Refrain*

³⁷ You led out your people with silver and gold;

in all their tribes there was not one that stumbled.

³⁸ Egypt was glad to see them go,

because they were afraid of them.

³⁹ You spread out a cloud for a covering

and a fire to give light by night.

⁴⁰ They asked, and you brought quail,

and satisfied them with bread from heaven.

⁴¹ You opened the rock, and water flowed,

so the river ran in the dry places.

⁴² For you remembered your holy word

and Abraham your servant.   *Refrain*

⁴³ So you led forth your people with gladness,

your chosen with shouts of joy.

⁴⁴ You gave your people the lands of the nations,

and they took the fruit of others' toil,

⁴⁵ that they might keep your statutes

and observe your teachings. Hallelujah!   *Refrain*

Tone

(To Refrain)

Lectionary: vv. 1-6, 37-45 Ordinary Time after Pentecost (A); vv. 1-6, 23-26 with 'Hallelujah' Ordinary Time after Pentecost (A); vv. 1-11 with 'Hallelujah' Ordinary Time after Pentecost (A); vv. 1-6, 16-22 with 'Hallelujah' Ordinary Time after Pentecost (A).

*Hallelujah is sung when the lection ends at this verse.

Music: Thomas Pavlechko © 2006 Thomas Pavlechko, admin. Augsburg Fortress Publishers
Psalm Text: from *Evangelical Lutheran Worship* © 2006 Evangelical Lutheran Church in America, admin. Augsburg Fortress Publishers
Tone: © 2006 Thomas Pavlechko, admin. Augsburg Fortress Publishers

Alternate Refrain

The stead-fast love of the Lord nev-er ceas-es; God's
mer-cies nev-er come to an end. They are
new ev-ery morn-ing, new ev-ery morn-ing; great is your
faith-ful-ness, O Lord, great is your faith-ful-ness.

Alternate Tone

Words: Lamentations 3:22-23
Music: Edith McNeill (b. 1920) © 1974, 1975 Celebration
Tone: © 2011 Faith Alive Christian Resources

105C Praise the Lord, the Day Is Won!

1 Praise the Lord, the day is won! Glo-ry, hal-le-lu-jah!
2 Loosed from chains by bond-age cast; glo-ry, hal-le-lu-jah!
3 As God's Spir-it moved the sea; glo-ry, hal-le-lu-jah!

God for us great things has done. Sing, shout hal-le-lu-jah!
God has freed our souls at last. Sing, shout hal-le-lu-jah!
set our hearts at lib-er-ty. Sing, shout hal-le-lu-jah!

Now let all the earth pro-claim res-ur-rec-tion won-der;
Slaves held cap-tive for so long, scarred by sin and sad-ness,
In our dark-est, dread-ful day, crushed by grief and mourn-ing;

in God's all-en-dur-ing name, death is cast a-sun-der!
lift a-new their vic-tory song, filled with joy and glad-ness!
God will roll the stone a-way, ra-diant love a-dorn-ing.

(continues)

4 God's great covenant is sealed!
Glory, hallelujah!
Our salvation is revealed.
Sing, shout hallelujah!
Plagues no more confound the flock,
flames nor flood assail us;
sure as water from the rock,
God will never fail us!

5 Faithful in the Lord rejoice.
Glory, hallelujah!
Raise to God your new-found voice.
Sing, shout hallelujah!
Crowned with full redemption's light,
by God's grace befriended;
life, behold the glorious sight;
death, your reign is ended!

Words: Michael Morgan © 2011 Michael Morgan, admin. Faith Alive Christian Resources
Music (GAUDEAMUS PARITER/AVE VIRGO VIRGINUM 7.6.7.6 D): Bohemian Brethren's *Gesangbuch*, 1544, P.D.

Psalm 106

¹ Praise the LORD! *

O give thanks to the LORD, for he is good;
for his steadfast love endures forever.

² Who can utter the mighty doings of the LORD, *
or declare all his praise?

³ Happy are those who observe justice, *
who do righteousness at all times.

⁴ **Remember me, O LORD, when you show favor to your people; ***
help me when you deliver them;

⁵ **that I may see the prosperity of your chosen ones, ***
that I may rejoice in the gladness of your nation,
that I may glory in your heritage.

⁶ Both we and our ancestors have sinned; *
we have committed iniquity, have done wickedly.

⁷ Our ancestors, when they were in Egypt,
did not consider your wonderful works; *
they did not remember the abundance of your steadfast love,
but rebelled against the Most High at the Red Sea.

⁸ **Yet he saved them for his name's sake, ***
so that he might make known his mighty power.

⁹ He rebuked the Red Sea, and it became dry; *
he led them through the deep as through a desert.

¹⁰ So he saved them from the hand of the foe, *
and delivered them from the hand of the enemy.

(continues)

11 The waters covered their adversaries; *
   not one of them was left.

12 Then they believed his words; *
   they sang his praise.

13 But they soon forgot his works; *
   they did not wait for his counsel.

14 But they had a wanton craving in the wilderness, *
   and put God to the test in the desert;

15 he gave them what they asked, *
   but sent a wasting disease among them.

16 They were jealous of Moses in the camp, *
   and of Aaron, the holy one of the LORD.

17 The earth opened and swallowed up Dathan, *
   and covered the faction of Abiram.

18 Fire also broke out in their company; *
   the flame burned up the wicked.

19 They made a calf at Horeb *
   and worshiped a cast image.

20 They exchanged the glory of God *
   for the image of an ox that eats grass.

21 They forgot God, their Savior, *
   who had done great things in Egypt,

22 wondrous works in the land of Ham, *
   and awesome deeds by the Red Sea.

23 Therefore he said he would destroy them—had not Moses, his chosen one, *
   stood in the breach before him, to turn away his wrath from destroying them.

24 Then they despised the pleasant land, *
   having no faith in his promise.

25 They grumbled in their tents, *
   and did not obey the voice of the LORD.

26 Therefore he raised his hand and swore to them *
   that he would make them fall in the wilderness,

27 and would disperse their descendants among the nations, *
   scattering them over the lands.

28 Then they attached themselves to the Baal of Peor, *
   and ate sacrifices offered to the dead;

²⁹ they provoked the LORD to anger with their deeds, *
  and a plague broke out among them.

³⁰ Then Phinehas stood up and interceded, *
  and the plague was stopped.

³¹ And that has been reckoned to him as righteousness *
  from generation to generation forever.

³² **They angered the LORD at the waters of Meribah,** *
  and it went ill with Moses on their account;

³³ **for they made his spirit bitter,** *
  and he spoke words that were rash.

³⁴ They did not destroy the peoples, *
  as the LORD commanded them,

³⁵ but they mingled with the nations *
  and learned to do as they did.

³⁶ They served their idols, *
  which became a snare to them.

³⁷ They sacrificed their sons *
  and their daughters to the demons;

³⁸ they poured out innocent blood, the blood of their sons and daughters, *
  whom they sacrificed to the idols of Canaan;
  and the land was polluted with blood.

³⁹ **Thus they became unclean by their acts,** *
  and prostituted themselves in their doings.

⁴⁰ **Then the anger of the LORD was kindled against his people,** *
  and he abhorred his heritage;

⁴¹ **he gave them into the hand of the nations,** *
  so that those who hated them ruled over them.

⁴² Their enemies oppressed them, *
  and they were brought into subjection under their power.

⁴³ Many times he delivered them, *
  but they were rebellious in their purposes,
  and were brought low through their iniquity.

⁴⁴ **Nevertheless he regarded their distress** *
  when he heard their cry.

⁴⁵ **For their sake he remembered his covenant,** *
  and showed compassion according to the abundance
  of his steadfast love.

(continues)

⁴⁶ He caused them to be pitied *

  by all who held them captive.

⁴⁷ **Save us, O Lᴏʀᴅ our God, and gather us from among the nations,** *

  that we may give thanks to your holy name

  and glory in your praise.

⁴⁸ **Blessed be the Lᴏʀᴅ, the God of Israel,**

  from everlasting to everlasting. *

  And let all the people say, "Amen." Praise the Lᴏʀᴅ!

Gracious God, your mercies are new every morning.
Great is your faithfulness!
Do not leave us to our faithless, wandering ways,
but shepherd us with your rod and staff
so that we will walk in the paths of righteousness
and dwell in your presence our whole life long. **Amen.**

Psalm 106, the final psalm of the fourth of the Psalter's five books, is a historical psalm that recounts God's history with Israel and calls particular attention to Israel's repeated unfaithfulness (vv. 6-46) and also to God's mercy (vv. 1-5, 47). This way of telling the story stands in contrast with other historical psalms that emphasize God's goodness (Pss. 78, 105, 136) or the drama of human repentance (Ps. 107). *Use in Worship: a call to confession; assurance of pardon; a model for contemporary narrative prayers (recounting an even larger sweep of God's mercy in the face of persistent human rebelliousness).*

106A It Is Good to Give Thanks to You, Lord

prais - es when you look on your peo - ple with love.
bond - age, paid no heed un - to all you had done.
des - ert; there they put you, O Lord, to the test.
res - cue when you heard all their cries of dis - tress.

Refrain
Harmony

O give thanks to the Lord, for God's love en-dures for - ev - er;

O give thanks to the Lord, for the Lord a - lone is good.

5 O_ God, save us now in your mercy;
bring us back from all that offends you.
Lord, look not alone at our evil,
but remember compassion and love.
Refrain

6 Now_ blest be the Lord, God of Israel.
Blest be God both now and forever.
Let nations and people cry, Amen!
Praise the Lord, hallelujah, Amen!
Refrain

Words: John L. Bell (b. 1949) © 1988 Wild Goose Resource Group, Iona Community, Scotland, GIA Publications, Inc., exclusive North American agent
Music (NEW 106TH 9.9.9.9 with refrain): John L. Bell (b. 1949) © 1989; arr. Marcus Hong © 2011 Wild Goose Resource Group, Iona Community, Scotland, GIA Publications, Inc., exclusive North American agent

106B Psalm 106:1-6, 19-23
A Responsorial Setting

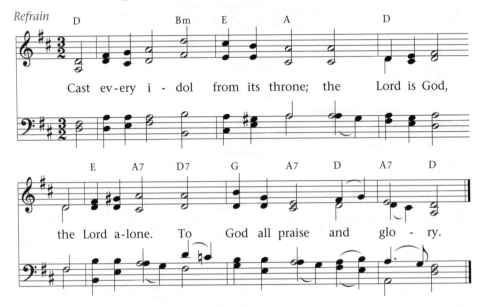

Cast ev-ery i-dol from its throne; the Lord is God, the Lord a-lone. To God all praise and glo-ry.

Refrain

1 Hallelujah! Give thanks to the LORD, for the LORD is good,
for God's mercy endures forever.

2 Who can declare the mighty acts of the LORD
or proclaim in full God's praise?

3 Happy are those who act with justice
and always do what is right.   *Refrain*

4 Remember me, O LORD, with the favor you have for your people,
and visit me with your salvation;

5 that I may see the prosperity of your elect
and be glad with the gladness of your people,
that I may glory with your inheritance.   *Refrain*

6 We have sinned as our forbears did;
we have done wrong and dealt wickedly.

19 They made a bullcalf at Horeb
and worshiped a molten image;

20 thus they exchanged their glory
for the image of an ox that feeds on grass.

21 They forgot God their Savior,
who had done great things in Egypt,

22 wonderful deeds in the land of Ham,
and fearful things at the Red Sea.

23 So you would have destroyed them,

  had not Moses your chosen stood in the breach,

   to turn away your wrath from consuming them.   *Refrain*

Tone

Lectionary: Ordinary Time after Pentecost (A).

Words: Johann J. Schütz, 1675; tr. Frances Cox, 1864; alt, P.D.
Music (MIT FREUDEN ZART fragment): Bohemian Brethren's *Kirchengesänge*, 1566; harm. Heinrich Reimann, 1895, P.D.
Psalm Text: from *Evangelical Lutheran Worship* © 2006 Evangelical Lutheran Church in America, admin. Augsburg Fortress Publishers
Tone: © 2011 Faith Alive Christian Resources

Psalm 107

1 O give thanks to the LORD, for he is good; *
   for his steadfast love endures forever.

2 **Let the redeemed of the LORD say so, ***
   those he redeemed from trouble

3 **and gathered in from the lands, ***
   from the east and from the west,
   from the north and from the south.

4 Some wandered in desert wastes, *
   finding no way to an inhabited town;

5 hungry and thirsty, *
   their soul fainted within them.

6 **Then they cried to the LORD in their trouble, ***
   and he delivered them from their distress;

7 **he led them by a straight way, ***
   until they reached an inhabited town.

8 **Let them thank the LORD for his steadfast love, ***
   for his wonderful works to humankind.

9 **For he satisfies the thirsty, ***
   and the hungry he fills with good things.

10 Some sat in darkness and in gloom, *
   prisoners in misery and in irons,

(continues)

¹¹ for they had rebelled against the words of God, *
>   and spurned the counsel of the Most High.

¹² Their hearts were bowed down with hard labor; *
>   they fell down, with no one to help.

¹³ **Then they cried to the Lord in their trouble, ***
>   **and he saved them from their distress;**

¹⁴ **he brought them out of darkness and gloom, ***
>   **and broke their bonds asunder.**

¹⁵ **Let them thank the Lord for his steadfast love, ***
>   **for his wonderful works to humankind.**

¹⁶ **For he shatters the doors of bronze, ***
>   **and cuts in two the bars of iron.**

¹⁷ Some were sick through their sinful ways, *
>   and because of their iniquities endured affliction;

¹⁸ they loathed any kind of food, *
>   and they drew near to the gates of death.

¹⁹ **Then they cried to the Lord in their trouble, ***
>   **and he saved them from their distress;**

²⁰ **he sent out his word and healed them, ***
>   **and delivered them from destruction.**

²¹ **Let them thank the Lord for his steadfast love, ***
>   **for his wonderful works to humankind.**

²² **And let them offer thanksgiving sacrifices, ***
>   **and tell of his deeds with songs of joy.**

²³ Some went down to the sea in ships, *
>   doing business on the mighty waters;

²⁴ they saw the deeds of the Lord, *
>   his wondrous works in the deep.

²⁵ For he commanded and raised the stormy wind, *
>   which lifted up the waves of the sea.

²⁶ They mounted up to heaven, they went down to the depths; *
>   their courage melted away in their calamity;

²⁷ they reeled and staggered like drunkards, *
>   and were at their wits' end.

²⁸ **Then they cried to the Lord in their trouble, ***
>   **and he brought them out from their distress;**

²⁹ **he made the storm be still, ***
>   **and the waves of the sea were hushed.**

30 Then they were glad because they had quiet, *
   and he brought them to their desired haven.

31 Let them thank the LORD for his steadfast love, *
   for his wonderful works to humankind.

32 Let them extol him in the congregation of the people, *
   and praise him in the assembly of the elders.

33 He turns rivers into a desert, *
   springs of water into thirsty ground,

34 a fruitful land into a salty waste, *
   because of the wickedness of its inhabitants.

35 He turns a desert into pools of water, *
   a parched land into springs of water.

36 And there he lets the hungry live, *
   and they establish a town to live in;

37 they sow fields, and plant vineyards, *
   and get a fruitful yield.

38 By his blessing they multiply greatly, *
   and he does not let their cattle decrease.

39 When they are diminished and brought low *
   through oppression, trouble, and sorrow,

40 he pours contempt on princes *
   and makes them wander in trackless wastes;

41 but he raises up the needy out of distress, *
   and makes their families like flocks.

42 The upright see it and are glad; *
   and all wickedness stops its mouth.

43 Let those who are wise give heed to these things, *
   and consider the steadfast love of the LORD.

Good and loving God, in Jesus you know the paths your children walk
and all that can frighten and discourage us.
Make your presence real to us as we make our journey,
that at any time and in every circumstance
we may remember your blessings—and rejoice! **Amen.**

Psalm 107, the first psalm in the fifth and final of the Psalter's five books, is a psalm of thanksgiving for God's faithfulness, deliverance, and covenant love in response to human repentance, turning away from sin and toward God. This is celebrated through a repeated pattern of describing various groups of people who have experienced calamity, turned toward God, and experienced deliverance (vv. 4-9, 10-16, 17-22, 23-32). The psalm concludes with a general hymn of praise to God (vv 33-41) and a proverb-like refrain that calls on the wise to "take this to heart." *Use in Worship: baptisms; services of testimony; in conjunction with confession of sin.*

107A Give Thanks to God Who Hears Our Cries

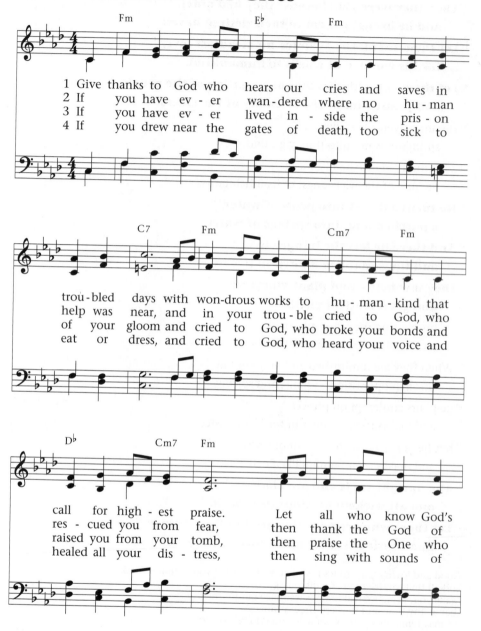

1 Give thanks to God who hears our cries and saves in
2 If you have ev - er wan - dered where no hu - man
3 If you have ev - er lived in - side the pris - on
4 If you drew near the gates of death, too sick to

trou - bled days with won - drous works to hu - man - kind that
help was near, and in your trou - ble cried to God, who
of your gloom and cried to God, who broke your bonds and
eat or dress, and cried to God, who heard your voice and

call for high - est praise. Let all who know God's
res - cued you from fear, then thank the God of
raised you from your tomb, then praise the One who
healed all your dis - tress, then sing with sounds of

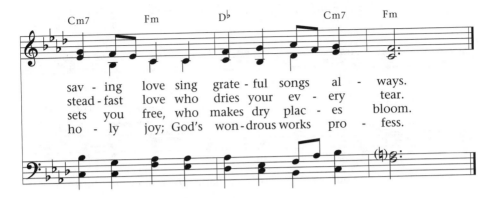

sav - ing   love sing   grate - ful songs   al - ways.
stead - fast love who   dries your   ev - ery   tear.
sets   you   free, who   makes dry plac - es   bloom.
ho - ly   joy; God's   won-drous works   pro - fess.

5 If you have felt your courage fail
   before a violent sea
   and cried to God, who stilled the storm,
   and made the wild wind flee,
   then in the congregation praise
   the God who heard your plea.

6 So praise the One whose love is great,
   whose kindness is well known,
   consider well the healing hand
   and help you have been shown,
   and tell the world what God has done.
   Praise God and God alone!

Alternate harmonization on p. 854.

Words: Ruth C. Duck © 2011 GIA Publications, Inc.
Music (MORNING SONG/CONSOLATION 8.6.8.6.8.6): J. Wyeth's *Repository of Sacred Music*, 1813; harm.
Jack Grotenhuis, 1983, © 1987 Faith Alive Christian Resources

107B Song: I Cry Out

I cry out for your hand of mer-cy to heal me. I am weak; I need your love to free me. O Lord, my rock, my strength in weak-ness, come res - cue me, O Lord. You are my hope; your prom-ise nev - er

Words and Music: Craig Musseau (b. 1965) © 1990 Vineyard Songs (Canada)/ION Publishing, admin. in North America by Music Services o/b/o Vineyard Music USA

Psalm 107:1-9, 17-37, 43
A Responsorial Setting

Refrain

Keyboard accompaniment on p. 693.

Refrain

1 Give thanks to the LORD, for the LORD is good,
    for God's mercy endures forever.

2 Let the redeemed of the LORD proclaim
    that God redeemed them from the hand of the foe,

3 gathering them in from the lands;
    from the east and from the west, from the north and from the south.   *Refrain*

4 Some wandered in desert wastes;
    they found no path to a city where they might dwell.

5 They were hungry and thirsty;
    their spirits languished within them.

6 Then in their trouble they cried to the LORD,
    and you delivered them from their distress.

7 You led them on a straight path
    to go to a city where they might dwell.

8 Let them give thanks to you, LORD, for your steadfast love
    and your wonderful works for all people.

9 For you satisfy the thirsty soul
    and fill the hungry with good things.   *Refrain*

17 Some were fools and took rebellious paths;
    through their sins they were afflicted.

18 They loathed all manner of food
    and drew near to death's door.

19 Then in their trouble they cried to the LORD
    and you delivered them from their distress.

20 You sent forth your word and healed them
    and rescued them from the grave.

21 Let them give thanks to you, LORD, for your steadfast love
    and your wonderful works for all people.

22 Let them offer sacrifices of thanksgiving
    and tell of your deeds with shouts of joy.   *Refrain*

23 Some went down to the sea in ships,
    plying their trade in deep waters.

24 They beheld the works of the LORD,
    God's wonderful works in the deep.

25 Then God spoke, and a stormy wind arose,
    which tossed high the waves of the sea.

(continues)

²⁶ They mounted up to the heavens and descended to the depths;
  their souls melted away in their peril.

²⁷ They staggered and reeled like drunkards,
  and all their skill was of no avail.

²⁸ Then in their trouble they cried to the LORD,
  and you delivered them from their distress.

²⁹ You stilled the storm to a whisper
  and silenced the waves of the sea.

³⁰ Then they were glad when it grew calm,
  when you guided them to the harbor they desired.

³¹ Let them give thanks to you, LORD, for your steadfast love
  and your wonderful works for all people.

³² Let them exalt you in the assembly of the people;
  in the council of the elders, let them sing hallelujah!   *Refrain*

³³ You change rivers into deserts,
  and water-springs into thirsty ground,

³⁴ fruitful land into salty waste,
  because of the wickedness of those who dwell there.

³⁵ You change deserts into pools of water
  and dry land into water-springs.

³⁶ You settle the hungry there,
  and they establish a city to dwell in.

³⁷ They sow fields and plant vineyards,
  and bring in a fruitful harvest.

⁴³ Whoever is wise will ponder these things,
  and consider well the LORD's steadfast love.   *Refrain*

Tone

For an alternate refrain and tone use "Thank You, Lord" on p. 903.

Lectionary: vv. 1-3, 17-22 Lent (B); vv. 1-3, 33-37 Ordinary Time after Pentecost (A); vv. 1-3, 23-32 Ordinary Time after Pentecost (B); vv. 1-9, 43 Ordinary Time after Pentecost (C).

Optional keyboard accompaniment

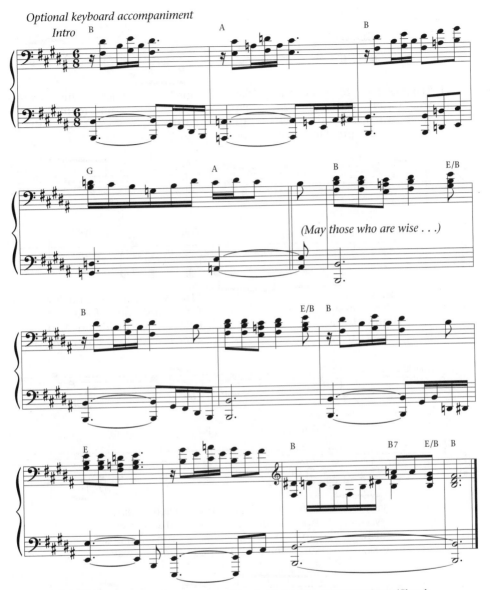

(May those who are wise . . .)

Music: Isaac Everett; arr. Paul Detterman © Isaac Everett, admin. Church Pension Group/Church Publishing, Inc.

107D Thanks Be to God Our Savior

1 "Thanks be to God our Savior," let his re-
2 Strangers without a city, some roamed the
3 Some groaned in bitter anguish, foes of the
4 Slaves to profane ambition, by evil

deemed ones say.
wilderness,
Most High's claims,
led astray,

"He shows us boundless
finding no food or
helpless, condemned to
some learned to know af-

favor; his love is sure each day."
pity, no hope in their distress.
languish, captives in iron chains.
fliction, suffered and pined away.

From earth's re - mot - est lands / a cho - sen folk he
Then, when they sought God's name, / he made their path - ways
Then, when they sought God's name, / he loos - ened all their
Then, when they sought God's name, / he brought them re - stor -

rais - es. O ran - somed from ty - rants' hands, join
flour - ish. O bless him, his love pro - claim: the
fet - ters. O bless him, his love pro - claim: the
a - tion. O bless him, his love pro - claim; bring

now to sound his prais - es.
hun - gry he will nour - ish.
pris - on bars he shat - ters.
thanks and a - dor - a - tion.

5 Storms thundered forth his power
to those who sailed the seas.
Winds lashed them hour by hour,
waves dashed them to their knees.
Then, when they sought God's name,
he calmed the raging weather.
O bless him, his love proclaim
where all his people gather.

6 His word brings desolation
where evil deeds abound,
but for his faithful nation
springs flow from barren ground.
He raises up the meek;
the mighty prince he plunders.
His loving-kindness seek;
consider all his wonders.

Words: David J. Diephouse, 1985, © 1987 Faith Alive Christian Resources
Music (DJ DEEP HOUSE 7.6.7.6.6.7.7.7): Greg Scheer © 2011 Greg Scheer

Psalm 108

A Song. A Psalm of David.

1 My heart is steadfast, O God, my heart is steadfast; *
   I will sing and make melody. Awake, my soul!

2 Awake, O harp and lyre! *
   I will awake the dawn.

3 **I will give thanks to you, O LORD, among the peoples, ***
   and I will sing praises to you among the nations.

4 **For your steadfast love is higher than the heavens, ***
   and your faithfulness reaches to the clouds.

5 **Be exalted, O God, above the heavens, ***
   and let your glory be over all the earth.

6 **Give victory with your right hand, and answer me, ***
   so that those whom you love may be rescued.

7 God has promised in his sanctuary: *
   "With exultation I will divide up Shechem,
   and portion out the Vale of Succoth.

8 Gilead is mine; Manasseh is mine; *
   Ephraim is my helmet; Judah is my scepter.

9 Moab is my washbasin; on Edom I hurl my shoe; *
   over Philistia I shout in triumph."

10 Who will bring me to the fortified city? *
   Who will lead me to Edom?

11 Have you not rejected us, O God? *
   You do not go out, O God, with our armies.

12 **O grant us help against the foe, ***
   for human help is worthless.

13 **With God we shall do valiantly; ***
   it is he who will tread down our foes.

God of unending faithfulness, Jesus promised that if we ask we will receive.
Guard and guide us by your Holy Spirit, and fill our hearts with confident joy.
Help us to know that the struggles we face are not against flesh and blood,
but against the power of evil beyond this world,
and that it is you who gives us the victory through Jesus Christ our Lord. **Amen.**

Psalm 108 is psalm of lament and a prayer for deliverance. It begins with a vow to praise God (vv. 1-4) that leads to a first prayer for deliverance (vv. 5-6) and continues with an oracle of promises from God (vv. 8-10), which leads to a second prayer for deliverance (vv. 11-13). The psalmist's intense prayer is thus grounded in both sides of covenantal engagement: the human worship of God and God's promise of deliverance. This, then, is an example of a lament prayer that, unlike Ps. 88, dwells primarily on positive assertions of faith and promise. It is an approach to times of difficulty and calamity that focuses more on claiming God's promises than on railing against God—a testimony to the range of approaches to lament found in the Psalter as a whole. *Use in Worship: call to worship (especially vv. 1-4); services of confession, lament, or healing; services held in times of crisis or difficulty.*

My Heart Is Firmly Fixed **108A**

1 My heart is firm-ly fixed; to God my song I raise.
2 A-mong the na-tions, LORD, to you my song will rise.
3 How great your love, O LORD: we praise your match-less worth.
4 Stretch forth your might-y hand in an-swer to our prayer,
5 God speaks: "All lands are mine, to serve me and o-bey;

A-wake, O harp, in joy-ful strains; a-wake, my soul, to praise.
Your faith-ful-ness out-shines the heavens, your mer-cies reach the skies.
Your glo-ry be ex-alt-ed high and cov-er all the earth.
and let your own be-lov-ed ones your great sal-va-tion share.
my peo-ple and their foes will serve my glo-ry day by day."

6 O who will lead us on
in triumph on this day?
LORD, why do you reject your own
and turn your face away?

7 An army's help is vain;
to God for help we plead.
With God we shall do valiantly;
with God we shall succeed.

Guitar chords do not correspond with keyboard harmony.

Words: *Psalter*, 1912; rev. *Psalter Hymnal*, 1987, © 1987 Faith Alive Christian Resources
Music (ST. THOMAS 6.6.8.6): Aaron Williams, 1763; harm. Lowell Mason (1792-1872), P.D.

108B Be Exalted, O God

I will give thanks to thee, O Lord, a-mong the peo-ples.

I will sing prais-es to thee a-mong the na-tions.

For thy stead - fast love is great, is great to the heav-ens;

and thy faith-ful-ness, thy faith-ful-ness to the clouds.

Be ex-alt-ed, O God, a-bove the heav - ens; let thy glo-ry be o - ver all the earth. Be ex-alt-ed, O God, a-bove the heav - ens; let thy glo-ry be o-ver all the earth. I will

Words and Music: Brent Chambers (b. 1948) © 1977 Universal Music—Brentwood-Benson Songs, admin. Music Services

Psalm 109

To the leader. Of David. A Psalm.

Voice 1:

1 Do not be silent, O God of my praise. *

   2 For wicked and deceitful mouths are opened against me,
   speaking against me with lying tongues.

3 They beset me with words of hate, *
   and attack me without cause.

4 In return for my love they accuse me, *
   even while I make prayer for them.

5 So they reward me evil for good, *
   and hatred for my love.

Voice 2:

6 They say, "Appoint a wicked man against him; *
   let an accuser stand on his right.

7 When he is tried, let him be found guilty; *
   let his prayer be counted as sin.

8 May his days be few; *
   may another seize his position.

9 May his children be orphans, *
   and his wife a widow.

10 May his children wander about and beg; *
   may they be driven out of the ruins they inhabit.

11 May the creditor seize all that he has; *
   may strangers plunder the fruits of his toil.

12 May there be no one to do him a kindness, *
   nor anyone to pity his orphaned children.

13 May his posterity be cut off; *
   may his name be blotted out in the second generation.

14 May the iniquity of his father be remembered before the LORD, *
   and do not let the sin of his mother be blotted out.

15 Let them be before the LORD continually, *
   and may his memory be cut off from the earth.

16 For he did not remember to show kindness, *
   but pursued the poor and needy
   and the brokenhearted to their death.

17 He loved to curse; let curses come on him. *
   He did not like blessing; may it be far from him.

¹⁸ He clothed himself with cursing as his coat, *
     may it soak into his body like water, like oil into his bones.

¹⁹ May it be like a garment that he wraps around himself, *
     like a belt that he wears every day."

²⁰ May that be the reward of my accusers from the LORD, *
     of those who speak evil against my life.

Voice 1:

²¹ But you, O LORD my Lord, act on my behalf for your name's sake; *
     because your steadfast love is good, deliver me.

²² For I am poor and needy, *
     and my heart is pierced within me.

²³ I am gone like a shadow at evening; *
     I am shaken off like a locust.

²⁴ My knees are weak through fasting; *
     my body has become gaunt.

²⁵ I am an object of scorn to my accusers; *
     when they see me, they shake their heads.

²⁶ Help me, O LORD my God! *
     Save me according to your steadfast love.

²⁷ Let them know that this is your hand; *
     you, O LORD, have done it.

²⁸ Let them curse, but you will bless. *
     Let my assailants be put to shame; may your servant be glad.

²⁹ May my accusers be clothed with dishonor; *
     may they be wrapped in their own shame as in a mantle.

³⁰ With my mouth I will give great thanks to the LORD; *
     I will praise him in the midst of the throng.

³¹ For he stands at the right hand of the needy, *
     to save them from those who would condemn them to death.

Lord and Judge of all,
where can we go with our darkest thoughts, our persistent hatreds?
You search all hearts and try all motives, so we entrust it all to you,
even as we seek your reign of righteousness and pray for those we despise,
as Jesus Christ our Lord taught us. **Amen.**

Psalm 109 is a prayer for divine intervention in the face of deceit and slander (vv. 1, 26) and a plea for justice in the face of injustice. The prayer curses against those who perpetuate evil (vv. 8-20). The curses—which are some of the most vicious in the entire Psalter—eventually give way to an acknowledgement of the psalmist's own weakness (vv. 22-24) and expressions of serenity and trust in God (vv. 27-31). The psalm does not specify whether this is the serenity of self-congratulation for having cursed or the serenity of peace that comes from surrendering vengeance over to God (which may be an appealing interpretation for many contemporary readers). Christian believers have long struggled with how to understand the psalm in light
(continues)

of the clear teaching of the NT to "love our enemies." Interpreters variously suggest that the psalm can be understood as the candid prayer of one who is unjustly wronged, as an indication of the ongoing significance of justice in human relationships, as a prophetic word to challenge us to make sure we do not perpetuate this kind of evil, and as a prayer for God (and not the victim) to establish justice—an act of surrender or relinquishment of justice to God. These interpretations leave us with a question: what kind of liturgical or musical setting might help us experience a text as a prophetic injunction against our own evil acts or an act of surrender and relinquishment? *Use in Worship: in conjunction with OT narratives of conflict; to provoke discussions about appropriate responses to injustice.*

109A Hymn: Give to the Winds Your Fears

Read Psalm 109:1-5 before singing stanza 1.

1 Give to the winds your fears; hope and be un - dis - mayed: God hears your sighs and counts your tears; God will lift up your head. *Read Ps. 109:6-20*
2 Why, heart, so heav - y still? Why, spir - it, so cast down? Bring ev - ery anx - ious thought to God, bid ev - ery fear be gone. *Read Ps. 109:21-26*
3 Leave to God's sov - ereign sway to choose and to com - mand; though won - dering, you will own God's way; how wise, how strong God's hand! *Read Ps. 109:27-31*
4 Let us in life and death, your stead - fast love de - clare, and pub - lish with our lat - est breath your love and guard - ian care.

This tune in a lower key: p. 489.

Words: sts. 1, 3, 4 Charles Wesley (1707-1788), alt., P.D.; st. 2 Martin Tel © 2011 Martin Tel, admin. Faith Alive Christian Resources
Music (GORTON 6.6.8.6): Ludwig van Beethoven (1770-1827), 1807, adapt., P.D.

Psalm 110

Of David. A Psalm.

¹ The LORD says to my lord, *

"Sit at my right hand until I make your enemies your footstool."

² **The LORD sends out from Zion your mighty scepter.** *

Rule in the midst of your foes.

³ Your people will offer themselves willingly

on the day you lead your forces on the holy mountains. *

From the womb of the morning, like dew, your youth will come to you.

⁴ **The LORD has sworn and will not change his mind,** *

"You are a priest forever according to the order of Melchizedek."

⁵ The Lord is at your right hand; *

he will shatter kings on the day of his wrath.

⁶ He will execute judgment among the nations, filling them with corpses; *

he will shatter heads over the wide earth.

⁷ **He will drink from the stream by the path;** *

therefore he will lift up his head.

Lord Jesus Christ, you were born as one of us,
you suffered and died, and you were raised for us.
You are our great high priest, and with true justice and unending mercy
you will return to judge and rule the earth.
In you we have nothing to fear, not even death itself.
All glory and praise are yours in this and every age. **Amen.**

Psalm 110 is a messianic psalm that is built around two divine promises (vv. 1, 4). The opening promise of God is to establish the rule of the king (v. 1); the second promise of God is to establish the priestly function of the king (v. 4), evoking the memory of Melchizadek (Gen. 14), the priest-king of the ancient city of Salem. Each is followed by assurances of God's promise and God's record of deliverance. In its original context, the psalm affirmed the monarchy, much like Ps. 2, and challenged the king to recognize that authority comes from God. The intertwining of political, military, and priestly roles in one person also suggests the importance of achieving integrity between worship and life, a theme that recurs again provocatively in Ps. 149 with its priestly and military language. In light of the NT, which quotes this psalm several times to describe the preeminence of Jesus, it can be understood as both a messianic prophecy and an altogether apt and evocative description of the kingly and priestly roles of Jesus Christ. *Use in Worship: Ascension Day; celebrations of the lordship and priestly role of Jesus Christ.*

110A The LORD unto My Lord Has Said

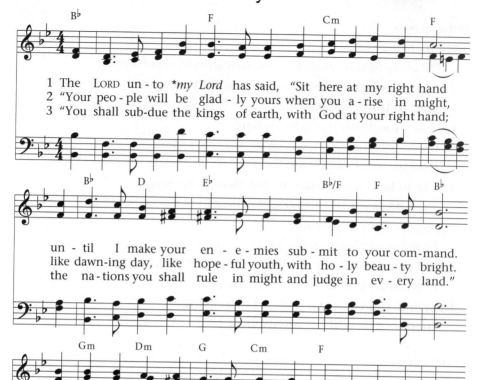

1 The LORD un-to *my Lord has said, "Sit here at my right hand
2 "Your peo-ple will be glad-ly yours when you a-rise in might,
3 "You shall sub-due the kings of earth, with God at your right hand;

un-til I make your en-e-mies sub-mit to your com-mand.
like dawn-ing day, like hope-ful youth, with ho-ly beau-ty bright.
the na-tions you shall rule in might and judge in ev-ery land."

A scep-ter pros-pered by the LORD your might-y hand shall wield;
The priest-hood of Mel-chiz-e-dek the LORD has giv-en you;
The *Lord, re-freshed by liv-ing streams, shall nei-ther faint nor fall,

from Zi-on you shall rule the world, and all your foes shall yield.
it shall re-main for-ev-er-more; God's word is al-ways true.
and he shall be the glo-rious head, ex-alt-ed o-ver all.

*Or "his Christ" (st. 1) and "Christ" (st. 3). This alternate (and original) text may be used to make the Christological interpretation of the psalm more explicit.

Guitar chords do not correspond with keyboard harmony.

Words: *Psalter*, 1912, alt., P.D.
Music (ALL SAINTS NEW 8.6.8.6 D): Henry S. Cutler, 1872, P.D.

The LORD Said to My Lord

Refrain

The LORD said to my Lord: "Sit at my right hand."

Solo Voice

1 The LORD said to my Lord, "Sit at my right
2 The LORD will ex-tend the scep-ter of your power from

3 The LORD has sworn and will not re-cant: "You are a

Choral or instrumental accompaniment

The LORD!

To Refrain

hand, un-til I make your en-e-mies your foot-stool."
Zi-on, say-ing, "Rule in the midst of your en-e-mies."

To Refrain

priest for-ev-er af-ter the or-der of Mel-chi-ze-dek."

The LORD! The LORD!

Words: Psalm 110:1-2, 4, from *Evangelical Lutheran Worship* © 2006 Evangelical Lutheran Church in America, admin. Augsburg Fortress Publishers
Music: Konstantin Zhigulin and Brad Cawyer © 2011 Konstantin Zhigulin

Psalm 111

¹ Praise the LORD! I will give thanks to the LORD with my whole heart, *
   in the company of the upright, in the congregation.

² **Great are the works of the LORD, ***
   studied by all who delight in them.

³ **Full of honor and majesty is his work, ***
   and his righteousness endures forever.

⁴ He has gained renown by his wonderful deeds; *
   the LORD is gracious and merciful.

⁵ He provides food for those who fear him; *
   he is ever mindful of his covenant.

⁶ He has shown his people the power of his works, *
   in giving them the heritage of the nations.

⁷ **The works of his hands are faithful and just; ***
   all his precepts are trustworthy.

⁸ **They are established forever and ever, ***
   to be performed with faithfulness and uprightness.

⁹ He sent redemption to his people; he has commanded his covenant forever. *
   Holy and awesome is his name.

¹⁰ **The fear of the LORD is the beginning of wisdom; ***
   all those who practice it have a good understanding.
   His praise endures forever.

Holy and generous God, giver of every good gift,
inspire in our hearts a desire for wisdom that begins with reverence for you.
Expand in our minds the knowledge of your Word,
and fill us with the love of your Son, Jesus, in whose name we pray. **Amen.**

Psalm 111 is an acrostic where each clause begins with a subsequent letter of the Hebrew alphabet. It focuses on the beauty and glory of God, celebrating God's greatness and goodness and emphasizing both God's covenant love (vv. 5, 9) and commands (v. 7). The psalm culminates by asserting the powerful interrelationship between worship and wisdom (v. 10), challenging any attempt to pursue practical advice for life apart from the worship of God. *Use in Worship: services focusing on themes of wisdom or guidance for life; a psalm of praise for any occasion.*

O Give the Lord Wholehearted Praise 111A

1 O give the Lord whole-heart-ed praise. To him thanks-
2 His saints de-light to search and trace his might-y
3 God's won-drous deeds of faith-ful-ness his peo-ple
4 God's prom-ise shall for-ev-er stand; he cares for

giv-ing I will bring; with all his peo-ple
works and won-drous ways. Ma-jes-tic glo-ry,
ev-er keep in mind. His works of love and
those who trust his word. Up-on his saints his

I will raise my voice and of his glo-ry sing.
bound-less grace, and right-eous-ness his work dis-plays.
gra-cious-ness re-veal that God the Lord is kind.
might-y hand the wealth of na-tions has con-ferred.

5 His works are true and just indeed;
his precepts are forever sure.
In truth and righteousness decreed,
they shall forevermore endure.

6 By God's own hand redemption came;
his covenant sure no change can know.
Let all revere his holy name
in heaven above and earth below.

7 In reverence and in godly fear
we find the key to wisdom's ways;
the wise his holy name revere.
Through endless ages sound his praise!

Guitar chords do not correspond with keyboard harmony.

This tune in a higher key: p. 593.

Words: *Psalter*, 1912, alt., P.D.
Music (GERMANY 8.8.8.8): W. Gardiner's *Sacred Melodies*, 1815, P.D.

111B Alleluia! Laud and Blessing

1 Al - le - lu - ia! Laud and bless - ing to our
2 Al - le - lu - ia! God sus - tains us, match - less
3 Al - le - lu - ia! Ho - ly Pa - rent, all your

God, whose Word is sure; by whose grace we
are the gifts we share: light in dark - ness,
chil - dren now re - claim; may our lives re -

find re - demp - tion, in whose love we live se - cure.
hope in con - flict, an - swers to our deep - est prayer.
flect your jus - tice, heirs to your most sa - cred name.

Right-eous - ness and rich com - pas - sion shall at - tend us
Ours to give as we are giv - en; arms to lift when
Fill our hearts with un - der - stand-ing, brace our weak - ness

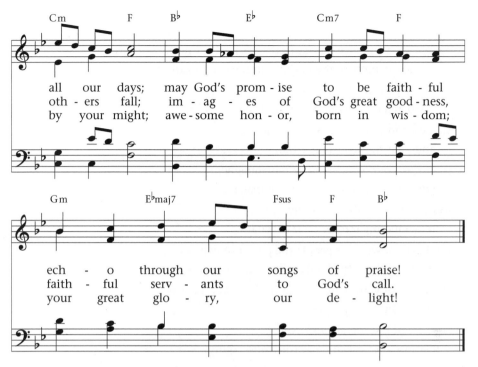

all   our   days;   may God's   prom - ise   to   be   faith - ful
oth - ers   fall;   im - ag - es   of   God's great   good - ness,
by   your might;   awe - some   hon - or,   born   in   wis - dom;

ech - o   through   our   songs   of   praise!
faith - ful   serv - ants   to   God's   call.
your   great   glo - ry,   our   de - light!

Words: Psalms 111 and 112; para. Michael Morgan © 2011 Michael Morgan, admin. Faith Alive Christian Resources
Music (ALL SAINTS/WEISSE FLAGGEN 8.7.8.7 D): as in *Tochter Sion*, Cologne, 1741, P.D.

Psalm 111 | A Responsorial Setting **111C**

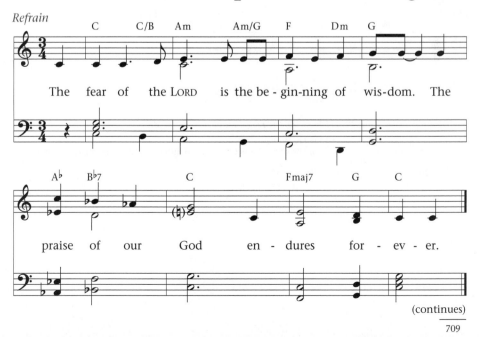

Refrain

The   fear   of   the LORD   is the be - gin-ning of   wis-dom.   The

praise   of   our   God   en - dures   for - ev - er.

(continues)

Refrain

¹ Hallelujah! I will give thanks to the LORD with my whole heart,

in the assembly of the upright, in the congregation.

² Great are your works, O LORD,

pondered by all who delight in them.

³ Majesty and splendor mark your deeds,

and your righteousness endures forever.   *Refrain*

⁴ You cause your wonders to be remembered;

you are gracious and full of compassion.

⁵ You give food to those who fear you,

remembering forever your covenant.

⁶ You have shown your people the power of your works

in giving them the lands of the nations.   *Refrain*

⁷ The works of your hands are faithfulness and justice;

all of your precepts are sure.

⁸ They stand fast forever and ever,

because they are done in truth and equity.

⁹ You sent redemption to your people and commanded your covenant forever;

holy and awesome is your name.

¹⁰ The fear of the LORD is the beginning of wisdom;

all who practice this have a good understanding.

God's praise endures forever.   *Refrain*

Tone

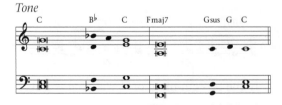

Lectionary: Ordinary Time after Epiphany (B); Ordinary Time after Pentecost (B,C).

Words and Music: Jay Wilkey © 2003 Jay Wilkey
Psalm Text: from *Evangelical Lutheran Worship* © 2006 Evangelical Lutheran Church in America, admin.
Augsburg Fortress Publishers
Tone: © 2011 Faith Alive Christian Resources

Rejoice in God, My Heart 111D

1 Re - joice in God, my heart, with all whose voic - es raise
2 The splen - dor of his reign in maj - es - ty ap - pears,
3 His deeds their Lord pro - claim, with all cre - a - ted things,

their thank - ful songs, and take your part in cease - less praise!
whose grace and mer - cy shall re - main to end - less years.
and from the hon - or of his name all wis - dom springs.

His words and works ex - tol, ex - alt his name on high,
Se - cure in him we stand, our God, whose ways are just;
Come share, my soul, the songs cel - es - tial voic - es raise,

and trace his glo - ries, O my soul, in earth and sky.
re - deemed by his al - might - y hand, in him we trust.
and wor - ship him to whom be - longs e - ter - nal praise!

Guitar chords do not correspond with keyboard harmony.

Words: Timothy Dudley-Smith (b. 1926) © Timothy Dudley-Smith in Europe and Africa, reproduced by permission of Oxford University Press; © 2006 Hope Publishing Company in the United States and the rest of the world
Music (LEONI/YIGDAL 6.6.8.4 D): Hebrew melody; adapt. Meyer Lyon (1751-1797), P.D.

Psalm 112

¹ Praise the LORD! Happy are those who fear the LORD, *
   who greatly delight in his commandments.

² **Their descendants will be mighty in the land;** *
   the generation of the upright will be blessed.

³ Wealth and riches are in their houses, *
   and their righteousness endures forever.

⁴ **They rise in the darkness as a light for the upright;** *
   they are gracious, merciful, and righteous.

⁵ It is well with those who deal generously and lend, *
   who conduct their affairs with justice.

⁶ **For the righteous will never be moved;** *
   they will be remembered forever.

⁷ They are not afraid of evil tidings; *
   their hearts are firm, secure in the LORD.

⁸ **Their hearts are steady, they will not be afraid;** *
   in the end they will look in triumph on their foes.

⁹ They have distributed freely, they have given to the poor; *
   their righteousness endures forever; their horn is exalted in honor.

¹⁰ **The wicked see it and are angry;** *
   they gnash their teeth and melt away;
   the desire of the wicked comes to nothing.

God of Light,
in your commandments we find life, and in your wisdom is true happiness.
Inspire us to live generously and to act justly,
so that our lives may reflect your love and righteousness,
and your name may be praised, through Christ our Lord. **Amen.**

Psalm 112 is an acrostic where each clause begins with a subsequent letter of the Hebrew alphabet. It opens with a call to praise (v. 1) and echoes themes found in both Proverbs and Jesus' Beatitudes (see Matt. 5:1-12). The psalm focuses on the blessings of godliness, complementing the reflections of Ps. 111 on the beauty and glory of God and echoing once again the message of Ps. 1. *Use in Worship: an act of proclamation (perhaps offered in conjunction with other scriptural calls to faithful living).*

For an additional setting of Ps. 112 see 111B.

How Blest Are Those 112A
Who Fear the LORD

1 How blest are those who fear the LORD and great-ly love God's ho-ly will. Their chil-dren share their great re-ward, and bless-ings all their days shall fill.

2 A-bound-ing wealth shall bless their home, their right-eous-ness for-e'er en-dure. To them shall light a-rise in gloom, for they are mer-ci-ful and pure.

3 The peo-ple who be-friend the weak in jus-tice shall their cause main-tain. True peace shall their whole life at-tend, and long their mem-ory shall re-main.

4 By e-vil tid-ings not dis-mayed, the right-eous trust in God a-lone. Their heart is stead-fast, un-a-fraid, for they shall see their foes o'er-thrown.

5 Dispersing gifts among the poor,
the righteous for their needs provide.
Their righteousness shall thus endure;
their strength in honor shall abide.

6 The wicked will be brought to shame,
while righteous ones will see the LORD.
Unrighteous hopes will not see gain,
for sin will find its due reward.

Guitar chords do not correspond with keyboard harmony.

Words: *Psalter*, 1887; rev. *Psalter Hymnal*, 1987, © Faith Alive Christian Resources
Music (MELCOMBE 8.8.8.8): Samuel Webbe, 1782, P.D.

Refrain

Hap-py are they who de-light, who de-light in the law of God.

Refrain

1 Hallelujah! Happy are they who fear the LORD
   and have great delight in God's commandments!

2 Their descendants will be mighty in the land;
   the generation of the upright will be blessed.

3 Wealth and riches will be in their house,
   and their righteousness will last forever.   *Refrain*

4 Light shines in the darkness for the upright;
   the righteous are merciful and full of compassion.

5 It is good for them to be generous in lending
   and to manage their affairs with justice.

6 For they will never be shaken;
   the righteous will be kept in everlasting remembrance.   *Refrain*

7 They will not be afraid of any evil rumors;
   their heart is steadfast, trusting in the LORD.

8 Their heart is established and will not shrink,
   until they see their desire upon their enemies.

9 They have given freely to the poor, and their righteousness stands fast forever;
   they will hold up their head with honor.

10 The wicked will see it and be angry; they will gnash their teeth and pine away;
   the desires of the wicked will perish.   *Refrain*

Tone

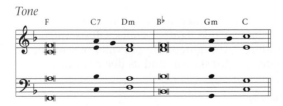

Lectionary: Ordinary Time after Epiphany (A); Ordinary Time after Pentecost (C).

Words and Music: Hal H. Hopson © 1987 Hope Publishing Company
Psalm Text: from *Evangelical Lutheran Worship* © 2006 Evangelical Lutheran Church in America, admin.
Augsburg Fortress Publishers
Tone: © 2011 Faith Alive Christian Resources

Psalm 113

1 Praïse the Lord! *

    Praise, O servants of the Lord; praise the name of the Lord.

2 **Blessed be the name of the Lord** *

    from this time on and forevermore.

3 **From the rising of the sun to its setting** *

    the name of the Lord is to be praised.

4 **The Lord is high above all nations,** *

    and his glory above the heavens.

5 Who is like the Lord our God, *

    who is seated on high,

6 who looks far down *

    on the heavens and the earth?

7 **He raises the poor from the dust,** *

    and lifts the needy from the ash heap,

8 **to make them sit with princes,** *

    with the princes of his people.

9 **He gives the barren woman a home,**

    making her the joyous mother of children. *

    Praïse the Lord!

Compassionate God,
your ears are open to the cries of the poor,
and you come to the aid of the needy.
Tune our hearts toward the least of these,
that we may meet our Lord Jesus in them
and that the great reversal of your kingdom may come. **Amen.**

Psalm 113 is a psalm of praise that focuses on God's regard for the lowly, the poor and needy, and those who cannot conceive children. This is a psalm of great contrasts: the exalted God looks down and lifts up those who are low. *Use in Worship: an act of praise for any occasion; morning and evening prayer services (see v. 3).*

Refrain

Leader

From the ris-ing of the sun to its go - ing down, let the
name of the Lord be praised! From the ris-ing of the sun to its
go - ing down, let the name of the Lord be praised!

Unison
All

Harmony

Hal-le - lu-jah! Hal-le - lu-jah! Hal-le - lu - jah!

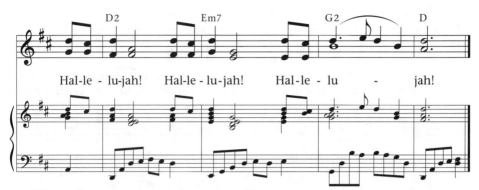

Hal-le - lu-jah! Hal-le - lu-jah! Hal-le - lu - jah!

Refrain

¹ Hallelujah! Give praise, you servants of the Lord;
  praise the name of the Lord.

² Let the name of the Lord be blessed,
  from this time forth forevermore.

³ From the rising of the sun to its going down
  let the name of the Lord be praised.

⁴ The Lord is high above all nations,
  God's glory above the heavens.

⁵ Who is like the Lord our God,
  who sits enthroned on high,

⁶ but stoops to behold
  the heavens and the earth?   *Refrain*

⁷ The Lord takes up the weak out of the dust
  and lifts up the poor from the ashes,

⁸ enthroning them with the rulers,
  with the rulers of the people.

⁹ The Lord makes the woman of a childless house
  to be a joyful mother of children. Hallelujah!   *Refrain*

Tone

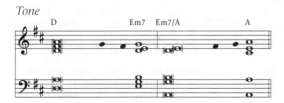

Lectionary: Ordinary Time after Pentecost (C).

Words and Music: Kathy Wonson Eddy © 2011 Kathy Wonson Eddy, admin. Faith Alive Christian Resources
Psalm Text: from *Evangelical Lutheran Worship* © 2006 Evangelical Lutheran Church in America, admin.
Augsburg Fortress Publishers
Tone: © 2011 Faith Alive Christian Resources

113B Bless the LORD, O Saints and Servants

1 Bless the LORD, O saints and ser - vants, praise the might of
2 Who in heaven can be God's e - qual, who on earth with

God's great name: age - less, match - less, filled with won - der,
God com - pare? Who can raise the poor from ash - es,

yes - ter - day, to - day, the same. When the dawn re -
lift the need - y from de - spair? God a - lone in -

ceives the sun - rise till the night re - turns its rays, shall the glo - ry
vites the help - less with the strong to share re - ward; fields once bar - ren

of God's good - ness be the theme of all our praise.
yield a har - vest, tongues once si - lent praise their LORD.

Guitar chords do not correspond with keyboard harmony.
Alternate tune: NETTLETON, p. 295.

Words: Michael Morgan © 2011 Michael Morgan, admin. Faith Alive Christian Resources
Music (AUSTRIAN HYMN 8.7.8.7 D): Franz Joseph Haydn (1732-1809), 1797, P.D.

¹ When Israel went out from Egypt, *
　　the house of Jacob from a people of strange language,

² Judah became God's sanctuary, *
　　Israel his dominion.

³ **The sea looked and fled; ***
　　Jordan turned back.

⁴ **The mountains skipped like rams, ***
　　the hills like lambs.

⁵ Why is it, O sea, that you flee? *
　　O Jordan, that you turn back?

⁶ O mountains, that you skip like rams? *
　　O hills, like lambs?

⁷ **Tremble, O earth, at the presence of the LORD, ***
　　at the presence of the God of Jacob,

⁸ **who turns the rock into a pool of water, ***
　　the flint into a spring of water.

We worship you, God of freedom and release;
you set us free from every form of slavery,
you quench our thirsty souls.
How can we keep from singing?
Drench your people with your Holy Spirit, so that we may praise you with all joy
through Jesus Christ, our Lord. **Amen.**

Psalm 114 is a psalm of praise that recalls Israel's deliverance from bondage and that depicts creation itself as a celebrant with mountains that "skip like rams" (v. 6). *Use in Worship: on or near Easter ("the Christian Passover") to celebrate God's redemptive work.*

114A When Israel Fled from Egypt Land

1 When Israel fled from Egypt land, from foreign
2 The sea rolled back to form dry land, the Jor-dan
3 What made you part, O might-y sea? Why, Jor-dan,
4 Now trem-ble, earth, the Lord is near; bow down and

tongue and cru - el hand, the LORD took Ju - dah
fled at God's com - mand. The moun - tains shook and
did you turn to flee? Why, moun - tains, shake, why
see your God ap - pear. His might makes springs to

for his home and Is - rael for his ver - y own.
skipped like rams; the hills leapt up like lit - tle lambs.
skip like rams? And hills, why leap like lit - tle lambs?
gush and glow; from flint the cool - ing wa - ters flow.

Words: Henrietta Ten Harmsel, 1985, alt. © 1987 Faith Alive Christian Resources
Music (ANDRE 8.8.8.8): William B. Bradbury (1816-1868), alt., P.D.

When Israel Fled from Egypt Land 114B

1 When Is-rael fled from E-gypt land, from for-eign
2 The sea rolled back to form dry land, the Jor-dan
3 What made you part, O might-y sea? Why, Jor-dan,
4 Now trem-ble, earth, the Lord is near; bow down and

tongue and cru-el hand, the LORD took Ju - dah
fled at God's com - mand. The moun-tains shook and
did you turn to flee? Why, moun-tains, shake, why
see your God ap - pear. His might makes springs to

for his home and Is-rael for his ver-y own.
skipped like rams; the hills leapt up like lit-tle lambs.
skip like rams? And hills, why leap like lit-tle lambs?
gush and glow; from flint the cool-ing wa-ters flow.

Guitar chords do not correspond with keyboard harmony.

Words: Henrietta Ten Harmsel, 1985, © 1987 Faith Alive Christian Resources
Music (O HEILAND, REISS DIE HIMMEL AUF 8.8.8.8): *Gesangbuch*, Augsburg, 1666; harm. Dale Grotenhuis, 1985, © 1987 Faith Alive Christian Resources

114C Psalm 114 | A Responsorial Setting

Refrain

¹ Hallelujah! When Israel came out of Egypt,
   the house of Jacob from a people of strange speech,

² Judah became God's sanctuary
   and Israel God's dominion.

3 The sea beheld it and fled;
    Jordan turned and went back.

4 The mountains skipped like rams,
    and the little hills like young sheep.   *Refrain*

5 What ailed you, O sea, that you fled,
    O Jordan, that you turned back,

6 you mountains, that you skipped like rams,
    you little hills like young sheep?   *Refrain*

7 Tremble, O earth, at the presence of the LORD,
    at the presence of the God of Jacob,

8 who turned the hard rock into a pool of water
    and flint-stone into a flowing spring.   *Refrain*

Tone

Lectionary: Easter Vigil (A,B,C); Eastertide (A,B,C); Ordinary Time after Pentecost (A).

Words and Music: South African © 1984 Peace of Music Publishing AB, admin. Walton Music Corporation
Psalm Text: from *Evangelical Lutheran Worship* © 2006 Evangelical Lutheran Church in America, admin.
Augsburg Fortress Publishers
Tone: © 2011 Faith Alive Christian Resources

Alternate Refrain 1

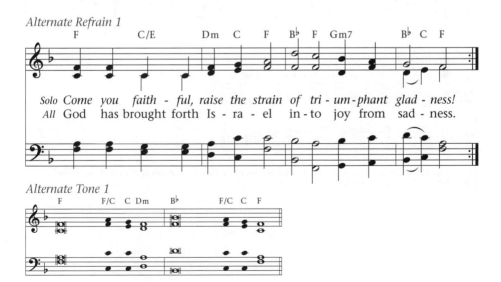

Alternate Tone 1

Words: John of Damascus (ca. 675-749); tr. John Mason Neale, 1859, alt., P.D.
Music (GAUDEAMUS PARITER/AVE VIRGO VIRGINUM fragment): Bohemian Brethren's *Gesangbuch*, 1544, P.D.
Tone: © 2011 Faith Alive Christian Resources

(continues)

Words and Music: Gregg DeMey © 2011 Re:Create Music; arr. Paul Detterman © 2011 Re:Create Music
Tone: © 2011 Faith Alive Christian Resources

1 Not to us, O LORD, not to us, but to your name give glory, *
    for the sake of your steadfast love and your faithfulness.

2 **Why should the nations say, ***
    "Where is their God?"

3 **Our God is in the heavens; ***
    he does whatever he pleases.

4 Their idols are silver and gold, *
    the work of human hands.

5 They have mouths, but do not speak; *
    eyes, but do not see.

6 They have ears, but do not hear; *
    noses, but do not smell.

7 They have hands, but do not feel; feet, but do not walk; *
    they make no sound in their throats.

8 **Those who make them are like them; ***
    so are all who trust in them.

9 O Israel, trust in the LORD! *
    He is their help and their shield.

10 O house of Aaron, trust in the LORD! *
    He is their help and their shield.

11 You who fear the LORD, trust in the LORD! *
    He is their help and their shield.

12 The LORD has been mindful of us; he will bless us; *
    he will bless the house of Israel; he will bless the house of Aaron;

13 **he will bless those who fear the LORD, ***
    both small and great.

14 May the LORD give you increase, *
    both you and your children.

15 May you be blessed by the LORD, *
    who made heaven and earth.

16 **The heavens are the LORD's heavens, ***
    but the earth he has given to human beings.

17 The dead do not praise the LORD, *
    nor do any that go down into silence.

18 **But we will bless the LORD from this time on and forevermore. ***
    Praise the LORD!

(continues)

The dead cannot praise you, O God;
wicked people do not want to praise you,
and careless people neglect to praise you.
Inspire your redeemed and faithful people to turn from all that is false
and to love and serve you alone, shouting "Hallelujah!" now for forever. **Amen.**

Psalm 115 is a psalm of praise that focuses on both the glory of God and the folly of idolatry. Like Ps. 135, which copies a portion of its text, this psalm makes explicit what is implicit in all psalms of praise: to turn toward God is to turn away from idols. Praise is an act of idolatry resistance. With its bitingly ironic depiction of idols as blind, deaf, mute, and inactive, the psalm echoes the taunting words of Isa. 42ff and evokes the memory of Elijah's taunting words to the idolatrous prophets of Baal (1 Kings 18:27). This irony gives way to a timeless proverb: people become like the idols they fashion (v. 8). The second half of the psalm echoes the imagery of the Aaronic benediction (and Ps. 67), describing the lavish blessing of God. *Use in Worship: services where attention is given to the implicit acts of idolatry resistance that every act of praise entails.*

115A A Litany of Praise

We lift our eyes to you and bless your name.

Not to us be praise, nor to the idols of our hearts.

You are the source of our strength.

Not to us be praise, nor to the idols of our hearts.

You are the source of our joy.

Not to us be praise, nor to the idols of our hearts.

You are the source of our hope.

Not to us be praise, nor to the idols of our hearts.

You are the source of peace.

We will bless the Lord from this time on and forevermore. Amen.

All sing a setting of Psalm 115, "Total Praise" (121B), or another psalm or hymn of praise.

Not unto Us, O Lord of Heaven 115B

Unison

1 Not un-to us, O Lord of heaven, but un-to you be
2 The i-dol gods of hea-then lands are but the work of
3 So let us trust in God a-lone, the Lord whose grace and

glo-ry given. In love and truth you do ful-fill
hu-man hands; they can-not see, they can-not speak,
power are known; and our com-plete al-le-giance yield

the coun-sels of your sov-ereign will; though na-tions fail
their ears are deaf, their hands are weak; like them shall be
to God who is our help and shield. Join, heaven and earth,

your power to own, yet you still reign, and you a-lone.
all those who hold to gods of sil-ver and of gold.
in sweet ac-cord; sing "Hal-le-lu-jah, praise the Lord!"

Guitar chords do not correspond with keyboard harmony.

Alternate harmonization on p. 1044.

Alternate tune: MELITA, p. 520.

Words: *Psalter*, 1912, alt., P.D.
Music (VATER UNSER 8.8.8.8.8.8): V. Schumann's *Geistliche Lieder*, 1539; arr. Alfred V. Fedak (b. 1953) © 2011
Faith Alive Christian Resources

115C Not for Ourselves, O Lord

1 Not for our-selves, O Lord, not for our-selves,
2 The world-ly say of us: "Where is their God?"
3 But we will trust in God, our help and shield,

would we claim glo - ry, but for you a - lone,
They vain-ly look for what they i - dol - ize,
tran - scend-ent Life on whom all lives de - pend,

be - cause of your great love and faith - ful - ness,
for flaunt-ed wealth, for burn-ished im - ag - es,
whose un - told mer - cies give our spir - its voice

the stead-fast care that makes your pres - ence known.
and trim all gods to their own shape and size.
to bless the Lord in songs that nev - er end.

Words: Carl P. Daw Jr. (b. 1944) © 1996 Hope Publishing Company
Music (TOULON 10.10.10.10): *Genevan Psalter*, 1551; adapt. from GENEVAN 124

Psalm 116

¹ I love the LORD, *

    because he has heard my voice and my supplications.

² Because he inclined his ear to me, *

    therefore I will call on him as long as I live.

³ The snares of death encompassed me;

  the pangs of Sheol laid hold on me; *

    I suffered distress and anguish.

⁴ **Then I called on the name of the LORD: ***

    "O LORD, I pray, save my life!"

⁵ **Gracious is the LORD, and righteous; ***

    our God is merciful.

⁶ **The LORD protects the simple; ***

    when I was brought low, he saved me.

⁷ **Return, O my soul, to your rest, ***

    for the LORD has dealt bountifully with you.

⁸ **For you have delivered my soul from death, ***

    my eyes from tears, my feet from stumbling.

⁹ I walk before the LORD *

    in the land of the living.

¹⁰ I kept my faith, even when I said, *

    "I am greatly afflicted";

¹¹ I said in my consternation, *

    "Everyone is a liar."

¹² **What shall I return to the LORD ***

    for all his bounty to me?

¹³ **I will lift up the cup of salvation ***

    and call on the name of the LORD,

¹⁴ **I will pay my vows to the LORD ***

    in the presence of all his people.

¹⁵ Precious in the sight of the LORD *

    is the death of his faithful ones.

¹⁶ O LORD, I am your servant; I am your servant, the child of your serving girl. *

    You have loosed my bonds.

¹⁷ **I will offer to you a thanksgiving sacrifice ***

    and call on the name of the LORD.

(continues)

¹⁸ **I will pay my vows to the LORD** ˙ *
   in the presence of all his people,

¹⁹ **in the courts of the house of the LORD, in your midst, Ȯ Jerusalem.** *
   Praise the LORD!

Compassionate God,
you protect us from unseen danger
and catch us when we stumble and fall.
You answer when we call to you in prayer.
Help our worship of you to be sacrificial and our vows to you to be sincere,
serving and rejoicing because of you as long as we live. **Amen.**

Psalm 116, like Ps. 30, is a psalm of thanksgiving for an experience of God's dramatic deliverance, this time
from death (vv. 3, 8). The first major section of the psalm (vv. 1-11) comprises a narrative testimony of
God's deliverance with references to specific prayers that God has answered (vv. 4, 10, 11) and a summary
statement of God's gracious, faithful, and compassionate nature (vv. 5-6). The second half of the psalm is
an act of dedication (vv. 12-19). While the original meaning of the "cup of salvation" (v. 13) is debated by
commentators, the psalm became associated with celebrations of Passover and the Christian Lord's Supper.
*Use in Worship: Maundy Thursday; celebrations of the Lord's Supper; funerals (v. 15); any occasion of experiencing
God's healing or deliverance.*

116A I Love You, LORD, for You Have Heard My Voice

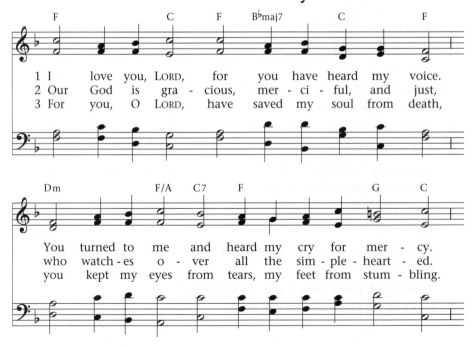

1 I love you, LORD, for you have heard my voice.
2 Our God is gra - cious, mer - ci - ful, and just,
3 For you, O LORD, have saved my soul from death,

You turned to me and heard my cry for mer - cy.
who watch - es o - ver all the sim - ple - heart - ed.
you kept my eyes from tears, my feet from stum - bling.

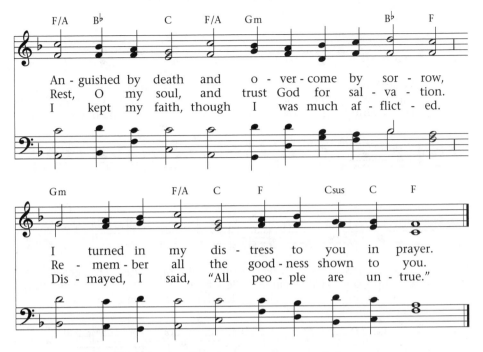

An - guished by death and o - ver - come by sor - row,
Rest, O my soul, and trust God for sal - va - tion.
I kept my faith, though I was much af - flict - ed.

I turned in my dis - tress to you in prayer.
Re - mem - ber all the good - ness shown to you.
Dis - mayed, I said, "All peo - ple are un - true."

4 How can I pay you, LORD, for all your gifts?
   I will lift up the cup of full salvation.
   I will fulfill my vows to you, my Savior.
   With all your saints, I'll call upon your name.

5 Precious to you the dying of your saints.
   I am your faithful servant, freed from bondage.
   I'll pay my vows and, with your people, thank you.
   Come to God's house, O people; praise the LORD!

Words: Helen Otte (b. 1931), 1980, alt. © 1987 Faith Alive Christian Resources
Music (GENEVAN 116 | 10.11.11.10): *Genevan Psalter*, 1562; harm. Seymour Swets, 1954, P.D.

116B What Shall I Render to the LORD

1 What shall I ren - der to the LORD for all his
2 Sal - va - tion's cup of bless - ing now I take and
3 His saints the LORD de - lights to save; their death is

ben - e - fits to me? How shall my life, by grace recall up - on God's name. Be - fore his saints I pay my
pre - cious in his sight. He has re - deemed me from the

stored, give wor - thy thanks, O LORD, to thee?
vow and here my grat - i - tude pro - claim.
grave, and in his ser - vice I de - light.

4 With thankful heart I offer now
my gift and call upon God's name.
Before his saints I pay my vow
and here my gratitude proclaim.

5 Within his house, the house of prayer,
I dedicate myself to God.
Let all his saints his grace declare
and join to sound his praise abroad.

Guitar chords do not correspond with keyboard harmony.

Words: *Psalter*, 1912, P.D.
Music (ROCKINGHAM 8.8.8.8): *Second Supplement to Psalmody in Miniature*, ca. 1780; adapt. Edward Miller (1731-1807), 1790, P.D.

I Love the Lord; He Heard My Cry 116C

1 I love the Lord; he heard my cry
2 I love the Lord; he heard my cry

and pit - ied ev - ery groan.
and chased my grief a - way.

Long as I live and trou-bles rise,
O let my heart no more des - pair

I'll has - ten to his throne.
while I have breath to pray.

Words: Isaac Watts (1674-1748), P.D.
Music: Afro-American spiritual; harm. Richard Smallwood (b. 1948) © 1975, 2003 Century Oak Publishing Group/Richwood Music, admin. Conexion Media Group, Inc.; arr. Dave Maddux

116D Psalm 116: 1-9, 12-19
A Responsorial Setting

Refrain

I love the Lord, who heard my cry.

Refrain

¹ I love the LORD, who has heard my voice,
    and listened to my supplication,

² for the LORD has given ear to me
    whenever I called.

³ The cords of death entangled me; the anguish of the grave came upon me;
    I came to grief and sorrow.

⁴ Then I called upon the name of the LORD:
    "O LORD, I pray you, save my life."   *Refrain*

⁵ Gracious is the LORD and righteous;
    our God is full of compassion.

⁶ The LORD watches over the innocent;
    I was brought low, and God saved me.

⁷ Turn again to your rest, O my soul,
    for the LORD has dealt well with you.

⁸ For you have rescued my life from death,
    my eyes from tears, and my feet from stumbling.

⁹ I will walk in the presence of the LORD
    in the land of the living.   *Refrain*

¹² How shall I repay the LORD
    for all the good things God has done for me?

¹³ I will lift the cup of salvation
    and call on the name of the LORD.

¹⁴ I will fulfill my vows to the LORD
    in the presence of all God's people.   *Refrain*

¹⁵ Precious in your sight, O LORD,
    is the death of your servants.

¹⁶ O LORD, truly I am your servant;
    I am your servant, the child of your handmaid;
    you have freed me from my bonds.

¹⁷ I will offer you the sacrifice of thanksgiving

and call upon the name of the L<small>ORD</small>.

¹⁸ I will fulfill my vows to the L<small>ORD</small>

in the presence of all God's people,

¹⁹ in the courts of the L<small>ORD</small>'s house,

in the midst of you, O Jerusalem. Hallelujah! *Refrain*

Tone

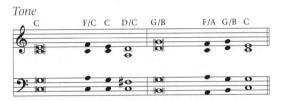

Lectionary: vv. 1-2, 12-19 Maundy Thursday (A,B,C) and Ordinary Time after Pentecost (A); vv. 1-4, 12-19 Eastertide (A); vv. 1-9 Ordinary Time after Pentecost (B).

Words: Isaac Watts (1674-1748), P.D.
Music: Afro-American spiritual; harm. Richard Smallwood (b. 1948) © 1975 Century Oak Publishing Group/Richwood Music, admin. Conexion Media Group, Inc.; arr. Dave Maddux
Psalm Text: from *Evangelical Lutheran Worship* © 2006 Evangelical Lutheran Church in America, admin. Augsburg Fortress Publishers
Tone: © 2011 Faith Alive Christian Resources

Words: Noel Donnelly © 1991 Noel Donnelly
Music (SCOTLAND fragment): Noel Donnelly © 1991 Noel Donnelly
Tone: © 2011 Faith Alive Christian Resources

116E I Will Walk in the Presence of God

Words: Noel Donnelly © 1991 Noel Donnelly
Music (SCOTLAND 9.8.8.9 with refrain): Noel Donnelly © 1991 Noel Donnelly

Psalm 117

1 Praise the LORD, all you nations! *

   Extol him, all you peoples!

2 For great is his steadfast love toward us,

   and the faithfulness of the LORD endures forever. *

   Praise the LORD!

God of all,
you have revealed your love to all the world through Jesus Christ your Son.
Gather all peoples to yourself so that in every tongue
one mighty hymn may rise to the glory of your holy name. **Amen.**

Psalm 117 is a call to praise with a universal scope; it calls all people to praise God. At the center of the psalm
are two of the most lovely and weighty images in the entire Psalter: God's covenantal love (*hesed*) and God's
truthfulness (*'emet*). Thus, while the psalm is short, it is also full of splendor. *Use in Worship: a call to worship
for any occasion.*

Bān-bîn ah / Let All Nations   117A

Words: Psalm 117, tr. Hsiang-chi Chang and I-to Loh (b. 1936), alt. © 1990 Christian Conference of Asia,
admin. GIA Publications, Inc.
Music (O-LÓ 7.7.7.7): Hsiang-chi Chang and I-to Loh (b. 1936) © 1990, 2000 and arr. I-to Loh (b. 1936) ©
2011 Christian Conference of Asia, admin. GIA Publications, Inc.

117B Laudate Dominum / Sing, Praise, and Bless the Lord

Ostinato Refrain

Latin Lau - da - te Do - mi - num, lau - da - te Do - mi - num

English Sing, praise, and bless the Lord. Sing, praise, and bless the Lord,

om - nes, gen - tes! al - le - lu - ia! al - le - lu - ia!

peo - ples! na - tions! Al - le - lu - ia! Al - le - lu - ia!

Solo Voice (sung over Ostinato Refrain)

Praise the Lord, all you na - tions; praise God all you peo - ples.

Al - le - lu - ia. Strong is God's love and mer - cy,

al - ways faith - ful for - ev - er. Al - le - lu - ia.

Al - le - lu - ia, al - le - lu - ia. Let ev - ery - thing

liv - ing give praise to the Lord. Al - le - praise to the Lord.

From All That Dwell Below the Skies 117C

1 From all that dwell be-low the skies let the Cre-a-tor's praise a-
2 In ev-ery land be-gin the song, to ev-ery land the strains be-
3 E-ter-nal are thy mer-cies, Lord; e-ter-nal truth at-tends thy

rise: Al-le-lu-ia! Al-le-lu-ia! Let the Re-deem-er's
long: Al-le-lu-ia! Al-le-lu-ia! In cheer-ful sound all
word: Al-le-lu-ia! Al-le-lu-ia! Thy praise shall sound from

name be sung through ev-ery land, in ev-ery tongue.
voic-es raise and fill the world with joy-ful praise. Al-le-lu-ia!
shore to shore, till suns shall rise and set no more.

Al-le-lu-ia! Al-le-lu-ia! Al-le-lu-ia! Al-le-lu-ia!

Guitar chords do not correspond with keyboard harmony.

Words: Isaac Watts (1674-1748), 1719, P.D.
Music (LASST UNS ERFREUEN 8.8.8.8 with alleluias): *Auserlesen Catholische Geistliche Kirchengesänge*, Cologne, 1623; adapt. and harm. Ralph Vaughan Williams (1872-1958), 1906, P.D.

117D Alabad al Señor / Praise the Lord!

Spanish A - la - bad al Se - ñor, na - cio - nes to - das; pue - blos
English Praise the Lord, praise the Lord! All tribes and na - tions, all you

to - dos, a - la - bad - le; por - que ha en - gran - de - ci - do so -
peo - ples join in prais - ing. For how great the lov - ing - kind - ness that

bre no - so - tros su mi - se - ri - cor - dia. La bon - dad del Se -
God in mer - cy show - ers down up - on us. And the grace of the

ñor es pa - ra siem - pre. ¡A - le - lu - ya, a - mén! La bon -
Lord en - dures for - ev - er. Al - le - lu - ia, a - men! Yes, the

dad del Se - ñor es pa - ra siem - pre. ¡A - le - lu - ya, a - mén!
grace of the Lord en - dures for - ev - er. Al - le - lu - ia, a - men!

Words: Psalm 117; tr. Mary Louise Bringle (b. 1953), 2011, © 2011 GIA Publications, Inc.
Music: traditional; arr. Marcus Hong © 2011 Faith Alive Christian Resources

Hallelujah, Hallelujah

Hal-le-lu-jah, hal-le-lu-jah; all you peo-ples, praise pro-claim. For God's grace and lov-ing-kind-ness O sing prais-es to his name. For the great-ness of God's mer-cy con-stant praise to him ac-cord. For God's faith-ful-ness e-ter-nal, hal-le-lu-jah, praise the LORD!

Guitar chords do not correspond with keyboard harmony.

Words: *Psalter*, 1887, alt., P.D.
Music (IN BABILONE 8.7.8.7 D): *Oude en Nieuwe Hollantse Boerenlities en Contradansen*, 1710, P.D.

O Praise the Lord Our God

O praise the Lord our God you na-tions; glo-ri-fy his ho-ly name heav-en and earth! For his lov-ing kind-ness is great u-pon us, and the truth of God for-ev-er shall reign.

O praise the Lord our God all you na-tions; glo-ri-fy his name all heaven and earth! For his lov-ing kind-ness is great toward us!

O praise the Lord our God; glo-ri-fy his name. For his lov-ing kind-ness is great toward us!

Al - le-lu - ia, al - le-lu - ia, al - le-lu - ia, al - le-lu - ia,
Al - le - lu - ia, al - le - lu - ia, al - le - lu - ia, al - le-lu - ia,

Al - le - lu - ia, al - le - lu - ia,

al - le-lu - ia, al - le-lu - ia, al - le-lu - ia.
al - le - lu - ia, al - le-lu - ia, al - le - lu - ia.

al - le - lu - ia, al - le - lu - ia.

Sing the first page four times. Begin with the lowest part alone, adding the middle part the second time, and then all parts together twice. After this, sing the Alleluias, repeating as desired.

Words and Music: Konstantin Zhigulin © 2011 Konstantin Zhigulin

Psalm 118

1 O give thanks to the LORD, for he is good; *
   his steadfast love endures forever!
2 Let Israel say, *
   "His steadfast love endures forever."
3 Let the house of Aaron say, *
   "His steadfast love endures forever."
4 Let those who fear the LORD say, *
   "His steadfast love endures forever."
5 Out of my distress I called on the LORD; *
   the LORD answered me and set me in a broad place.
6 **With the LORD on my side I do not fear. ***
   What can mortals do to me?
7 The LORD is on my side to help me; *
   I shall look in triumph on those who hate me.
8 **It is better to take refuge in the LORD ***
   than to put confidence in mortals.
9 **It is better to take refuge in the LORD ***
   than to put confidence in princes.
10 All nations surrounded me; *
   in the name of the LORD I cut them off!
11 They surrounded me, surrounded me on every side; *
   in the name of the LORD I cut them off!
12 They surrounded me like bees; they blazed like a fire of thorns; *
   in the name of the LORD I cut them off!
13 **I was pushed hard, so that I was falling, ***
   but the LORD helped me.
14 **The LORD is my strength and my might; ***
   he has become my salvation.
15 There are glad songs of victory in the tents of the righteous: *
   "The right hand of the LORD does valiantly;
16 the right hand of the LORD is exalted; *
   the right hand of the LORD does valiantly."
17 **I shall not die, but I shall live, ***
   and recount the deeds of the LORD.
18 The LORD has punished me severely, *
   but he did not give me over to death.
19 **Open to me the gates of righteousness, ***
   that I may enter through them and give thanks to the LORD.

²⁰ **This is the gate of the Lord;** *
> **the righteous shall enter through it.**

²¹ **I thank you that you have answered me** *
> **and have become my salvation.**

²² The stone that the builders rejected *
> has become the chief cornerstone.

²³ **This is the Lord's doing;** *
> **it is marvelous in our eyes.**

²⁴ **This is the day that the Lord has made;** *
> **let us rejoice and be glad in it.**

²⁵ Save us, we beseech you, O Lord! *
> O Lord, we beseech you, give us success!

²⁶ **Blessed is the one who comes in the name of the Lord.** *
> **We bless you from the house of the Lord.**

²⁷ **The Lord is God, and he has given us light.** *
> **Bind the festal procession with branches,**
> **up to the horns of the altar.**

²⁸ **You are my God, and I will give thanks to you;** *
> **you are my God, I will extol you.**

²⁹ **O give thanks to the Lord, for he is good,** *
> **for his steadfast love endures forever.**

Lord Jesus Christ, you are the foundation of our life and faith.
Even when the world rejects you, we sing your praise.
Help us to love and serve others even when they reject us and you.
In your name there is healing, in your death there is life,
in your resurrection there is hope, and at your return every knee will bow.
Lord Jesus, come quickly. **Amen.**

Psalm 118 is a psalm of thanksgiving that features two primary emphases: a grand testimony regarding the deliverance of God (vv. 5-7, 10-18, 22-23) and a strong vow to praise and confess God in worship (vv. 19-21, 24, 26-29). An unusually complex psalm, these emphases are complemented by exhortations to worship God (vv. 1-4) and to trust God (vv. 8-9) and a short prayer for God's continued deliverance (v. 25). It describes the work of God in terms of deliverance (v. 14), discipline (v. 18), and enlightenment (v. 27). The psalm offers a vivid imagery of salvation as the move from claustrophobic constraint (v. 5), made maddening by an enemy that felt like "buzzing bees" (vv. 5, 12) to a place of spaciousness (v. 5) marked by the joyful praise of God's people (v. 15). This psalm is quoted several times in the NT. *Use in Worship: call to worship (v. 24); Palm Sunday worship (v. 26); liturgies for the Lord's Supper (v. 26); during Christmas and Easter (vv. 22-23); Easter worship (a form of use that can only be enriched by attention to the entire psalm).*

118A The Glorious Gates of Righteousness

1 The glo-rious gates of right-eous-ness throw
2 This is your tem-ple gate, O LORD: the
3 The stone re-ject-ed and de-spised is

o-pen un-to me, and I will come to
just shall en-ter there. My Sav-ior, I will
now the cor-ner-stone. How won-drous are the

them with praise and en-ter thank-ful-ly; and I will
give you thanks, for you have heard my prayer; my Sav-ior,
ways of God, un-fath-omed and un-known; how won-drous

come to them with praise and en-ter thank-ful-ly.
I will give you thanks, for you have heard my prayer.
are the ways of God, un-fath-omed and un-known.

4 Hosanna! Ever blest is he who comes in God's own name.
The blessing of God's holy house upon you we proclaim. *(2x)*

5 O praise the LORD, for he is good; let all in heaven above
and all his saints on earth proclaim his everlasting love. *(2x)*

Words: *Psalter*, 1912, alt., P.D.
Music (ZERAH 8.6.8.6 with repeat): Lowell Mason (1792-1872), 1837, P.D.

Psalm 118:19-29 | A Responsorial Setting   **118B**

Refrain

Hail and Ho-san-na! Blest is he who comes in God's own name to make our world God's home!

Refrain

¹⁹ Open for me the gates of the righteous; *
     I will enter and give thanks to the LORD.

²⁰ **This is the gate of the LORD ***
     through which the righteous may enter.

²¹ I will give you thanks, for you answered me; *
     you have become my salvation.   *Refrain*

²² The stone the builders rejected *
     has become the cornerstone;

²³ the LORD has done this, *
     and it is marvelous in our eyes.

²⁴ **The LORD has done it this very day; ***
     let us rejoice today and be glad.

²⁵ LORD, save us! *
     LORD, grant us success!

²⁶ Blessed is he who comes in the name of the LORD. *
     From the house of the LORD we bless you.   *Refrain*

²⁷ The LORD is God, and he has made his light shine on us. *
     With boughs in hand,
     join in the festal procession up to the horns of the altar.

²⁸ **You are my God, and I will praise you; ***
     you are my God, and I will exalt you.

²⁹ Give thanks to the LORD, for he is good; *
     his love endures forever.   *Refrain*

                                                     (continues)

Tone

Accompaniment pattern for singing in canon; may be played by handbells or on keyboard.

118C Psallite Deo / This Is the Day

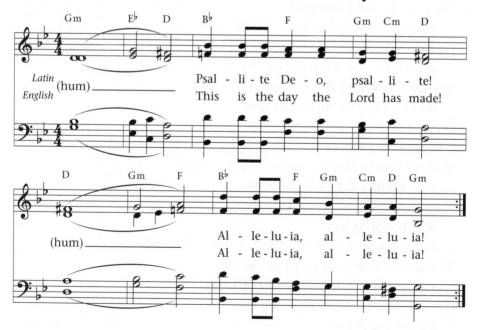

Latin (hum) _____ Psal - li - te De - o, psal - li - te!
English This is the day the Lord has made!

(hum) _____ Al - le - lu - ia, al - le - lu - ia!
Al - le - lu - ia, al - le - lu - ia!

Psallite Deo means 'sing a psalm to the Lord.'

Solo voice sings verses while the congregation hums. Where the solo voice music divides, either part may be sung.

Words: Psalm 118, alt.
Music: Jacques Berthier (1923-1994) © 1982, 1998 Ateliers et Presses de Taizé, Taizé Community, France, GIA Publications, Inc., exclusive North American agent

118D This Is the Day the Lord Has Made

1 This is the day the Lord has made; in it will
2 God is my ref - uge and my strength, my might, my
3 O - pen the gates of right - eous - ness, Lord, let me
4 See now the won - der God has done: the once - re -

we re - joice, prais - ing God's ev - er -
joy, my song, my shield, sal - va - tion,
en - ter there, that I may lift my
ject - ed stone has now be - come the

last - ing love with heart and mind and voice.
sure de - fense through - out my whole life long.
thanks to you in hymn and song and prayer.
cor - ner - stone, the Lord's own Cho - sen One.

5 Blest is the One who comes to us
   in God our maker's name,
   bringing to us God's life and light,
   to every age the same.

6 This is the day the Lord has made;
   in it will we rejoice,
   praising God's everlasting love
   with heart and mind and voice.

Words: Joy F. Patterson (b. 1931) © 1993 Hope Publishing Company
Music (THIS IS THE DAY 8.6.8.6): Joy F. Patterson (b. 1931) © 1993 Hope Publishing Company

This Is the Day the Lord Hath Made 118E

1 This is the day the Lord hath made, the hours are
2 Ho - san - na to the a - noint - ed King, to Da - vid's
3 Blest be the Lord, who comes in power with mes - sag -
4 Ho - san - na in the high - est strains the church on

all God's own; let heaven re - joice, let
ho - ly Son! Help us, O Lord; de -
es of grace, who comes in this ac -
earth can raise! The high - est heavens in

earth be glad, and praise sur - round the throne.
scend and bring sal - va - tion from the throne.
cept - ed hour to save our sin - ful race.
which God reigns shall now re - sound with praise.

Words: Isaac Watts (1674-1748), 1719, alt., P.D.
Music (NUN DANKET ALL' UND BRINGET EHR' 8.6.8.6): Johann Crüger (1598-1662), 1647, P.D.

Psalm 118:14-15 may be read before the singing of each stanza.

The LORD is my strength and my defense; he has become my salvation.
Shouts of joy and victory resound in the tents of the righteous:
"The LORD's right hand has done mighty things!"

1 The right hand of God is writ-ing in our land,
2 The right hand of God is point-ing in our land,
3 The right hand of God is strik-ing in our land,
4 The right hand of God is heal-ing in our land,

writ - ing with pow - er and with love,
point - ing the way we must go,
strik-ing out at en - vy, hate, and greed.
heal-ing bro - ken bod - ies, minds, and souls,

our con - flicts and our fears, our tri-umphs and our tears
so cloud-ed is the way, so eas - i - ly we stray,
Our self - ish - ness and lust, our pride and deeds un - just,
so won-drous is its touch with love that means so much,

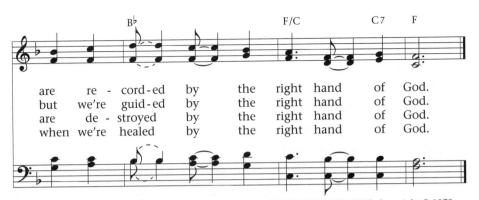

are re - cord-ed by the right hand of God.
but we're guid-ed by the right hand of God.
are de - stroyed by the right hand of God.
when we're healed by the right hand of God.

Psalm 118:1-2, 14-29 **118G**
A Responsorial Setting

Refrain

This is the day the Lord has made;

let us re - joice and be glad.

(continues)

Refrain

¹ Give thanks to the LORD, for the LORD is good;
    God's mercy endures forever.

² Let Israel now declare,
    "God's mercy endures forever."

¹⁴ The LORD is my strength and my song,
    and has become my salvation.

¹⁵ Shouts of rejoicing and salvation echo in the tents of the righteous:
    "The right hand of the LORD acts valiantly!

¹⁶ The right hand of the LORD is exalted!
    The right hand of the LORD acts valiantly!"

¹⁷ I shall not die, but live,
    and declare the works of the LORD.   *Refrain*

¹⁸ The LORD indeed punished me sorely,
    but did not hand me over to death.

¹⁹ Open for me the gates of righteousness:
    I will enter them and give thanks to the LORD.

²⁰ "This is the gate of the LORD;
    here the righteous may enter."

²¹ I give thanks to you, for you have answered me
    and you have become my salvation.   *Refrain*

²² The stone that the builders rejected
    has become the chief cornerstone.

²³ By the LORD has this been done;
    it is marvelous in our eyes.

²⁴ This is the day that the LORD has made;
    let us rejoice and be glad in it.   *Refrain*

²⁵ Hosanna! O LORD, save us!
    We pray to you, LORD, prosper our days!

²⁶ Blessed is the one who comes in the name of the LORD;
    we bless you from the house of the LORD.

²⁷ The LORD is God and has given us light.
    Form a procession with branches up to the corners of the altar.

²⁸ You are my God, and I will thank you;
    you are my God, and I will exalt you.

²⁹ Give thanks to the LORD, for the LORD is good;
    God's mercy endures forever.   *Refrain*

Tone

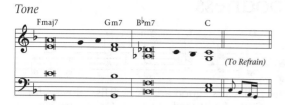

Lectionary: vv. 1-2, 14-24 Resurrection of the Lord (A,B,C); vv. 1-2, 19-29 Lent (Liturgy of the Palms) (A,B,C); vv. 14-29 Eastertide (C).

Words: Psalm 118:24
Music: Leon C. Roberts © 1987 Leon C. Roberts
Psalm Text: from *Evangelical Lutheran Worship* © 2006 Evangelical Lutheran Church in America, admin. Augsburg Fortress Publishers
Tone: © 2011 Faith Alive Christian Resources

Alternate Refrain

Alternate Tone

Music: Fintan O'Carroll (1922-1981) and Christopher Walker (b. 1947) © 1985 Fintan O'Carroll and Christopher Walker, admin. OCP Publications
Tone: © 2011 Faith Alive Christian Resources

Give Thanks to God
for All His Goodness

1 Give thanks to God for all his good-ness: "His love for-
2 Brought low, I cried to God; he heard me. He an-swered
3 Hark! right-eous and vic-to-rious sing-ing: "The LORD's right

ev - er is the same." Give thanks to God, O ho - ly
me and set me free. The LORD with me, no one can
hand does val - iant - ly." For life re-stored my prais-es

na - tion: "His love for - ev - er is the same."
hurt me. He is my strength, my vic - to - ry.
bring - ing: "The LORD's right hand does val - iant - ly."

Give thanks to God, O ho - ly priest - hood: "His love for-
Put not your con - fi - dence in princ - es. When en - e -
When gates of right-eous - ness stand o - pen, I en - ter

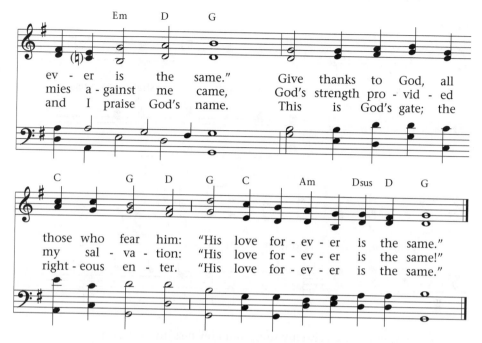

ev - er is the same." Give thanks to God, all
mies a - gainst me came, God's strength pro - vid - ed
and I praise God's name. This is God's gate; the

those who fear him: "His love for - ev - er is the same."
my sal - va - tion: "His love for - ev - er is the same!"
right - eous en - ter. "His love for - ev - er is the same."

4 The stone the builders had rejected
   is now the foremost cornerstone.
   The LORD has done it, we have seen it—
   his ways confound what we had known.
   This is the day of days: God made it!
   And we are glad, we praise his name:
   "Save us and let us know your blessing.
   Your love forever is the same."

5 Our voices join in glad confession:
   "God's love forever is the same."
   Blest is the one in our procession
   who comes triumphant in God's name.
   Let branches mark the festal highway.
   Bring to the altar glad acclaim:
   "You are my God and I will praise you:
   Your love forever is the same!"

Guitar chords do not correspond with keyboard harmony.

Alternate harmonization on p. 616.

Words: Stanley Wiersma (1930-1986), 1982, alt. © 1987 Faith Alive Christian Resources
Music (RENDEZ À DIEU/GENEVAN 98/118 | 9.8.9.8 D): *Genevan Psalter*, 1551; harm. Claude Goudimel
(ca. 1505-1572), 1564, P.D.

Psalm 118:14-24
A Paraphrase for Easter

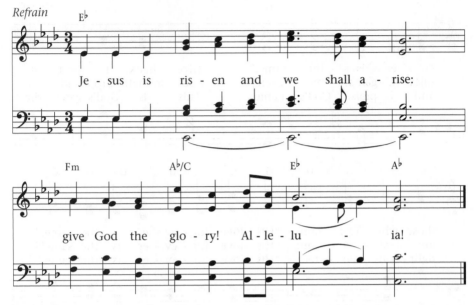

Refrain

Je-sus is ris-en and we shall a-rise:
give God the glo-ry! Al-le-lu-ia!

Refrain

GOD's my strength, he's also my song, and now he's my salvation.
Hear the shouts, hear the triumph songs in the camp of the saved?

"The hand of GOD has turned the tide!
The hand of GOD is raised in victory!
The hand of GOD has turned the tide!" *Refrain*

I didn't die. I lived! And now I'm telling the world what GOD did.
GOD tested me, he pushed me hard, but didn't hand me over to Death.

Swing wide the city gates—the righteous gates!
    I'll walk right through and thank GOD!
This Temple Gate belongs to GOD,
    so the victors can enter and praise. *Refrain*

Thank you for responding to me; you've truly become my salvation!
The stone the masons discarded as flawed is now the capstone!

This is GOD's work.
    We rub our eyes—we can hardly believe it!
This is the very day GOD acted—
    let's celebrate and be festive! *Refrain*

Guitar chords do not correspond with keyboard harmony.

Surrexit Christus / The Lord Is Risen 118J

Solo voice sings verses while the congregation hums. Where the solo voice music divides, either part may be sung.

Words: Psalm 118, alt.
Music: Jacques Berthier (1923-1994) © 1982, 1998 Ateliers et Presses de Taizé, Taizé Community, France,
GIA Publications, Inc., exclusive North American agent

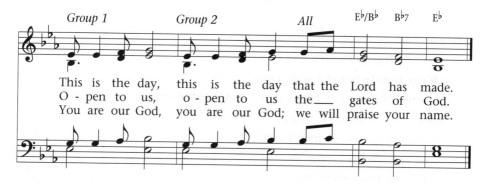

Words: Psalm 118:19, 24, 28
Music (THIS IS THE DAY): Fijian folk melody; Les Garrett, 1967, © 1967, 1980 Universal Music—
Brentwood-Benson Songs, admin. Music Services

Psalm 119

Alef א

1 Happy are those whose way is blameless, *
    who walk in the law of the LORD.

2 Happy are those who keep his decrees,*
    who seek him with their whole heart,

3 who also do no wrong, *
    but walk in his ways.

4 You have commanded your precepts *
    to be kept diligently.

5 O that my ways may be steadfast *
    in keeping your statutes!

6 Then I shall not be put to shame, *
    having my eyes fixed on all your commandments.

7 I will praise you with an upright heart, *
    when I learn your righteous ordinances.

8 I will observe your statutes; *
    do not utterly forsake me.

(continues)

Bet ב

9 How can young people keep their way pure? *
    By guarding it according to your word.

10 With my whole heart I seek you; *
    do not let me stray from your commandments.

11 I treasure your word in my heart, *
    so that I may not sin against you.

12 Blessed are you, O Lord; *
    teach me your statutes.

13 With my lips I declare *
    all the ordinances of your mouth.

14 I delight in the way of your decrees *
    as much as in all riches.

15 I will meditate on your precepts, *
    and fix my eyes on your ways.

16 I will delight in your statutes; *
    I will not forget your word.

Gimel ג

17 Deal bountifully with your servant, *
    so that I may live and observe your word.

18 Open my eyes, so that I may behold *
    wondrous things out of your law.

19 I live as an alien in the land; *
    do not hide your commandments from me.

20 My soul is consumed with longing *
    for your ordinances at all times.

21 You rebuke the insolent, accursed ones, *
    who wander from your commandments;

22 take away from me their scorn and contempt, *
    for I have kept your decrees.

23 Even though princes sit plotting against me, *
    your servant will meditate on your statutes.

24 Your decrees are my delight, *
    they are my counselors.

Dalet ד

25 My soul clings to the dust; *

    revive me according to your word.

26 **When I told of my ways, you answered me; ***

    teach me your statutes.

27 **Make me understand the way of your precepts, ***

    and I will meditate on your wondrous works.

28 My soul melts away for sorrow; *

    strengthen me according to your word.

29 Put false ways far from me; *

    and graciously teach me your law.

30 **I have chosen the way of faithfulness; ***

    I set your ordinances before me.

31 **I cling to your decrees, O LORD; ***

    let me not be put to shame.

32 **I run the way of your commandments, ***

    for you enlarge my understanding.

He ה

33 Teach me, O LORD, the way of your statutes, *

    and I will observe it to the end.

34 **Give me understanding, that I may keep your law ***

    and observe it with my whole heart.

35 Lead me in the path of your commandments, *

    for I delight in it.

36 **Turn my heart to your decrees, ***

    and not to selfish gain.

37 Turn my eyes from looking at vanities; *

    give me life in your ways.

38 **Confirm to your servant your promise, ***

    which is for those who fear you.

39 Turn away the disgrace that I dread, *

    for your ordinances are good.

40 **See, I have longed for your precepts; ***

    in your righteousness give me life.

(continues)

Vav ו

⁴¹ Let your steadfast love come to me, O LORD, *
　　your salvation according to your promise.

⁴² Then I shall have an answer for those who taunt me, *
　　for I trust in your word.

⁴³ **Do not take the word of truth utterly out of my mouth,** *
　　for my hope is in your ordinances.

⁴⁴ **I will keep your law continually,** *
　　forever and ever.

⁴⁵ I shall walk at liberty, *
　　for I have sought your precepts.

⁴⁶ I will also speak of your decrees before kings, *
　　and shall not be put to shame;

⁴⁷ **I find my delight in your commandments,** *
　　because I love them.

⁴⁸ **I revere your commandments, which I love,** *
　　and I will meditate on your statutes.

Zayin ז

⁴⁹ Remember your word to your servant, *
　　in which you have made me hope.

⁵⁰ **This is my comfort in my distress,** *
　　that your promise gives me life.

⁵¹ The arrogant utterly deride me, *
　　but I do not turn away from your law.

⁵² **When I think of your ordinances from of old,** *
　　I take comfort, O LORD.

⁵³ Hot indignation seizes me because of the wicked, *
　　those who forsake your law.

⁵⁴ **Your statutes have been my songs** *
　　wherever I make my home.

⁵⁵ I remember your name in the night, O LORD, *
　　and keep your law.

⁵⁶ **This blessing has fallen to me,** *
　　for I have kept your precepts.

Het ח

⁵⁷ The LORD is my portion; *
　I promise to keep your words.

⁵⁸ **I implore your favor with all my heart; ***
　be gracious to me according to your promise.

⁵⁹ When I think of your ways, *
　I turn my feet to your decrees;

⁶⁰ **I hurry and do not delay ***
　to keep your commandments.

⁶¹ Though the cords of the wicked ensnare me, *
　I do not forget your law.

⁶² **At midnight I rise to praise you, ***
　because of your righteous ordinances.

⁶³ I am a companion of all who fear you, *
　of those who keep your precepts.

⁶⁴ **The earth, O LORD, is full of your steadfast love; ***
　teach me your statutes.

Tet ט

⁶⁵ You have dealt well with your servant, *
　O LORD, according to your word.

⁶⁶ Teach me good judgment and knowledge, *
　for I believe in your commandments.

⁶⁷ **Before I was humbled I went astray, ***
　but now I keep your word.

⁶⁸ **You are good and do good; ***
　teach me your statutes.

⁶⁹ The arrogant smear me with lies, *
　but with my whole heart I keep your precepts.

⁷⁰ Their hearts are fat and gross, *
　but I delight in your law.

⁷¹ **It is good for me that I was humbled, ***
　so that I might learn your statutes.

⁷² **The law of your mouth is better to me ***
　than thousands of gold and silver pieces.

(continues)

Yod　　י

73 Your hands have made and fashioned me; *
　　give me understanding that I may learn your commandments.

74 Those who fear you shall see me and rejoice, *
　　because I have hoped in your word.

75 I know, O LORD, that your judgments are right, *
　　and that in faithfulness you have humbled me.

76 Let your steadfast love become my comfort *
　　according to your promise to your servant.

77 Let your mercy come to me, that I may live; *
　　for your law is my delight.

78 Let the arrogant be put to shame, because they have
　　subverted me with guile; *
　　as for me, I will meditate on your precepts.

79 Let those who fear you turn to me, *
　　so that they may know your decrees.

80 May my heart be blameless in your statutes, *
　　so that I may not be put to shame.

Kaf　　כ

81 My soul languishes for your salvation; *
　　I hope in your word.

82 My eyes fail with watching for your promise; *
　　I ask, "When will you comfort me?"

83 For I have become like a wineskin in the smoke, *
　　yet I have not forgotten your statutes.

84 How long must your servant endure? *
　　When will you judge those who persecute me?

85 The arrogant have dug pitfalls for me; *
　　they flout your law.

86 All your commandments are enduring; *
　　I am persecuted without cause; help me!

87 They have almost made an end of me on earth; *
　　but I have not forsaken your precepts.

88 In your steadfast love spare my life, *
　　so that I may keep the decrees of your mouth.

Lamed ל

89 The LORD exists forever; *
>   your word is firmly fixed in heaven.

90 **Your faithfulness endures to all generations; ***
>   **you have established the earth, and it stands fast.**

91 By your appointment they stand today, *
>   for all things are your servants.

92 **If your law had not been my delight, ***
>   **I would have perished in my misery.**

93 **I will never forget your precepts, ***
>   **for by them you have given me life.**

94 **I am yours; save me, ***
>   **for I have sought your precepts.**

95 The wicked lie in wait to destroy me, *
>   but I consider your decrees.

96 **I have seen a limit to all perfection, ***
>   **but your commandment is exceedingly broad.**

Mem מ

97 Oh, how I love your law! *
>   It is my meditation all day long.

98 Your commandment makes me wiser than my enemies, *
>   for it is always with me.

99 **I have more understanding than all my teachers, ***
>   **for your decrees are my meditation.**

100 **I understand more than the aged, ***
>   **for I keep your precepts.**

101 I hold back my feet from every evil way, *
>   in order to keep your word.

102 I do not turn away from your ordinances, *
>   for you have taught me.

103 **How sweet are your words to my taste, ***
>   **sweeter than honey to my mouth!**

104 **Through your precepts I get understanding; ***
>   **therefore I hate every false way.**

(continues)

Nun נ

105 Your word is a lamp to my feet *
　　and a light to my path.

106 I have sworn an oath and confirmed it, *
　　to observe your righteous ordinances.

107 **I am severely afflicted; ***
　　give me life, O LORD, according to your word.

108 **Accept my offerings of praise, O LORD, ***
　　and teach me your ordinances.

109 I hold my life in my hand continually, *
　　but I do not forget your law.

110 The wicked have laid a snare for me, *
　　but I do not stray from your precepts.

111 **Your decrees are my heritage forever; ***
　　they are the joy of my heart.

112 **I incline my heart to perform your statutes ***
　　forever, to the end.

Samech ס

113 I hate the double-minded, *
　　but I love your law.

114 **You are my hiding place and my shield; ***
　　I hope in your word.

115 Go away from me, you evildoers, *
　　that I may keep the commandments of my God.

116 **Uphold me according to your promise, that I may live, ***
　　and let me not be put to shame in my hope.

117 **Hold me up, that I may be safe ***
　　and have regard for your statutes continually.

118 You spurn all who go astray from your statutes; *
　　for their cunning is in vain.

119 All the wicked of the earth you count as dross; *
　　therefore I love your decrees.

120 **My flesh trembles for fear of you, ***
　　and I am afraid of your judgments.

Ayin ע

121 I have done what is just and right; *
    do not leave me to my oppressors.

122 Guarantee your servant's well-being; *
    do not let the godless oppress me.

123 **My eyes fail from watching for your salvation,** *
    and for the fulfillment of your righteous promise.

124 **Deal with your servant according to your steadfast love,** *
    and teach me your statutes.

125 I am your servant; give me understanding, *
    so that I may know your decrees.

126 It is time for the LORD to act, *
    for your law has been broken.

127 **Truly I love your commandments** *
    more than gold, more than fine gold.

128 **Truly I direct my steps by all your precepts;** *
    I hate every false way.

Pe פ

129 Your decrees are wonderful; *
    therefore my soul keeps them.

130 The unfolding of your words gives light; *
    it imparts understanding to the simple.

131 **With open mouth I pant,** *
    because I long for your commandments.

132 **Turn to me and be gracious to me,** *
    as is your custom toward those who love your name.

133 Keep my steps steady according to your promise, *
    and never let iniquity have dominion over me.

134 Redeem me from human oppression, *
    that I may keep your precepts.

135 **Make your face shine upon your servant,** *
    and teach me your statutes.

136 **My eyes shed streams of tears** *
    because your law is not kept.

(continues)

Tsade צ

137 You are righteous, O LORD, *
    and your judgments are right.

138 You have appointed your decrees in righteousness *
    and in all faithfulness.

139 My zeal consumes me *
    because my foes forget your words.

140 Your promise is well tried, *
    and your servant loves it.

141 I am small and despised, *
    yet I do not forget your precepts.

142 Your righteousness is an everlasting righteousness, *
    and your law is the truth.

143 Trouble and anguish have come upon me, *
    but your commandments are my delight.

144 Your decrees are righteous forever; *
    give me understanding that I may live.

Kof ק

145 With my whole heart I cry; answer me, O LORD. *
    I will keep your statutes.

146 I cry to you; save me, *
    that I may observe your decrees.

147 I rise before dawn and cry for help; *
    I put my hope in your words.

148 My eyes are awake before each watch of the night, *
    that I may meditate on your promise.

149 In your steadfast love hear my voice; *
    O LORD, in your justice preserve my life.

150 Those who persecute me with evil purpose draw near; *
    they are far from your law.

151 Yet you are near, O LORD, *
    and all your commandments are true.

152 Long ago I learned from your decrees *
    that you have established them forever.

Resh ר

¹⁵³ Look on my misery and rescue me, *
for I do not forget your law.

¹⁵⁴ **Plead my cause and redeem me;** *
give me life according to your promise.

¹⁵⁵ Salvation is far from the wicked, *
for they do not seek your statutes.

¹⁵⁶ **Great is your mercy, O Lᴏʀᴅ;** *
give me life according to your justice.

¹⁵⁷ Many are my persecutors and my adversaries, *
yet I do not swerve from your decrees.

¹⁵⁸ I look at the faithless with disgust, *
because they do not keep your commands.

¹⁵⁹ **Consider how I love your precepts;** *
preserve my life according to your steadfast love.

¹⁶⁰ **The sum of your word is truth;** *
and every one of your righteous ordinances endures forever.

Shin ש

¹⁶¹ Princes persecute me without cause, *
but my heart stands in awe of your words.

¹⁶² **I rejoice at your word** *
like one who finds great spoil.

¹⁶³ I hate and abhor falsehood, *
but I love your law.

¹⁶⁴ **Seven times a day I praise you** *
for your righteous ordinances.

¹⁶⁵ Great peace have those who love your law; *
nothing can make them stumble.

¹⁶⁶ **I hope for your salvation, O Lᴏʀᴅ,** *
and I fulfill your commandments.

¹⁶⁷ **My soul keeps your decrees;** *
I love them exceedingly.

¹⁶⁸ **I keep your precepts and decrees,** *
for all my ways are before you.

(continues)

Tav ת

169 Let my cry come before you, O LORD; *
    give me understanding according to your word.

170 Let my supplication come before you; *
    deliver me according to your promise.

171 **My lips will pour forth praise, ***
    because you teach me your statutes.

172 **My tongue will sing of your promise, ***
    for all your commandments are right.

173 Let your hand be ready to help me, *
    for I have chosen your precepts.

174 **I long for your salvation, O LORD, ***
    and your law is my delight.

175 **Let me live that I may praise you, ***
    and let your ordinances help me.

176 **I have gone astray like a lost sheep; seek out your servant, ***
    for I do not forget your commandments.

Holy God,
your ways are just and your commandments are true.
Help us to understand your law, and when understanding fails
inspire us to follow you in joyful obedience, so that we may faithfully serve you,
for the sake of Jesus Christ our Lord. **Amen.**

Psalm 119 is an acrostic psalm with twenty-two eight-verse segments, each beginning with a subsequent letter in the Hebrew alphabet. The psalm focuses on the decrees, laws, commands, and promises of God. It depicts life as a walk or journey down a path; it lifts up the importance of a righteous heart, mouth, and voice, and righteous feet; it challenges us to treasure and take delight; it presents God's law as both command and promise; and it gives us hope. The carefully constructed structure of the psalm fits the message: God's Torah represents the establishment of order and poise in the middle of chaos and strife. Note that within the psalm's precise and highly regulated structure there are many references to chaos and strife—including references to enemies, the arrogant, persecutors, and the psalmist's own "wandering like a lost sheep" (v. 176). *Use in Worship: daily morning prayer services; congregations could consider the discipline of using one eight-verse segment of the psalm prior to the reading and preaching of Scripture each week.*

Let Me Sing of Your Law 119A

Refrain *Harmony*

Let me sing of your law, O my God;
let your love come up-on your peo - ple.

Unison

1 Through your own word, Lord, give us life;
2 I have made known to you my ways;
3 Show me the way to keep your law;
4 Deep in my soul my sor - row lies;

in your ho - ly keep - ing, hap - py is my soul.
you have heard my plead - ing; now teach me your laws.
let your ho - ly pre - cepts, dwell with - in my mind.
ev - er keep your prom - ise, let my heart be glad.

To Refrain

5 O take me far from evil ways,
  and in your great mercy
  guide me in your paths. *To Refrain*

6 Within your law I choose to live;
  in the paths of wisdom
  I walk evermore. *To Refrain*

7 My heart is strong, my joy is full;
  following your law, Lord,
  freely do I walk. *To Refrain*

Guitar chords do not correspond with keyboard harmony.

Words and Music: Lucien Deiss (1921-2007) © 1970 World Library Publications

119B How Shall the Young Direct Their Way?

1 How shall the young di - rect their way? What light shall
2 Sin - cere - ly I have sought you, Lord, O let me
3 O bless - ed Lord, teach me your law, your right-eous
4 Up - on your pre - cepts and your ways my heart will

be their per - fect guide? Your Word, O Lord, will
not from you de - part; to know your will and
judg - ments I de - clare; your tes - ti - mo - nies
med - i - tate with awe; your Word shall be my

safe - ly lead if in its wis - dom they con - fide.
keep from sin, your Word I cher - ish in my heart.
make me glad, for they are wealth be - yond com - pare.
chief de - light, and I will not for - get your law.

Words: Psalm 119:9-16; *Psalter*, 1912, P.D.
Music (ST. CRISPIN 8.8.8.8): George J. Elvey, 1862, P.D.

Teach Me, O Lord, Your Way of Truth 119C

1 Teach me, O Lord, your way of truth,
   and from it I will not depart.
   That I may steadfastly obey,
   give me an understanding heart.

2 In your commandments make me walk,
   for in your law my joy shall be.
   Give me a heart that loves your will,
   from discontent and envy free.

3 Turn heart and eye from vanities,
   preserve my life within your way.
   Confirm to me your holy word
   promised to those who fear your name.

4 Lord, turn away disgrace and dread.
   Your righteous judgments I confess.
   To know your word is my desire.
   Revive me in your righteousness.

Tune: ST. CRISPIN on facing page

Words: Psalm 119:33-40; *Psalter*, 1912, P.D.

Your Word Sheds Light upon My Path 119D

1 Your word sheds light upon my path;
   a shining light, it guides my feet.
   Your righteous judgments to observe,
   my solemn vow I now repeat.

2 In my distress I plead with you;
   send help according to your word.
   Accept my sacrifice of praise
   and make me know your judgments, Lord.

3 When danger brings me close to death,
   your law stays with me night and day.
   The wicked lay a snare for me,
   yet from your truth I will not stray.

4 Your precepts are my heritage,
   they make my heart and soul rejoice.
   To keep your statutes faithfully
   shall ever be my willing choice.

Tune: ST. CRISPIN on facing page

Words: Psalm 119:105-112; *Psalter*, 1912, P.D.

O Let My Supplicating Cry 119E

1 O let my supplicating cry
   by you, my gracious Lord, be heard.
   Give wisdom and deliver me
   according to your faithful word.

2 Instructed in your holy law,
   to praise your word I lift my voice.
   Come, Lord, and be my present help,
   for your commandments are my choice.

3 For your salvation I have longed,
   my joy is in your law, O Lord.
   Now, let me live, your praise to sing;
   sustain me by your holy word.

4 Your servant, like a wandering sheep,
   has lost the path and gone astray.
   Restore my soul and lead me home,
   for your commands I would obey.

Tune: ST. CRISPIN on facing page

Words: Psalm 119:167-176; *Psalter*, 1912, P.D.

These verses from Psalm 119 may be framed by the singing of "Order My Steps."

⁹ How can a young person stay pure?
    By obeying your word.
¹⁰ I have tried hard to find you—
    don't let me wander from your commands.
¹¹ I have hidden your word in my heart,
    that I might not sin against you.

³³ Teach me your decrees, O LORD;
    I will keep them to the end.
³⁴ Give me understanding and I will obey your instructions;
    I will put them into practice with all my heart.
³⁵ Make me walk along the path of your commands,
    for that is where my happiness is found.

⁶⁵ You have done many good things for me, LORD,
    just as you promised.
⁶⁶ I believe in your commands;
    now teach me good judgment and knowledge.
⁶⁷ I used to wander off until you disciplined me;
    but now I closely follow your word.

¹⁰⁵ Your word is a lamp to guide my feet
    and a light for my path.
¹³³ Guide my steps by your word,
    so I will not be overcome by evil.

119G Psalm 119:1-8
A Responsorial Setting

Refrain

O LORD, my de-light, my de-light is in your law.

Refrain

1 Happy are they whose way is blameless,
      who follow the teaching of the LORD!

2 Happy are they who observe your decrees
      and see you with all their hearts,

3 who never do any wrong,
      but always walk in your ways.

4 You laid down your commandments,
      that we should fully keep them.   *Refrain*

5 Oh, that my ways were made so direct
      that I might keep your statutes!

6 Then I should not be put to shame,
      when I regard all your commandments.

7 I will thank you with a true heart,
      when I have learned your righteous judgments.

8 I will keep your statues;
      do not utterly forsake me.   *Refrain*

Tone

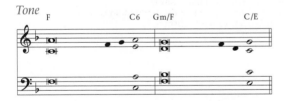

Lectionary: Ordinary Time after Epiphany (A); Ordinary Time after Pentecost (B).

Words and Music: Hal H. Hopson © 1987 Hope Publishing Company
Psalm Text: from *Evangelical Lutheran Worship* © 2006 Evangelical Lutheran Church in America, admin.
Augsburg Fortress Publishers
Tone: © 1987 Hope Publishing Company

Psalm 119:97-104 119H
A Responsorial Setting

Use refrain and tone from 119G.

Refrain

⁹⁷ Oh, how I love your teaching!
  All the day long it is in my mind.

⁹⁸ Your commandment has made me wiser than my enemies,
  for it is always with me.

⁹⁹ I have more understanding than all my teachers,
  for your decrees are my study.

¹⁰⁰ I am wiser than the elders,
  because I observe your commandments.   *Refrain*

¹⁰¹ I restrain my feet from every evil way,
  that I may keep your word.

¹⁰² I do not turn aside from your judgments,
  because you yourself have taught me.

¹⁰³ How sweet are your words to my taste!
  They are sweeter than honey to my mouth.

¹⁰⁴ Through your commandments I gain understanding;
  therefore I hate every lying way.   *Refrain*

Lectionary: Ordinary Time after Pentecost (C).

Psalm Text: from *Evangelical Lutheran Worship* © 2006 Evangelical Lutheran Church in America, admin.
Augsburg Fortress Publishers

1191 Psalm 119:9-16
A Responsorial Setting

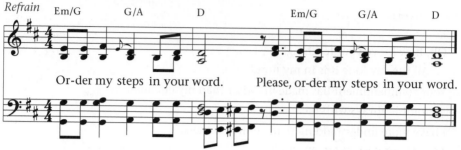

Refrain

Or-der my steps in your word.   Please, or-der my steps in your word.

Refrain

9 How shall the young keep their way clean?
  By keeping to your word.

10 With my whole heart I seek you;
   let me not stray from your commandments.

11 I treasure your promise in my heart,
   that I may not sin against you.

12 Blessed are you, O LORD;
   instruct me in your statutes.   *Refrain*

13 With my lips I recite
   all of the judgments of your mouth.

14 I take greater delight in the way of your decrees
   than in all manner of riches.

15 I will meditate on your commandments
   and give attention to your ways.

16 My delight is in your statutes;
   I will not forget your word.   *Refrain*

Tone

Lectionary: Lent (B).

At the conclusion of the psalm, 119F may be sung.

Words: Glenn Burleigh © 1991 Glenn Burleigh, Burleigh Inspirations Music
Music (IN YOUR WORD fragment): Glenn Burleigh © 1991 Glenn Burleigh, Burleigh Inspirations Music
Psalm Text: from *Evangelical Lutheran Worship* © 2006 Evangelical Lutheran Church in America, admin.
Augsburg Fortress Publishers
Tone: © 2011 Faith Alive Christian Resources

Psalm 119:33-40 119J
A Responsorial Setting

Use refrain and tone from 119I.

Refrain

33 Teach me, O LORD, the way of your statutes,
    and I shall keep them to the end.

34 Give me understanding, and I shall keep your teaching;
    I shall keep it with all my heart.

35 Lead me in the path of your commandments,
    for that is my desire.   *Refrain*

36 Incline my heart to your decrees
    and not to unjust gain.

37 Turn my eyes from beholding falsehood;
    give me life in your way.   *Refrain*

38 Fulfill your promise to your servant,
    which is for those who fear you.

39 Turn away the reproach that I dread,
    because your judgments are good.

40 Behold, I long for your commandments;
    by righteousness enliven me.   *Refrain*

Lectionary: Ordinary Time after Epiphany (A); Ordinary Time after Pentecost (A).

At the conclusion of the psalm, 119F may be sung.

119K Psalm 119:105-112
A Responsorial Setting

Refrain

Send out your light, Lord, send your truth to be my guide.
Then let them lead me to the place where you re - side.

Refrain

¹⁰⁵ Your word is a lamp to my feet
and a light upon my path.

¹⁰⁶ I have sworn and am determined
to keep your righteous judgments.

¹⁰⁷ I am deeply troubled;
preserve my life, O LORD, according to your word.

¹⁰⁸ Accept, O LORD, the willing tribute of my lips,
and teach me your judgments. *Refrain*

¹⁰⁹ My life is always in danger,
yet I do not forget your teaching.

¹¹⁰ The wicked have set a trap for me,
but I have not strayed from your commandments.

¹¹¹ Your decrees are my inheritance forever;
truly, they are the joy of my heart.

¹¹² I have applied my heart to fulfill your statutes
forever and to the end. *Refrain*

Tone

Lectionary: Ordinary Time after Pentecost (A).

Words (from Psalm 43:3) and Music: The Iona Community © 1995 Wild Goose Resource Group, Iona Community, Scotland, GIA Publications, Inc., exclusive North American agent
Psalm Text: from *Evangelical Lutheran Worship* © 2006 Evangelical Lutheran Church in America, admin. Augsburg Fortress Publishers
Tone: © 2011 Faith Alive Christian Resources

Psalm 119:129-136 119L
A Responsorial Setting

Use refrain and tone from 119K.

Refrain

129 Your decrees are wonderful;
    therefore I obey them with all my heart.

130 When your word is opened it gives light;
    it gives understanding to the simple.

131 I open my mouth and pant
    because I long for your commandments.

132 Turn to me and be gracious to me,
    as you always do to those who love your name.   *Refrain*

133 Order my footsteps in your word;
    let no iniquity have dominion over me.

134 Rescue me from those who oppress me,
    and I will keep your commandments.

135 Let your face shine upon your servant
    and teach me your statutes.

136 My eyes shed streams of tears,
    because people do not keep your teaching.   *Refrain*

Lectionary: Ordinary Time after Pentecost (A).

For another refrain option see p. 780, "Order My Steps."

Psalm Text: from *Evangelical Lutheran Worship* © 2006 Evangelical Lutheran Church in America, admin. Augsburg Fortress Publishers

Psalm 119:137-144
A Responsorial Setting

Refrain

¹³⁷ You are righteous, O LORD,
   and upright are your judgments.

¹³⁸ You commanded your decrees in righteousness
   and in all faithfulness.

¹³⁹ My indignation has consumed me,
   because my enemies forget your words.   *Refrain*

¹⁴⁰ Your word is very pure,
   and your servant loves it.

¹⁴¹ I am small and of little account,
   yet I do not forget your commandments.

¹⁴² Your righteousness is everlasting
   and your teaching is true.   *Refrain*

¹⁴³ Trouble and distress have come upon me,
   yet your commandments are my delight.

¹⁴⁴ The righteousness of your decrees is everlasting;
   grant me understanding that I may live.   *Refrain*

Tone

Lectionary: Ordinary Time after Pentecost (C).

Words: Psalm 119
Music: Bradley Ellingboe from *Psalter for Worship, Year C* © 2006 Augsburg Fortress Publishers
Psalm Text: from *Evangelical Lutheran Worship* © 2006 Evangelical Lutheran Church in America, admin.
Augsburg Fortress Publishers
Tone: from *Psalter for Worship, Year C* © 2006 Augsburg Fortress Publishers

Thou Art My Portion, Lord  119N

1 Thou art my por - tion, Lord; thy
2 I thought up - on my ways, thy
3 While snares be - set my path, thy
4 All those who fear thy name shall

words I ev - er heed; with all my heart thy
tes - ti - mo - nies learned; with ear - nest haste, and
law I keep in view; at mid - night I will
my com - pan - ions be; thy mer - cy fills the

grace I seek, thy prom - is - es I plead.
wait - ing not, to thy com - mands I turned.
give thee praise for all thy judg - ments true.
earth, O Lord; thy stat - utes teach thou me.

Words: anonymous, based on Psalm 119:57-64
Music (CARLISLE 6.6.8.6): Charles Lockhart (1745-1815), 1769, P.D.

1190 All Your Commandments, Father Almighty

bring to your chil - dren heal - ing and bless - ing;
each of your stat - utes stands firm for - ev - er;
how can the young ones keep their way ho - ly?
keep - ing them brings us close to your king - dom—

1 All your com-mand - ments, Fa - ther al - might - y,
2 Dai - ly in - struct us as your dis - ci - ples:
3 God of all mer - cy, grant me your guid - ance;
4 Joy comes to na - tions know - ing your judg - ments;

Chris - tians who keep them find here their com - fort.
faith - ful your prom - ise, free your for - give - ness.
I have found trea - sure in your in - struc - tion.
laws that spell free - dom, true lib - er - a - tion.

5 My heart is listening for you each morning,
never desert me; speak in the nighttime;
open my eyes, Lord, then lead me onward.

6 Put right my passions by your clear precept,
quell my rebellions, rescue me quickly:
raise and restore me, mighty Redeemer.

(continues)

7 Savior whose Spirit gave us the Scriptures,
train me to trust them when I am tempted;
unless you helped me, I would go under.

8 Vain are my own ways; yours is the vic<u>tory</u>.
Wonderful Coun<u>se</u>lor, you are my wisdom:
your word shall teach me; I will obey you.

Words: Christopher Idle © 1990 The Jubilate Group, admin. Hope Publishing Company
Music (KANCIONAL NEW 5.5.5.5.5.5): Alfred V. Fedak (b. 1953), 1999, © 2000 Selah Publishing Company, Inc.

Psalm 120

A Song of Ascents.

1 In my distress I cry to the LORD, *
   that he may answer me:

2 **"Deliver me, O LORD,** *
   from lying lips, from a deceitful tongue."

3 What shall be given to you? *
   And what more shall be done to you, you deceitful tongue?

4 A warrior's sharp arrows, *
   with glowing coals of the broom tree!

5 Woe is me, that I am an alien in Meshech *
   that I must live among the tents of Kedar.

6 **Too long have I had my dwelling** *
   among those who hate peace.

7 **I am for peace;** *
   but when I speak, they are for war.

God, our deliverer,
when we find ourselves in unfamiliar territory, surrounded by deceit and hostility,
shield us from harm and lead us to the pathway of your peace,
through Christ, our Prince of Peace. **Amen.**

Psalm 120, the first of fifteen Psalms of Ascents, is a complex psalm about peace and deceit. Its central theme is reliance on God in the face of the brokenness of shalom through both deceitful speech and warfare. The psalmist expresses a desire for peace (v. 7) and a desire to be forgiven for deceit (v. 2). Verse 3 is ambiguous: is it an expression of judgment on the deceit of others, possibly those who are "for war"? Is it a reflection on the psalmist's own deceit? Or is the entire psalm a reflection on the way war is made by the tongue? Many commentators note that this ambiguity is a strength that invites reflection on the links between deceitful speech and warfare and on the moral ambiguity of both the psalmist and the enemy. *Use in Worship: services focusing on the themes of warfare or peace; as a guide to prayer that brings both warfare and peace—in all their ambiguity—before God.*

120A O Lord, Deliver Me from Liars

1 O Lord, de - liv - er me from li - ars. O Lord, de - liv - er me from li - ars. O Lord, de - liv - er me from li - ars, and from my own hy - po - cri - sy.

2 O Lord, I'm sick and tired of try - ing. O Lord, I'm sick and tired of try - ing. O Lord, I'm sick and tired of try - ing to quench the fire of a ly - ing tongue.

3 O woe is me for I am dwell - ing; O woe is me for I am dwell - ing; O woe is me for I am dwell - ing a - mong a peo - ple who hate peace.

4 I am for peace, but when I speak; I am for peace, but when I speak; I am for peace, but when I speak they are for war, they are for war.

Repeat for Stanzas

Final Ending

Sing stanza 1

Consider what a great forest is set on fire by a small spark. The tongue is also a fire, a world of evil among the parts of the body. It corrupts the whole body, sets the whole course of one's life on fire, and is itself set on fire by hell.

Sing stanza 2

With the tongue, we praise our Lord and Father, and with it we curse human beings, who have been made in God's likeness. Out of the same mouth come praise and cursing. My brothers and sisters, this should not be. Can both fresh water and salt water flow from the same spring? My brothers and sisters, can a fig tree bear olives, or a grapevine bear figs? Neither can a salt spring produce fresh water. Who is wise and understanding among you? Let them show it by their good life, by deeds done in the humility that comes from wisdom.

Sing stanza 3

But if you harbor bitter envy and selfish ambition in your hearts, do not boast about it or deny the truth. Such "wisdom" does not come down from heaven but is earthly, unspiritual, demonic. For where you have envy and selfish ambition, there you find disorder and every evil practice.

Sing stanza 4

But the wisdom that comes from heaven is first of all pure; then peace-loving, considerate, submissive, full of mercy and good fruit, impartial and sincere. Peacemakers who sow in peace reap a harvest of righteousness.

Let us pray.

O Lord our God, who with a word spoke creation into being and declared it good, so lead us that our words and deeds might reflect your beauty and righteousness.

Among strangers, help us to show love;

at the prospect of war, help us to speak peace;

and in the midst of deception and lies, help us to uncover truth.

We pray these things through Jesus Christ,

confident that our deliverance comes from you. **Amen.**

120B When My Troubles Arose

Drum pattern

Solo Voice

Filipino Nang a - ko'y ma - nga - nib kay Yah-
English 1 When my trou-bles a - rose I called
       2 What will hap-pen to you, when you
       3 Far too long I have lived a - mong

All

Go forth, Go forth, Go forth,

weh du - ma - ing, di - ni - nig N'ya a - ko sa a - king da - la-
out to the Lord, and the Lord heard my voice, my God an-swered my
speak with de - ceit? What mis-for - tune and grief will at-tend all your
those who hate peace. When I speak a - bout peace, then I hear them re-

Go forth, Go forth, Go

ngin. Sa ta - ong di ta - pat, ga - wa - i'y man - lin - lang,
call; O de - liv - er me, Lord, from the lips of de - ceit;
sin? Bit - ter sor-rows like ar - rows will pierce you with woe;
ply; "It's not peace that we want, we are on - ly for war!"

forth, Go forth, Go forth,

Yah - weh, i - lig - tas mo a - ko't i - sang - ga - lang.
spare me from the curs-ing of those who would harm me.
live coals, burn-ing fire___ to purge all your e - vil.
O Lord, show me how to go forth. Help me seek peace.

Go forth, seek peace.

Words: Psalm 120; para. Rolando S. Tinio © 1990, 2000 Christian Conference of Asia, admin. GIA
Publications, Inc.
Music (CORDILLERA): Judith Laoyan, Philippines melody © 1990, 2000 Christian Conference of Asia,
admin. GIA Publications, Inc.; ostinato, Francisco F. Feliciano © 1990 Francisco F. Feliciano

O God of Love, Forever Blest 120C

Unison

1 O God of love, for-ev-er blest, pit-y my suf-fering state.
2 I cried in trou-ble to the Lord, and he has an-swered me.

When will you set my soul at rest from lips that love de-ceit?
From ly-ing lips and craft-y tongue, O Lord, my soul set free.

Men: Women: Men: Women:

Too long my soul with those who lift the
has made its home *who lift the*

Men: Women: All:

sword. I am for peace they make for war.
sword. *but when I speak they make for war.*

Optional concluding prayer

O God, for too long the world has called us to war, and our dead lay sprawled across the bleeding centuries. But you break the bow and shatter the spear, calling us to sow the seeds of peace in the midst of despair. In tenderness, may we take the tiniest sprouts and plant them where they can safely grow into blossoms of hope. **Amen.**

Words: Isaac Watts (1674-1748), alt., P.D.
Music (SHALOM 120 | 8.6.8.6 with refrain): Bruce Benedict © 2009 Cardiphonia Music; arr. Greg Scheer
© 2011 Greg Scheer
Prayer: Linea Reimer Geiser © 1988 Geiser

Psalm 121

A Song of Ascents.

¹ I lift up my eyes to the hills— *
   from where will my help come?

² **My help comes from the LORD, ***
   who made heaven and earth.

³ He will not let your foot be moved; *
   he who keeps you will not slumber.

⁴ **He who keeps Israel ***
   will neither slumber nor sleep.

⁵ The LORD is your keeper; *
   the LORD is your shade at your right hand.

⁶ **The sun shall not strike you by day, ***
   nor the moon by night.

⁷ The LORD will keep you from all evil; *
   he will keep your life.

⁸ **The LORD will keep your going out and your coming in ***
   from this time on and forevermore.

Maker of heaven and earth,
we trust you to keep us in your care.
Guard us from evil, protect us from harm.
Help us to know you, and knowing you to follow you,
so that all our comings and goings may conform to your purpose for our lives,
through Jesus Christ our Lord. **Amen.**

Psalm 121, the second of the Psalms of Ascents, is a declaration of trust. The opening imagery can be interpreted in two ways: either that the mountains represent God, who made them, or that they represent an alternative source of hope. The psalmist's question of v. 1 is answered in v. 2—our help comes from God. Like Ps. 91, it offers a strong testimony to the care and protection offered by God, a sentiment echoed in Romans 8 ("nothing shall separate us from the love of God"). *Use in Worship: funerals; occasions of great difficulty.*

To the Hills I Lift My Eyes 121A

1 To the hills I lift my eyes; whence shall help for
  me a - rise? From the LORD comes all my aid,
  who the heavens and earth has made. He will guard through
  dan - gers all, will not let you slip or fall. He who
  safe his peo - ple keeps nev - er slum - bers, nev - er sleeps.

2 Your pro - tec - tor is the LORD; shade for you he
  will af - ford. Nei - ther sun nor moon shall smite;
  God shall guard by day and night. He will ev - er
  keep your soul; what would harm he will con - trol. In the
  home and by the way God will keep you day by day.

Words: *Psalter*, 1912, alt., P.D.
Music (GUIDE 7.7.7.7 D): Marcus M. Wells, 1858, P.D.

121B Total Praise

Alzo a los montes mis ojos /
Lift Your Eyes Up to the Mountains

Spanish

1 Al - zo a los mon-tes mis o - jos, ¿Dón-de en-con-tra - ré re -
2 Es Ya - vé quien te pro - te - ge y quien con-du - ce tu

English

1 Lift your eyes up to the moun-tains. Where can sav-ing help be
2 God the Lord is here be - side us, watch-ing o - ver us to

fu - gio? De Dios vie - ne mi con - sue - lo, ha - ce -
vi - da, te a - com - pa - ña - rá en la no - che y al sol
found? God who formed the world and made us comes to
guide us, with us through the night's de - clin - ing to the

dor del an - cho mun-do. No va - ci - la - rá tu pa - so,
del ra - dian - te dí - a. To - da pe - na se - rá ex - tra - ña,
com - fort and to aid us. God will keep our feet from stum-bling,
day - light, bright - ly shin-ing. Ev - ery e - vil will be van-quished;

tu cus - to - dia se - rá Él; pues siem-pre es - tá vi - gi -
Él au - xi - lia - rá tus dí - as. Des - de aho - ra y pa - ra
and a watch-ful eye is keep-ing, faith - ful Guard-ian o - ver
God will speed each good en - deav-or, Light and Lead - er on our

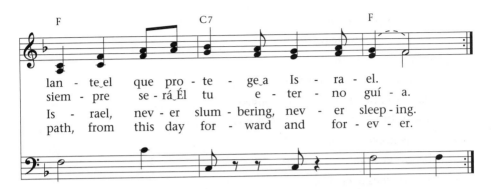

lan - te el que pro - te - ge a Is - ra - el.
siem - pre se - rá Él tu e - ter - no guí - a.
Is - rael, nev - er slum - bering, nev - er sleep - ing.
path, from this day for - ward and for - ev - er.

Words: anonymous, Psalm 121 © Plegaria Colombia; tr. Mary Louise Bringle (b. 1953), 2011
Music: anonymous; arr. Marcus Hong, 2011, © Plegaria Colombia

Psalm 121 | A Responsorial Setting 121D

Refrain

My help comes on - ly from the Lord. The mak - er of

heav - en and earth. My help comes on - ly from the

Lord. The mak - er of heav - en and earth. earth.

To Vamp or Tone | *Final ending*

(continues)

Refrain

1 I lift up my eyes to the hills;
  from where is my help to come?

2 My help comes from the LORD,
  the maker of heaven and earth.   *Refrain*

3 The LORD will not let your foot be moved
  nor will the one who watches over you fall asleep.

4 Behold, the keeper of Israel
  will neither slumber nor sleep;

5 the LORD watches over you;
  the LORD is your shade at your right hand;

6 the sun will not strike you by day,
  nor the moon by night.   *Refrain*

7 The LORD will preserve you from all evil
  and will keep your life.

8 The LORD will watch over your going out and your coming in,
  from this time forth forevermore.   *Refrain*

Tone

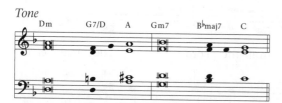

Optional vamp during the reading of the psalm

Lectionary: Lent (A); Ordinary Time after Pentecost (C).

Words: Psalm 121
Music: Daniel Richardson and Angel Napieralski © 2010 Daniel Richardson and Angel Napieralski, admin.
Faith Alive Christian Resources
Psalm Text: from *Evangelical Lutheran Worship* © 2006 Evangelical Lutheran Church in America, admin.
Augsburg Fortress Publishers
Tone: © 2011 Faith Alive Christian Resources

I to the Hills Will Lift My Eyes 121E

1 I to the hills will lift my eyes; from
2 God will not let your foot be moved, your
3 Your faith - ful keep - er is the Lord, your
4 From e - vil God will keep you safe, pro -

whence shall come my aid? My help is from the
guard - ian nev - er sleeps; God's watch - ful and un -
shel - ter and your shade; 'neath sun or moon, by
vide for all you need; your go - ing out, your

Lord a - lone, who heaven and earth has made.
slum - bering care pro - tects and safe - ly keeps.
day or night, you shall not be a - fraid.
com - ing in, God will for - ev - er lead.

Guitar chords do not correspond with keyboard harmony.

Words: *Psalter*, 1912, alt. 1988, P.D.
Music (UNION 8.6.8.6): *Genuine Church Music*, 1832, attr. Stephen Jenks, P.D.; arr. Alice Parker © 2000 Alice Parker

121F Naega sanŭl hyanghayŏ / To the Hills I Lift My Eyes

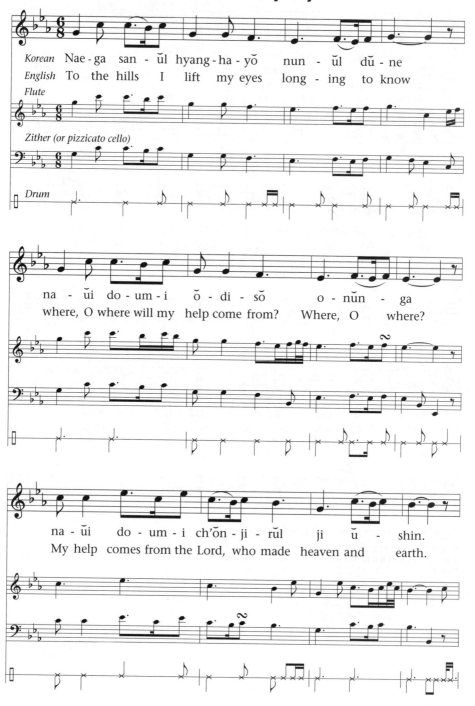

Korean: Nae-ga san-ŭl hyang-ha-yŏ nun-ŭl dŭ-ne
English: To the hills I lift my eyes long-ing to know

na-ŭi do-um-i ŏ-di-sŏ o-nŭn-ga
where, O where will my help come from? Where, O where?

na-ŭi do-um-i ch'ŏn-ji-rŭl ji ŭ-shin.
My help comes from the Lord, who made heaven and earth.

Yŏ - ho - wa ha - na - nim - e - ge - sŏ o - ne.
God the Cre - a - tor will keep my life. God is my help.

Korean

내가 산을 향하여 눈을 드니
나의 도움이 어디서 오는가
나의 도움이 천지를 지으신
여호와 하나님에게서 오네

A Benediction 121G

The benediction may begin by singing or speaking "Our help comes from the Lord, the maker of heaven and earth." If singing, 121F, 121H, or the refrain from 121D or 121I may be used.

May the Lord watch over you—
your going out and coming in,
your sleeping and waking,
your labor and your rest,
your dying and your rising.
Truly, the Lord will keep your life—forever. **Amen**.

121H I Lift My Eyes Up to the Mountains

I lift my eyes up to the moun-tains;
where does my help come from?
My help comes from you, Mak-er of heav - en,
Cre - a - tor of the earth.

Fine

Words and Music: Brian Doerksen (b. 1965) © 1990 Vineyard Songs (Canada)/ION Publishing, admin. in North America by Music Services o/b/o Vineyard Music USA

1211 Our Help Is from the Lord

Flute

Refrain

Our help is from the Lord who made heav - en and earth.

1 I look to the hills, to the far - a - way
2 The Lord is your keep - er, the Lord is your
3 The Lord will pro - tect you and keep you from

hills, from where, from where will my
shade; the sun, the moon can - not
harm, the Lord will keep you from

help come? / harm you. / dan - ger.

A7sus / A7 / Bm

My help comes from the / Through the light of the / And wher - ev - er you

Lord who made heav - en and earth. From the / day and the dark of the night, nev - er / go for the length of your days, you are

F♯m/C♯ / G / D/A

To Refrain

Lord who made heav - en and earth. / fear; God is at your right hand. / safe, ev - er safe in God's care.

Bm / Em7 / Asus / A

Psalm 122

A Song of Ascents. Of David.

¹ I was glad when they said to me, *
  "Let us go to the house of the LORD!"

² **Our feet are standing ***
  within your gates, O Jerusalem.

³ **Jerusalem—built as a city ***
  that is bound firmly together.

⁴ To it the tribes go up, the tribes of the LORD, *
  as was decreed for Israel, to give thanks to the name of the LORD.

⁵ For there the thrones for judgment were set up, *
  the thrones of the house of David.

⁶ **Pray for the peace of Jerusalem: ***
  "May they prosper who love you.

⁷ **Peace be within your walls, ***
  and security within your towers."

⁸ For the sake of my relatives and friends *
  I will say, "Peace be within you."

⁹ **For the sake of the house of the LORD our God, ***
  I will seek your good.

O Lord, we long for the day when our feet will stand
within the gates of the New Jerusalem.
Until then, as we journey toward home, guide and protect your church:
be our unity, clothe us in truth, and keep us in your peace.
We pray in the name of Jesus the Christ. **Amen.**

Psalm 122, the third Psalm of Ascents, expresses joy over and prayers for Jerusalem, the city identified with God's presence in the temple. It is divided into two inter-related parts: a rhapsodic description of Jerusalem as the destination for the procession of ascent and the site for both communal worship and political authority (vv. 1-5) and a series of prayers for Jerusalem's well-being (vv. 6-9). The prayers for Jerusalem feature a delightful word-play, asking God to provide "shalom" (peace) for the "city of shalom" (Jeru-salem). *Use in Worship: an opening to worship; during the season of Advent; a prayer for peace in the middle of inter-religious conflict; in services that focus on the joy of processing into the new Jerusalem (see Isa. 60); prayer for the ultimate embodiment of shalom in the fullness of God's kingdom.*

Rejoice, Rejoice, Come Sing with Me 122A

1 Re-joice, re-joice, come sing with me: "This is the house of God!"
2 In mar-ket square and cit-y street we seek the peace of God.

The tem-ple gates swing wide and free—this is the house of God!
Be-fore the rul-er's judg-ment seat, we seek the peace of God.

For ev-ery tribe and ev-ery race this is the house of God!
In joy-ful song and whis-pered prayer we seek the peace of God.

God calls us to this ho-ly place—this is the house of God!
God's cit-y can be an-y-where we seek the peace of God.

May be sung responsively between solo voice and congregation or antiphonally between two groups of singers.

Words: Adam M. L. Tice, 2010, © 2011 GIA Publications, Inc.
Music (FOREST GREEN 8.6.8.6 D): English; harm. J. Michael Joncas (b. 1951) © 1987 GIA Publications, Inc.

122B I Rejoiced When I Heard Them Say

1 I re-joiced when I heard them say: "Let us go to the
2 Like a tem-ple of u - ni - ty is the cit - y, Je -
3 It is faith-ful to Is - rael's law, there to praise the
4 For the peace of all na - tions, pray: for God's peace with-
5 For the love of my friends and kin I will bless you with

house of God." And now our feet are
ru - sa - lem. It is there all tribes will
name of God. All the judg - ment seats of
in your homes. May God's last - ing peace sur -
signs of peace. For the love of God's own

stand - ing in your gates, O Je - ru - sa - lem!
gath - er, all the tribes of the house of God.
Da - vid were set down in Je - ru - sa - lem.
round us; may it dwell in Je - ru - sa - lem.
peo - ple I will la - bor and pray for you.

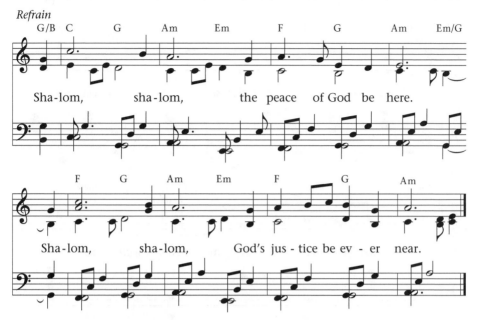

Sha-lom, sha-lom, the peace of God be here.

Sha-lom, sha-lom, God's jus-tice be ev-er near.

Words: Bernadette Farrell © 1993 Bernadette Farrell, admin. OCP Publications
Music (ENGLAND 8.8.8.8 with refrain): Bernadette Farrell © 1993 Bernadette Farrell, admin. OCP Publications

A Litany for Peace in Places of Conflict 122C

The refrain "Dona nobis pacem" (p. 811) may be used as an alternate response throughout the prayer.

God of righteousness and peace,
grant us your peace.

When warfare haunts our streets,
grant us your peace.

When anxieties haunt our minds and hearts,
grant us your peace.

For the people of [,_____,] who face the fear and violence of conflict today:
grant us your peace.

For all the people of Jerusalem and its surrounding lands,
who live in shadow of so many centuries of conflict,
grant us your peace.

Turn our hearts toward the Prince of Peace, we pray,
grant us your peace. Amen.

122D Psalm 122 | A Responsorial Setting

Refrain

¹ I was glad when they said to me,

  "Let us go to the house of the LORD."

² Now our feet are standing

  within your gates, O Jerusalem.

³ Jerusalem is built as a city

  that is at unity with itself;

4 to which the tribes go up, the tribes of the LORD,
  the assembly of Israel, to praise the name of the LORD.   *Refrain*

5 For there are the thrones of judgment,
  the thrones of the house of David.

6 Pray for the peace of Jerusalem:
  "May they prosper who love you.

7 Peace be within your walls
  and quietness within your towers.

8 For the sake of my kindred and companions,
  I pray for your prosperity.

9 Because of the house of the LORD our God,
  I will seek to do you good."   *Refrain*

Tone

Lectionary: Advent (A).

Words and Music: David Haas (b. 1957) © 1994 GIA Publications, Inc.
Psalm Text: from *Evangelical Lutheran Worship* © 2006 Evangelical Lutheran Church in America, admin.
Augsburg Fortress Publishers
Tone: © 2011 Faith Alive Christian Resources

Alternate Refrain
May be sung in canon

Do - na, do - na, do - na no - bis pa - cem!

Alternate Tone

Dona nobis pacem means 'grant us your peace.'

Music: Hermann Rauhe © Bosse-Verlag, Kassel
Tone: © 2011 Faith Alive Christian Resources

122E Let Us Go Rejoicing

1 Let us go re - joic - ing, re - joic - ing to the house of
2 Now our feet are stand - ing with - in your gates, Je - ru - sa -
3 Peace reign in this cit - y, the peace of God with - in these
4 Let us go re - joic - ing, re - joic - ing to the house of

God. Let us join to - geth - er, who
lem. Gath - ered as one peo - ple, we
walls. May this peace em - power us to
God. Let us sit at ta - ble with

come from near and far, who seek the ho - ly
of - fer thanks and praise be - fore the throne of
put an end to war, to seek the reign of
Christ the ris - en Lord. Then guid - ed by his

cit - y, the new Je - ru - sa - lem,
jus - tice, com - pas - sion and all grace,
jus - tice with dig - ni - ty for all,
Spir - it as ser - vants we'll go forth,

re - joic-ing be - fore the liv - ing God.

God, re-joic-ing be - fore the liv-ing God.

Words: Bob Hurd (b. 1950) © 1999, 2000 Bob Hurd, admin. OCP Publications
Music (POINT HILL 6.8.6.6.7.6.9): Bob Hurd (b. 1950); acc. Craig S. Kingsbury (b. 1952) © 1999, 2000
Bob Hurd, admin. OCP Publications

122F With Joy I Heard My Friends Exclaim

1 With joy I heard my friends ex-claim: "Come,
2 How beau - ti - ful does Zi - on stand, a
3 They come to learn the will of God, to

let us in God's tem - ple meet;" With - in your gates, O
cit - y built com - pact and fair; the peo - ple of the
pay their vows, God's grace to own, for there is judg-ment's

Zi - on blest, shall ev - er stand our will - ing feet.
Lord u - nite with joy and praise to wor - ship there.
roy - al seat, Mes - si - ah's sure and last - ing throne.

Refrain

Come, let us go to the house of the Lord.

Zi - on, sing; sing out your peace and joy.

(continues)

4 For Zion's peace let prayers be made;
  may all that love you prosper well!
  Within your walls let peace abide,
  and gladness with your children dwell.
  Refrain

5 For love of friends and kindred dear,
  my heart's desire is Zion's peace,
  and for the house of God, the Lord,
  my loving care shall never cease.
  Refrain

Words: *Psalter*, 1912, alt.; ref. Hal H. Hopson © 2008 Birnamwood Publications, a division of MorningStar Music Publishers, Inc.
Music (SUSSEX CAROL 8.8.8.8.8.8): English carol; arr. Ralph Vaughan Williams (1872-1958) © 1919 Stainer & Bell Ltd.

Psalm 123

A Song of Ascents.

1 To you I lift up my eyes, *

  O you who are enthroned in the heavens!

2 As the eyes of servants look to the hand of their master, *

  as the eyes of a maid to the hand of her mistress,

  so our eyes look to the Lord our God, *

  until he has mercy upon us.

3 **Have mercy upon us, O Lord, have mercy upon us, ***

  for we have had more than enough of contempt.

4 **Our soul has had more than its fill ***

  of the scorn of those who are at ease,

  of the contempt of the proud.

Lord Jesus, our only comfort in life and in death,
the world's contempt did not dissuade you from accomplishing our salvation.
May we look to no one but you to sustain us
now, and through all that is yet to come. **Amen.**

Psalm 123, the fourth Psalm of Ascents, is a prayer for God's grace, mercy, and favor in the context of feelings of shame and scorn (vv. 3-4). It portrays God as master and people as servants, an image that, in this context, especially highlights God's role as protector and provider. This psalm anticipates the prominent Christian liturgical prayer "Kyrie eleison, Lord, have mercy." *Use in Worship: the opening of worship (emphasizing the humility that is proper for worship); in conjunction with prayers of confession or lament; in preparation for the benediction; a significant resource in contexts where shame is rarely mentioned in worship.*

123A Psalm 123 | A Responsorial Setting

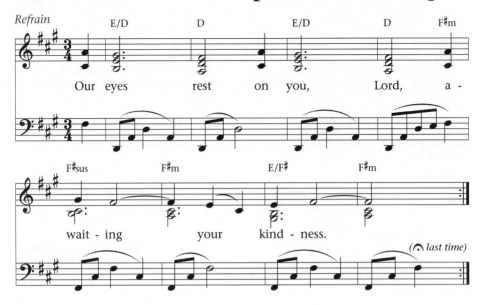

Refrain

Our eyes rest on you, Lord, a-wait-ing your kind-ness.

(⌒ last time)

Refrain

1 To you I lift up my eyes,
    to you enthroned in the heavens.

2 As the eyes of servants look to the hand of their masters,
    and the eyes of a maid to the hand of her mistress,
        so our eyes look to you, O LORD our God,
        until you show us your mercy.   *Refrain*

3 Have mercy upon us, O LORD, have mercy
    for we have had more than enough of contempt,

4 too much of the scorn of the indolent rich,
    and of the derision of the proud.   *Refrain*

Tone

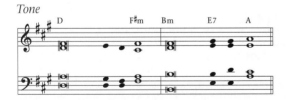

Lectionary: Ordinary Time after Pentecost (A,B).

Words: Psalm 123 from the *Liturgical Psalter* © 1969, 1981, 1997 International Commission on English in the Liturgy Corporation
Music: David Haas (b. 1957) © 1997 GIA Publications, Inc.
Psalm Text: from *Evangelical Lutheran Worship* © 2006 Evangelical Lutheran Church in America, admin. Augsburg Fortress Publishers
Tone: © 2011 Faith Alive Christian Resources

Up to You I Lift My Eyes   123B

1 Up to you I lift my eyes, high en-throned a-
2 As a ser - vant watch - es still, set to know his
3 As a maid re - ceives com-mand from her grac - ious
4 When in ar - ro - gance de-spised, when re-buffed or

bove the skies: teach me, Lord, to fol - low you,
mas - ter's will: so we fix our eyes on you,
mis - tress' hand: so, our God, we look to you,
vic - tim - ized— we seek mer - cy, Lord, from you:

see your hand in all_____ I do.
seek your hand in all_____ we do.
seek your hand in all_____ we do.
be our guide in all_____ we do.

Words: Emma Turl © Emma Turl, admin. Praise Trust
Music (THE CALL 7.7.7.7): Ralph Vaughan Williams (1872-1958); adapt. E. Harold Geer © 1911, 1956
Stainer & Bell Ltd.

Psalm 124

A Song of Ascents. Of David.

¹ If it had not been the LORD who was on our side *
   —let Israel now say—

² **if it had not been the LORD who was on our side, ***
   when our enemies attacked us,

³ then they would have swallowed us up alive, *
   when their anger was kindled against us;

⁴ **then the flood would have swept us away, ***
   the torrent would have gone over us;

⁵ then over us would have gone *
   the raging waters.

⁶ **Blessed be the LORD, ***
   who has not given us as prey to their teeth.

⁷ We have escaped like a bird from the snare of the fowlers; *
   the snare is broken, and we have escaped.

⁸ **Our help is in the name of the LORD, ***
   who made heaven and earth.

Maker of heaven and earth,
as you rescued Daniel from the lions, protect us from the evil that would consume us.
As you saved Noah from the flood, keep us from drowning in trouble.
You have freed us from the power of sin, blessed the work of our minds and hands,
and given us eternal life—all through Jesus Christ.
We praise and thank you, now and always. **Amen.**

Psalm 124, the fifth of the Psalms of Ascents, is a corporate statement of trust in God in light of God's past deliverance. It is a confession that it is God alone who saves, not human strength. Its phrasing anticipates the rhetorical question in Rom. 8:31: "If God is for us, who can be against us?" The phrase "our help is in the name of the LORD" (v. 8) has functioned as a standard line for the opening of worship in several Christian traditions, including the Reformed tradition (where it is known as the "votum" or vow) and in some monastic traditions of night prayer. *Use in Worship: in conjunction with testimonies of faith (modeling a form of testimony that is God-centered, not human-centered); in conjunction with biblical accounts of divine deliverance (from the exodus to Easter).*

Our Help Is in the Name of God the LORD 124A

1 Our help is in the name of God the LORD; the one who
2 When e-vil seems to have the up-per hand, call on God's
3 Praise God the LORD who hears the cap-tives' prayer; like birds es-

made the heav-ens with a word; Cre - a - tor of the
name: the LORD, the great "I AM." When trou-bles rise and
cap - ing from the fowl-er's snare we are set free; our

world, each liv - ing thing. Come, bless the LORD, lift up your hearts and
all a-round gives way, re - mem-ber God stays with us night and
prais - es now as - cend: "Blessed be the LORD: Cre - a - tor, Sav - ior,

sing: "Our help is in the name of God the LORD."
day. Our help is in the name of God the LORD.
Friend. Our help is in the name of God the LORD."

Guitar chords do not correspond with keyboard harmony.

Words: Martin Tel © 2011 Martin Tel, admin. Faith Alive Christian Resources
Music (OLD 124TH/GENEVAN 124 | 10.10.10.10.10): *Genevan Psalter*, 1551, P.D.

1 Our help is in the name of the Lord,
(2 Our) help is in the name of the Lord,

who made the heavens, who made the earth.
who made the heavens, who made the earth.

A shel - ter from the cold and wear - ing storm,
The liv - ing hope that gives the blind - ed sight.

pro - tect - or of my heart, my home.
I rest up - on your strength and might.

You

are the ev-er-last-ing glo-ry of the un-i-verse,

Refrain

and I have come to wor-ship, to

sing, _____ to fall be-fore my King, _____ to

lift my hands in praise. _____ To you a-lone I

raise my voice in wor-ship.

2 Our

(continues)

*During the final singing of the refrain a group of singers may sing a countermelody repeating this short motif and using the text of the bridge. The refrain may be repeated ad lib.

Words: Paul Thé © 2007 Votum Publishing, admin. Faith Alive Christian Resources
Music: Paul Thé © 2007 Votum Publishing, admin. Faith Alive Christian Resources; arr. Eelco Vos © 2011
Votum Publishing, admin. Faith Alive Christian Resources

124C Psalm 124 | A Responsorial Setting

Refrain

Our help   is in the name of the L{ORD}.

Refrain

¹ If the L{ORD} had not been on our side,
    let Israel now say;

² if the L{ORD} had not been on our side,
    when enemies rose up against us,

³ then would they have swallowed us up alive
    in their fierce anger toward us;

⁴ then would the waters have overwhelmed us
    and the torrent gone over us.

⁵ then would the raging waters
    have gone right over us.   *Refrain*

⁶ Blessed be the L{ORD}
    who has not given us over to be a prey for their teeth.

⁷ We have escaped like a bird from the snare of the fowler;
    the snare is broken, and we have escaped.

⁸ Our help is in the name of the L{ORD},
    the maker of heaven and earth.   *Refrain*

Tone

Lectionary: Ordinary Time after Pentecost (A,B).

Words: Psalm 124
Music: Anne Krentz Organ from *Psalter for Worship, Year C* © 2006 Augsburg Fortress Publishers
Psalm Text: from *Evangelical Lutheran Worship* © 2006 Evangelical Lutheran Church in America, admin.
Augsburg Fortress Publishers
Tone: from *Psalter for Worship, Year C* © 2006 Augsburg Fortress Publishers

Psalm 125

A Song of Ascents.

¹ Those who trust in the LORD are like Mount Zion, *
  which cannot be moved, but abides forever.

² **As the mountains surround Jerusalem,**
  so the LORD surrounds his people, *
  from this time on and forevermore.

³ For the scepter of wickedness shall not rest
  on the land allotted to the righteous, *
  so that the righteous might not stretch out their hands to do wrong.

⁴ **Do good, O LORD, to those who are good,** *
  and to those who are upright in their hearts.

⁵ But those who turn aside to their own crooked ways
  the LORD will lead away with evildoers. *
  Peace be upon Israel!

Zion's God—our God—renew our trust in you:
ground us in your righteousness, protect us in times of trouble,
guide us through times of testing, and deliver us from the Evil One.
We ask all this through Jesus Christ our Lord. **Amen.**

Psalm 125, the sixth of the Psalms of Ascents, is a psalm of trust and petition focusing on God's provision for faithful people. Echoing the description of faithful and faithless people in Ps. 1, this psalm depicts faithful people as those who rely on God (v. 1), are protected by God (v. 2), and are "upright" rather than "crooked" (vv. 4-5). The permanence of Mount Zion serves as an image for God's protection of the faithful. *Use in Worship: services focusing on the role, mission, and calling of the Church as the people of God; exploring a fully biblical ecclesiology, the doctrine or understanding of the Church (joining with Pss. 133 [unity] and 87 [universality and diversity]).*

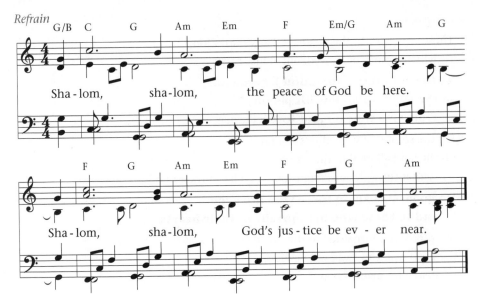

Refrain

¹ Those who trust in the LORD are like Mount Zion,

    which cannot be moved, but stands fast forever.

² The mountains surround Jerusalem;

    so you surround your people, O LORD,

    from this time forth forevermore.   *Refrain*

³ The scepter of the wicked shall not hold sway over the land allotted to the just,

    so that the just shall not put their hands to evil.

⁴ Show your goodness, O LORD, to those who are good

    and to those who are true of heart.

⁵ As for those who turn aside to crooked ways,

    the LORD will lead them away with the evildoers;

    but peace be upon Israel.   *Refrain*

Tone

Lectionary: Ordinary Time after Pentecost (B).

Words and Music: Bernadette Farrell © 1999 Bernadette Farrell, admin. OCP Publications
Psalm Text: from *Evangelical Lutheran Worship* © 2006 Evangelical Lutheran Church in America, admin.
Augsburg Fortress Publishers
Tone: © 2011 Faith Alive Christian Resources

Those Who Rely on the Lord 125B

Words: Christopher Idle © 1987 The Jubilate Group, admin. Hope Publishing Company
Music (CLERMONT PARK 12.10.12.10): Roy Hopp © 2011 Roy Hopp

125C Those Who Place on God Reliance

1 Those who place on God re - li - ance in de - spair shall
2 Ev - er - last - ing is Mount Zi - on, from cre - a - tion's
3 God's good bless - ings shall be giv - en to all those who
4 Those who work a - gainst God's heal - ing have their ill with

not be moved. As the moun - tains hug the val - ley,
dawn till night; so e - ter - nal is God's prom - ise
do God's will. Just re - wards shall be their for - tune;
ill re - paid. All the faith - ful of the king - dom

so em - braced are God's be - loved.
to all those who live a - right.
God is with us, with us still.
find their full re - demp - tion made.

Optional stanzas from Psalm 126

1 When the Lord restored our blessing,
all delights were like a dream;
in defeat, a shout of victory;
in the sand, a flowing stream.

2 Mouths that once were parched
with anguish
now with shouts of joy are filled;
laughter now displaces sadness
for the goodness God has willed.

3 Bring us back to former glory,
lost through years of exile's pain;
generations long forgotten
seek God's favor to regain.

4 Those who plant their seeds
with grieving,
wetting soil with falling tears,
shall rejoice in time of harvest,
reaping hope for all their years.

Words: Michael Morgan © 1999, 2011 Michael Morgan, admin. Faith Alive Christian Resources
Music (HATIKVAH 8.7.8.7): traditional Hebrew melody; arr. Hal H. Hopson © 2008 Birnamwood
Publications, a division of MorningStar Music Publishers, Inc.

Psalm 126

A Song of Ascents.

1 When the LORD restored the fortunes of Zion, *
   we were like those who dream.

2 **Then our mouth was filled with laughter,**
   and our tongue with shouts of joy; *
      then it was said among the nations,
      "The LORD has done great things for them."

3 **The LORD has done great things for us,** *
   and we rejoiced.

4 Restore our fortunes, O LORD, *
   like the watercourses in the Negeb.

5 **May those who sow in tears** *
   reap with shouts of joy.

6 **Those who go out weeping, bearing the seed for sowing,** *
   shall come home with shouts of joy, carrying their sheaves.

We are overwhelmed, O Lord, by your love and saving goodness.
In Christ Jesus you restore both our lives and our world.
Like reapers at an unexpected harvest,
we shout your praise and sing your goodness. **Amen.**

Psalm 126, the seventh of the Psalms of Ascents, remembers the restoration of Zion and expresses hope in God's continued restoration (see also Ps. 85). Its imagery of transformation (weeping to rejoicing, sowing to reaping) makes this psalm rich with evocative possibilities, especially when linked with other scriptural texts that depict conversion, deliverance, or resurrection using the images of weeping and rejoicing (e.g., Ps. 30 or the raising of Lazarus) and sowing and reaping (Luke 8:1-9, 1 Cor. 15:35-42, 2 Cor. 9:6-10, James 3:18). *Use in Worship: Thanksgiving Day (due to harvest imagery, suggesting that harvest festivals can themselves be viewed as an allegory or parable of a spiritual harvest).*

For an additional setting of Ps. 126 see 125C.

126A When God First Brought Us Back

1 When God first brought us back from ex-ile, we were as dazed
2 Once more, O Lord, re-store your peo-ple; come with your sav-

as those who dream. Then were our mouths brim-ming with
-ing help a-gain, as to the brook-beds in the

laugh-ter; joy from our lips gushed like a stream. The god-less
des-ert you bring the sweet, re-viv-ing rain. Let those who

cried in en-vious won-der, "Look what the Lord
sow with tears and sigh-ing sing as they reap

Words: Carl P. Daw Jr. (b. 1944) © 1996 Hope Publishing Company
Music (WAYFARING STRANGER 9.8.9.8 D): traditional American; arr. Horace Clarence Boyer (1935-2009)
© 1992 Horace Clarence Boyer

126B Psalm 126 | A Responsorial Setting

Refrain

¹ When the LORD restored the fortunes of Zion,
   then were we like those who dream.

² Then was our mouth filled with laughter, and our tongue with shouts of joy.
   Then they said among the nations,
   "The LORD has done great things for them."

³ The LORD has done great things for us,
   and we are glad indeed.   *Refrain*

⁴ Restore our fortunes, O LORD,
   like the watercourses of the Negeb.

⁵ Those who sowed with tears
   will reap with songs of joy.

⁶ Those who go out weeping, carrying the seed,
   will come again with joy, shouldering their sheaves.   *Refrain*

Tone

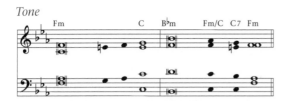

Lectionary: Advent (B); Lent (C); Ordinary Time after Pentecost (B); Thanksgiving Day (B).

Words and Music: Andrew Donaldson © 1995 Andrew Donaldson
Psalm Text: from *Evangelical Lutheran Worship* © 2006 Evangelical Lutheran Church in America, admin.
Augsburg Fortress Publishers
Tone: © 2011 Faith Alive Christian Resources

Alternate Refrain

Those who sow in tears and sor - row one day will reap with joy.

Alternate Tone

Words: Ladies of the Grail © 1963, 1986 The Grail, England, GIA Publications, Inc., exclusive North American agent
Music: Joseph Gelineau © 1963, 1986 The Grail, England, GIA Publications, Inc., exclusive North American agent
Tone: © 2011 Faith Alive Christian Resources

126C A Prayer for Deliverance

The following may be prayed between stanzas 2 and 3 of "When God Restored Our Common Life" (126E).

Lord God, we pause now to recall with joy all those times that your people have experienced your liberating power—with Moses and Miriam at the Red Sea, with Nehemiah at the rebuilding of the temple, with Peter at the Pentecostal outpouring of your Holy Spirit [add other examples as appropriate]. Emboldened by such memories, we pray for all those who long for this kind of liberation today [list those persecuted for faith or other examples as appropriate]. Strengthen us in prayer and fill us with hope so that your people may sing with joy.

126D When the Lord Brought Back

1 When the Lord brought back from cap-ti-vi-ty his flock,
2 Then they said a-mong the na-tions, "God for them has done great things;
3 Re - store, O Lord, our for-tunes as of old,

we were all like peo-ple in a dream.
might-y mar-vels he has done in - deed."
like the tor-rents of the des-erts in the south.

Then our throats with laugh-ter rang, and our tongues burst out in
Yes, the Lord has won-ders done, end-less pow - er he has
Those who weep-ing sow the seed shall in joy the har-vest

song; we a-woke like peo-ple from a dream.
shown, and we are glad in - deed.
reap. Life shall be re-stored as tor-rents of the south.

Refrain

Though with tears we set out sad-ly in the ear-ly morn, bear-ing

forth the seed to be sown, we shall come back re-joic-ing at the

set-ting of the sun; we shall come back car-ry-ing the sheaves.

We shall come back re-joic-ing, car-ry-ing the sheaves; we shall

come back re-joic-ing all the way. Though we left in the morn-ing with a

To Stanzas

bit-ter seed to sow, we shall come back re-joic-ing all the way.

Coda (to be sung after last Refrain)

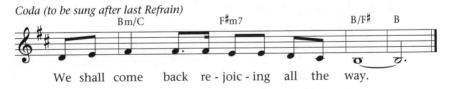

We shall come back re-joic-ing all the way.

Keyboard accompaniment on p. 836.

Words: Henry Bryan Hays, O. S. B. (b. 1920) © 1979 Liturgical Press
Music (LOOKOUT MOUNTAIN): Henry Bryan Hays, O. S. B. (b. 1920) © 1979, 1991 Liturgical Press

Keyboard Accompaniment

Music (LOOKOUT MOUNTAIN): Henry Bryan Hays, O. S. B. (b. 1920) © 1979, 1991 Liturgical Press

When God Restored Our Common Life

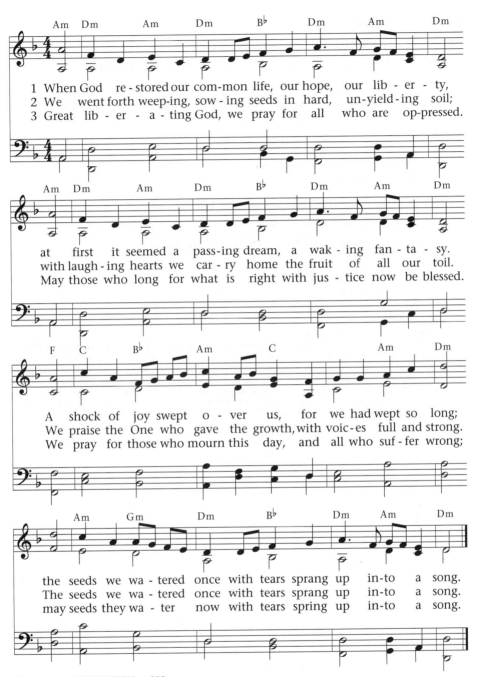

1 When God re-stored our com-mon life, our hope, our lib-er-ty,
2 We went forth weep-ing, sow-ing seeds in hard, un-yield-ing soil;
3 Great lib-er-a-ting God, we pray for all who are op-pressed.

at first it seemed a pass-ing dream, a wak-ing fan-ta-sy.
with laugh-ing hearts we car-ry home the fruit of all our toil.
May those who long for what is right with jus-tice now be blessed.

A shock of joy swept o-ver us, for we had wept so long;
We praise the One who gave the growth, with voic-es full and strong.
We pray for those who mourn this day, and all who suf-fer wrong;

the seeds we wa-tered once with tears sprang up in-to a song.
The seeds we wa-tered once with tears sprang up in-to a song.
may seeds they wa-ter now with tears spring up in-to a song.

Alternate tune: RESIGNATION, p. 908.

Words: Ruth C. Duck, 1982, © 1992 GIA Publications, Inc.
Music (SALVATION 8.6.8.6 D): *Kentucky Harmony*, 1816; harm. Kenneth Munson (1916-1988), P.D.

Psalm 127

A Song of Ascents. Of Solomon.

1 Unless the LORD builds the house, those who build it labor in vain. *
    Unless the LORD guards the city, the guard keeps watch in vain.

2 **It is in vain that you rise up early and go late to rest,** *
    eating the bread of anxious toil; for he gives sleep to his beloved.

3 Sons are indeed a heritage from the LORD, *
    the fruit of the womb a reward.

4 Like arrows in the hand of a warrior *
    are the sons of one's youth.

5 **Happy is the man who has his quiver full of them.** *
    He shall not be put to shame
    when he speaks with his enemies in the gate.

Heavenly Father,
in all our toil and striving, at work and in the home,
may we always trust in your blessing rather than in our own efforts,
through the finished work of Jesus Christ our Lord. **Amen.**

Psalm 127, the eighth of the Psalms of Ascents, describes the utter necessity of divine agency in anything of lasting value. Apart from God's activity, there is only vanity and endless, fruitless toil—a message that echoes Ecclesiastes. It suggests that God's activity engages both civic and family life, and may include everything from building houses and guarding cities to enabling sleep and providing children. The psalm calls for dependence on God in every aspect of life and challenges the pretension that our own endless striving, by itself, can achieve anything of lasting significance. *Use in Worship: services focusing on civic and cultural engagement, family life, or vocation; services focusing on the theme of divine agency (a theme that permeates many NT texts [e.g., 1 Cor., Phil. 3]).*

Unless the Lord Constructs the House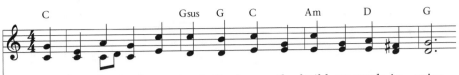

1 Un - less the Lord con - structs the house, the build-ers work in vain;
2 Un - less the Lord is keep - ing watch, the cit - y can - not stand;
3 In vain you la - bor night and day, by con-stant care op-pressed;

the Lord a - lone de - signs and builds foun - da - tions that re - main.
the sen - try guards the gates in vain with - out God's might-y hand.
the Lord sup-plies your loved ones' needs and grants them sleep and rest.

4 The Lord designed the family,
   providing earthly love;
   our children are God's heritage—
   a gift from heaven above.

5 Like weapons in a warrior's hand
   are those who bear our name;
   with them we face a hostile world
   assured and free from shame.

Guitar chords do not correspond with keyboard harmony.

Words: Mollie Knight © 1990 The Jubilate Group, admin. Hope Publishing Company
Music (ST. ANNE 8.6.8.6): William Croft, 1708, P.D.

Refrain

1 Unless the LORD builds the house, their labor is in vain who build it.
　　Unless the LORD watches over the city, in vain the sentinel keeps vigil.

2 It is in vain to rise so early and go to bed so late;
　　vain, too, to eat the bread of toil;
　　for you, LORD, give sleep to your beloved.　*Refrain*

3 Children are a heritage from the LORD,
　　and the fruit of the womb is a gift.

4 Like arrows in the hand of a warrior
　　are the children of one's youth.

5 Happy is the one whose quiver is full of them!
　　Such a one will not be put to shame
　　when contending with enemies in the gate.　*Refrain*

Tone

Lectionary: Ordinary Time after Pentecost (B).

Words and Music: Gregg DeMey © 2011 Re:Create Music; arr. Paul Detterman © 2011 Re:Create Music
Psalm Text: from *Evangelical Lutheran Worship* © 2006 Evangelical Lutheran Church in America, admin.
Augsburg Fortress Publishers
Tone: © 2011 Faith Alive Christian Resources

A Prayer of Trust for Psalms 127 and 131 　127C

Sing or read Psalm 127

Loving God,
when our striving makes us anxious,
when our efforts seem vain,
help us to hear again the beauty of your promise:
　　"The Lord gives rest to his beloved."

Quiet our hearts, we pray,
and teach us to trust in you.

Sing or read Psalm 131

John D. Witvliet, 2011, © Creative Commons Attribution-NonCommercial-ShareAlike

Psalm 128

A Song of Ascents.

¹ Happy is everyone who fears the LORD, *
  who walks in his ways.

² **You shall eat the fruit of the labor of your hands; ***
  you shall be happy, and it shall go well with you.

³ Your wife will be like a fruitful vine within your house; *
  your children will be like olive shoots around your table.

⁴ **Thus shall the man be blessed ***
  who fears the LORD.

⁵ The LORD bless you from Zion. *
  May you see the prosperity of Jerusalem all the days of your life.

⁶ **May you see your children's children. ***
  Peace be upon Israel!

Source of unending blessings,
be present in our homes and families
and in the fellowship and ministry of your church.
As we gather at our tables, and as we gather at your table,
unite us in the vision of the great wedding feast of the Lamb,
in whose name we ask this. **Amen.**

Psalm 128, the ninth of the Psalms of Ascents, is a proverb-like statement about the blessings of labor and family life that come to those who revere God (see also Ps. 112). The psalm is expressed in the form of a beatitude (vv. 1-4) and benediction (vv. 5-6). In the ordinary activities of life, it stresses that true blessing comes because of God's work through human activities; God is the source of every good gift (see James 1:17). The psalm focuses on the head of the household as a representative of the entire family unit, just as some royal psalms speak of the king as representative of the entire nation. *Use in Worship: services focusing on family life and human labor; services based on other proverbs or beatitudes.*

Blest Are They Who Trust 128A

Refrain
Harmony

Blest are they who trust, who trust in the Lord.

Unison

1 Joy a - bounds for all the faith - ful; those who trust the
2 Joy a - bounds for all the faith - ful; those who trust the
3 Like a fruit - ful vine they flour - ish, branch - es of a

Lord are filled; all the good wrought by their la - bor
Lord are filled; right - eous minds, in - fused with jus - tice;
faith - ful tree, so shall chil - dren's chil - dren gath - er

is their gain, so God has willed.
stead - fast hearts, with love in - stilled.
at your ta - ble, you to see.

Words: ref. Hal H. Hopson © 2008 Birnamwood Publications, a division of MorningStar Music Publishers, Inc.; sts. Michael Morgan © 1999, 2011 Michael Morgan, admin. Faith Alive Christian Resources
Music (RUSSIAN TUNE OLD 8.7.8.7 with refrain): adapt. from traditional Russian Orthodox chant; arr. Hal H. Hopson © 2008 Birnamwood Publications, a division of MorningStar Music Publishers, Inc.

128B Psalm 128 | A Responsorial Setting

Refrain

Blest are those who love you, hap-py those who fol-low you, blest are those who seek you, O God.

Refrain

1. Happy are they all who fear the LORD,
    and who follow in God's ways!

2. You shall eat the fruit of your labor;
    happiness and prosperity shall be yours.

3. Your wife shall be like a fruitful vine within your house,
    your children like olive shoots round about your table.

4. The one who fears the LORD
    shall thus indeed be blessed.   *Refrain*

5. The LORD bless you from Zion,
    and may you see the prosperity of Jerusalem all the days of your life.

6. May you live to see your children's children;
    may peace be upon Israel.   *Refrain*

Tone

Lectionary: Ordinary Time after Pentecost (A).

Words and Music: Marty Haugen (b. 1950) © 1987, 1993 GIA Publications, Inc.
Psalm Text: from *Evangelical Lutheran Worship* © 2006 Evangelical Lutheran Church in America, admin.
Augsburg Fortress Publishers
Tone: © 2011 Faith Alive Christian Resources

Whoever Fears the Lord 128C

1 Who-ev - er fears the Lord and lives as God in - tends
2 We cel - e - brate the joys of home and fam - i - ly,
3 His kind-ness is re - vealed where bit - ter con - flicts cease;

will find the whole of life is filled with gifts he sends.
where love's en - dur-ing bonds pro - vide se - cu - ri - ty.
far more, with - in our hearts, his mer - cy brings us peace.

When work is more than toil and reaps a just re - ward,
God nur-tures ev - ery child for life's de-mand - ing race;
May God pro - long our days to see our chil-dren's heirs,

when strength and health are ours, all these are from the Lord!
each day he of - fers us new fruit - ful - ness, new grace.
and may his gra-cious gifts be ours and al - so theirs.

Words: Martin Leckebusch © 2003 Kevin Mayhew Ltd.
Music (OLD DOMINION 6.6.6.6 D): Roy Hopp © 2011 Roy Hopp

Psalm 129

A Song of Ascents.

¹ "Often have they attacked me from my youth" *
  —let Israel now say—

² "often have they attacked me from my youth, *
  yet they have not prevailed against me.

³ The plowers plowed on my back; *
  they made their furrows long."

⁴ **The LORD is righteous; ***
  he has cut the cords of the wicked.

⁵ **May all who hate Zion ***
  be put to shame and turned backward.

⁶ Let them be like the grass on the housetops *
  that withers before it grows up,

⁷ with which reapers do not fill their hands *
  or binders of sheaves their arms,

⁸ while those who pass by do not say, *
  "The blessing of the LORD be upon you!
  We bless you in the name of the LORD!"

O God, the cords of sin are strong—they bind us close to death.
But the victory you have given us in Jesus Christ
has severed those cords and loosed the bonds of evil.
We now live to bless you and to sing your praise in all the world. **Amen.**

Psalm 129, the tenth Psalm of Ascents, is a psalm about how the past deliverance of God grounds our current approach to threats. It looks back at God's past deliverance (vv. 1-4) and ahead to the continued need for deliverance (vv. 5-8). The Hebrew grammar of the psalm is ambiguous enough to allow for it to be read as either a prayer expressing desire for God to turn away the enemy or as a confident assurance that God will do so. The imagery is especially poignant, depicting those who are against God as the withered grass of an empty harvest (in contrast to the plentiful harvest suggested in Pss. 126:6 and 128:2). *Use in Worship: as a way to enter into the experience of ancient Israel (in conjunction with readings about Israel's struggle with enemies); in conjunction with NT texts about the principalities and powers that oppose God's purposes.*

I Will Sing a Song of Triumph 129A

1 I will sing a song of triumph, sing to
2 When the con-flicts I en-coun-tered left me
3 Those who hate what God has cho-sen: in the
4 Those who trust the Lord to save them: may they

re - as - sert the truth, sing al-though un-num-bered
wound-ed, scarred, and sore, God the Right-eous One was
end, how can they thrive? Plants with nei-ther earth nor
find, in-stead of shame, kind-ness from the One they

trou - bles have be - set me since my youth:
with me to de-stroy the chains I bore.
mois-ture, what can help them to sur - vive?
wor - ship, end - less bless - ings in God's name.

Alternate harmonization on p. 897.

Words: Martin Leckebusch © 2003 Kevin Mayhew Ltd.
Music (CAPTIVITY/KAS DZIEDAJA 8.7.8.7): Latvian melody; arr. Greg Scheer © 2008 Greg Scheer

Psalm 130

A Song of Ascents.

1 Out of the depths I cry to you, O LORD. *
  2 Lord, hear my voice!

Let your ears be attentive *
to the voice of my supplications!

3 If you, O LORD, should mark iniquities, *
  Lord, who could stand?

4 **But there is forgiveness with you, ***
so that you may be revered.

5 **I wait for the LORD, my soul waits, ***
and in his word I hope;

6 **my soul waits for the Lord ***
more than those who watch for the morning,
more than those who watch for the morning.

7 O Israel, hope in the LORD! *
  For with the LORD there is steadfast love,
  and with him is great power to redeem.

8 **It is he who will redeem Israel ***
from all its iniquities.

When we realize the depth of our sin, O God, we are driven into dark despair.
It is only when we realize the height of your mercy
and the breadth of your forgiveness,
that we begin to see the dawning of new life in Jesus Christ.
Thanks be to you, O Lord our Redeemer. **Amen.**

Psalm 130, the eleventh of the Psalms of Ascents and one of the seven penitential psalms, is a profound expression of the human predicament and a strong statement of God's grace. It is often identified by its opening words in Latin *de profundis*, and has been associated with prayers to God in concentration camps and prisons, hospitals, and places of devastation. The central motifs of the psalm are waiting for God and the pardon and redemption that God provides for a people who have taken the wrong path. Though confident of God's sovereign grace, the psalm ends with a call to hope in the Lord. *Use in Worship: in conjunction with prayers of lament; in conjunction with confession and the assurance of God's grace and pardon; during the season of Advent; on any occasion as a testimony of God's sovereign grace.*

Out of the Depths I Cry to You 130A

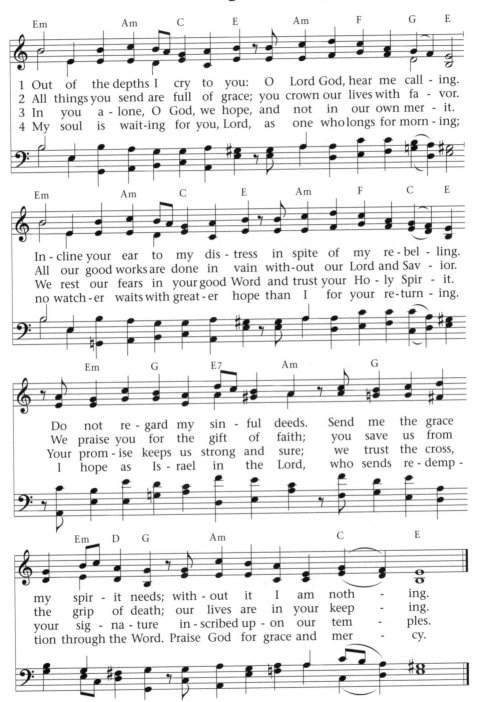

1 Out of the depths I cry to you: O Lord God, hear me call - ing.
2 All things you send are full of grace; you crown our lives with fa - vor.
3 In you a - lone, O God, we hope, and not in our own mer - it.
4 My soul is wait-ing for you, Lord, as one who longs for morn - ing;

In - cline your ear to my dis - tress in spite of my re - bel - ling.
All our good works are done in vain with-out our Lord and Sav - ior.
We rest our fears in your good Word and trust your Ho - ly Spir - it.
no watch - er waits with great - er hope than I for your re-turn - ing.

Do not re - gard my sin - ful deeds. Send me the grace
We praise you for the gift of faith; you save us from
Your prom - ise keeps us strong and sure; we trust the cross,
I hope as Is - rael in the Lord, who sends re - demp -

my spir - it needs; with - out it I am noth - ing.
the grip of death; our lives are in your keep - ing.
your sig - na - ture in - scribed up - on our tem - ples.
tion through the Word. Praise God for grace and mer - cy.

Guitar chords do not correspond with keyboard harmony.

Words: Martin Luther, 1524; tr. Gracia Grindal © 1978, 2006 Augsburg Fortress Publishers
Music (AUS TIEFER NOT 8.7.8.7.8.8.7): Martin Luther, 1524; harm. Austin C. Lovelace, 1963, © 1964
Abingdon Press, admin. The Copyright Company

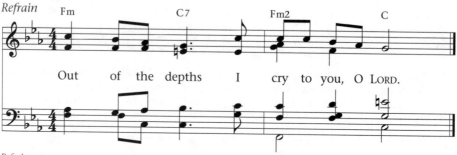

Refrain

Out of the depths I cry to you, O LORD.

Refrain

¹ Out of the depths
   I cry to you, O LORD;

² O LORD, hear my voice!
   Let your ears be attentive to the voice of my supplication.

³ If you were to keep watch over sins,
   O LORD, who could stand?

⁴ Yet with you is forgiveness,
   in order that you may be feared.   *Refrain*

⁵ I wait for you, O LORD; my soul waits;
   in your word is my hope.

⁶ My soul waits for the Lord more than those who keep watch for the morning,
   more than those who keep watch for the morning.   *Refrain*

⁷ O Israel, wait for the LORD, for with the LORD there is steadfast love;
   with the LORD there is plenteous redemption.

⁸ For the LORD shall redeem Israel
   from all their sins.   *Refrain*

Tone

Lectionary: Lent (A); Ordinary Time after Pentecost (B).

Words: Psalm 130:1
Music: Kathleen Harmon, S. N. D. de N. © 1993 Institute for Liturgical Ministry, admin. Faith Alive Christian Resources
Psalm Text: from *Evangelical Lutheran Worship* © 2006 Evangelical Lutheran Church in America, admin. Augsburg Fortress Publishers
Tone: © 2011 Faith Alive Christian Resources

Out of the Depths I Cry to You on High 130C

1 Out of the depths I cry to you on high; Lord, hear my
2 I wait for God, I trust his ho-ly word; he hears my
3 Hope in the Lord: un-fail-ing is his love; in him con-

call. Bend down your ear and lis-ten to my sigh,
sighs. My soul still waits and looks un-to the Lord;
fide. Mer-cy and full re-demp-tion from a-bove

for-giv-ing all. If you should mark our sins, who then could
my prayers a-rise. I look for him to drive a-way my
he does pro-vide. From sin and e-vil, might-y though they

stand? But grace and mer-cy dwell at your right hand.
night— yes, more than those who watch for morn-ing light.
seem, his arm al-might-y will his saints re-deem.

Words: *Psalter*, 1912, alt., P.D.
Music (SANDON 10.4.10.4.10.10): Charles H. Purday, 1860, P.D.

130D Out of the Depths I Cry to You

1 Out of the depths I cry to you.
2 Out of the woe - ful depths I cry,
4 Lord, from the depths I wait for you,
5 Lord, here I find your mer - cy now,

O Lord please hear my call. O Lord be mer -
from the depths of sin— of e - vil done
my hope is in your Word. All through the night
as ev - er was with you. Be - fore your throne

- ci - ful to me; at your throne of grace I fall;
in days gone by, and of e - vil now with - in;
till day is nigh, my soul waits up - on the Lord;
of grace I bow, Lord, be mer - ci - ful to me;

at your throne of grace I fall.
and of e - vil now with - in.
my soul waits up - on the Lord.
Lord, be mer - ci - ful to me.

Words: Karl Digerness, adapt. from *Out of the Deep I Call*, by Henry W. Baker, 1868, © 2005 Karl Digerness
Music: Karl Digerness © 2005 Karl Digerness; arr. Eelco Vos © 2011 Karl Digerness

130E In Deep Despair I Cry to You

1 In deep de-spair I cry to you—Lord, hear my
2 The sound-less whis-per of your voice, your hov-ering
3 Be-cause your love is stead-fast, Lord, on you our

voice, my prayer. If you should mark in-iq-ui-ties, who
pres-ence near, for these my long-ing spir-it waits as
hope re-lies; you will re-deem your Is-ra-el from

would stand guilt-less there? But, Lord, with you for-
for the morn-ing clear, as those who watch through-
all in-iq-ui-ties and turn to songs of

give-ness dwells and love be-yond com-pare.
out the night till morn-ing shall ap-pear.
thanks and praise our sor-row and our sighs.

Guitar chords do not correspond with keyboard harmony.

Alternate harmonization on p. 686.

Words: Joy F. Patterson (b. 1931), 1991, © 1994 Selah Publishing Company, Inc.
Music (MORNING SONG/CONSOLATION 8.6.8.6.8.6): *Sixteen Tune Settings*, 1812; attr. Elkanah Kelsey
Dare; harm. David Ashley White, 1994, © 1994 Selah Publishing Company, Inc.

From the Depths of Sin and Sadness 130F

1 From the depths of sin and sad-ness, I have called un-to the Lord.
2 If you, Lord, re-cord our sin-ning, who could then be-fore you stand?
3 For the Lord my heart is long-ing, for God's Word I hope and wait.
4 Hope, O peo-ple, in your Sav-ior, who will save you from your sins.

Be not deaf to my poor plead-ing, in your mer-cy, hear my voice. voice.
But with you there is for-give-ness, you shall ev-er be re-vered. vered.
More than watch-ers for the sun-rise, I am wait-ing for the Lord. Lord.
Ky - ri - e e-le - i - son. In your mer-cy hear my voice. voice.

Kyrie eleison means 'Lord, have mercy.'

Words: Willard F. Jabusch, ca. 1966, © 1966 Willard F. Jabusch, admin. OCP Publications
Music (RUSSIAN 8.7.8.7 with repeat): Russian folk melody; harm. Susan G. Wente © 1977 World Library Publications

For You, My God, I Wait

1 For you,   my God,   I wait
2 Lord, hear   my plead - ing voice,
3 If you   should list   my faults,
4 For ev - en   from   the deep

with hope   born of   the Word.
and let   me know   you hear!
the sins   of heart   and hand,
I know   you hear   my cries.

Like sleep - less ones   who long   to dream
As sleep - less ones   feel rest   ap-proach,
like sleep - less ones   who groan   at dawn
Like sleep - less ones   who dream   at last,

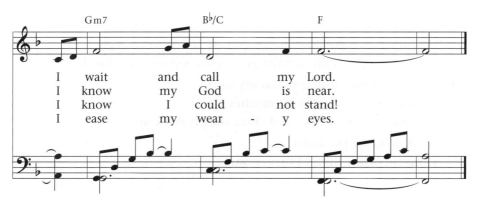

(Psalm 131)

5 And once my soul is still,
    in you I find my rest,
    at peace as though a child upon
    a gentle mother's breast.

6 O God, you are my hope;
    I know that you forgive.
    Your love redeems me from the depths
    so I may rise and live.

Words: Adam M. L. Tice © 2011 GIA Publications, Inc.
Music (SPRINGTIME 6.6.8.6): David Ward © 2011 David Ward, admin. Faith Alive Christian Resources

A Prayer of Hope 130H

Out of the depths of my soul I cry to you,
    in times of need, doubt, and fear,
    sorrow and loneliness,
    pain and powerlessness.

There, in the depths of my despair,
    marked by my sin and shortcomings,
    you hear my voice and attend to my cries.

You meet me with forgiveness and steadfast love.

Even in the depths, I can wait in confidence,
    trusting that you are journeying with me from darkness to light,
    for with you is transformation and redemption.

My soul waits for you,
    and in your word I hope.

Melissa Haupt, 2011, © Creative Commons Attribution-NonCommercial-ShareAlike

Psalm 131

A Song of Ascents. Of David.

¹ O Lᴏʀᴅ, my heart is not lifted up, my eyes are not raised too high; *
   I do not occupy myself with things too great and too marvelous for me.

² **But I have calmed and quieted my soul,**
   like a weaned child with its mother; *
      my soul is like the weaned child that is with me.

³ **O Israel, hope in the Lᴏʀᴅ ***
   from this time on and forevermore.

O Christ,
our lives and our world seem so tangled and complicated.
Help us to desire nothing else but that you will always be present to us,
and that we may always be present to you. **Amen.**

Psalm 131, the twelfth of the Psalms of Ascents, is a poignant expression of serene contentment and utter dependence upon God. At the center of the psalm is a dramatic comparison of the person of faith to a weaned and satisfied child in the arms of its mother. Like Ps. 130, it calls the people to wait on God, but this time from a place of less despair. It announces that trust in God need not demand answers to all of life's questions and stands as a call to set aside anxiety and to rest in God (see also Matt. 11:28). *Use in Worship: services focusing on the call to rest in God; a response to sermons that explore either the grandeur of God or the problem of evil—sermons that will likely end not only with answers but also with questions; night prayer; a response to celebrations of the Lord's Supper (after which God's people may be asked to pause to experience the contentment of weaned children).*

For an additional setting of Ps. 131 see 130G.

131A A Prayer of Surrender and Trust

Loving God,
   may our words be simple,
   our hearts humbled,
   our attention focused,
   and our thoughts pure.
Thank you that we may lean upon you,
   as a child with its mother.
You are our hope and we praise you,
   now and forever. **Amen.**

In You, O Lord, 131B
I Have Found My Peace

Refrain

In you, O Lord, I have found my peace, I have found my peace.

(last time)

1 My heart is not proud, my eyes not a-bove you; you fill my soul. I am not filled with great things, nor with thoughts be-yond me.

2 My soul is still, my soul stays qui-et, long-ing for you like a weaned child in its moth-er's arms; so is my soul a child with you.

To Refrain

Words and Music: David Haas (b. 1957) © 1985 GIA Publications, Inc.

131C Psalm 131 | A Responsorial Setting

Refrain

Like a child that is qui-et-ed is my soul,
like a child that is qui-et-ed is my soul.

Refrain

¹ O Lord, I am not proud; I have no haughty looks.

    I do not occupy myself with great matters,

      or with things that are too hard for me.   *Refrain*

² But I still my soul and make it quiet, like a child upon its mother's breast;

    my soul is quieted within me.

³ O Israel, wait upon the Lord,

    from this time forth forevermore.   *Refrain*

Tone

Lectionary: Ordinary Time after Epiphany (A); Ordinary Time after Pentecost (A).

If the psalm is read, the first two measures of the alto, tenor, and bass parts may be repeated as an ostinato under the reading.

Words: Loretta Ellenberger © 1973 Hope Publishing Company
Music: Loretta Ellenberger © 1973 Hope Publishing Company; arr. Rupert Lang © 1999 Hope Publishing Company
Psalm Text: from *Evangelical Lutheran Worship* © 2006 Evangelical Lutheran Church in America, admin. Augsburg Fortress Publishers
Tone: © 2011 Faith Alive Christian Resources

For You the Pride  131D
from My Heart Is Banished

1 For you the pride from my heart is ban - ished, for you false
2 Now is my soul calm from all its test - ing, like a weaned

dreams from my eyes have van - ished; for you vain glo - ry
child on her moth - er rest - ing. May all who hear join

I leave ad-mir - ing, end-less am - bi - tion I cease de - sir - ing.
such cel - e - bra - tion; wait for the Lord. God is worth our wait-ing.

Words: The Iona Community © 1993 Wild Goose Resource Group, Iona Community, Scotland, GIA Publications, Inc., exclusive North American agent
Music (THE ISLE OF MULL 10.10.10.10): Scottish traditional; arr. © 1993 Wild Goose Resource Group, Iona Community, Scotland, GIA Publications, Inc., exclusive North American agent

131E # Like A Child Rests

Refrain

Like a child rests in its moth-er's arms, so will I rest in you.

Like a child rests in its moth-er's arms, so will I rest in you.

To Refrain

1 My God, I am not proud. I do not look for things too great.
2 My God, I trust in you. You care for me, you give me peace.
3 O Is - rael, trust in God; now and al - ways trust in God.

Guitar chords do not correspond with keyboard harmony.

Words and Music: Christopher Walker (b. 1947) © 1988, 1989 Christopher Walker, admin. OCP Publications

A Song of Ascents.

1 O LORD, remember in David's favor *
   all the hardships he endured;

2 how he swore to the LORD *
   and vowed to the Mighty One of Jacob,

3 **"I will not enter my house ***
   or get into my bed;

4 **I will not give sleep to my eyes ***
   or slumber to my eyelids,

5 **until I find a place for the LORD, ***
   a dwelling place for the Mighty One of Jacob."

6 We heard of it in Ephrathah; *
   we found it in the fields of Jaar.

7 **"Let us go to his dwelling place; ***
   let us worship at his footstool."

8 **Rise up, O LORD, and go to your resting place, ***
   you and the ark of your might.

9 **Let your priests be clothed with righteousness, ***
   and let your faithful shout for joy.

10 **For your servant David's sake ***
   do not turn away the face of your anointed one.

11 The LORD swore to David a sure oath from which he will not turn back: *
   "One of the sons of your body I will set on your throne.

12 If your sons keep my covenant and my decrees that I shall teach them, *
   their sons also, forevermore, shall sit on your throne."

13 **For the LORD has chosen Zion; ***
   he has desired it for his habitation:

14 "This is my resting place forever; *
   here I will reside, for I have desired it.

15 I will abundantly bless its provisions; *
   I will satisfy its poor with bread.

16 **Its priests I will clothe with salvation, ***
   and its faithful will shout for joy.

17 There I will cause a horn to sprout up for David; *
   I have prepared a lamp for my anointed one.

18 **His enemies I will clothe with disgrace, ***
   but on him, his crown will gleam."

(continues)

Psalm 132 (continued)

Eternal God,
you fulfilled your promise to give us a Messiah of David's household.
In Jesus Christ you have clothed us with life and fed us the living bread of his body.
Crowned with the victory of his resurrection, we shout for joy. **Amen.**

Psalm 132, the thirteenth of the Psalms of Ascents, is a call and response statement of covenant faithfulness. The psalm opens with a prayer (vv. 1-10) that rehearses David's vows of commitment to God and closes with a rehearsal of God's vows to David (vv. 11-18) that focus on God's election of Zion and of David and his descendants. It is an example of the ideal personal exchange between God and the covenantal community: the prayer to God speaks glowingly of "their priests clothed in faithfulness, the people committed to rejoicing in God," and God responds by promising to "clothe the priests in deliverance and the people with rejoicing" (vv. 9, 16). *Use in Worship: celebrations of the lordship of Christ (especially in light of the promise of v. 11 "the fruit of your body I will place on the throne"); any season of covenantal renewal.*

132A When David Had a Longing

1 When Da - vid had a long - ing to build the Lord a house,
2 The Lord then vowed to Da - vid: his house would sure - ly last

he voiced his heart's in - ten - tion by means of sol - emn vows.
if on - ly his suc - ces - sors held God's com - mand - ments fast;

His peo - ple caught the vi - sion: to build a sa - cred place
God longed to set a - mong them a throne for heav - en's King;

where ho - ly joy and wor - ship would please the God of grace.
what joy and what a - bun - dance his pres - ence there would bring!

Let Da - vid be re - mem - bered, your faith - ful ser - vant, Lord:
Let Da - vid's Lamp be light - ed, your cho - sen ser - vant, Lord:

the depth of his de - vo - tion, the hard - ships he en - dured.
his king - dom be es - tab - lished, his tri - umph be as - sured.

Words: Martin Leckebusch © 2003 Kevin Mayhew Ltd.
Music (THAXTED 7.6.7.6 triple): Gustav Holst, 1921, P.D.

Once in Royal David's City, When the King Was in Distress

1 Once in roy - al Da - vid's cit - y, when the king was
in dis - tress, God re - deemed his shep - herd ser - vant through a
cov - e - nant to bless: "I have made this realm your
home— yours, and chil - dren yet to come."

2 God of trials and per - se - ver - ance, Da - vid's strength, and
Is - rael's stay, grant the ref - uge then pro - vi - ded to our
trou - bled lives to - day. Help us fash - ion through your
grace hearts to be your dwell - ing place.

3 Might - y Lord, by proph - ets prom - ised, come and reign in
right - eous - ness; let your peo - ple shout sal - va - tion, jus - tice
show, and love con - fess. May our songs with joy pro -
claim bound - less bless - ings in your name.

4 Al - ways loy - al to your chil - dren, in your word we
rest se - cure; gifts be - yond our ex - pec - ta - tions, mer - cy
full, and love so pure; bread for all whose plates are
bare; loaves to break, to feast, to share.

(continues)

5 Faithful to your ancient promise,
  Lord of present, future, past;
  flesh and Spirit, dwell among us,
  face to face with God at last!
  Born to show each child the way
  to your resurrection day.

6 Heir to David's royal lineage,
  God of heaven, child of earth;
  join us through your Holy Spirit,
  brothers, sisters in one birth.
  Love and light to us come down,
  by your gleaming star and crown.

Words: Michael Morgan © 2011 Michael Morgan, admin. Faith Alive Christian Resources
Music (IRBY 8.7.8.7.7.7): Henry J. Gauntlett, 1849, P.D.

Psalm 132 | A Responsorial Setting 132C

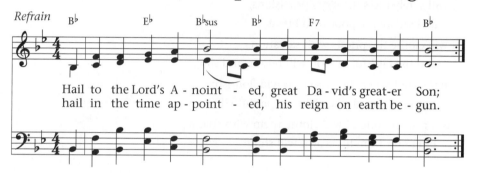

Refrain

Hail to the Lord's A - noint - ed, great Da - vid's great-er Son;
hail in the time ap - point - ed, his reign on earth be - gun.

Refrain

¹ LORD, remember David,

   and all the hardships he endured;

² how he swore an oath to the LORD

   and vowed a vow to the Mighty One of Jacob:

³ "I will not come under the roof of my house,

   nor climb up into my bed;

⁴ I will not allow my eyes to sleep,

   nor let my eyelids slumber;

⁵ until I find a place for the LORD,

   a dwelling for the Mighty One of Jacob."   *Refrain*

⁶ "The ark! We heard it was in Ephrathah;

   we found it in the fields of Ja'ar.

⁷ Let us go to God's dwelling-place;

   let us fall upon our knees before God's footstool."

⁸ Arise, O LORD, into your resting-place,

   you and the ark of your strength.

⁹ Let your priests be clothed with righteousness;

   let your faithful people sing with joy.

(continues)

¹⁰ For your servant David's sake,
     do not turn away the face of your anointed.   *Refrain*

¹¹ The L<small>ORD</small> has sworn an oath to David, and in truth, will not break it:
     "A son, the fruit of your body, will I set upon your throne.

¹² If your children keep my covenant and my testimonies that I shall teach them,
     their children will sit upon your throne forevermore."

¹³ For the L<small>ORD</small> has chosen Zion,
     desiring Jerusalem for a habitation:

¹⁴ "This shall be my resting-place forever;
     here will I dwell, for I delight in Zion.

¹⁵ I will surely bless the city's provisions,
     and satisfy the poor with bread.

¹⁶ I will clothe the priests with salvation,
     and the faithful in Zion will rejoice and sing.

¹⁷ There will I make the horn of David flourish;
     I have prepared a lamp for my anointed.

¹⁸ As for his enemies, I will clothe them with shame;
     but as for him, his crown will shine."   *Refrain*

Tone

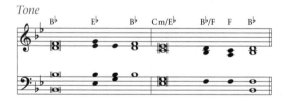

Lectionary: Reign of Christ (B).

Words: James Montgomery, 1822, P.D.
Music (ST. THEODULPH/VALET WILL ICH DIR GEBEN fragment): Thomas Tertius Noble, 1615, P.D.
Psalm Text: from *Evangelical Lutheran Worship* © 2006 Evangelical Lutheran Church in America, admin. Augsburg Fortress Publishers
Tone: © 2011 Faith Alive Christian Resources

A Song of Ascents.

¹ How very good and pleasant it is *
when kindred live together in unity!

² **It is like the precious oil on the head, ***
running down upon the beard, on the beard of Aaron,
running down over the collar of his robes.

³ **It is like the dew of Hermon, which falls on the mountains of Zion. ***
For there the LORD ordained his blessing, life forevermore.

O God, let the overflowing of your Holy Spirit
cover your church with the blessing of unity
and the anointing of your peace,
through our Lord Jesus Christ. **Amen.**

Psalm 133, the fourteenth of the Psalms of Ascents, is a celebration of the unity of God's people, a unity that is not to be taken for granted as the history of Israel attests. The psalm uses dramatic imagery to convey the beauty of unity, comparing it to fragrant oil and mountain dew. *Use in Worship: any occasion focusing on the nature, purpose, and mission of God's people (joining Pss. 87 [universality, diversity], 67 [mission], 125 [divine establishment], 15 and 24 [holiness]) in having an ecclesial focus.*

Behold the Goodness of Our Lord 133A

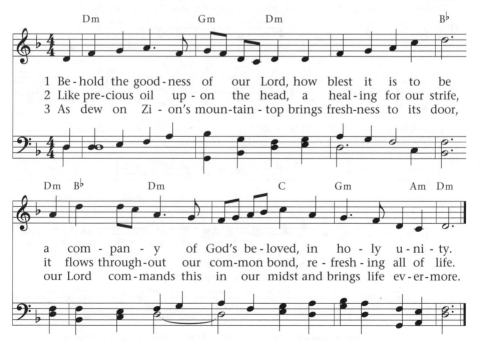

1 Be-hold the good-ness of our Lord, how blest it is to be
2 Like pre-cious oil up - on the head, a heal-ing for our strife,
3 As dew on Zi - on's moun-tain - top brings fresh-ness to its door,

a com - pan - y of God's be - loved, in ho - ly u - ni - ty.
it flows through-out our com-mon bond, re - fresh-ing all of life.
our Lord com-mands this in our midst and brings life ev-er-more.

Alternate harmonization on p. 114.

Words: Fred R. Anderson (b. 1941), 1986, © 1986 Fred R. Anderson, from *Singing Psalms of Joy and Praise*
Music (DETROIT 8.6.8.6): *Supplement to Kentucky Harmony*, 1820; P.D.; harm. Emily R. Brink (b. 1940), 1986,
© Faith Alive Christian Resources

Mirad cuán bueno y cuán delicioso / Behold, How Good and Delightful

Spanish: Mi - rad cuán bue - no y cuán de - li - cio - so es;
English: Be - hold, how good and de - light - ful a gift it is;

mi - rad cuán bue - no y cuán de - li - cio - so es
be - hold, how good and de - light - ful a gift it is

ha - bi - tar los her - ma - nos jun - tos en ar - mo - ní - a,
when sis - ters and broth - ers join hands to live in u - ni - ty.

por - que_a - llí en - ví - a_el Se - ñor ben - di - ción y vi - da_e - ter - na,
There the bless - ing of God de - scends; there is life now and for - ev - er.

por - que_a - llí en - ví - a_el Se - ñor ben - di - ción.
There the bless - ing of God de - scends: end - less life.

Words: traditional Puerto Rican; English tr. Martin A. Seltz © 1998 Augsburg Fortress Publishers
Music: traditional Puerto Rican; arr. Marcus Hong © 2011 Faith Alive Christian Resources

How Very Good and Pleasant 133C

How ver-y good and pleas-ant when we live in u-ni-ty. It is like pre-cious oil, like fresh morn-ing dew. We gath-er here to-geth-er with our hearts and voic-es raised to God, who's the cen-ter of our u-ni-ty and praise!

Words and Music: Barbara Boertje (b. 1959) © 1997 Barbara Boertje

133D Miren qué bueno / Oh, Look and Wonder

Refrain

To stanzas after repeat

Last time

Spanish ¡Mi - ren qué bue - no, qué bue - no es!
English Oh, look and won - der how good it is!

Stanzas

1 ¡Mir - en qué bue-no es cuan - do los her - ma - nos es - tán jun - tos!
1 How good it is when broth - ers dwell in peace with one an - oth - er:
2 How good it is when sis - ters dwell in peace with one an - oth - er:
3 How good it is when all earth's peo - ple dwell in peace to - geth - er:

To Refrain

Es co - mo a - cei - te bue - no de - rra - ma - do so - bre Aa - rón.
it is like pre - cious oil when run - ning fresh on Aa - ron's beard.
fresh like the morn - ing dew that falls on Zi - on's ho - ly hill.
there is where God will pour the bless - ing, life for - ev - er - more.

2 ¡Miren qué bueno es cuando
las hermanas están juntas!
Se parace al rocío
sobre los montes de Sión. *To Refrain*

3 ¡Miren qué bueno es cuando
nos reunimos todos juntos!
Porque el Señor envía
vida eterna y bendición. *To Refrain*

Words: Pablo Sosa (b. 1933) © 1972 GIA Publications, Inc.
Music (MIREN QUÉ BUENO): Pablo Sosa (b. 1933) © 1972 GIA Publications, Inc.

Psalm 133 | A Responsorial Setting

1 How good and how pleasant it is
   when kindred live together in unity!

2 It is like fine oil upon the head, flowing down upon the beard,
   upon the beard of Aaron, flowing down upon the collar of his robe.

3 It is like the dew of Hermon flowing down upon the hills of Zion.
   For there the LORD has commanded the blessing: life forevermore. *Refrain*

Tone

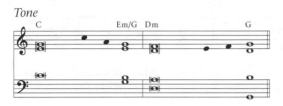

Lectionary: Eastertide (B); Ordinary Time after Pentecost (A,B).

*Use refrain from 133D on facing page. At each occurence the refrain is sung in Spanish and then in English.

Psalm Text: from *Evangelical Lutheran Worship* © 2006 Evangelical Lutheran Church in America, admin. Augsburg Fortress Publishers
Tone: © 2011 Faith Alive Christian Resources

Psalm 134

A Song of Ascents.

1 Come, bless the LORD, all you servants of the LORD, *
   who stand by night in the house of the LORD!

2 Lift up your hands to the holy place, *
   and bless the LORD.

3 **May the LORD, maker of heaven and earth, ***
   bless you from Zion.

O God, you have made and redeemed all that is,
and blessed your people in immeasurable ways.
We lift our hands and hearts to you in worship,
glorifying and enjoying you forever, through Jesus Christ our Lord. **Amen.**

Psalm 134, the fifteenth and final of the Psalms of Ascents, is a call to covenantal engagement with God in temple worship. Like Ps. 132, this psalm points to the relational, dialogical structure of worship: the people bless God in worship (vv. 1-2), and God is asked to bless the people (v. 3). The reference to "lifting up hands" points to the embodied nature of worship (see also Ps. 141:2). *Use in Worship: evening prayer; appropriate for any occasion.*

Come, All You Servants of the Lord

Instrumental Introduction, Interlude and Ending

1 Come, all you ser-vants of the Lord, who work and pray by
2 The Lord now bless from heaven a-bove and shine on you with

night, by day. Come, bless the Lord with-in this place;
ra-diant face; the Lord who heaven and earth has made

with lift-ed hands your hom-age pay.
il-lu-mine you with peace and grace.

Alternate harmonization on p. 623.

Words: Arlo D. Duba, 1984, © 1986 Arlo D. Duba
Music (GENEVAN 134/OLD HUNDREDTH 8.8.8.8): Louis Bourgeois (ca. 1510-1561), 1551, P.D.; arr. Eelco
Vos © 2011 Eelco Vos, admin. Faith Alive Christian Resources

Come Bless the Lord 134B

Words: Psalm 134:1-2
Music: traditional; arr. Martin Tel © 2011 Faith Alive Christian Resources

134C We Will Rest in You

Words and Music: Mike Hay (1953-1999) © 1993 World Library Publications

Psalm 135

¹ Praise the LORD! Praise the name of the LORD; *
 give praise, O servants of the LORD,

² you that stand in the house of the LORD, *
 in the courts of the house of our God.

³ **Praise the LORD, for the LORD is good; ***
 sing to his name, for he is gracious.

⁴ For the LORD has chosen Jacob for himself, *
 Israel as his own possession.

⁵ **For I know that the LORD is great; ***
 our Lord is above all gods.

⁶ **Whatever the LORD pleases he does, in heaven and on earth, ***
 in the seas and all deeps.

⁷ **He it is who makes the clouds rise at the end of the earth; ***
 he makes lightnings for the rain
 and brings out the wind from his storehouses.

⁸ He it was who struck down the firstborn of Egypt, *
 both human beings and animals;

⁹ he sent signs and wonders *
 into your midst, O Egypt, against Pharaoh and all his servants.

¹⁰ He struck down many nations *
 and killed mighty kings—

¹¹ Sihon, king of the Amorites, and Og, king of Bashan, *
 and all the kingdoms of Canaan—

¹² and gave their land as a heritage, *
 a heritage to his people Israel.

¹³ **Your name, O LORD, endures forever, ***
 your renown, O LORD, throughout all ages.

¹⁴ **For the LORD will vindicate his people, ***
 and have compassion on his servants.

¹⁵ The idols of the nations are silver and gold, *
 the work of human hands.

16 They have mouths, but they do not speak; *
    they have eyes, but they do not see;

17 they have ears, but they do not hear, *
    and there is no breath in their mouths.

18 Those who make them and all who trust them *
    shall become like them.

19 O house of Israel, bless the LORD! *
    O house of Aaron, bless the LORD!

20 O house of Levi, bless the LORD! *
    You that fear the LORD, bless the LORD!

21 Blessed be the LORD from Zion, he who resides in Jerusalem. *
    Praise the LORD!

Lord of creation, you shape human history
and form your people to accomplish your purpose;
yet we continue to be drawn to idols of our own making.
In Jesus Christ, deliver us from false gods.
Set us free to sing your songs and to bless your name forever and ever. **Amen.**

Psalm 135 is a grand hymn of praise that offers a resounding affirmation of the power and glory of God, as well as resounding denial of the power of idols and other gods. The psalm praises God for acts both of creation (vv. 5-7) and redemption (vv. 8-12), joining several other psalms that also feature this pairing (e.g., Pss. 33, 103, 104, and 136). The opening of the psalm closely resembles Ps. 134, and the section on the folly of idols (vv. 15-18) is nearly identical to portions of Ps. 113. Its anti-idolatry message is also closely related to Isa. 40-46 and several other prophetic texts that call Israel to both affirm God and reject idols. *Use in Worship: services focusing on the nature of Jesus and what Jesus reveals of God's character; acclamation of praise appropriate for use on any occasion.*

135A Exalt the LORD, His Praise Proclaim

1 Ex - alt the LORD, his praise pro - claim; all you his ser - vants, praise his name, who in the LORD's house ev - er stand and hum - bly serve at his com - mand. The LORD is good, his praise pro-claim; since

2 I know the LORD is high in state; a - bove all gods our Lord is great. The LORD per - forms what he de - crees, in heaven and earth, in depths and seas. He makes the va - pors to as - cend in

3 Ex - alt the LORD, his praise pro - claim; all you his ser - vants, praise his name, who in the LORD's house ev - er stand and hum - bly serve at his com - mand. For - ev - er praise and bless his name, and

it is pleas - ant, praise his name. His peo - ple
clouds from earth's re - mot - est end; the light - nings
in the church his praise pro - claim. In Zi - on

for his own he takes and his be -
flash at his com - mand; he holds the
is his dwell - ing place; O praise the

lov - ed trea - sure makes.
tem - pest in his hand.
LORD, show forth his grace.

Words: *Psalter*, 1887; rev. *Psalter*, 1912, alt., P.D.
Music (CREATION 8.8.8.8 D): Franz Joseph Haydn (1732-1809), 1798, P.D.

135B O Praise God's Name Together

1 O praise God's name to-geth-er, you ser-vants of the LORD;
2 O LORD, no mind can mea-sure the great-ness of your might;
3 For you, LORD of cre-a-tion, con-trol your vast do-main;
4 False gods may rise be-fore us, their van-i-ty dis-play;

O LORD, for all your fa-vor to us, you are a-dored!
you gave the earth its or-bit and set the stars to flight.
you speak, and na-tions trem-ble; in ho-ly peace you reign.
but as the hands that made them, they too shall fade a-way.

With-in your ho-ly tem-ple, be-fore your sa-cred throne,
The clouds you raised in heav-en give to the fields their rain;
When kings en-slave your cho-sen, your might un-bars the door;
Your name, O God Al-might-y, en-dures for end-less days;

the cho-sen heirs of Ja-cob pro-claim you God a-lone!
your Word lifts waves from o-ceans and moun-tains from the plain.
and ty-rants, once in pow-er, now kneel be-fore the poor.
and new-born gen-er-a-tions u-nite to sing your praise.

Guitar chords do not correspond with keyboard harmony.

Words: Michael Morgan © 2011 Michael Morgan, admin. Faith Alive Christian Resources
Music (AURELIA 7.6.7.6 D): Samuel S. Wesley, 1864, P.D.

Voice 1:

1 O give thanks to the LORD, for he is good, *

for his steadfast love endures forever.

2 O give thanks to the God of gods, *

for his steadfast love endures forever.

3 O give thanks to the Lord of lords, *

for his steadfast love endures forever;

Voice 2:

4 who alone does great wonders, *

for his steadfast love endures forever;

5 who by understanding made the heavens, *

for his steadfast love endures forever;

6 who spread out the earth on the waters, *

for his steadfast love endures forever;

7 who made the great lights, *

for his steadfast love endures forever;

8 the sun to rule over the day, *

for his steadfast love endures forever;

9 the moon and stars to rule over the night, *

for his steadfast love endures forever;

Voice 1:

10 who struck Egypt through their firstborn, *

for his steadfast love endures forever;

11 and brought Israel out from among them, *

for his steadfast love endures forever;

12 with a strong hand and an outstretched arm, *

for his steadfast love endures forever;

13 who divided the Red Sea in two, *

for his steadfast love endures forever;

14 and made Israel pass through the midst of it, *

for his steadfast love endures forever;

15 but overthrew Pharaoh and his army in the Red Sea, *

for his steadfast love endures forever;

16 who led his people through the wilderness, *

for his steadfast love endures forever;

17 who struck down great kings, *

for his steadfast love endures forever;

(continues)

¹⁸ and killed famous kings, *

for his steadfast love endures forever;

¹⁹ Sihon, king of the Amorites, *

for his steadfast love endures forever;

²⁰ and Og, king of Bashan, *

for his steadfast love endures forever;

²¹ and gave their land as a heritage, *

for his steadfast love endures forever;

²² a heritage to his servant Israel, *

for his steadfast love endures forever.

Voice 2:

²³ It is he who remembered us in our low estate, *

for his steadfast love endures forever;

²⁴ and rescued us from our foes, *

for his steadfast love endures forever;

²⁵ who gives food to all flesh, *

for his steadfast love endures forever.

²⁶ O give thanks to the God of heaven, *

for his steadfast love endures forever.

Everlasting God,
your love is a banner unfurled over all times and places.
Help us to live into the story of your redemption,
joining the cast of those called to love and serve in your name.
All glory be to you, Father, Son, and Holy Spirit. **Amen.**

Psalm 136 is a litany of gratitude for God's action in creation both in redeeming the people of Israel. The specific references in the psalm extend to each of the first five books of the Bible, making this psalm a response to the entirety of Torah. The second half of each verse is an acclamation of praise appropriate for use by the assembly. This narrative or history-telling prayer follows a similar form to Christian prayers at the Lord's Supper. *Use in Worship: services focusing on the grateful remembrance of God's covenant faithfulness; Thanksgiving Day; new year's celebrations; Easter; baptisms; celebrations of the Lord's Supper.*

Let Us with a Gladsome Mind 136A

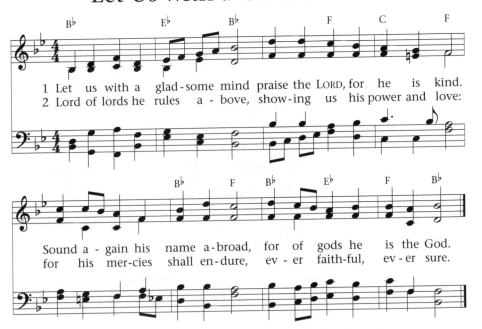

1 Let us with a glad-some mind praise the LORD, for he is kind.
2 Lord of lords he rules a-bove, show-ing us his power and love:

Sound a-gain his name a-broad, for of gods he is the God.
for his mer-cies shall en-dure, ev-er faith-ful, ev-er sure.

3 Heavens and earth with seas he made;
still his wonders are displayed.
He, with all-commanding might,
filled his new-made world with light—

4 Sun to stride across the day,
moon and stars in vast array:
for his mercies shall endure,
ever faithful, ever sure.

5 He with thunder-clasping hand
smote the sons of Egypt land,
split the Red Sea floods in two,
guided Israel safely through.

6 He brought walls of water down,
made the hosts of Pharaoh drown:
for his mercies shall endure,
ever faithful, ever sure.

7 Flowing springs and manna blessed
Israel in the wilderness.
Og and Sihon, heathen kings,
found what wicked action brings.

8 Then the land of heavy yoke
God gave to his chosen folk:
for his mercies shall endure,
ever faithful, ever sure.

9 He remembered us when low,
rescued us from every foe.
His love feeds all living things,
shelters them beneath his wings.

10 Let us, then, with thankful mind,
praise the LORD, for he is kind:
for his mercies shall endure,
ever faithful, ever sure.

Guitar chords do not correspond with keyboard harmony.

Words: John Milton (1608-1674); alt. Marie J. Post, 1985, © 1987 Faith Alive Christian Resources
Music (MONKLAND 7.7.7.7): J. Freylinghausen's *Geistreiches Gesangbuch*, 1704; adapt. John Antes, ca. 1800; arr. John Wilkes, 1861, P.D.

136B Let Us with a Gladsome Mind

1 Let us with a glad-some mind
2 Let us blaze God's name a - broad;
3 God has with a gra - cious eye
4 All things liv - ing God does feed;

*For God's mer - cies shall en - dure,

praise the Lord, so good and kind,
of all gods the Lord is God.
looked up - on our mis - er - y;
with full hand sup - plies their need.

ev - er faith - ful, ev - er sure.

for God's mer - cies shall en - dure,
God with all com - mand - ing might
for God's mer - cies shall en - dure,
Let us then with glad-some mind

For God's mer - cies shall en - dure,

ev - er faith - ful, ev - er sure.

ev - er faith - ful, ev - er sure. *(To Stanza 2)*
filled the new-made world with light. *(To Refrain)*
ev - er faith - ful, ev - er sure. *(To Stanza 4)*
praise the Lord, so good and kind. *(To Refrain)*

1st and 3rd times to Stanzas; 2nd and 4th times to Refrain

Refrain *(sing 4 times; may be sung antiphonally)*

For God's mer-cies shall en-dure, ev - er faith - ful, ev - er sure.

(⌢ last time)

To Stanza 3

For traditional harmony and rhythm see 66E. When using the traditional version do not sing the refrain.

*Sing echo beginning with stanza 3.

Words: John Milton (1608-1674), P.D.
Music (GENEVAN 136 adapt. 7.7.7.7 with refrain): *Genevan Psalter*, 1562; arr. Eelco Vos © 2011 Eelco Vos,
admin. Faith Alive Christian Resources

136C We Give Thanks unto You

Leader

Em   Am7   B7

1 We give thanks un - to you,   O   God   of   might,
2 In your wis - dom and love   you shaped the skies,
3 You have filled all the skies   with glo - ry and light,
4 From of old you have led   your peo - ple in faith,

All   Em   B

for your love is nev - er end - ing;

Leader   B7   Em

we give thanks un - to you, the God of gods,
you spread out the earth up - on the sea,
the sun for the day and moon for night,
you have shown your com-pas - sion, strength, and love,

All   G   Am   B7   Em

for your love is nev - er end - ing.

5 You delivered the ones who called_ unto you,
   for your love is never ending;
   from_ bondage to freedom, you brought them forth,
   for your love is never ending.

6 You have opened the sea and brought your people through,
   for your love is never ending;
   brought them into a land that_ flows with life,
   for your love is never ending.

(continues)

7 You remember your promise age_ to_ age,
   for your love is never ending;
   you show mercy on those of_ low degree,
   for your love is never ending.

8 You give food and_ life to all_ living things,
   for your love is never ending;
   we give thanks unto you, the_ God of all,
   for your love is never ending.

Words and Music: Marty Haugen (b. 1950) © 1987 GIA Publications, Inc.

Psalm 136:1-9, 23-36 **136D**
A Responsorial Setting

*Tone and Refrain

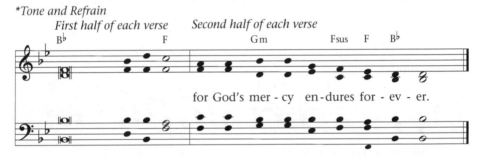

for God's mer - cy en-dures for - ev - er.

Refrain

1 Give thanks to the LORD, for the LORD is good,
   for God's mercy endures forever.

2 Give thanks to the God of gods,
   for God's mercy endures forever.

3 Give thanks to the Lord of lords,
   for God's mercy endures forever;

4 who alone does great wonders,
   for God's mercy endures forever;   *Refrain*

5 who by wisdom made the heavens,
   for God's mercy endures forever;

6 who spread out the earth upon the waters,
   for God's mercy endures forever;

7 who made the great lights—
   for God's mercy endures forever;

(continues)

⁸ the sun to govern the day,
>   for God's mercy endures forever;

⁹ the moon and the stars to govern the night,
>   for God's mercy endures forever;   *Refrain*

²³ who remembered us in our low estate,
>   for God's mercy endures forever;

²⁴ and rescued us from our enemies,
>   for God's mercy endures forever;

²⁵ who gives food to all creatures,
>   for God's mercy endures forever.

²⁶ Give thanks to the God of heaven,
>   for God's mercy endures forever.   *Refrain*

Lectionary: Easter Vigil (A,B,C).

*Disregard refrain indications in the psalm text when using this tone and refrain.

Refrain and Tone: Frederick A. Gore Ouseley, P.D.
Psalm Text: from *Evangelical Lutheran Worship* © 2006 Evangelical Lutheran Church in America, admin.
Augsburg Fortress Publishers

Alternate Refrain

All cre-a-tion join to say: Al - le - lu - ia!

Alternate Tone

Words: Charles Wesley (1707-1788), 1739, alt. P.D.
Music (EASTER HYMN fragment): *Lyra Davidica*, 1708, P.D.
Tone: © 2011 Faith Alive Christian Resources

Give Thanks to God, for Good Is He 136E

1 Give thanks to God, for good is he:
2 His wis-dom made the heavens to be: his love a-bides for-ev-er.
3 He helped us in our deep-est woes:

To him all praise and glo-ry be:
He spread the earth up-on the sea: his mer-cy lasts for-ev-er.
He ran-somed us from all our foes:

His won-drous works with praise re-cord:
Praise him whose sun a-wakes the day: his love a-bides for-ev-er.
Each crea-ture's need he will sup-ply:

The on-ly God, the sov-ereign Lord:
The moon and stars his might dis-play: his mer-cy lasts for-ev-er.
Give thanks to God, en-throned on high:

Words: *Psalter*, 1912, alt., P.D.
Music (CONSTANCE 8.7.8.7 D): Arthur S. Sullivan, 1875, P.D.

136F We Thank You, Lord, for You Are Good

1 We thank you, Lord, for you are good;
2 You, Lord, a-lone did won-drous deeds;
3 You made the star-ry lights to rise;
4 You res-cue us from ev-ery foe;

Your mer-cy lives for-ev-er.

your kind-ness from of old has stood;
from you a-lone all good pro-ceeds;
your glo-ries shine in ra-diant skies;
you feed your crea-tures here be-low;

Your love will keep us ev-er.

O God of gods, O sov-ereign Lord, we bless you
your wis-dom made the heavens to be; you formed the
your glow-ing moon en-hanc-es night; your sun brings
we give you thanks, Cre-a-tor, Lord; we sing the

now with one ac-cord:
earth a-bove the sea:
forth each morn-ing's light:
glo-ries of your Word.

Your love is ev-er-last-ing.

Guitar chords do not correspond with keyboard harmony.

Words: John G. Dunn, 1985, © John G. Dunn
Music (WAS GOTT TUT 8.7.8.7.8.8.7): Severus Gastorius, 1681; P.D.

Give Thanks unto the Lord `136G`

Solo voice — F

1 Give thanks un - to the Lord for God is ev - er good.
2 God is the God of gods, God is the Lord of lords.
3 Our God a - lone does won-ders, God made the earth and stars.

4 God made the sun for day, and moon and stars for night.
5 God stretched a might - y arm, led Is - rael out of E-gypt.
6 God con-quered Phar-aoh's ar - my, led Is - rael through the des-ert.

7 God con-quered might - y kings, and blessed the land of Is-rael.
8 God frees us from op-pres-sion, gives life to ev - ery crea-ture.
9 Give thanks un - to the Lord, the God of earth and heav-en.

All
Ahom   Ahom   Ahom   Ahom

Gm   F/C   F

Swahili A - na - fa - thi - li za mi - le - le!
English A - men, A - le - le, Al - le - lu - ia!
         A - men, God's love will last for - ev - er!

Words: Psalm 136; traditional Swahili; Mwalimu Glenn T. Boyd; tr. C. Michael Hawn, from *Four African Hymns*
© 1994 Choristers Guild
Music (KIHAYA): Kihaya melody; arr. Mwalimu Glenn T. Boyd and J. Nathan Corbitt from *Four African Hymns*
© 1994 Choristers Guild

136H O Give Thanks to the LORD

1 O give thanks to the LORD, for the LORD is good.
2 O give thanks to the one who is God of gods.
3 O give thanks to the LORD, to the LORD of lords.

Refrain
All
For God's stead - fast love en - dures for - ev - er.

4 Who a - lone does great won - ders,

5 Who by un - der - stand - ing made the heav - ens,

6 Who spread out the earth on the wa - ters,

Words and Music: Pamela Ruiter-Feenstra © 2011 Pamela Ruiter-Feenstra, admin. Faith Alive Christian Resources

Psalm 137

¹ By the rivers of Babylon— *
   there we sat down and there we wept when we remembered Zion.

² On the willows there *
   we hung up our harps.

³ For there our captors asked us for songs, *
   and our tormentors asked for mirth, saying,
   "Sing us one of the songs of Zion!"

⁴ **How could we sing the LORD's song** *
   in a foreign land?

⁵ **If I forget you, O Jerusalem,** *
   let my right hand wither!

⁶ **Let my tongue cling to the roof of my mouth,** *
   if I do not remember you,
   if I do not set Jerusalem above my highest joy.

⁷ Remember, O LORD, against the Edomites the day of Jerusalem's fall, *
   how they said, "Tear it down! Tear it down! Down to its foundations!"

⁸ O daughter Babylon, you devastator! *
   Happy shall they be who pay you back what you have done to us!

⁹ Happy shall they be who take your little ones *
   and dash them against the rock!

God of justice, we pray for all refugees and wanderers,
the abused and the tortured, the exiles of every land and people.
When loss and grief rob us of song,
may we entrust our hurts and hatreds to you,
the true and final judge of all. **Amen.**

Psalm 137 ruminates on the despair of captivity. It remembers how the songs of the people were silenced, while the taunting requests of the captors to sing the songs of God (v. 3) and the taunting calls of captors to destroy Jerusalem (v. 7) continue to echo in memory. The psalm's rumination culminates with one of the most biting curses of the Psalter. The curse intensifies a theme present in the Psalter since Ps. 1, suggesting that the blessed are not only those who avoid the scorners but also those who take vengeance against them. This psalm helps modern readers enter into the unspeakable despair of the people of Israel, a correction to overly sentimental readings of the OT narrative. Many commentators pause in contemplative silence as they reflect on other contemporary appropriations of this psalm. *Use in Worship: in conjunction with OT narratives of conflict and exile; to provoke discussions about appropriate responses to injustice.*

By the Babylonian Rivers 137A

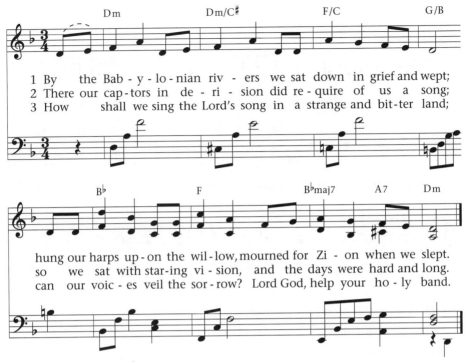

1 By the Bab-y-lo-nian riv-ers we sat down in grief and wept;
2 There our cap-tors in de-ri-sion did re-quire of us a song;
3 How shall we sing the Lord's song in a strange and bit-ter land;

hung our harps up-on the wil-low, mourned for Zi-on when we slept.
so we sat with star-ing vi-sion, and the days were hard and long.
can our voic-es veil the sor-row? Lord God, help your ho-ly band.

Alternate harmonization on p. 847.

Words: Ewald Bash, 1964, © 1964 American Lutheran Church, admin. Augsburg Fortress Publishers
Music (CAPTIVITY/KAS DZIEDAJA 8.7.8.7): Latvian melody, P.D.; arr. Greg Scheer © 2011 Greg Scheer

A Reflection 137B

I pray the psalm of wrath in the certainty of its wonderful fulfillment; I leave the vengeance in God's hands and pray for the carrying out of God's justice to all enemies. I know that God has remained true and has secured justice in wrathful judgment on the cross, and that this wrath has become grace and joy for us. Jesus Christ himself prays for the execution of God's vengeance on his body, and thus Christ leads me back daily to the gravity and the grace of his cross for me and all the enemies of God.

Dietrich Bonhoeffer, taken from *Psalms: The Prayer Book of the Bible*, p. 59 © 1970 Augsburg Fortress Publishers

137C Psalm 137 | A Responsorial Setting

Refrain
May be sung as a round

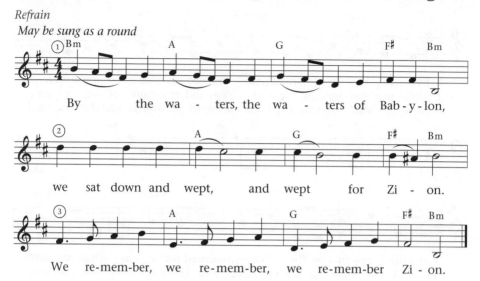

By the wa - ters, the wa - ters of Bab-y-lon,

we sat down and wept, and wept for Zi - on.

We re-mem-ber, we re-mem-ber, we re-mem-ber Zi - on.

Refrain

1 By the waters of Babylon we sat down and wept,
   when we remembered you, O Zion.

2 As for our harps, we hung them up
   on the trees in the midst of that land.

3 For those who led us away captive asked us for a song,
  and our oppressors called for mirth;
     "Sing us one of the songs of Zion."

4 How shall we sing the LORD's song
     upon an alien soil?   *Refrain*

5 If I forget you, O Jerusalem,
     let my right hand forget its skill.

6 Let my tongue cleave to the roof of my mouth if I do not remember you,
     if I do not set Jerusalem above my highest joy.

7 Remember the day of Jerusalem, O LORD, against the people of Edom,
     who said, "Down with it! down with it! even to the ground!"   *Refrain*

8 O daughter of Babylon, doomed to destruction,
     happy shall they be who repay you for what you have done to us!

9 Happy shall they be who take your little ones
     and dash them against the rock!   *Refrain*

Tone
Unaccompanied

Lectionary: Ordinary Time after Pentecost (C). (Lection may end at v. 6.)

To sing this refrain in a different key see stanza 1 of 137D (below).

Words: Psalm 137
Music (BY THE WATERS): traditional Jewish melody
Psalm Text: from *Evangelical Lutheran Worship* © 2006 Evangelical Lutheran Church in America, admin. Augsburg Fortress Publishers
Tone: © 2011 Faith Alive Christian Resources

By the Waters of Babylon **137D**

Three-part canon

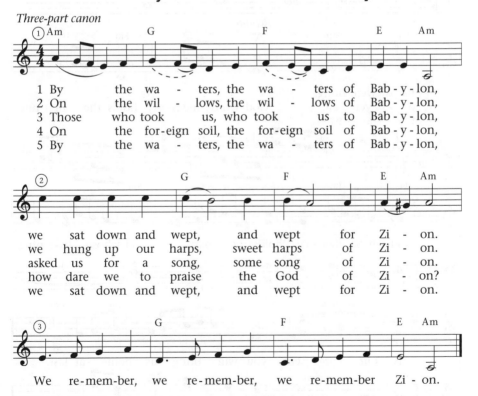

This tune in a different key: p. 898.

Words: sts. 1, 5 traditional; sts. 2-4 Carl P. Daw Jr. (b. 1944) © 1996, 2011 Hope Publishing Company
Music (BY THE WATERS): traditional Jewish melody

137E God of Memory

1 God of mem-ory, I re-mem-ber how our cap-tors want-ed song.
2 God of mem-ory, I re-mem-ber burn-ing, bro-ken cit-y wall.
3 God of mem-ory, I re-mem-ber chil-dren tumb-ling, not in play.

I will not for-get the wil-lows where our si-lent
I will not for-get the cit-y, cher-ish Zi-on
I will not for-get the long-ing to strike back in

Refrain

harps were hung.
o-ver all. God whose mem-ory holds the fu-ture,
that same way.

God whose mer-cy holds the past, God whose lis-tening

is our pre-sent, you will bring us home at last.

Guitar chords do not correspond with keyboard harmony.
Alternate harmonization on p. 182.
Alternate tune: AUTHORITY, p. 372.

Words: Richard Leach, 1994, © 1996 Selah Publishing Company, Inc.
Music (EBENEZER 8.7.8.7 D): Thomas J. Williams, 1890; harm. Alfred V. Fedak (b. 1953) © 2011 Faith Alive
Christian Resources

Psalm 138

Of David.

1 I give you thanks, O LORD, with my whole heart; *
   before the gods I sing your praise;

2 **I bow down toward your holy temple and give thanks to your name**
   for your steadfast love and your faithfulness; *
   for you have exalted your name and your word above everything.

3 **On the day I called, you answered me,** *
   you increased my strength of soul.

4 All the kings of the earth shall praise you, O LORD, *
   for they have heard the words of your mouth.

5 They shall sing of the ways of the LORD, *
   for great is the glory of the LORD.

6 **For though the LORD is high, he regards the lowly;** *
   but the haughty he perceives from far away.

7 **Though I walk in the midst of trouble,**
   you preserve me against the wrath of my enemies; *
   you stretch out your hand, and your right hand delivers me.

8 **The LORD will fulfill his purpose for me;**
   your steadfast love, O LORD, endures forever. *
   Do not forsake the work of your hands.

We lift our hearts in thankful praise to you, O Lord,
for you do not forsake the work of your hands,
but you continue to redeem and restore your creation
through your Son, Jesus Christ, our living Lord.
By your Spirit, enable us to fulfill your purpose in our lives
and, in so doing, to discover true joy. **Amen.**

Psalm 138 is a psalm of thanksgiving and trust. Its focus moves from the past, offering thanks for answered prayer (v. 3), to the present, testifying about God's continued presence in the midst of difficulty (v. 7), to the future, expressing confidence in God's purposes (v. 8). Like Ps. 113, it depicts God as exalted, deeply concerned for the lowly (v. 6), and distant from the arrogant (v. 6). *Use in Worship: celebrations of the Lord's Supper (focus on past, present, and future); appropriate for any occasion.*

With Grateful Heart
My Thanks I Bring

1 With grate-ful heart my thanks I bring; be - fore the "gods" your praise I sing. I wor-ship in your ho - ly place and praise you for your truth and grace; for truth and grace to - geth - er shine in your most ho - ly Word di - vine,

2 I cried to you, and you did save; your word of grace new cour - age gave. The kings of earth shall thank you, LORD, for they have heard your won-drous word; yes, they shall come with songs of praise for great and glo - rious are your ways,

3 O LORD, en-throned in glo - ry bright, you reign a - lone in heaven-ly height; the proud in vain your fa - vor seek, but you have mer - cy for the meek. Through trou - ble though my path-way be, you will re - vive and strength-en me,

4 You will stretch forth your might-y arm to save me when my foes a - larm. The work you have for me be - gun shall by your grace be ful - ly done. Your love for - ev - er will en - dure: your mer - cy, LORD, is ev - er sure;

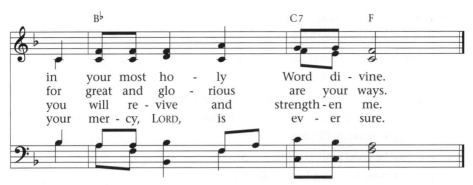

in your most ho - ly   Word di - vine.
for great and glo - rious   are your ways.
you will re - vive and   strength - en me.
your mer - cy, LORD, is   ev - er sure.

Alternate tune: MELITA, p. 520.

Words: *Psalter*, 1912, alt., P.D.
Music (SOLID ROCK 8.8.8.8.8.8 with repeat): William B. Bradbury (1816-1868), 1863, P.D.

Psalm 138 | A Responsorial Setting 138B

Refrain

1 Thank you, Lord, thank you, Lord, thank you, Lord.
2 Been so good, been so good, been so good.

I just want to thank you, Lord.

Refrain

¹ I will give thanks to you, O LORD, with my whole heart;
    before the gods I will sing your praise.

² I will bow down toward your holy temple and praise your name,
    because of your steadfast love and faithfulness;
        for you have glorified your name and your word above all things.   *Refrain*

³ When I called, you answered me;
    you increased my strength within me.

⁴ All the rulers of the earth will praise you, O LORD,
    when they have heard the words of your mouth.   (continues)

⁵ They will sing of the ways of the LORD,
    that great is the glory of the LORD.   *Refrain*

⁶ The LORD is high, yet cares for the lowly,
    perceiving the haughty from afar.

⁷ Though I walk in the midst of trouble, you keep me safe;
    you stretch forth your hand against the fury of my enemies;
    your right hand shall save me.

⁸ You will make good your purpose for me;
    O LORD, your steadfast love endures forever;
    do not abandon the works of your hands.   *Refrain*

Tone

Lectionary: Ordinary Time after Epiphany (C); Ordinary Time after Pentecost (A,B,C).

Words: traditional
Music: Afro-American spiritual; arr. Stephen Key © 2000 GIA Publications, Inc.
Psalm Text: from *Evangelical Lutheran Worship* © 2006 Evangelical Lutheran Church in America, admin.
Augsburg Fortress Publishers
Tone: © 2011 Faith Alive Christian Resources

138C With All My Heart I Thank You, LORD

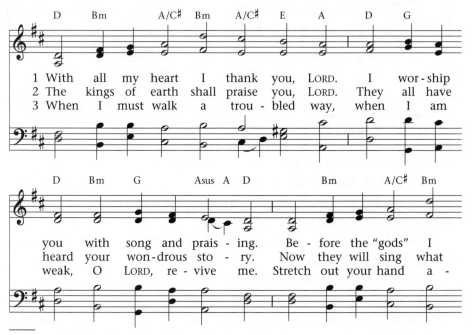

bless your name and praise you for your love un - fail - ing.
they have heard: "Great is the LORD and great his glo - ry."
gainst all hate. From sin and all things harm - ful save me.

Your stead - fast love, your faith - ful - ness, your name, your
The LORD is high in maj - es - ty, yet he re -
Your right hand gives me vic - to - ry. Work in my

word are high ex - alt - ed. The day I cried, you
spects the meek and low - ly. The LORD is high in
life your full in - ten - tion. Your stead - fast love can

an - swered me. Your strength has made my soul un - daunt - ed.
maj - es - ty; he keeps his dis - tance from the haugh - ty.
nev - er die. Bring what you start - ed to per - fec - tion.

Words: Stanley Wiersma (1930-1986), 1981, © Faith Alive Christian Resources
Music (GENEVAN 138 | 8.9.8.9 D): *Genevan Psalter*, 1551; harm. Dale Grotenhuis, 1985, © 1987 Faith Alive
Christian Resources

Psalm 139

To the leader. Of David. A Psalm.

¹ O LORD, you have searched me and known me. *
   ² You know when I sit down and when I rise up;
   you discern my thoughts from far away.
³ You search out my path and my lying down, *
   and are acquainted with all my ways.
⁴ **Even before a word is on my tongue, ***
   O LORD, you know it completely.
⁵ You hem me in, behind and before, *
   and lay your hand upon me.
⁶ Such knowledge is too wonderful for me; *
   it is so high that I cannot attain it.
⁷ **Where can I go from your spirit? ***
   Or where can I flee from your presence?
⁸ **If I ascend to heaven, you are there; ***
   if I make my bed in Sheol, you are there.
⁹ **If I take the wings of the morning ***
   and settle at the farthest limits of the sea,
¹⁰ **even there your hand shall lead me, ***
   and your right hand shall hold me fast.
¹¹ If I say, "Surely the darkness shall cover me, *
   and the light around me become night,"
¹² even the darkness is not dark to you; *
   the night is as bright as the day, for darkness is as light to you.
¹³ **For it was you who formed my inward parts; ***
   you knit me together in my mother's womb.
¹⁴ **I praise you, for I am fearfully and wonderfully made. ***
   Wonderful are your works; that I know very well.
¹⁵ **My frame was not hidden from you,**
   when I was being made in secret, *
   intricately woven in the depths of the earth.
¹⁶ Your eyes beheld my unformed substance. *
   In your book were written all the days that were formed for me,
   when none of them as yet existed.
¹⁷ **How weighty to me are your thoughts, O God! ***
   How vast is the sum of them!
¹⁸ **I try to count them—they are more than the sand; ***
   I come to the end—I am still with you.

[19] O that you would kill the wicked, O God, *
    and that the bloodthirsty would depart from me—
[20] those who speak of you maliciously, *
    and lift themselves up against you for evil!
[21] Do I not hate those who hate you, O LORD? *
    And do I not loathe those who rise up against you?
[22] I hate them with perfect hatred; *
    I count them my enemies.
[23] **Search me, O God, and know my heart; ***
    test me and know my thoughts.
[24] **See if there is any wicked way in me, ***
    and lead me in the way everlasting.

Almighty God, creator of all things, you know each of us so intimately
that no thought in our minds or cell in our bodies is hid from your eyes.
Secure in the loving embrace of our brother, Jesus Christ,
we open our hearts and lives to your searching gaze. **Amen.**

Psalm 139 is a psalm of testimony about the limitless capacity for God to know us (v. 1) and to be present throughout all creation (vv. 7-12). It includes a poignant testimony about God's mysterious and majestic role in human conception and birth (vv. 13-16). The psalm then features a dramatic change, asking for God's vengeance on faithless people (v. 19) and guidance in the way of truth (v. 24). The opening sections of the psalm are the most often used; the concluding section, however, makes it clear that the psalm is about the choice for righteousness (cf. Ps. 1) and expression of awareness not only of God's pervasive knowledge about us but also readiness for God to examine and test us (vv. 23-24). *Use in Worship: services marking seasons of human life, from birth to death (opening sections); a call to confession (especially in light of vv. 23-24).*

My Lord, You Have Examined Me

1 My Lord, you have ex-am-ined me, you know me through and through;
2 The pres-ence of your Spir-it will be with me to the last;
3 You made me in my moth-er's womb, so in-tri-cate your ways,
4 And yet I find my soul per-turbed by bit-ter-ness and grief,

you see my deeds, per-ceive my thoughts, my speech, my mot-ives too.
wher-ev-er I de-cide to go your love will hold me fast.
and ev-en then, be-fore my birth, you num-bered all my days.
for man-y choose to treat your word with scorn-ful un-be-lief—

You wrap me round on ev-ery side; on me you place your hand:
If I should try to run from you I know with-out a doubt
Be-fore I sleep and as I wake I know that you are there:
so search me, Lord, and cleanse my heart from all that you ab-hor,

such knowl-edge is too won-der-ful for me to un-der-stand!
no dark-ness could con-ceal my path— your light would shine me out.
how could I ev-er sound the depths of your un-fail-ing care?
then teach me how to walk with you to-day and ev-er-more.

Words: Martin Leckebusch © 2006 Kevin Mayhew Ltd.
Music (RESIGNATION 8.6.8.6 D): W. Walker's *Southern Harmony*, 1835, P.D.; harm. *Hymnal for Colleges and Schools*, 1956, © 1956 Yale University Press

LORD, You Have Searched Me **139B**

1 LORD, you have searched me, and you know where I take
rest and where I go. LORD, you know all that
I have planned, and all my ways are in your hand.

2 If I the wings of morn-ing take and far a-
way my dwell-ing make, if I should sink in
deep-est sea, your right hand keeps its hold on me.

3 All that I am I owe to you; you knit me,
LORD, with-in the womb. I give my Mak-er
thank-ful praise, whose won-drous works my soul a-maze.

4 When I was formed within the earth,
you knew my frame before my birth.
My life in all your perfect plan
was known before my days began.

5 Search me, O God, my heart discern;
try me, my inmost thoughts to learn;
and lead me, if in sin I stray,
to choose the everlasting way.

Words: *Psalter*, 1912; rev. Marie J. Post, 1986, © 1987 Faith Alive Christian Resources
Music (FEDERAL STREET 8.8.8.8): Henry K. Oliver, 1832, P.D.

139C Psalm 139:1-18, 23-24
A Responsorial Setting

Refrain

Lord, you have searched me; you know me through and through.

Refrain

¹ LORD, you have searched me out;
    O LORD, you have known me.

² You know my sitting down and my rising up;
    you discern my thoughts from afar.

³ You trace my journeys and my resting-places
    and are acquainted with all my ways.

⁴ Indeed, there is not a word on my lips,
    but you, O LORD, know it altogether.

⁵ You encompass me, behind and before,
    and lay your hand upon me.

⁶ Such knowledge is too wonderful for me;
    it is so high that I cannot attain to it.   *Refrain*

⁷ Where can I go then from your Spirit?
    Where can I flee from your presence?

⁸ If I climb up to heaven, you are there;
    if I make the grave my bed, you are there also.

⁹ If I take the wings of the morning
    and dwell in the uttermost parts of the sea,

¹⁰ even there your hand will lead me
    and your right hand hold me fast.

¹¹ If I say, "Surely the darkness will cover me,
    and the light around me turn to night,"

¹² darkness is not dark to you; the night is as bright as the day;
    darkness and light to you are both alike.   *Refrain*

¹³ For you yourself created my inmost parts;

you knit me together in my mother's womb.

¹⁴ I will thank you because I am marvelously made;

your works are wonderful,

and I know it well.

¹⁵ My body was not hidden from you,

while I was being made in secret and woven in the depths of the earth.

¹⁶ Your eyes beheld my limbs, yet unfinished in the womb;

all of them were written in your book;

my days were fashioned before they came to be.

¹⁷ How deep I find your thoughts, O God!

How great is the sum of them!

¹⁸ If I were to count them, they would be more in number than the sand;

to count them all, my life span would need to be like yours.   *Refrain*

²³ Search me out, O God, and know my heart;

try me and know my restless thoughts.

²⁴ Look well whether there be any wickedness in me

and lead me in the way that is everlasting.   *Refrain*

Tone

Lectionary: vv. 1-6, 13-18 Ordinary Time after Epiphany (B) and Ordinary Time after Pentecost (B,C); vv. 1-12, 23-24 Ordinary Time after Pentecost (A).

Words and Music: Hal H. Hopson © 1989 Hope Publishing Company
Psalm Text: from *Evangelical Lutheran Worship* © 2006 Evangelical Lutheran Church in America, admin. Augsburg Fortress Publishers
Tone: © 2011 Faith Alive Christian Resources

139D You Are Before Me, Lord

1 You are be-fore me, Lord; you are be-hind,
2 Then from your Spir-it where, Lord, shall I go,
3 If I should take my flight in-to the dawn,
4 If I should say, "Let dark-ness cov-er me,
5 Search me, O God, search me and know my heart:

and o-ver me you have spread out your hand;
and from your pres-ence where, Lord, shall I fly?
if I should dwell on o-cean's far-thest shore,
and I shall hide with-in the veil of night,"
try me, O God, my mind and spir-it try;

such knowl-edge is too won-der-ful for me,
If I as-cend to heav-en you are there,
your might-y hand will rest up-on me still,
sure-ly the dark-ness is not dark to you:
keep me from an-y path that gives you pain,

too high to grasp, too great to un-der-stand.
and still are with me if in hell I lie.
and your right hand will guard me ev-er-more.
the night is as the day, the dark-ness, light.
and lead me in the ev-er-last-ing way.

Words: Ian Pitt-Watson (1923-1995) © 1973 Ian Pitt-Watson Trust; alt.
Music (HIGHLAND CATHEDRAL 10.10.10.10): Uli Roever and Michael Korb © Universal Music Publishing Group (Germany)

O Lord, My God, You Know All My Ways 139E

1 O Lord, my God, you know all my ways, when I
2 Where can I go to be far from you? In the
3 O Lord, my God, you cre - a - ted me, in a

sleep and I rise, when I sit or stand; and be -
deep - est of caves, in the heights of heaven? If I
won - der - ful way you have fash - ioned me. Test my

fore an - y word is up - on my tongue you dis -
rise up and fly on the wings of dawn, still your
spir - it and see what is in my heart; lead me

Last time

cern it as though I had spo-ken it.
right hand will guide me and hold me fast.
on in the way to e - ter-nal life.

Words: Paul Wigmore © 1992 The Jubilate Group, admin. Hope Publishing Company
Music (SHEPHERDSWELL): John Barnard © 1992 The Jubilate Group, admin. Hope Publishing Company

139F Oh Señor, tú me has examinado / Oh, Lord God, You Have Searched Me

fue - re, a - hí tú_es-ta - rás, y_aun a - llí tu
wan-der, your Spir - it is there, and your hand will

ma - no me guia - rá.
guide and guard my way.

Words: Marisol Díaz © Marisol Díaz; tr. Mary Louise Bringle (b. 1953), 2011
Music: Marisol Díaz © Marisol Díaz; arr. Marcus Hong, 2011

Psalm 140

To the leader. A Psalm of David.

Voice 1:

¹ Deliver me, O Lord, from evildoers; *

  protect me from those who are violent,

² who plan evil things in their minds *

  and stir up wars continually.

³ They make their tongue sharp as a snake's, *

  and under their lips is the venom of vipers. *Selah*

Voice 2:

⁴ Guard me, O Lord, from the hands of the wicked; *

  protect me from the violent who have planned my downfall.

⁵ The arrogant have hidden a trap for me,

  and with cords they have spread a net; *

  along the road they have set snares for me. *Selah*

⁶ **I say to the Lord, "You are my God; ***

  give ear, O Lord, to the voice of my supplications." (continues)

7 **O Lord, my Lord, my strong deliverer,** *
   you have covered my head in the day of battle.

8 **Do not grant, O Lord, the desires of the wicked;** *
   do not further their evil plot.   *Selah*

Voice 1:

9 Those who surround me lift up their heads; *
   let the mischief of their lips overwhelm them!

Voice 2:

10 Let burning coals fall on them! *
   Let them be flung into pits, no more to rise!

11 Do not let the slanderer be established in the land; *
   let evil speedily hunt down the violent!

12 **I know that the Lord maintains the cause of the needy,** *
   and executes justice for the poor.

13 **Surely the righteous shall give thanks to your name;** *
   the upright shall live in your presence.

Lord, you taught us to pray,
"Save us from the time of trial, and deliver us from evil."
By the power of your Holy Spirit enable us to turn to you
and find our strong Deliverer. **Amen.**

Psalm 140 is a prayer for rescue from and retribution for a violent enemy (vv. 1-11), grounded in a confession that God is a God of justice for the weak and needy (v. 12). It includes an unsentimental description of human malice, memorably comparing evil to a poisonous snake's tongue and to a luring trap. The psalm expresses the honest cries of the oppressed and a longing for God's intervention in the world. In the NT, Paul quotes this psalm in his depiction of human depravity (Rom. 3:13). *Use in Worship: a call to confession; in conjunction with lament over human evil and suffering.*

Deliver Me from Evil

1 De - liv - er me from e - vil; de - fend me, LORD, from wrong.
2 O LORD, I have con - fessed you to be my God a - lone.
3 Let their own e - vil strike them and cause their o - ver - throw,

The vi - o - lent have gath - ered, with poi - son on their tongue.
Now hear my cry for mer - cy and make your pow - er known.
so that the poor see jus - tice when e - vil is brought low.

From those who plot to hurt me or catch me in their snare,
O sov - ereign LORD and Sav - ior, my ar - mor in the strife,
The right - eous will sing prais - es, pro - claim your name and grace;

pro - tect me, LORD, and keep me safe - guard - ed in your care.
let not the wick - ed tri - umph who wish to take my life.
the up - right will live safe - ly with - in your sure em - brace.

Guitar chords do not correspond with keyboard harmony.

Words: *Psalter*, 1912; rev. Bert Witvoet, 1985, © 1987 Faith Alive Christian Resources
Music (PASSION CHORALE/HERZLICH TUT MICH VERLANGEN 7.6.7.6 D): Hans Leo Hassler, 1601; adapt. and harm. Johann S. Bach (1685-1750), in *St. Matthew Passion*, 1729, P.D.

Psalm 141

A Psalm of David.

1 I call upon you, O Lᴏʀᴅ; come quickly to me; *
     give ear to my voice when I call to you.

2 **Let my prayer be counted as incense before you,** *
     and the lifting up of my hands as an evening sacrifice.

3 **Set a guard over my mouth, O Lᴏʀᴅ;** *
     keep watch over the door of my lips.

4 **Do not turn my heart to any evil, to busy myself with wicked deeds**
   in company with those who work iniquity; *
     do not let me eat of their delicacies.

5 Let the righteous strike me; let the faithful correct me. *
       Never let the oil of the wicked anoint my head,
         for my prayer is continually against their wicked deeds.

6 When they are given over to those who shall condemn them, *
     then they shall learn that my words were pleasant.

7 Like a rock that one breaks apart and shatters on the land, *
     so shall their bones be strewn at the mouth of Sheol.

8 **But my eyes are turned toward you, O Gᴏᴅ, my Lord;** *
     in you I seek refuge; do not leave me defenseless.

9 **Keep me from the trap that they have laid for me,** *
     and from the snares of evildoers.

10 **Let the wicked fall into their own nets,** *
     while I alone escape.

Holy God, we offer ourselves to you:
our hands in prayer, our lips in praise, and our hearts in full devotion.
Take us as we are, and then mold us to your design,
so that we may serve you with joy all the days of our lives.
We pray this in the name of Jesus. **Amen.**

Psalm 141 is cry for God's help when facing the choice between good and evil. Echoing the imagery of Ps. 1, it expresses hope that the faithful and righteous would offer correction (v. 5) and describes the folly of sin (v. 7). As in Ps. 140, the psalmist is deeply aware of the lurking danger that comes from the enemy, and prays that the wicked will self-destruct (v. 10); here, however, the psalmist's first prayer is to remain true to God and to avoid the temptation of becoming evil (vv. 3-5). This psalm acknowledges that divine assistance is needed not only for teaching the law but also for enabling obedience. *Use in Worship: evening prayer services.*

O LORD, Come Quickly; 141A
Hear Me Pray

Four-part canon

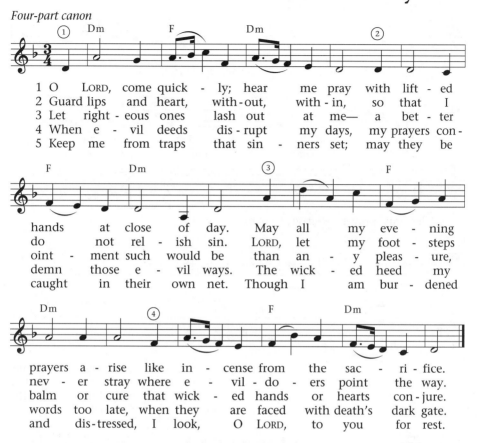

1 O LORD, come quick - ly; hear me pray with lift - ed hands at close of day. May all my eve - ning prayers a - rise like in - cense from the sac - ri - fice.

2 Guard lips and heart, with - out, with - in, so that I do not rel - ish sin. LORD, let my foot - steps nev - er stray where e - vil - do - ers point the way.

3 Let right - eous ones lash out at me— a bet - ter oint - ment such would be than an - y pleas - ure, balm or cure that wick - ed hands or hearts con - jure.

4 When e - vil deeds dis - rupt my days, my prayers con - demn those e - vil ways. The wick - ed heed my words too late, when they are faced with death's dark gate.

5 Keep me from traps that sin - ners set; may they be caught in their own net. Though I am bur - dened and dis - tressed, I look, O LORD, to you for rest.

Alternate tune: FEDERAL STREET, p. 909.

Words: sts. 1, 2, 4, 5 Marie J. Post, 1985, © 1987 Faith Alive Christian Resources; st. 3 Martin Tel © 2011 Martin Tel, admin. Faith Alive Christian Resources
Music (WHEN JESUS WEPT 8.8.8.8): William Billings, *The New England Psalm Singer*, 1770, P.D.

141B Like Burning Incense, O Lord

you;   O   lis - ten to me now.   I
you;   let good - ness rule my heart.
ones   al - ways at my side.
you;   spare me from all wrong.

raise my hands in of - fering to you.
Keep me far from those   who do harm.
Plant your wis - dom deep   in my soul.
Keep all e - vil far   from my heart.

The refrain may be sung in canon with the second voice entering two measures after the first.

141C Let My Prayer Rise Up

All

Let my prayer rise up like in-cense be-fore you, the lift-ing up of my hands as an of-fer-ing to you.

Leader / Group One

O God, I call to you, come to me now; oh,

All / Group Two

O God, I call to you,

hear my voice when I cry to you.

come to me now; oh, hear my voice when I cry to

Let my prayer rise up like in-cense be-fore you, the

you. Let my prayer rise up like in-cense be-

(continues)

Keyboard accompaniment on facing page.

Words: from *Holden Evening Prayer*, Marty Haugen (b. 1950) © 1990 GIA Publications, Inc.
Music: Marty Haugen (b. 1950) © 1990 GIA Publications, Inc.

Music: Marty Haugen (b. 1950) © 1990 GIA Publications, Inc.

141D O Lord, I Have Cried to You

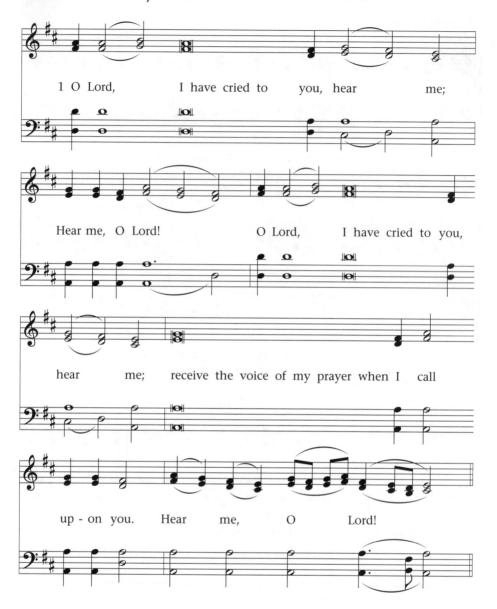

1 O Lord, I have cried to you, hear me;
Hear me, O Lord! O Lord, I have cried to you,
hear me; receive the voice of my prayer when I call
up-on you. Hear me, O Lord!

2 Let my prayer rise like incense be - fore you;

and the lifting up of my hands as an eve-ning sac - ri - fice.

Hear me, O Lord!

Words and Music: Galician *Samohlasen* © 2004 Metropolitan Andrey Sheptytsky Institute of Eastern Christian Studies

I Lift My Hands

Refrain

I lift my hands, I lift my hands like an eve-ning of-fer-
ing; as day-light fades I give my-self to you.

1 I call you, Lord; come now to help me!
2 In all my words, Lord, be my guard-ian,
3 Keep me from shar-ing the feast of the wick-ed;
4 O cher-ished God, you are my vi-sion!
5 *Praise to you, Lord, Fa - ther Al - might - y,*

O hear my voice as I cry out to you.
keep stead-fast watch at the door of my lips!
if I am struck, let me an - swer with love.
A shel-ter strong when my soul cries to you!
and praise to you, Christ the Sav - ior and Son.

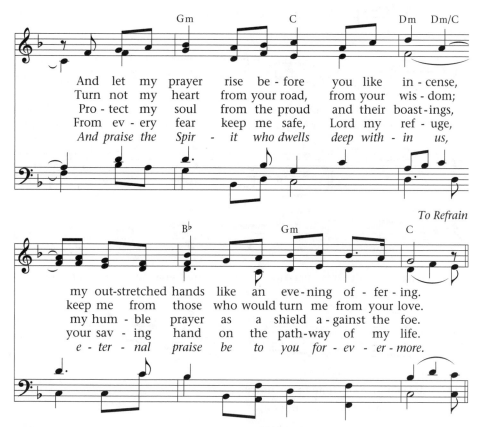

Gm ... C ... Dm ... Dm/C

And let my prayer rise be - fore you like in - cense,
Turn not my heart from your road, from your wis - dom;
Pro - tect my soul from the proud and their boast-ings,
From ev - ery fear keep me safe, Lord my ref - uge,
And praise the Spir - it who dwells deep with - in us,

To Refrain

Bb ... Gm ... C

my out-stretched hands like an eve-ning of - fer - ing.
keep me from those who would turn me from your love.
my hum - ble prayer as a shield a - gainst the foe.
your sav - ing hand on the path-way of my life.
e - ter - nal praise be to you for - ev - er - more.

Words and Music: Steven C. Warner © 2006 World Library Publications

Psalm 141:1-4a, 8
A Responsorial Setting

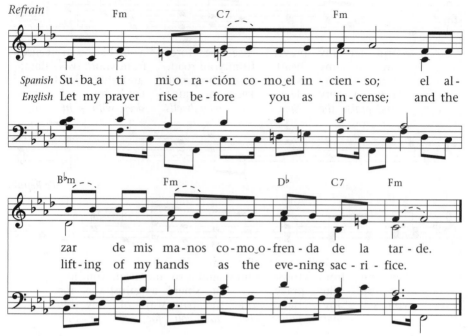

Refrain

Spanish Su-ba a ti mi o-ra-ción co-mo el in-cien-so; el al-
English Let my prayer rise be-fore you as in-cense; and the

zar de mis ma-nos co-mo o-fren-da de la tar-de.
lift-ing of my hands as the eve-ning sac-ri-fice.

Refrain

¹ O Lord, I call to you; come to me quickly;
  hear my voice when I cry to you.

² Let my prayer rise before you as incense;
  the lifting up of my hands as the evening sacrifice. *Refrain*

³ Set a watch before my mouth, O LORD,
  and guard the door of my lips.

⁴ᵃ Let not my heart incline to any evil thing.
  Let me not be occupied in wickedness with evildoers.

⁸ But my eyes are turned to you, Lord GOD;
  in you I take refuge; strip me not of my life. *Refrain*

Tone

Words: Psalm 141
Music: Gerhard Cartford © 1998 Augsburg Fortress Publishers; arr. Bethany Vrieland © 2011 Augsburg
Fortress Publishers
Psalm Text: from *Evangelical Lutheran Worship* © 2006 Evangelical Lutheran Church in America, admin.
Augsburg Fortress Publishers
Tone: © 1996 Augsburg Fortress Publishers

A Prayer at Bedtime

The prayer may begin each night with this, Psalm 141:2, or another Scripture recitation.
The phrases may be spoken in alteration with the child reciting the words in italics.

Lord, come quickly,
listen to my voice as I pray.
May these words be like a sweet smell rising up,
as I close my eyes and fold my hands in prayer.   *based on Psalm 141:1-2*

Option 1

Dear Lord,
Watch over me as I sleep even as you do when I am awake.
Keep all bad thoughts from me so that I may sleep in peace.
Amen.

Option 2

The boldface words may be used as a prayer alone, or you may choose to allow time for the child to voice his/her own words.

Lord, I love you . . .

[Allow the child to add his/her own reasons for loving God, such as . . .]

because you made the beautiful world, the color red,
race cars and little ponies.
You gave me people who love me, and sent Jesus to save me.

But sometimes I don't show my love very well.
I am sorry for my sins. Please forgive me . . .

[Allow the child to add specific confessions at the end of each of the following lines.]

for the things I said and did today that were wrong,
and for the things I should have done but I didn't.

Thank you for all the good things you give me . . .

[Allow the child to add his/her own thanksgivings, such as. . .]

for food to eat and my warm bed,
for my family and my friends,
for my body so I can run and jump,
and for my mind so I can learn and dream.

Help everyone who needs you . . .

[Allow the child to add his/her prayers for others, such as. . .]

people who don't have food to eat, a warm bed, or people who love them;
and for people who are sick.

Help me to love and care for others . . .

[Allow the child to name people and things for which he/she can show love and care, such as. . .]

for people who don't know you, for kids at my school and church,
for the world around me—the plants and animals,
and for my family.

Now, at the end of this day, bless me with a good night's sleep so I can
be ready for tomorrow.

[Allow the child an opportunity to voice any concerns he/she may have for the following day.]

Amen.

The prayer may conclude with the singing or speaking of the Lord's Prayer (see pp. 1034, 1038, 1044, 1045, 1049)
and/or a blessing given to the child (see 20C, 121G, p. 1052).

Joyce Borger, 2011, © Creative Commons Attribution-NonCommercial-ShareAlike

Psalm 142

A Maskil of David. When he was in the cave. A Prayer.

1 With my voice I cry to the LORD; *

    with my voice I make supplication to the LORD.

2 **I pour out my complaint before him;** *

    I tell my trouble before him.

3 When my spirit is faint, you know my way. *

    In the path where I walk they have hidden a trap for me.

4 Look on my right hand and see—there is no one who takes notice of me; *

    no refuge remains to me; no one cares for me.

5 **I cry to you, O LORD; I say, "You are my refuge,** *

    my portion in the land of the living."

6 **Give heed to my cry, for I am brought very low.** *

    Save me from my persecutors, for they are too strong for me.

7 **Bring me out of prison, so that I may give thanks to your name.** *

    The righteous will surround me,

    for you will deal bountifully with me.

Lord Jesus, loving Savior,
few things in life are worse than to be in trouble and to be alone.
When the burden of living is great and the snares of the world are complex,
be our companion and our peace.
Cover us with your presence until we again find tranquility and joy. **Amen.**

Psalm 142 is an individual cry for God's help from a person overwhelmed by persecution (v. 6) and imprisonment (v. 7). The psalmist expresses deep loneliness and isolation (vv. 3-4) but also sturdy hope of joining the community of the righteous and of the future blessing of God (v. 7). *Use in Worship: a prayer by or on behalf of those who face persecution or imprisonment.*

Hear My Cry and Supplication 142A

1 Hear my cry and sup-pli-ca-tion; LORD, I
2 When my path is filled with dan-gers, no one
3 LORD, I am op-pressed and low-ly; I de-
4 When you lead me from this pris-on, right-eous

pour out my com-plaint. Heed my tale of
comes to res-cue me. When I am en-
pend up-on your care. Save me now, O
friends will gath-er round. When from depths I

trib-u-la-tion; lead the way when I am faint.
snared by strang-ers, no one comes to set me free.
God most ho-ly, hear me in my deep de-spair.
have a-ris-en, I will make your praise re-sound.

Optional refrain or final stanza

I will arise and go to Jesus,
he will embrace me in his arms;
in the arms of my dear Savior,
Oh, there are ten thousand charms.

Guitar chords do not correspond with keyboard harmony.

Words: sts. Clarence P. Walhout, 1982, © 1987 Faith Alive Christian Resources; opt. ref. American, 17th c., P.D.
Music (ARISE/RESTORATION 8.7.8.7): W. Walker's *Southern Harmony*, 1835, P.D.; harm. Charles H. Webb
(b. 1933), P.D.

142B When I Lift Up My Voice

1 When I lift up my voice and I cry for your help and I
2 When I see no one cares and I walk all a - lone and my
3 When you come to my side and you an-swer my prayers and you

pour out my trou - bles be - fore you: I say,
spir - it grows wea - ry with - in me: I say,
set my life free from its pris - on, I say:

Refrain

"You are my ref - uge; I will praise your name; you are good to me,

O Lord!" Lord!"

Words: Michael Perry © 1990 The Jubilate Group, admin. Hope Publishing Company
Music (WHEN I LIFT UP MY VOICE 6.6.10 with refrain): Michael Perry; arr. David Peacock © 1990 The
Jubilate Group, admin. Hope Publishing Company

Psalm 143

A Psalm of David.

1 Hear my prayer, O LORD;
give ear to my supplications in your faithfulness; *
answer me in your righteousness.

2 **Do not enter into judgment with your servant,***
for no one living is righteous before you.

3 For the enemy has pursued me, crushing my life to the ground, *
making me sit in darkness like those long dead.

4 Therefore my spirit faints within me; *
my heart within me is appalled.

5 **I remember the days of old, I think about all your deeds, ***
I meditate on the works of your hands.

6 **I stretch out my hands to you; ***
my soul thirsts for you like a parched land.   *Selah*

7 Answer me quickly, O LORD; my spirit fails. *
Do not hide your face from me,
or I shall be like those who go down to the Pit.

8 **Let me hear of your steadfast love in the morning,**
for in you I put my trust. *
Teach me the way I should go, for to you I lift up my soul.

9 Save me, O LORD, from my enemies; *
I have fled to you for refuge.

10 **Teach me to do your will, for you are my God. ***
Let your good spirit lead me on a level path.

11 For your name's sake, O LORD, preserve my life. *
In your righteousness bring me out of trouble.

12 **In your steadfast love cut off my enemies,**
and destroy all my adversaries, *
for I am your servant.

Merciful God, with souls parched by sin
and spirits withered by enemies within and without, we lift our hands to you.
Lead us by your Spirit on the path of truth and guard us from all harm,
trusting in Jesus Christ, our refuge and our righteousness. **Amen.**

Psalm 143, one of the seven penitential psalms, is a cry for help in the midst of hopelessness. It evokes the memory of God's faithfulness in the past (v. 5) as the basis for the petition for God to lead forward into the future (v. 8). The psalmist prays for God to be not only deliverer but also teacher (v. 8), asking both for deliverance and obedience (v. 10). The psalm echoes many themes from earlier in the Psalter: no one is righteous (v. 2, echoing Pss. 14 and 53), a longing for God with parched thirst (v. 6, echoing Ps. 42), the memory of God's deeds (v. 5, echoing Ps. 77), the prayer for God to serve as teacher and guide (vv. 8-10, echoing Ps. 119), and imprecation against the enemy (v. 12, echoing Pss. 52, 109). *Use in Worship: a prayer of confession or a supplication for help.*

143A Hear My Prayer, O God

1 Hear my prayer, O God, and lis-ten to my plea;
2 Hound-ed by a foe who crushed me to the ground,
3 An-swer soon, O God; my spir-it faints in me;
4 Keep me safe, O God, and help me learn your will;

faith-ful, right-eous One, give ear and an-swer me.
I am like the dead or those in pris-on bound.
do not hide your face, or I will cease to be.
let your Spir-it lead through lev-el path-ways still.

Judge me not, I pray; no mer-it dare I claim;
Hope-less, numbed by fear, I pon-der all your care;
When the morn-ing dawns, make known your love a-new;
For your great Name's sake, my griefs and fears dis-pel;

know-ing my own faults, I trust in your just Name.
thirst-y as parched earth, I lift my hands in prayer.
show me how to walk, for I will trust in you.
free me from my foes, that I may serve you well.

Words: Carl P. Daw Jr. (b. 1944) © 2005 Hope Publishing Company
Music (HYMN CHANT 5.6.5.6 D): Hal H. Hopson © 2006 Hope Publishing Company

Psalm 143 | A Responsorial Setting 143B

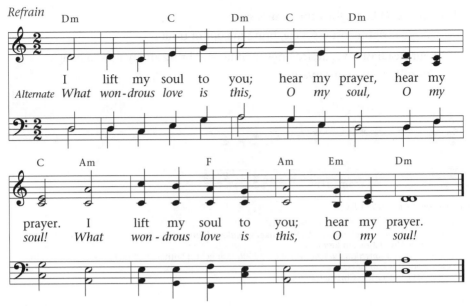

Refrain

Dm   C   Dm   C   Dm

I lift my soul to you; hear my prayer, hear my

Alternate What won-drous love is this, O my soul, O my

C   Am   F   Am   Em   Dm

prayer. I lift my soul to you; hear my prayer.

soul! What won-drous love is this, O my soul!

Refrain

¹ LORD, hear my prayer, and in your faithfulness heed my supplications;
   answer me in your righteousness.

² Enter not into judgment with your servant,
   for in your sight shall no one living be justified.

³ For my enemy has sought my life and has crushed me to the ground,
   making me live in dark places like those who are long dead.   *Refrain*

⁴ My spirit faints within me;
   my heart within me is desolate.

⁵ I remember the time past; I ponder all your deeds;
   I consider the works of your hands.

⁶ I spread out my hands to you;
   my soul gasps to you like a thirsty land.

⁷ O LORD, make haste to answer me; my spirit fails me;
   do not hide your face from me,
   or I shall be like those who go down to the pit.   *Refrain*

⁸ Let me hear of your lovingkindness in the morning, for I put my trust in you;
   show me the road that I must walk, for I lift up my soul to you.

⁹ Deliver me from my enemies, O LORD,
   for I flee to you for refuge.

¹⁰ Teach me to do what pleases you, for you are my God;
   let your good Spirit lead me on level ground.   (continues)

¹¹ Revive me, O Lord, for your name's sake;

for your righteousness' sake, bring me out of trouble.

¹² In your steadfast love, destroy my enemies and bring all my foes to naught,

for truly I am your servant.   *Refrain*

Tone

Lectionary: Easter Vigil (A,B,C).

Words: S. Mead's *A General Selection,* 1811, P.D.
Music (WONDROUS LOVE fragment): W. Walker's *Southern Harmony,* 1835; arr. Emily R. Brink (b. 1940)
© 1987 Faith Alive Christian Resources
Psalm Text: from *Evangelical Lutheran Worship* © 2006 Evangelical Lutheran Church in America, admin.
Augsburg Fortress Publishers
Tone: © 2011 Faith Alive Christian Resources

Psalm 144

Of David.

¹ Blessed be the Lord, my rock, *

who trains my hands for war, and my fingers for battle;

² **my rock and my fortress, my stronghold and my deliverer,** *

my shield, in whom I take refuge,

who subdues the peoples under me.

³ O Lord, what are human beings that you regard them, *

or mortals that you think of them?

⁴ They are like a breath; *

their days are like a passing shadow.

⁵ **Bow your heavens, O Lord, and come down;** *

touch the mountains so that they smoke.

⁶ **Make the lightning flash and scatter them;** *

send out your arrows and rout them.

⁷ Stretch out your hand from on high; *

set me free and rescue me from the mighty waters, from the hand of aliens,

⁸ whose mouths speak lies, *

and whose right hands are false.

9 **I will sing a new song to you, O God;** *
   upon a ten-stringed harp I will play to you,

10 **the one who gives victory to kings,** *
   who rescues his servant David.

11 Rescue me from the cruel sword, and deliver me from the hand of aliens, *
   whose mouths speak lies, and whose right hands are false.

12 **May our sons in their youth be like plants full grown,** *
   our daughters like corner pillars, cut for the building of a palace.

13 May our barns be filled, with produce of every kind; *
   may our sheep increase by thousands, by tens of thousands in our fields,

14 and may our cattle be heavy with young. *
   May there be no breach in the walls, no exile,
   and no cry of distress in our streets.

15 **Happy are the people to whom such blessings fall;** *
   happy are the people whose God is the LORD.

Praise be to you, O God, for you have given us in Christ every spiritual blessing
and have delivered us from the powers of sin and death.
By your Spirit's power help us in the struggle to bring all things into conformity
with your kingdom of righteousness and peace. **Amen.**

Psalm 144 is a prayer for deliverance in battle (vv. 5-8, 10-11) that is juxtaposed with a series of reflections about praise and thanksgiving for God's protection and guidance (vv. 1-2), the fleetingness of human life (vv. 3-4), a vow to praise God (v. 9), and the flourishing of human life that has accompanied the fear of God (vv. 12-15). The psalm helps us to enter into the drama of all those who engaged in battle throughout the history of the OT, revealing the mixture of emotions and sentiments they must have felt. As with Ps. 149, Christian responses to the battle imagery vary widely. Nearly every tradition laments the way this psalm has been misused to justify Crusades and misguided acts of terror and warfare. Many traditions appropriate this text primarily with reference to spiritual, not military, warfare. In traditions that affirm the legitimacy of just warfare, the psalm is a prophetic call to ensure that every military action is conducted in light of and in praise for God's longing for justice, peace, and reconciliation. *Use in Worship: in conjunction with OT battle narratives; in services that focus on spiritual warfare; in discussions about just warfare.*

144A Hymn: O Morning Star, O Radiant Sun

Refrain

1 O Morn - ing Star, O ra - diant Sun, when will our
2 Our lives are frail— a fleet - ing breath. We face our
3 O Sav - ior, rend the heav - ens wide; come down, come
4 There shall we all our prais - es bring ev - er to

hearts be - hold your dawn? O Sun, a - rise; with -
foe: the sting of death. Stretch out your hand, Lord,
down with might - y stride; un - lock the gates, the
you, our Sav - ior King; there shall we praise you

out your light we grope in gloom and dark of night.
hold us fast, un - til the storms of life are past.
doors break down; un - bar the way to heav - en's crown.
and a - dore for - ev - er and for - ev - er - more.

Refrain (sing stanza 1)

1 Praise be to the LORD my Rock,

who trains my hands for war, my fingers for battle.

2a He is my loving God and my fortress, my stronghold and my deliverer,

my shield, in whom I take refuge.

3 LORD, what are human beings that you care for them,

mere mortals that you think of them?

4 They are like a breath;

their days are like a fleeting shadow.

Refrain (sing stanza 2)

5 Part your heavens, LORD, and come down;

touch the mountains, so that they smoke.

6 Send forth lightning and scatter the enemy;

shoot your arrows and rout them.

7a Reach down your hand from on high;

deliver me and rescue me from the mighty waters.

Refrain (sing stanza 3)

9 I will sing a new song to you, my God;

on the ten-stringed lyre I will make music to you.

14b There will be no breaching of walls, no going into captivity,

no cry of distress in our streets.

15 Blessed is the people of whom this is true;

blessed is the people whose God is the LORD.

Refrain (sing stanza 4)

Tone

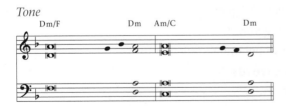

Guitar chords do not correspond with keyboard harmony.

Words: sts. 1, 3, 4 F. von Spee (1591-1635); tr. M. L. Seltz (1909-1967); st. 2 Martin Tel © 2011 Martin Tel, admin. Faith Alive Christian Resources
Music (O HEILAND, REISS DIE HIMMEL AUF 8.8.8.8): *Gesangbuch*, Augsburg, 1666; harm. Dale Grotenhuis, 1985, © 1987 Faith Alive Christian Resources
Text: Psalm 144 © THE HOLY BIBLE, NEW INTERNATIONAL VERSION®, NIV® Copyright © 1973, 1978, 1984, 2011 by Biblica, Inc.™ Used by permission. All rights reserved worldwide.
Tone: © 2006 Augsburg Fortress Publishers

Psalm 145

Praise. Of David.

1 I will extol you, my God and King, *
    and bless your name forever and ever.

2 Every day I will bless you, *
    and praise your name forever and ever.

3 Great is the LORD, and greatly to be praised; *
    his greatness is unsearchable.

4 One generation shall laud your works to another, *
    and shall declare your mighty acts.

5 On the glorious splendor of your majesty, *
    and on your wondrous works, I will meditate.

6 The might of your awesome deeds shall be proclaimed, *
    and I will declare your greatness.

7 They shall celebrate the fame of your abundant goodness, *
    and shall sing aloud of your righteousness.

8 The LORD is gracious and merciful, *
    slow to anger and abounding in steadfast love.

9 The LORD is good to all, *
    and his compassion is over all that he has made.

10 All your works shall give thanks to you, O LORD, *
    and all your faithful shall bless you.

11 They shall speak of the glory of your kingdom, *
    and tell of your power,

12 to make known to all people your mighty deeds, *
    and the glorious splendor of your kingdom.

13 Your kingdom is an everlasting kingdom, *
    and your dominion endures throughout all generations.

The LORD is faithful in all his words, *
    and gracious in all his deeds.

14 The LORD upholds all who are falling, *
    and raises up all who are bowed down.

15 The eyes of all look to you, *
    and you give them their food in due season.

16 You open your hand, *
    satisfying the desire of every living thing.

17 The LORD is just in all his ways, *
    and kind in all his doings.

¹⁸ The LORD is near to all who call on him, *
   to all who call on him in truth.

¹⁹ **He fulfills the desire of all who fear him; ***
   he also hears their cry, and saves them.

²⁰ The LORD watches over all who love him, *
   but all the wicked he will destroy.

²¹ **My mouth will speak the praise of the LORD, ***
   and all flesh will bless his holy name forever and ever.

Great God, we exalt and worship you.
In Christ you offer us everything we need.
Embolden us to go out into the streets and alleys of our world,
urging others to come to your banqueting house;
and there may we discover the table of forgiveness and healing, of laughter and joy.
We ask this in Jesus' name. **Amen.**

Psalm 145, the first of six praise psalms that conclude the Psalter, is a grand hymn of praise. As an acrostic where each verse begins with the subsequent letter in the Hebrew alphabet, the psalm alternates between vows to praise (vv. 1-2, 10, 21) and reasons for praise (vv. 3-9, 11-20), focusing on both the grandeur and the compassion of God. The psalm explores in detail the quartet of divine virtues (covenant love, faithfulness, truthfulness, and righteousness) that have recurred throughout the Psalter. The use of the terms "all" and "every" throughout the psalm highlights its theme of complete praise. Some commentators have noticed correspondences between Ps. 145 and nearly every petition in the Lord's Prayer. *Use in Worship: services focusing on the importance and meaning of praise; significant occasions and festivals; appropriate for any occasion.*

A Table Prayer **145A**

Blessed are you, Lord our God, King of the universe:
   we celebrate your abundant goodness.

For all who hunger and thirst this day,
   we pray, "Lord, have mercy."

As we remember your righteousness and compassion,
   we look to you with gratitude and hope.

Lord Jesus, as you were at Emmaus, be our guest
   and open our eyes to help us recognize your presence.

Holy Spirit, as we eat and drink and fellowship together,
   bless and strengthen us for your service.

Alleluia. **Amen.**

John D. Witvliet, 2011, © Creative Commons Attribution-NonCommercial-ShareAlike

I Will Exalt My God and King

Unison

1 I will ex - alt my God and King, and I will
2 On your most glo - rious maj - es - ty and on your
3 The LORD our God is rich in grace, ten - der to
4 All you have made will praise you, LORD; your might-y

ev - er praise your name. I will ex - tol you ev - ery
deeds my mind will dwell. Your deeds will fill the world with
us, com - pas - sion - ate. His an - ger is most slow to
acts your saints will show, till all the peo - ples on the

day and ev - er - more your praise pro - claim. You, LORD, are
awe, and all your great-ness I will tell. Your match-less
rise; his love and kind-ness are most great. The LORD is
earth the splen-dor of your king - dom know. E - ter - nal

great - ly to be praised; your great-ness is be - yond all
good - ness and your grace your peo - ple will com - mem - o -
good in all his ways; his crea-tures know his con-stant
is your king-dom, LORD, for - ev - er strong and ev - er

thought. From age to age your peo-ple tell the might-y
rate; and all your truth and right-eous-ness our joy-ful
care. To all his works his love ex-tends; all crea-tures
sure; while gen-er-a - tions rise and die, your glo-rious

Interlude

won-ders you have wrought.
song will cel - e - brate.
in his mer - cies share.
reign will still en - dure.

Final ending

5 The LORD is faithful to his word;
he will extend his gracious hand.
The LORD upholds the faltering feet
and makes the weak securely stand.
The eyes of all look up to you
for food and drink, which you supply;
your open hand is bountiful,
and every need you satisfy.

6 The LORD is just in all his ways;
in all his works the LORD is kind,
and all who call on him in truth
in him a present helper find.
He will fulfill the heart's desire
of those who fear him and obey.
The LORD will surely hear their cry,
will save them when to him they pray.

7 The LORD in grace preserves his saints,
redeeming those who love his name.
The wicked he will overthrow
and put his enemies to shame.
My mouth will sing the glorious praise
of God, whom earth and heaven adore.
Let every creature praise his name
forever and forevermore.

Words: *Psalter*, 1912, alt., P.D.
Music (JERUSALEM 8.8.8.8 D): C. Hubert H. Parry (1848-1918), 1916; arr. Janet Wyatt, 1977, © 1977
Roberton Publications. Reprinted by permission of the publisher Goodmusic Publishing, Ltd.

145C Te exaltaré, mi Dios, mi Rey / I Will Exalt My God, My King

Words: Casiodoro Cárdenas, 1979; tr. composite; st. 2 tr. Mary Louise Bringle (b. 1953), 2011
Music (ECUADOR): Casiodoro Cárdenas, 1979; arr. Raquel Mora Martínez, 1979, © Raquel Mora Martínez

145D Psalm 145 | A Responsorial Setting

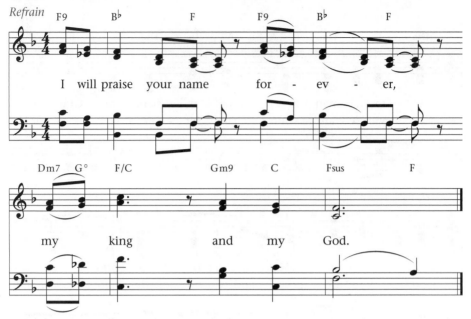

Refrain

I will praise your name for - ev - er,
my king and my God.

Refrain

1 I will exalt you, my God and king,
and bless your name forever and ever.

2 Every day will I bless you
and praise your name forever and ever.

3 Great is the LORD and greatly to be praised!
There is no end to your greatness.

4 One generation shall praise your works to another
and shall declare your power.

5 I will speak of the glorious splendor of your majesty
and all your marvelous works.   *Refrain*

6 They shall tell of the might of your wondrous acts,
and I will recount your greatness.

7 They shall publish the remembrance of your great goodness;
they shall sing joyfully of your righteousness.

8 The LORD is gracious and full of compassion,
slow to anger and abounding in steadfast love.   *Refrain*

9 LORD, you are good to all,
and your compassion is over all your works.

10 All your works shall praise you, O LORD,
and your faithful ones shall bless you.

¹¹ They shall tell of the glory of your kingdom
> and speak of your power,

¹² that all people may know of your power
> and the glorious splendor of your kingdom.

¹³ Your kingdom is an everlasting kingdom;
> your dominion endures throughout all ages.
>> You, LORD, are faithful in all your words,
>> and loving in all your works.   *Refrain*

¹⁴ The Lord upholds all those who fall
> and lifts up those who are bowed down.

¹⁵ The eyes of all wait upon you, O LORD,
> and you give them their food in due season.

¹⁶ You open wide your hand
> and satisfy the desire of every living thing.

¹⁷ You are righteous in all your ways
> and loving in all your works.   *Refrain*

¹⁸ You are near to all who call upon you,
> to all who call upon you faithfully.

¹⁹ You fulfill the desire of those who fear you;
> and hear their cry and save them.

²⁰ You watch over all those who love you,
> but all the wicked you shall destroy.

²¹ My mouth shall speak the praise of the LORD;
> let all flesh bless God's holy name forever and ever.   *Refrain*

Tone

Lectionary: vv. 1-8 Ordinary Time after Pentecost (A); vv. 8-9, 14-21 Ordinary Time after Pentecost (A); vv. 8-14 Ordinary Time after Pentecost (A); vv. 10-18 Ordinary Time after Pentecost (B); vv. 1-5, 17-21 Ordinary Time after Pentecost (C).

Words: © 1969, 1981, 1997 International Commission on English in the Liturgy Corporation
Music: Rawn Harbor © 2006 Rawn Harbor, admin. OCP Publications
Psalm Text: from *Evangelical Lutheran Worship* © 2006 Evangelical Lutheran Church in America, admin.
Augsburg Fortress Publishers
Tone: © 2011 Faith Alive Christian Resources

145E I Will Extol You, O My God

1 I will ex-tol you, O my God, and praise you, O my King;
2 Each gen-er-a-tion to the next shall tes-ti-mo-ny bear,
3 Your might-y acts and glo-rious deeds we shall with awe con-fess.

yes, ev-ery day and ev-er-more your prais-es I will sing.
and to your praise, from age to age, your won-drous acts de-clare.
Your good-ness we will cel-e-brate and sing your right-eous-ness.

Great is the LORD, our might-y God, and great-ly to be praised;
Up-on your glo-rious maj-es-ty and hon-or I will dwell,
Most gra-cious and com-pas-sion-ate is God, who reigns a-bove;

his great-ness is un-search-a-ble, a-bove all glo-ry raised.
and all your grand and glo-rious works and great-ness I will tell.
his wrath is ev-er slow to rise, un-bound-ed is his love.

Guitar chords do not correspond with keyboard harmony.

Words: *Psalter*, 1912, alt., P.D.
Music (NOEL/GERARD 8.6.8.6 D): English; adapt. Arthur S. Sullivan, 1874, P.D.

O My God and King and Savior 145F

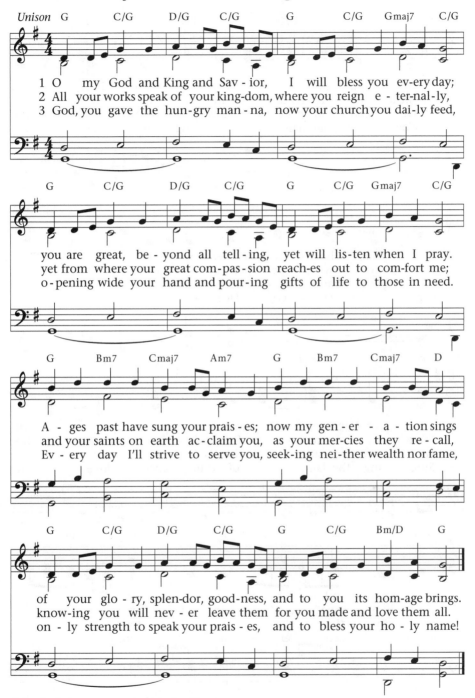

Guitar chords do not correspond with keyboard harmony.

Words: Rae E. Whitney, 2001, © 2001 Selah Publishing Company, Inc.
Music (HOLY MANNA 8.7.8.7 D): W. Moore's *The Columbian Harmony*, 1825; harm. Norman E. Johnson, 1973,
© 1973, 1996 Covenant Publications

We Will Extol You, God and King

Words: Greg Scheer © 2006 Faith Alive Christian Resources
Music (SCARECROW 8.7.8.7 with refrain): Greg Scheer © 2006 Faith Alive Christian Resources

Psalm 146

¹ Praise the LORD! *
> Praise the LORD, O my soul!

² **I will praise the LORD as long as I live;** *
> **I will sing praises to my God all my life long.**

³ Do not put your trust in princes, *
> in mortals, in whom there is no help.

⁴ When their breath departs, they return to the earth; *
> on that very day their plans perish.

⁵ **Happy are those whose help is the God of Jacob,** *
> **whose hope is in the LORD their God,**

⁶ **who made heaven and earth, the sea, and all that is in them;** *
> **who keeps faith forever;**

⁷ **who executes justice for the oppressed;**
who gives food to the hungry. *
> The LORD sets the prisoners free;

⁸ the LORD opens the eyes of the blind. *
> The LORD lifts up those who are bowed down;
> the LORD loves the righteous.

⁹ The LORD watches over the strangers; *
> he upholds the orphan and the widow,
> but the way of the wicked he brings to ruin.

¹⁰ **The LORD will reign forever,** *
> **your God, O Zion, for all generations. Praise the LORD!**

Sovereign God,
when confronted by would-be messiahs promising prosperity and peace,
grant us your wisdom and discernment.
Help us to place our confidence in no one but you.
You are our only Savior and our only Lord. **Amen.**

Psalm 146, the second of six praise psalms that conclude the Psalter, is noteworthy for giving particular attention to God's love for the lowly: prisoners, strangers, orphans, and widows (vv. 7-9). The psalm highlights divine agency, describing God as the one who creates, keeps faith, renders justice, provides bread, frees prisoners, opens eyes, raises up the lowly, loves the righteousness, guards immigrants, and sustains orphans and widows. The salvation that God provides comes in the form of liberation, nourishment, illumination, and protection. The psalm also pauses from its praise to instruct us to refrain from relying on human deliverers (v. 3). *Use in Worship: occasions focusing on astonishingly countercultural ways that divine power is expressed (including Christmas and Good Friday); appropriate for any occasion.*

I'll Praise My Maker While I've Breath

146A

1 I'll praise my Mak - er while I've breath, and when my voice
2 Hap - py are those whose hopes re - ly on God the Lord,
3 The Lord gives eye - sight to the blind, he calms and heals
4 I'll praise you while you lend me breath, and, when my voice

is lost in death, praise shall em - ploy my no - blest powers;
who made the sky, and earth, the sea, the night and day;
the trou-bled mind, and sends the wound-ed con-science peace.
is lost in death, praise shall em - ploy my no - blest powers;

my days of praise are nev - er past while life and thought
God's truth for - ev - er stands se - cure, he keeps his prom -
God helps the strang - er in dis - tress, the wid - ow and
my days of praise are nev - er past while life and thought

and be - ing last or im - mor - tal - i - ty en - dures.
ise to the poor, and none who seeks is turned a - way.
the fa - ther - less, and grants the pris - oner glad re - lease.
and be - ing last or im - mor - tal - i - ty en - dures.

Guitar chords do not correspond with keyboard harmony.

Words: Isaac Watts (1674-1748), John Wesley (1703-1791), P.D.
Music (OLD 113TH 8.8.8.8.8.8): Matthäus Greiter (ca. 1500-1552), *Strassburger Kirchenamt*, 1525; harm.
V. Earle Copes (b. 1921) © 1964 Abingdon Press, admin. The Copyright Company

146B Psalm 146 | A Responsorial Setting

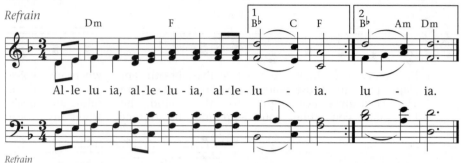

Refrain

Al - le - lu - ia, al - le - lu - ia, al - le - lu - ia. lu - ia.

Refrain

1 Hallelujah!
  Praise the LORD, O my soul!

2 I will praise the LORD as long as I live;
  I will sing praises to my God while I have my being.   *Refrain*

3 Put not your trust in rulers,
  in mortals in whom there is no help.

4 When they breathe their last, they return to earth,
  and in that day their thoughts perish.

5 Happy are they who have the God of Jacob for their help,
  whose hope is in the LORD their God;

6 who made heaven and earth, the seas, and all that is in them;
  who keeps promises forever;

7 who gives justice to those who are oppressed, and food to those who hunger.
  The LORD sets the captive free.   *Refrain*

8 The LORD opens the eyes of the blind;
  the LORD lifts up those who are bowed down;
  the LORD loves the righteous.

9 The LORD cares for the stranger;
  the LORD sustains the orphan and widow,
  but frustrates the way of the wicked.

10 The LORD shall reign forever,
  your God, O Zion, throughout all generations. Hallelujah!   *Refrain*

Tone

Lectionary: vv. 1-10 Ordinary Time after Pentecost (B,C); vv. 5-10 Advent.

Music: Jacques Berthier (1923-1994) © 1986 Ateliers et Presses de Taizé, Taizé Community, France, GIA
Publications, Inc., exclusive North American agent
Psalm Text: from *Evangelical Lutheran Worship* © 2006 Evangelical Lutheran Church in America, admin.
Augsburg Fortress Publishers
Tone: © 2011 Faith Alive Christian Resources

Alternate Refrain 1

May be sung in canon

Muscogee He - le - lu - yan, he - le - lu - yan; he - le, he - le - lu - yan.

English Hal - le - lu - jah, hal - le - lu - jah; hal - le, hal - le - lu - jah.

He - le - lu - yan, he - le - lu - yan; he - le, he - le - lu - yan.

Hal - le - lu - jah, hal - le - lu - jah; hal - le, hal - le - lu - jah.

Alternate Tone 1

Words: traditional Muscogee Creek Indian
Music: Muscogee Creek Indian; trans. Charles H. Webb (b. 1933) © 1989 The United Methodist Publishing House, admin. The Copyright Company
Tone: © 2011 Faith Alive Christian Resources

Alternate Refrain 2

Indonesian Pu - ji Tu - han, Pu - ji Tu - han, Pu - ji Tu - han.

English Hal - le - lu - jah, hal - le - lu - jah, hal - le - lu - jah.

Alternate Tone 2

Words: traditional
Music: Christian I. Tamaela, Indonesian © Christian I. Tamaela
Tone: © 2011 Faith Alive Christian Resources

146C Praise the LORD! Sing Hallelujah!

1 Praise the LORD! Sing hal - le - lu - jah! Come, our great Re - deem - er praise. I will sing the glo - rious prais - es of my God through all my days. Put no con - fi - dence in princ - es, nor on hu - man

2 Hap - py are the ones pro - fess - ing Ja - cob's God to be their aid. They are blest whose hope of bless - ing on the LORD their God is stayed. Heaven and earth the LORD cre - at - ed, seas and all that

3 Food he dai - ly gives the hun - gry, sets the mourn - ing pris - oner free, rais - es those bowed down with an - guish, makes the sight - less eyes to see. God our Sav - ior loves the right - eous, and the strang - er

4 Praise the LORD! Sing hal - le - lu - jah! Come, our great Re - deem - er praise. I will sing the glo - rious prais - es of my God through all my days. O - ver all God reigns for - ev - er; through all a - ges

help de-pend. They shall die, to dust re-turn-ing;
they con-tain. He de-liv-ers from op-pres-sion;
he be-friends, helps the or-phan and the wid-ow,
he is King. Un-to him, your God, O Zi-on,

all their thoughts and plans shall end.
right-eous-ness he will main-tain.
judg-ment on the wick-ed sends.
joy-ful hal-le-lu-jahs sing.

Alternate tune: HOLY MANNA, see p. 951.

Words: *Psalter*, 1887, alt., P.D.
Music (8.7.8.7 D): Darwin Jordan © Darwin Jordan Music; arr. Marcus Hong

146D Praise the LORD! Sing Hallelujah!

1 Praise the LORD! Sing hal - le - lu - jah! Come, our great Re - deem - er praise. I will sing the glo - rious prais - es of my God through all my days. Put no con - fi - dence in princ - es, nor on hu - man

2 Hap - py are the ones pro - fess - ing Ja - cob's God to be their aid. They are blest whose hope of bless - ing on the LORD their God is stayed. Heaven and earth the LORD cre - at - ed, seas and all that

3 Food he dai - ly gives the hun - gry, sets the mourn-ing pris - oner free, rais - es those bowed down with an - guish, makes the sight - less eyes to see. God our Sav - ior loves the right - eous, and the strang - er

4 Praise the LORD! Sing hal - le - lu - jah! Come, our great Re - deem - er praise. I will sing the glo - rious prais - es of my God through all my days. O - ver all God reigns for - ev - er; through all a - ges

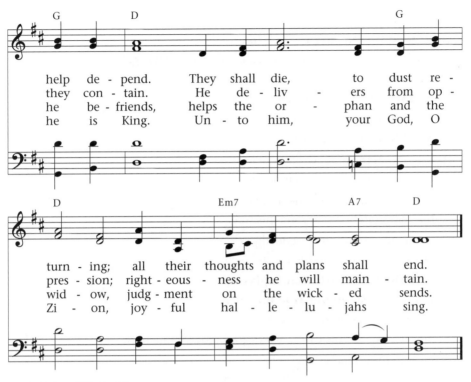

help de - pend. They shall die, to dust re -
they con - tain. He de - liv - ers from op -
he be - friends, helps the or - phan and the
he is King. Un - to him, your God, O

turn - ing; all their thoughts and plans shall end.
pres - sion; right - eous - ness he will main - tain.
wid - ow, judg - ment on the wick - ed sends.
Zi - on, joy - ful hal - le - lu - jahs sing.

Words: *Psalter*, 1887, alt., P.D.
Music (RIPLEY 8.7.8.7 D): Lowell Mason (1792-1872), 1839, P.D.

A Prayer for Illumination 146E

Sing stanzas 1-2 of 146 A, C, or D

Almighty and loving God,
the highest heavens and the depths of the oceans convey the wonders of your splendor and majesty.

Open our eyes to see your glory also revealed in places of despair and brokenness, and in times of grief and fear.

Truly, our hope is in you.

Sing stanzas 3-4 of 146 A, C, or D

John D. Witvliet, 2011, © Creative Commons Attribution-NonCommercial-ShareAlike

Psalm 147

¹ Praise the LORD!

How good it is to sing praises to our God; *
for he is gracious, and a song of praise is fitting.

² **The LORD builds up Jerusalem;** *
he gathers the outcasts of Israel.

³ **He heals the brokenhearted,** *
and binds up their wounds.

⁴ He determines the number of the stars; *
he gives to all of them their names.

⁵ Great is our Lord, and abundant in power; *
his understanding is beyond measure.

⁶ The LORD lifts up the downtrodden; *
he casts the wicked to the ground.

⁷ **Sing to the LORD with thanksgiving;** *
make melody to our God on the lyre.

⁸ He covers the heavens with clouds, *
prepares rain for the earth, makes grass grow on the hills.

⁹ He gives to the animals their food, *
and to the young ravens when they cry.

¹⁰ His delight is not in the strength of the horse, *
nor his pleasure in the speed of a runner;

¹¹ but the LORD takes pleasure in those who fear him, *
in those who hope in his steadfast love.

¹² **Praise the LORD, O Jerusalem!** *
Praise your God, O Zion!

¹³ **For he strengthens the bars of your gates;** *
he blesses your children within you.

¹⁴ **He grants peace within your borders;** *
he fills you with the finest of wheat.

¹⁵ He sends out his command to the earth; *
his word runs swiftly.

¹⁶ He gives snow like wool; *
he scatters frost like ashes.

¹⁷ He hurls down hail like crumbs— *
who can stand before his cold?

¹⁸ He sends out his word, and melts them; *
he makes his wind blow, and the waters flow.

¹⁹ **He declares his word to Jacob,** *
   his statutes and ordinances to Israel.

²⁰ **He has not dealt thus with any other nation;** *
   they do not know his ordinances. Praise the Lᴏʀᴅ!

We worship you, O God, builder, healer, counter of stars.
We sing praise to you, O God, provider, delighter, protector of your people.
You give us life and joy through your Son.
By the power of your Spirit may we never stop rejoicing in you. **Amen.**

Psalm 147, the third of six praise psalms that conclude the Psalter, intertwines acclamations about God's creation and preservation of the cosmos (vv. 4-5, 8-9, 15-18) with acclamations about God's present-day acts of healing and restoration to the brokenhearted and outcasts (vv. 2-3, 6, 10-11, 13-14, 19-20). Addressed to the community that had returned from exile (see v. 2), this intertwining is a way of saying both that the one who heals and restores us is none other than the Creator of the cosmos and that the Creator of the astonishing cosmos is the one who cares about nurturing and healing us. *Use in Worship: celebrations of the Lord's Supper (reference to the "finest of wheat" [v. 14]); appropriate for any occasion.*

Psalm 147 | A Responsorial Setting 147A

Refrain

¹ Hallelujah! How good it is to sing praises to our God!
   How pleasant it is to honor God with praise!

² The Lᴏʀᴅ rebuilds Jerusalem,
   and gathers the exiles of Israel.

³ The Lᴏʀᴅ heals the brokenhearted
   and binds up their wounds.

(continues)

⁴ The Lord counts the number of the stars
  and calls them all by their names.

⁵ Great is our Lord and mighty in power;
  there is no limit to God's wisdom. *Refrain*

⁶ The Lord lifts up the lowly,
  but casts the wicked to the ground.

⁷ Sing to the Lord with thanksgiving;
  make music upon the harp to our God,

⁸ who covers the heavens with clouds
  and prepares rain for the earth,
  making grass to grow upon the mountains.

⁹ God provides food for the cattle
  and for the young ravens when they cry.

¹⁰ God is not impressed by the might of a horse,
  and has no pleasure in the speed of a runner,

¹¹ but finds pleasure in those who fear the Lord,
  in those who await God's steadfast love. *[Hallelujah!] *Refrain*

¹² Worship the Lord, O Jerusalem;
  praise your God, O Zion,

¹³ who has strengthened the bars of your gates
  and has blessed your children within you.

¹⁴ God has established peace on your borders
  and satisfies you with the finest wheat. *Refrain*

¹⁵ God sends out a command to the earth,
  a word that runs very swiftly.

¹⁶ God gives snow like wool,
  scattering frost like ashes.

¹⁷ God scatters hail like bread crumbs.
  Who can stand against God's cold?

¹⁸ The Lord sends forth the word and melts them;
  the wind blows, and the waters flow.

¹⁹ God declares the word to Jacob,
  statutes and judgments to Israel.

²⁰ The Lord has not done so to any other nation;
  they do not know God's judgments. Hallelujah! *Refrain*

Tone

Lectionary: vv. 1-11 with 'Hallelujah' Ordinary Time after Epiphany (B); vv. 12-20 Christmastide (A,B,C).

*Hallelujah is sung when the lection ends at this verse.

Words: Honduran traditional
Music: Honduran traditional; arr. John L. Bell (b. 1949) © 1995 Wild Goose Resource Group, Iona
Community, Scotland, GIA Publications, Inc., exclusive North American agent
Psalm Text: from *Evangelical Lutheran Worship* © 2006 Evangelical Lutheran Church in America, admin.
Augsburg Fortress Publishers
Tone: © 2011 Faith Alive Christian Resources

Alternate Refrain

Optional keyboard accompaniment for Alternate Refrain

Alternate Tone

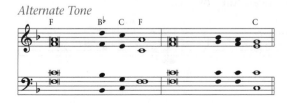

When using as a refrain for the reading or chanting of the psalm, sing only the first line. At the conclusion of the psalm the entire refrain may be sung in canon.

Music (MOZART ALLELUIA): W. A. Mozart (1756-1791), from *Exultate, Jubilate*, adapt., P.D.
Tone: © 2011 Faith Alive Christian Resources

147B Praise the Lord Who Heals

Refrain

Praise, praise the Lord who heals the bro - ken - heart - ed.

Praise, praise the Lord, our God, who heals the heart full of woe.

1 Give thanks for God is gra - cious.
2 The Lord con - soles the griev - ing
3 Great is our God al - might - y

Sing out and lift your praise.
and heals their bit - ter pain.
God's wis - dom knows no bounds.

The Lord re - builds all na - tions
The stars in night sky shin - ing
The Lord sus - tains the low - ly

To Refrain

and gath - ers those a - stray.
the Lord calls each by name.
and casts the wick - ed out.

Sing to God, with Joy and Gladness

O Praise the Lord, for It Is Good 147D

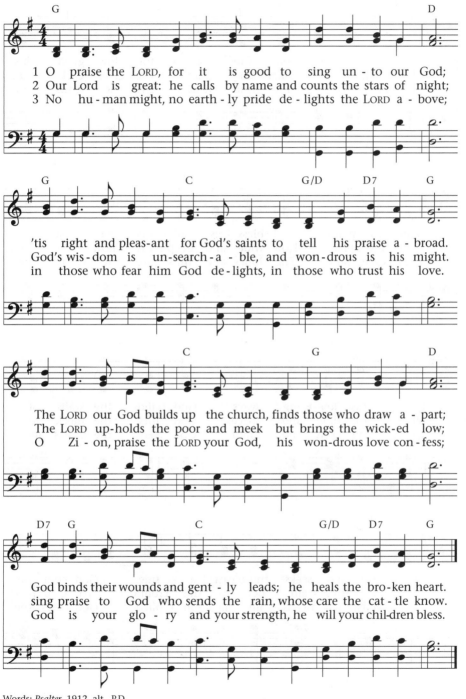

1 O praise the LORD, for it is good to sing un - to our God;
2 Our Lord is great: he calls by name and counts the stars of night;
3 No hu - man might, no earth - ly pride de - lights the LORD a - bove;

'tis right and pleas-ant for God's saints to tell his praise a - broad.
God's wis - dom is un-search-a - ble, and won-drous is his might.
in those who fear him God de - lights, in those who trust his love.

The LORD our God builds up the church, finds those who draw a - part;
The LORD up-holds the poor and meek but brings the wick-ed low;
O Zi - on, praise the LORD your God, his won-drous love con - fess;

God binds their wounds and gent - ly leads; he heals the bro-ken heart.
sing praise to God who sends the rain, whose care the cat - tle know.
God is your glo - ry and your strength, he will your chil-dren bless.

Words: *Psalter*, 1912, alt., P.D.
Music (MINERVA 8.6.8.6 D): John H. Stockton, 1874, P.D.

147E Sing Praise to Our Creator

1 Sing praise to our Cre - a - tor. How good his name to praise! God bless - es all his peo - ple in count - less lov - ing ways. God builds the walls of Zi - on and seeks those cast a - side. God com - forts

2 God num - bers stars and plan - ets, gives each a name and place. How wide and deep his pow - er through all of time and space! God lifts the meek to hon - or, drives sin - ners to the ground. To God pour

3 With clouds God fills the heav - ens; he sends the wel - come rain. The slopes and hills are fer - tile with spring - ing grass and grain. God feeds the beasts and ra - vens; their needs are all sup - plied. God loves the

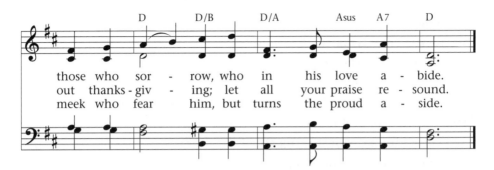

those who sor - row, who in his love a - bide.
out thanks - giv - ing; let all your praise re - sound.
meek who fear him, but turns the proud a - side.

4 Extol the LORD, O Zion: he blesses you with peace.
He blesses all your children; his gracious gifts increase.
God speaks and makes the snow fall like wool upon the land.
God's word sends warmth; the seasons are gathered in his hand.

5 He speaks to all his people; they know his law and word.
No other land is favored, nor is their conscience stirred.
Let all who know God's blessing, his loving, righteous ways,
sing praise to their Creator. How good God's name to praise!

Guitar chords do not correspond with keyboard harmony.

Words: Marie J. Post, 1985, © 1987 Faith Alive Christian Resources
Music (HARTFORD 7.6.7.6 D): John B. Dykes (1823-1876), P.D.

A Prayer of Praise 147F

God of Abraham, Isaac, and Jacob,
our hearts are filled with gratitude
that we have been grafted into your people
through our union with your Son, Jesus Christ, our Lord.
We bless you as the one who blesses and builds up,
the one who comforts and creates,
the one who speaks and nourishes.
Strengthen our capacity to remember all your works—and to take courage.
Help us to contemplate and savor how great and how good you are.
How good it is to praise your name. Amen.

John D. Witvliet, 2011, © Creative Commons Attribution-NonCommercial-ShareAlike

Psalm 148

¹ Praise the LORD!

Praise the LORD from the heavens; *
   praise him in the heights!

² Praise him, all his angels; *
   praise him, all his host!

³ **Praise him, sun and moon; ***
   praise him, all you shining stars!

⁴ Praise him, you highest heavens, *
   and you waters above the heavens!

⁵ **Let them praise the name of the LORD, ***
   for he commanded and they were created.

⁶ He established them forever and ever; *
   he fixed their bounds, which cannot be passed.

⁷ **Praise the LORD from the earth, ***
   you sea monsters and all deeps,

⁸ fire and hail, snow and frost, *
   stormy wind fulfilling his command!

⁹ **Mountains and all hills, ***
   fruit trees and all cedars!

¹⁰ Wild animals and all cattle, *
   creeping things and flying birds!

¹¹ **Kings of the earth and all peoples, ***
   princes and all rulers of the earth!

¹² Young men and women alike, *
   old and young together!

¹³ **Let them praise the name of the LORD,**
   for his name alone is exalted; *
   his glory is above earth and heaven.

¹⁴ He has raised up a horn for his people, praise for all his faithful, *
   for the people of Israel who are close to him.
   Praise the LORD!

O God, beginning with the angels and descending through the skies,
your call to worship unites all creation in song.
Give us wisdom and strength, enabling our wholehearted praise,
for you alone are worthy; you alone are Lord. **Amen.**

Psalm 148, the fourth of the six concluding praise psalms, is noteworthy for its vivid depiction of all of creation praising (a similar theme in Pss. 96, 97, 98 and implied in Gen. 1, Ps. 33, and Job 38-39). The pervasiveness of praise is underscored in the recurrence of "all" (nine times). It was incorporated into the canticle of Shadrach, Meshach, and Abednego (Dan. 1-3), which is known as *benedicite*, the first word of its Latin translation. The psalm is an invitation to wonder at the astonishing beauty of God seen in creation and stands in contrast to mechanical and utilitarian conceptions of nature. *Use in Worship: during the season of Christmas (as a precursor to the angels' hymn of praise sung in response to Jesus' birth); appropriate for any occasion.*

Let All Creation's Wonders 148A

1 Let all cre - a - tion's won - ders and count-less an - gel hordes
2 From far be - neath the o - ceans let joy - ful songs a - rise,
3 So let us lift our voic - es for all that we are worth

u - nite in cease - less wor - ship to praise the Lord of lords:
while hail and wind and light - ning toss psalms a - cross the skies.
to God whose time - less splen - dor sur - pass - es heaven and earth:

he spoke, and formed the cos - mos; he set the stars in place;
You beasts of farm and jun - gle, let na - ture's hymn be heard;
in love he chose and called us, a peo - ple of his own,

his voice de - fines the con - tours of in - ter - stel - lar space—
tell out your mak - er's great-ness, each in - sect, ev - ery bird;
and gave to us a Sav - ior to make his mer - cy known.

let sun and moon ex - tol him and ev - ery plan - et sing;
you peo - ples and you rul - ers, ac - knowl-edge him as King—
His name a - lone we hon - or; our life - long praise we bring;

a - cross the con - stel - la - tions let al - le - lu - ias ring.
from ev - ery gen - er - a - tion let al - le - lu - ias ring.
from deep with - in our spir - its let al - le - lu - ias ring!

For accompaniment see p. 864.

Words: Martin Leckebusch © 2001 Kevin Mayhew Ltd.
Music (THAXTED 7.6.7.6 triple): Gustav Holst, 1921, P.D.

148B O Bless the Lord

Refrain

O bless the Lord, the God of our sal - va - tion, Rock of strength and a ref - uge sure! O bless the Lord, the God of ev-ery na-tion, o - ver all the earth!

To Stanzas | *Fine*

Stanzas

1 O bless the Lord, high - est heav - ens a - bove!
2 Let all the earth sing with joy to the Lord,
3 Let all the na - tions on earth bless the Lord,
4 Let all the peo - ples on earth bless the Lord!

Bless the Lord! Glo - ri - fy his name!
all the seas, crea-tures of the deep!
for the Lord gov - erns all the world!
Young and old, glo - ri - fy his name!

Sun in the day, moon and stars in the night,
Moun-tains and hills, birds and beasts in the fields,
Let all the rul - ers on earth bless the Lord!
Let ev - ery voice sing with joy to the Lord:

To Refrain

wor - ship and praise!
wor - ship and praise!
Wor - ship and praise!
"Glo - ry and praise!"

Words and Music: John Michaels (b. 1947) © 1984 OCP Publications

148C Praise the LORD, Sing Hallelujah

1 Praise the LORD, sing hal - le - lu - jah, from the heav-ens
2 Let them praise the LORD their Mak - er: they were made at
3 All you fruit - ful trees and ce - dars, ev - ery hill and

praise his name; praise the LORD, our great Cre - a - tor;
his com-mand. God es - tab - lished them for - ev - er;
moun-tain high, creep-ing things and beasts and cat - tle,

all his an - gels, praise pro - claim. All his hosts, to - geth - er
his de - cree shall ev - er stand. Let the earth sing hal - le -
birds that in the heav - ens fly, kings of earth and all you

praise him, sun and moon and stars on high; praise the
lu - jah: rag - ing seas, you mon - sters all, fire and
peo - ple, princ - es great, earth's judg - es all; praise his

LORD, O heavens of heav - ens, and the floods a - bove the sky.
hail and snow and va - pors, storm-y winds that hear his call.
name, young men and maid - ens, a - ged men, and chil-dren small.

Refrain (may be sung after stanza 3 only)

Praise the LORD, sing hal - le - lu - jah, for his
Praise the LORD,

name a - lone is high, and his glo - ry is ex-
and his glo - ry

alt - ed, and his glo - ry is ex - alt - ed, and his
and his glo - ry

glo - ry is ex - alt - ed, far a - bove the earth and sky.
and his glo - ry

Words: *Bible Songs Hymnal*, 1927, alt., P.D.
Music (PRAISE JEHOVAH 8.7.8.7 with refrain): William J. Kirkpatrick (1838-1921), P.D.

All the Saints Join In

1 Praise him, praise him from the heav - ens.
3 Praise him, praise him from the earth here be-low.

Praise him in the heights up a - bove.
Praise him all crea-tures and storm winds that blow.

Praise him all his an - gels.
Praise him you moun-tains that tow-er so high.

Praise him all of his heav-en - ly hosts. 2 O
Praise him you o-ceans so deep, far, and wide. 4 O

praise him,   O you sun and moon   and all of you
(4) praise him, praise him all you kings,   you princ-es and

shin - ing stars. Praise him from a - bove.   O
rul-ers of earth. Praise him with all pow - er.   O

praise him   O you high-est heav-ens;   you wa-ters a -
praise him   both young and the old,   to-geth-er with

bove   the skies. Praise the name of the LORD.
one might-y voice. Praise the name of the LORD.

First time to Stanza 3, Second time to Vamp

(continues)

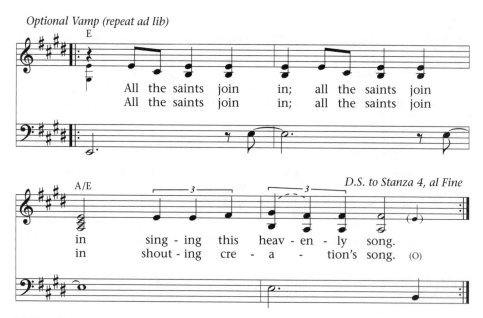

Optional Vamp (repeat ad lib)

All the saints join in; all the saints join
All the saints join in; all the saints join

D.S. to Stanza 4, al Fine

in sing - ing this heav - en - ly song.
in shout - ing cre - a - tion's song. (O)

Words and Music: Tommy Walker © 1988, 2005 Universal Music—Brentwood-Benson Songs, admin. Music Services; arr. Eelco Vos © 2011 Universal Music—Brentwood-Benson Songs, admin. Music Services

148E Hallelujah! Sing Praise to Your Creator

Indonesian Nya - nyi - kan - lah nya - nyi - an ba - ru ba - gi
English 1 Hal - le - lu - jah! Sing praise to your Cre - a - tor,
2 Praise the LORD, all moun - tains and o - ceans, roll - ing
3 Give to God all glo - ry and hon - or. From the

Al - lah, Pen - cip - ta ca - kra - wa - la. Se -
sun, moon, and stars and an - gels a - bove. Praise the
thun - der and wind and storm clouds on high. Praise the
depths to the heights let prais - es re - sound to the

ga - la se - ra - fim ke - ru - bim, pu - ji - lah
LORD, whose word es - tab - lished the heav - ens, who up -
LORD your Mak - er, all liv - ing crea - tures, all the
LORD, the source of strength and sal - va - tion for all

Di - a be - sar - kan - lah Na - ma - Nya.
holds all his works in his sov - ereign love.
beasts in the fields and birds in the sky.
peo - ple on whom his fa - vor is found.

Ber - so - rak so - rai ba - gi Ra - ja - mu!
God reigns on high, let the heav - ens re - joice!
Both young and old, come and join in the song!
Praise God, you saints he has claimed for his own! (Oh!)

Ber - so - rak so - rai ba - gi Ra - ja - mu!
God reigns on high, let the heav - ens re - joice!
Both young and old, come and join in the song!
Praise God, you saints he has claimed for his own!

Words: Indonesian, Tilly Lubis © 2009 Yamuger, Indonesian Institute for Sacred Music; English vers. David
J. Diephouse © 2009 Faith Alive Christian Resources
Music (NYANYIKANLAH): traditional Batak melody, Toba, Indonesia; arr. H. A. Pandopo © 1999 H. A. Pandopo

148F Praise the LORD! O Heavens, Adore Him

1 Praise the LORD! O heavens, a - dore him; praise him, an - gels in the height. Sun and moon, re - joice be - fore him; praise him, shin - ing stars of light. Praise the LORD, for he has spo - ken; worlds his might - y voice o - beyed. Laws which

2 In the earth let all things praise him: seas and all that they con - tain, storm - y winds that do his plea - sure, hail and light-ning, snow and rain. Hills and moun-tains, praise your Mak - er; praise him, all you flocks and herds. Fields and

3 All you na - tions, come be - fore him: earth - ly rul - ers and all kings, men and wom - en, par - ents, chil - dren, join with all cre - at - ed things. Praise the God of our sal - va - tion, who re - stores from sin and shame. Heaven and

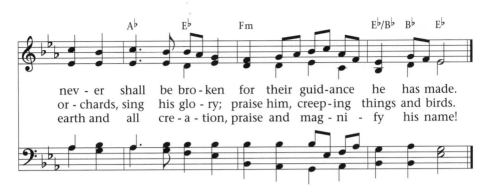

nev - er shall be bro - ken for their guid-ance he has made.
or - chards, sing his glo - ry; praise him, creep-ing things and birds.
earth and all cre - a - tion, praise and mag - ni - fy his name!

Guitar chords do not correspond with keyboard harmony.

Alternate tune: HOLY MANNA, see p. 951.

Words: st. 1 *Foundling Hospital Collection*, 1796, alt.; sts. 2-3 *Psalter*, 1912, alt., P.D.
Music (AUSTRIAN HYMN 8.7.8.7 D): Franz Joseph Haydn (1732-1809), 1797, P.D.

Psalm 148 | A Responsorial Setting 148G

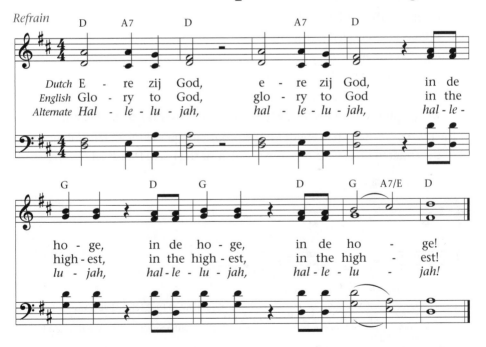

Refrain

Dutch E - re zij God, e - re zij God, in de
English Glo - ry to God, glo - ry to God, in the
Alternate Hal - le - lu - jah, hal - le - lu - jah, hal - le -

ho - ge, in de ho - ge, in de ho - ge!
high - est, in the high - est, in the high - est!
lu - jah, hal-le - lu - jah, hal - le - lu - jah!

Refrain

¹ Hallelujah! Praise the LORD from the heavens;
  praise God in the heights.

² Praise the LORD, all you angels;
  sing praise, all you hosts of heaven. *(continues)*

3 Praise the LORD, sun and moon;
   sing praise all you shining stars.
4 Praise the LORD, heaven of heavens,
   and you waters above the heavens.
5 Let them praise the name of the LORD,
   who commanded, and they were created,
6 who made them stand fast forever and ever,
   giving them a law that shall not pass away.   *Refrain*
7 Praise the LORD from the earth,
   you sea monsters and all deeps;
8 fire and hail, snow and fog,
   tempestuous wind, doing God's will;
9 mountains and all hills,
   fruit trees and all cedars;
10 wild beasts and all cattle,
   creeping things and flying birds;
11 sovereigns of the earth and all peoples,
   princes and all rulers of the world;
12 young men and maidens,
   old and young together.   *Refrain*
13 Let them praise the name of the LORD,
   whose name only is exalted, whose splendor is over earth and heaven.
14 The LORD has raised up strength for the people and praise for all faithful servants,
   the children of Israel, a people who are near the LORD. Hallelujah!   *Refrain*

Tone

Lectionary: Christmastide (A,B,C); Eastertide (C).

Words: Luke 2:14; para F. A. Schultz, ca. 1870; tr. *Psalter Hymnal*, 1987, © 1987 Faith Alive Christian Resources
Music (ERE ZIJ GOD fragment): F. A. Schultz, ca. 1870, P.D.
Psalm Text: from *Evangelical Lutheran Worship* © 2006 Evangelical Lutheran Church in America, admin.
Augsburg Fortress Publishers
Tone: © 2011 Faith Alive Christian Resources

Alternate Refrain

Alternate Tone

Words: traditional
Music: Abraham Maraire; arr. Patrick Matsikenyiri © Zimbabwe East Annual Conference, admin. General Board of Global Ministries t/a GBGMusik
Tone: © 2011 Faith Alive Christian Resources

148H Hallelujah! Praise the LORD from the Heavens

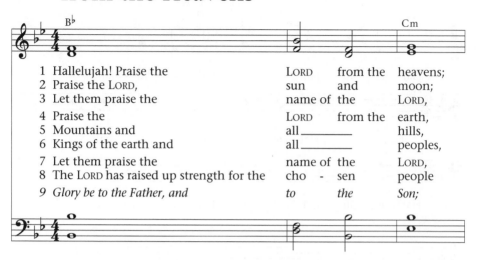

1 Hallelujah! Praise the   LORD   from the   heavens;
2 Praise the LORD,   sun   and   moon;
3 Let them praise the   name of the   LORD,

4 Praise the   LORD   from the   earth,
5 Mountains and   all_____   hills,
6 Kings of the earth and   all_____   peoples,

7 Let them praise the   name of the   LORD,
8 The LORD has raised up strength for the   cho - sen   people

9 *Glory be to the Father, and*   *to*   *the*   *Son;*

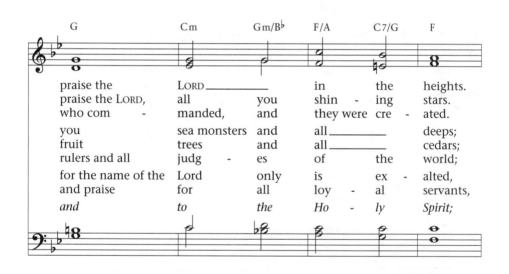

praise the   LORD_____   in   the   heights.
praise the LORD,   all   you   shin - ing   stars.
who com - manded,   and   they were cre - ated.

you   sea monsters and   all_____   deeps;
fruit   trees   and   all_____   cedars;
rulers and all   judg - es   of   the   world;

for the name of the   Lord   only   is   ex - alted,
and praise   for   all   loy - al   servants,

and   *to*   *the*   *Ho - ly*   *Spirit;*

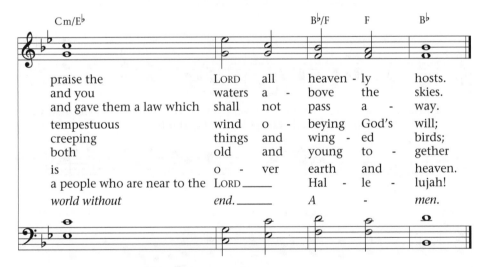

Words: from *Psalter for the Christian People* © Liturgical Press
Music: George Thalben-Ball © Evelyn P. Thalben-Ball, admin. Calder & Co.

1481 Let the Whole Creation Cry

1 Let the whole cre - a - tion cry, "Glo-ry to the Lord on high."
2 Men and wom-en, young and old, raise the an-them man - i - fold;

Heaven and earth, a - wake and sing, "God is our e - ter - nal King."
join with chil-dren's songs of praise, wor-ship God through length of days.

Praise God, all ye hosts a-bove, ev - er shin-ing forth in love;
From the north to south-ern pole let the might-y cho-rus roll:

sun and moon, up - lift your voice; night and stars in God re-joice!
"Ho-ly, ho - ly, ho - ly One, glo-ry be to God a-lone!"

Guitar chords do not correspond with keyboard harmony.

Words: Stopford A. Brooke, 1881, P.D.
Music (SALZBURG 7.7.7.7 D): Jakob Hintze, 1678; harm. Johann S. Bach (1685-1750); from *Hymns Ancient and Modern*, 1861, P.D.

Psalm 149

¹ Praise the LORD!

Sing to the LORD a new song, *

his praise in the assembly of the faithful.

² **Let Israel be glad in its Maker;** *

let the children of Zion rejoice in their King.

³ **Let them praise his name with dancing,** *

making melody to him with tambourine and lyre.

⁴ **For the LORD takes pleasure in his people;** *

he adorns the humble with victory.

⁵ Let the faithful exult in glory; *

let them sing for joy on their couches.

⁶ Let the high praises of God be in their throats *

and two-edged swords in their hands,

⁷ to execute vengeance on the nations *

and punishment on the peoples,

⁸ to bind their kings with fetters *

and their nobles with chains of iron,

⁹ to execute on them the judgment decreed. *

This is glory for all his faithful ones. Praise the LORD!

Sovereign God,
we dance and sing for joy because you have called us to be your people
and have given us victory through our Lord Jesus Christ.
Armor us with his grace and embolden us with the Spirit's power,
so that we may faithfully struggle for peace and justice everywhere. **Amen.**

Psalm 149, the fifth of six praise psalms that conclude the Psalter, is a song of praise that envisions God's people as both those who sing praise in public worship (v. 1) and those who conduct warfare in the name of justice and covenantal commitment to God (vv. 5-9). The psalm serves to help us enter into the experience of the people of Israel and the way in which they perceived an intimate relationship between praise and fighting just and holy wars. As with Ps. 144, Christian responses to the battle imagery vary widely. Nearly every tradition laments the way this psalm has been misused to justify crusades and misguided acts of terror and warfare. Many traditions appropriate this text primarily with reference to spiritual, not military, warfare. In traditions that affirm the legitimacy of warfare in some contexts, the psalm is a prophetic call to ensure that every military action is done in light of and in praise for God's longing for justice, peace, and reconciliation. Pacifist traditions are more inclined to see the psalm as an example of OT experience that is challenged by the NT's call for peacemaking and reconciliation. It is, then, a psalm to handle with great care. It is also a psalm that can provoke instructive conversations about the nature of faithful obedience in a world of injustice. *Use in Worship: in conjunction with OT battle narrative; services focusing on spiritual warfare; in discussions about just warfare.*

Refrain (or sing stanza 1)

1 Hallelujah! Sing to the LORD a new song,
   God's praise in the assembly of the faithful.

2 Let Israel rejoice in their maker;
   let the children of Zion be joyful in their ruler.

3 Let them praise their maker's name with dancing;
   let them sing praise with tambourine and harp.   *Refrain (or sing stanza 2)*

4 For the LORD takes pleasure in the people
   and adorns the poor with victory.

5 Let the faithful rejoice in triumph;
   let them sing for joy on their beds.   *Refrain (or sing stanza 3)*

6 Let the praises of God be in their throat
   and a two-edged sword in their hand,

7 to wreak vengeance on the nations
   and punishment on the peoples,

8 to bind their kings in chains
   and their nobles with links of iron,

9 to inflict on them the judgment decreed;
   this is glory for all God's faithful ones. Hallelujah!   *Refrain (or sing stanza 4)*

Tone

Lectionary: Ordinary Time after Pentecost (A); All Saints' Day (C).

Words: Te Deum, 4th c.; vers. Ignaz Franz, ca. 1774; tr. Clarence A. Walworth, 1853, alt., P.D.
Music (GROSSER GOTT fragment): *Katholisches Gesangbuch*, Vienna, 1774, P.D.
Psalm Text: from *Evangelical Lutheran Worship* © 2006 Evangelical Lutheran Church in America, admin.
Augsburg Fortress Publishers
Tone: © 2011 Faith Alive Christian Resources

Alternate Refrain

Al - le - lu - ia, al - le - lu - ia, al - le - lu - ia.

Alternate Tone

Music: Plainsong, mode VI; arr. © 2006 Augsburg Fortress Publishers
Tone: © 2011 Faith Alive Christian Resources

149B Give Praise to Our God

1 Give praise to our God and sing a new song,
amid all the saints God's prais-es pro-long;
a song to your mak-er and rul-er now raise,
all chil-dren of Zi-on, re-joice and give praise.

2 With tim-brel and harp and joy-ful ac-claim,
with glad-ness and mirth, we praise your great name;
for now in your peo-ple your plea-sure you seek,
with robes of sal-va-tion a-dorn-ing the meek.

3 In glo-ry ex-ult, you saints of the Word;
with songs in the night high prais-es ac-cord;
go forth in God's ser-vice, be strong in God's might
to con-quer all e-vil and stand for the right.

4 For this is God's word: the saints shall not fail,
but o-ver the earth the hum-ble pre-vail;
all rul-ers and na-tions shall yield to their sway,
To God give the glo-ry; sing prais-es for aye.

Guitar chords do not correspond with keyboard harmony.

Alternate tune: LYONS, p. 664.

Words: *Psalter*, 1912, alt. 1995, P.D.
Music (LAUDATE DOMINUM 10.10.11.11): C. Hubert H. Parry (1848-1918), 1894, P.D.

Psalm 150

1 Praise the LORD! Praise God in his sanctuary; *

praise him in his mighty firmament!

2 Praise him for his mighty deeds; *

praise him according to his surpassing greatness!

3 Praise him with trumpet sound; *

praise him with lute and harp!

4 Praise him with tambourine and dance; *

praise him with strings and pipe!

5 Praise him with clanging cymbals; *

praise him with loud clashing cymbals!

6 Let everything that breathes praise the LORD! *

Praise the LORD!

Lord of all creation,
tune the instruments of our lives and choreograph the dance of your church
so that, through word and deed,
your people may persistently proclaim your glory, majesty, love, and goodness,
until everything that breathes sings "Hallelujah!"
We pray through Jesus Christ our Lord and Redeemer. **Amen.**

Psalm 150 is an exuberant call to praise. Its placement as the final psalm suggests that all of life is finally aimed at the praise of God. The Psalter, which began with instruction and a call to faithful journeying with God, now ends with a doxology, a testimony to the true end or goal of human existence before God's face. The psalm's call for various instruments to take up praise crescendos to the climatic call for "everything that breathes" to offer praise to God. The psalm does not offer specific reasons for praise; these have been offered all the way along throughout the Psalter. *Use in Worship: appropriate for any occasion (especially when reasons for praise have already been made clear); a fitting first act of worship, as well as a climactic conclusion.*

150A Sing Praise to the Lord, You People of Grace

1 Sing praise to the Lord, you people of grace; fill
heaven with the songs that sound from this place; since you are God's
ser - vants and meet in his name, his won - ders de -
clare and his glo - ry pro - claim.

2 His great-ness ex - ceeds what words can ex - plain, and
his is the power no force can re - strain; with fan - fares of
horns and cre - scend - os of strings raise an - thems to
ho - nor the King of all kings.

3 Where mu - sic is made, let rhy - thms a - bound: let
cym - bals and drums add weight to the sound; with dance that is
grace - ful and words that are clear, bring joy to the
God you a - dore and re - vere.

4 Yield all that you are to wor - ship the Lord— see
life as a psalm, each mo - ment a chord; let har - mo - nies
flour - ish and mel - o - dies soar— let all that has
breath praise the Lord ev - er - more.

Refrain
Two part

150B Praise Ye the Lord, Hallelujah

Omit final time

1 Praise God with the sound of the trum - pet, praise God with the
2 Praise God with ho - ly cym - bals, praise God with
3 Praise God in the ho - ly tem - ple, praise God for al -
4 Praise God on top of the moun - tains, praise God both

lute and the harp; praise God with tim - brel and danc-
strings and with pipes; praise God with clash - ing cym-
might - y deeds; praise God for those boun - ti - ful mer-
day and night; praise God down in the low val -

- ing, praise God wher - ev - er you are.
- bals, praise God with all of your might.
- cies, for God ful - fills our needs.
- leys, praise God be - cause it's al - right.

150C Blest Be God, Praised Forever

Introduction (may be sung by Leader)

Ra - bə ki ho - ve sa - naa ha - me - shaa,
Blest be God, praised for - ev - er and wor - shiped;

ra - bə ki ho - ve sa - naa.
blest be God, praised for - ev - er and ev - er.

Refrain

Punjabi Ra - bə ki ho - ve sa - naa ha - me - shaa,
English Blest be God, praised for - ev - er and wor - shiped;

Fine

ra - bə ki ho - ve sa - naa.
blest be God, praised for - ev - er.

Leader

Ra - bə ki ho - ve me - dha se - ra - i

1 In God's house sing out, join - ing the heav - ens.
2 Praise your Lord bright - ly, loud - sound - ing trum - pet.
3 Tam - bour - ines, keep the pulse in our mu - sic.
4 Clap and sing, praise God, now and for - ev - er.

All

Ra - bə ki ho - ve me - dha se - ra - i

In God's house sing out, join - ing the heav - ens.
Praise your Lord bright - ly, loud - sound - ing trum - pet.
Tam - bour - ines, keep the pulse in our mu - sic.
Clap and sing, praise God, now and for - ev - er.

Leader

| u - sə | ke | naa - mə | ki | sa - naa, | ha - le - lu - ya |

Praise God's name now and for - ev - er, hal - le - lu - jah!
Flute and harp, height - en the mu - sic, hal - le - lu - jah!
Cym - bals crash, fill us with rhy - thm, hal - le - lu - jah!
All that breathes, all that is liv - ing, hal - le - lu - jah!

All

u - sə ke naa - mə ki sa - naa ha - me - shaa
Praise God's name now and for - ev - er; come wor - ship:
Flute and harp, height - en the mu - sic; come wor - ship:
Cym - bals crash, fill us with rhy - thm; come wor - ship:
All that breathes, all that is liv - ing, come wor - ship:

To Refrain

ra - bə ki ho - ve sa - naa.
blest be God, praised for - ev - er and ev - er.
blest be God, praised for - ev - er and ev - er.
blest be God, praised for - ev - er and ev - er.
blest be God, praised for - ev - er and ev - er.

Finger Cymbals (o = open + = closed)

Drums

Words: anonymous; tr. Samuel Paul, Pakistan; vers. James Minchin, alt. © 2000 Christian Conference of Asia, admin. GIA Publications, Inc.; English adapt.
Music (SANAA): Punjabi melody, Pakistan © 2000 Christian Conference of Asia, admin. GIA Publications, Inc.

150D Alabad a nuestro Dios / Praise the Lord

Spanish A - la - bad / a nues - tro Dios en su san - tua - rio,
A - la - bad - le / por la gran - de - za de su nom - bre,

English Praise the Lord. / Give praise with - in the ho - ly tem - ple
Praise the Lord, / whose name sur - pas - ses all in great - ness.

por la_her - mo - su - ra de su cie - lo, / por sus pro -
con el so - ni - do de bo - ci - na, / sal - te - rio
for all the beau - ty of the heav - ens, / for might - y
Praise with the sound - ing of the trum - pet, / with harp and

e - zas a - la - bad - le_a Él.
y_ar - pa, a la vez can - tad.
acts of pow - er, praise the Lord.
lyre to - geth - er, praise and sing.

A - la - bad - le con el a - le - gre pan - de - ro,
A - la - bad - le con cuer - das, flau - tas y cím - ba - los
Praise the Lord with tam - bour - ines bright - ly shak - ing,
Praise the Lord with strings and flutes and with cym - bals,

con el can-dor de la dan-za, can-tad con go-zo al Se-
de jú-bi-lo re-so-
and with the sweet-ness of danc-ing, sing out with joy un-to the
with jub-i-la-tion re-

ñor.
Lord.
nan-tes. En su len-gua-je, to-do
sound-ing. Each in its lang-uage, now let

lo que res-pi-ra a-la-be al Se-ñor.
all that have life and have breath praise the Lord.

ñor. A - mén.
Lord. A - men.

Words: Osdy Sorian, Mexico, 1976; tr. Mary Louise Bringle (b. 1953), 2011
Music (ACAPULCO): Osdy Soriano, Mexico, 1976; arr. Obed Valencia Lozada, 2001, © 2001 Obed Valencia Lozada

150E Hallelujah! Praise God in His Holy Temple

Hallelujah! Praise God in his holy temple; praise him in the firmament of his power. Praise him for his mighty acts; praise him for his excellent greatness. Praise him with the blast of the ram's horn; praise him with lyre and harp. Praise him with timbrel and dance; praise him with strings and pipe.

Tenor and Bass

Praise him with re - sound - ing cym - bals; praise him with loud

Organ

All

Let everything that has breath

clang - ing cymbals.

praise the Lord. Hal - le - lu - jah!

(continues)

Glory to the Father, and to the Son, and to the Ho - ly Spirit:

as it was in the be - gin - ning, is now, and will be for -

ev - er. A - - - men.

Words and Music: Charles Villiers Stanford (1852-1924), P.D.

Praise the LORD, to God Give Praises

1 Praise the LORD, to God give prais - es;
Praise him in his might - y heav - ens;

2 Praise with harp and lyre and trum - pet;
Praise with tam - bou - rine and danc - ing;

praise him in his ho - ly place.
for his might - y deeds give praise.
praise from strings and pipes be poured.
with loud cym - bals, praise ac - cord.

Hal - le - lu - jah, hal - le - lu - jah, hal - le -
Hal - le - lu - jah, hal - le - lu - jah, hal - le -

lu - jah, he is ex - cel - lent and great.
lu - jah, all with breath, O praise the LORD.

Words: Psalm 150, alt., P.D.
Music (HELMSLEY 8.7.8.7.4.4.4.7): attr. Augustine Arne; adapt. Thomas Olivers, 1763, P.D.

Refrain

Refrain

1 Hallelujah! Praise God in the holy temple;
       praise God in the mighty firmament.

2 Praise God for mighty acts;
       praise God for exceeding greatness.   *Refrain*

3 Praise God with trumpet sound;
       praise God with lyre and harp.

4 Praise God with tambourine and dance;
       praise God with strings and pipe.   *Refrain*

5 Praise God with resounding cymbals;
       praise God with loud clanging cymbals.

6 Let everything that has breath
       praise the LORD. Hallelujah!   *Refrain*

Tone

Lectionary: Eastertide (C).

Words and Music: J. Jefferson Cleveland (1937-1986) © 1981 Abingdon Press, admin. The Copyright Company
Psalm Text: from *Evangelical Lutheran Worship* © 2006 Evangelical Lutheran Church in America, admin.
Augsburg Fortress Publishers
Tone: © 2011 Faith Alive Christian Resources

Alternate Refrain 1

Alternate Tone 1

Words: Charles Wesley (1707-1788), 1739, alt., P.D.
Music (EASTER HYMN fragment): *Lyra Davidica*, 1708, P.D.
Tone: © 2011 Faith Alive Christian Resources

Alternate Refrain 2

Hal - le, hal - le, hal - le - lu - jah.

Hal - le, hal - le, hal - le - lu - jah.
Hal - le - lu - jah.

Hal - le, hal - le, hal - le - lu - jah.

Hal - le - lu - jah. Hal - le - lu - jah.

(continues)

150G (continued)

Words: Caribbean traditional
Music: Caribbean traditional; arr. Mark Sedio (b. 1954) © 1995 Augsburg Fortress Publishers
Tone: © 2011 Faith Alive Christian Resources

150H Hallelujah, Praise the Lord

1 Hal - le - lu - jah, praise the Lord. Praise him with each
2 Praise him in his ho - ly place. Shout his power through
3 Praise him with the pluck - ing string, cym - bal clang and
4 Praise with in - stru - ments of wood, for the Lord is

note and word. Praise him for his might - y ways,
out - er space. Ev - ery - thing that breathes, pro - claim
trum - pet ring, tap - ping foot and clap - ping hand;
just and good. Praise with u - ni - son and chord.

who with love ex - alts our days. Hal - le - lu - jah.
praise and hon - or to God's name. Hal - le - lu - jah.
praise the Lord through all the land. Hal - le - lu - jah.
Hal - le - lu - jah, praise the Lord! Hal - le - lu - jah.

Words: Marie J. Post, 1974, alt. © 1974 Faith Alive Christian Resources
Music (ORIENTIS PARTIBUS 7.7.7.7 with hallelujah): French, 13th c., P.D.

Praise the Lord Who Reigns Above

1 Praise the Lord who reigns a - bove and keeps his court be - low;
2 Cel - e - brate the e - ter - nal God with harp and psal - ter - y,
3 God, in whom they move and live, let ev - ery crea - ture sing,

praise the ho - ly God of love, and all his great - ness show;
tim - brels soft and cym - bals loud in this high praise a - gree;
glo - ry to their Mak - er give, and hom - age to their King.

praise God for his no - ble deeds, praise God for his match - less power;
praise God, ev - ery tune - ful string; all the reach of heaven - ly art,
Hal - lowed be his name be - neath, as in heaven on earth a - dored;

God from whom all good pro - ceeds let earth and heaven a - dore.
all the powers of mu - sic bring, the mu - sic of the heart.
praise the Lord in ev - ery breath, let all things praise the Lord.

Guitar chords do not correspond with keyboard harmony.

Words: Charles Wesley (1707-1788), P.D.
Music (AMSTERDAM 7.6.7.6.7.7.7.6): *Foundery Collection*, 1742, P.D.

150J Praise God! Earth and Heaven Rejoice!

1 Praise God! Earth and heaven re-joice! All cre-a-tion,
2 Trum-pets, raise the joy-ful song; strings and pipes, now

with one voice, God's great maj-es-ty de-clare to all
play a-long! Cym-bals crash, as ne'er be-fore; danc-ing

peo-ple, ev-ery-where: Sing, shout, "Glo-ry, hal-le-lu-jah!"
feet, be still no more! Sing, shout, "Glo-ry, hal-le-lu-jah!"

God, who won-drous deeds has done; who for us sal-
May our breath through-out our days fill the earth with

va-tion won: Al-le-lu-ia, al-le-lu-ia!
songs of praise: Al-le-lu-ia, al-le-lu-ia!

Guitar chords do not correspond with keyboard harmony.

Words: Michael Morgan © 2011 Michael Morgan, admin. Faith Alive Christian Resources
Music (GENEVAN 150 | 7.7.7.7.8.7.7.8): *Genevan Psalter*, 1562, P.D.; harm. Dale Grotenhuis, 1985, © 1987
Faith Alive Christian Resources

Canticles

Services of Prayer

Luke 1:68-79
The Song of Zechariah

⁶⁸ Blessed be the Lord God of Israel, *

    for he has looked favorably on his people and redeemed them.

⁶⁹ He has raised up a mighty savior for us *

    in the house of his servant David,

⁷⁰ as he spoke through the mouth of his holy prophets from of old, *

    ⁷¹ that we would be saved from our enemies

    and from the hand of all who hate us.

⁷² Thus he has shown the mercy promised to our ancestors, *

    and has remembered his holy covenant,

⁷³ the oath that he swore to our ancestor Abraham, *

    to grant us ⁷⁴ that we, being rescued from the hands of our enemies,

might serve him without fear, ⁷⁵ in holiness and righteousness *

    before him all our days.

⁷⁶ And you, child, will be called the prophet of the Most High; *

    for you will go before the Lord to prepare his ways,

⁷⁷ to give knowledge of salvation to his people *

    by the forgiveness of their sins.

⁷⁸ By the tender mercy of our God, *

    the dawn from on high will break upon us,

⁷⁹ to give light to those who sit in darkness

and in the shadow of death, *

    to guide our feet into the way of peace.

O God, our Sun of Righteousness,
you wake us from sleep, you free us from the fetters of sin and doubt,
and one day you will raise us to eternal life with you.
Unseal our lips and fill us with your Spirit,
so that our mouths may declare your praise
and our lives may be spent in service to our Savior, Jesus Christ. **Amen.**

The Song of Zechariah is often named the *Benedictus* (the first word in its Latin text). It emphasizes the themes of God's liberation and redemption, as well as God's faithfulness as a promise-making and promise-keeping God. The text also points to the shape of a faithful way of life that God's redemptive act makes possible, a life of holiness, righteousness, and peace. *Use in Worship: a regular canticle in morning prayer services; a response to the reading of Scripture.*

For an additional setting of the Song of Zechariah see p. 1032.

You Have Come to Your People

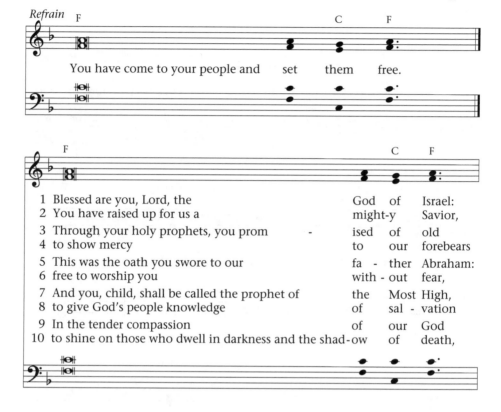

1 Blessed are you, Lord, the — God of Israel:
2 You have raised up for us a — might-y Savior,
3 Through your holy prophets, you prom - ised of old
4 to show mercy — to our forebears
5 This was the oath you swore to our — fa - ther Abraham:
6 free to worship you — with - out fear,
7 And you, child, shall be called the prophet of — the Most High,
8 to give God's people knowledge — of sal - vation
9 In the tender compassion — of our God
10 to shine on those who dwell in darkness and the shad-ow of death,

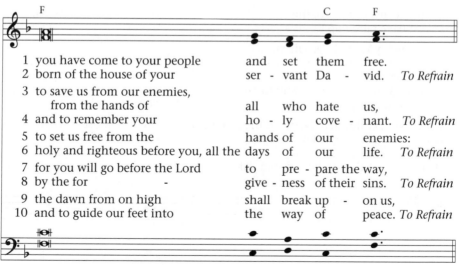

1 you have come to your people and set them free.
2 born of the house of your ser - vant Da - vid. *To Refrain*
3 to save us from our enemies,
   from the hands of all who hate us,
4 and to remember your ho - ly cove - nant. *To Refrain*
5 to set us free from the hands of our enemies:
6 holy and righteous before you, all the days of our life. *To Refrain*
7 for you will go before the Lord to pre - pare the way,
8 by the for - give - ness of their sins. *To Refrain*
9 the dawn from on high shall break up - on us,
10 and to guide our feet into the way of peace. *To Refrain*

Words: Luke 1:68-79 © 1988 English Language Liturgical Consultation (ELLC)
Music: Byzantine chant; arr. John A. Melloh, S. M. © 1979 GIA Publications, Inc.

THE SONG OF ZECHARIAH

In the Tender Compassion of Our God

Optional introduction

Refrain

In the ten-der com-pas-sion of our God the dawn from on high shall break up-on us.

1 Blessed are you, Lord, the God of Israel,
2 You have raised up for us a might - y Savior,

3 Through your holy prophets,
        you promised of old to save us from our enemies,
4 to show mercy to our forebears,
5 This was the oath you swore to our fa - ther Abraham:
6 free to worship you without fear,

7 And you, child, shall be called the prophet of the Most High,
8 to give God's people knowledge of sal - vation
9 In the tender compassion of our God
10 to shine on those who dwell in darkness and the shadow of death,

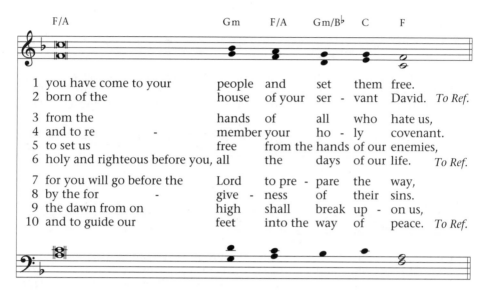

1 you have come to your people and set them free.
2 born of the house of your ser - vant David. *To Ref.*

3 from the hands of all who hate us,
4 and to re - member your ho - ly covenant.
5 to set us free from the hands of our enemies,
6 holy and righteous before you, all the days of our life. *To Ref.*

7 for you will go before the Lord to pre - pare the way,
8 by the for - give - ness of their sins.
9 the dawn from on high shall break up - on us,
10 and to guide our feet into the way of peace. *To Ref.*

Words: Luke 1:68-79
Music: Mark Mummert © 2004, 2006 Augsburg Fortress Publishers

Our God and Father Bless

1 Our God and Fa - ther bless, for by his sworn de - cree he
2 His an - cient pur - pose stands, un - changed for ev - er - more, that
3 Let truth pre - pare his path, let right - eous - ness in - crease! That

sends to us in power di - vine the prom - ised Lord of Da - vid's line,
we and all who find a place with - in his cov - e - nant of grace
from the shade of na - ture's night to dawn of heav - en's glo - ry bright

ful - fill - ing all his love's de - sign to save and set us free.
may free - ly come be - fore his face to wor - ship and a - dore.
the ran - somed chil - dren of the light may walk the way of peace.

Guitar chords do not correspond with keyboard harmony.

Words: Timothy Dudley-Smith (b. 1926) © 1988 Hope Publishing Company
Music (PELAW WOOD 6.6.8.8.8.6): David Lee © 1991, 2011 David Lee

Luke 1:46b-55
The Song of Mary

⁴⁶ᵇ My soul magnifies the Lord, *

    ⁴⁷ and my spirit rejoices in God my Savior,

⁴⁸ **for he has looked with favor on the lowliness of his servant.** *

    Surely, from now on all generations will call me blessed;

⁴⁹ for the Mighty One has done great things for me, *

    and holy is his name.

⁵⁰ **His mercy is for those who fear him** *

    from generation to generation.

⁵¹ He has shown strength with his arm; *

    he has scattered the proud in the thoughts of their hearts.

⁵² **He has brought down the powerful from their thrones,** *

    and lifted up the lowly;

⁵³ he has filled the hungry with good things, *

    and sent the rich away empty.

⁵⁴ **He has helped his servant Israel,** *

    in remembrance of his mercy,

⁵⁵ **according to the promise he made to our ancestors,** *

    to Abraham and to his descendants forever.

O God of Love, in your justice we find joy.
Help us to be so open to your purposes for us,
that we may become bearers of your Word,
speaking truth to power and bringing hope to the poor and the downtrodden.
We pray this in Jesus' name. **Amen.**

The Song of Mary is often called the *Magnificat* (the first word in its Latin text). The text celebrates the mighty acts of God, which subvert human reliance on power and wealth. The text is both personal and corporate, as well as occasional and general, referring tenderly to Mary's own experience of God's work in her life and also to the breadth of God's work through the people of Israel. It bears significant resemblance to the song of Hannah, mother of Samuel (1 Sam. 2:1-10). *Use in Worship: a regular canticle in morning or evening prayer services; a regular response to the reading of Scripture.*

For additional settings of the Song of Mary see pp. 462 and 1042.

Magnificat / Sing Out My Soul

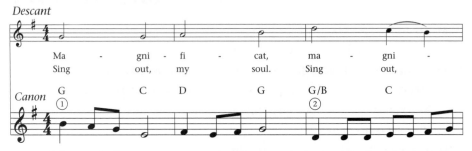

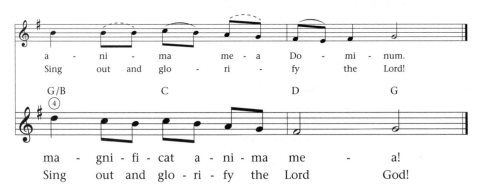

Words: from the *Song of Mary*, Luke 1:46-49 © 1978, 1980, 1981 Ateliers et Presses de Taizé, Taizé Community, France, GIA Publications, Inc., exclusive North American agent
Music (MAGNIFICAT): Jacques Berthier (1923-1994) © 1978, 1980, 1981 Ateliers et Presses de Taizé, Taizé Community, France, GIA Publications, Inc., exclusive North American agent

My Spirit Glorifies the Lord

1 My spirit glorifies the Lord; in God my
2 All generations from now on shall call me
3 His mercy shall extend to those who fear the

Savior I rejoice, for he beheld my
blest and spread my fame, for he has done great
Lord from age to age; he has revealed his

hum-ble state and in his love made me his choice.
things for me— might-y and ho-ly is his name.
might-y arm, scat-tering the proud in all their rage.

4 He brought down rulers from their thrones,
but lifted those of low degree.
He filled the hungry with good things,
but empty sent the rich away.

5 He helped his servant Israel,
remembering to be merciful,
keeping his word to Abraham
and to his seed forevermore.

Words: Luke 1:46-55; vers. Dewey Westra, 1931; rev. *Psalter Hymnal*, 1987, © 1987 Faith Alive Christian Resources
Music (PENTECOST 8.8.8.8): William Boyd, 1868, P.D.

Holy Is Your Name

1 My soul is filled with joy as I
2 I am low - ly as a child, but I
3 I pro-claim the power of God, you do

sing to God my Sav - ior: you have looked up - on your
know from this day for-ward that my name will be re -
mar - vels for your ser-vants; though you scat - ter the proud-

ser - vant, you have vis - i - ted your peo - ple.
mem-bered, for all will call me bless-ed.
heart - ed, and de - stroy the might of princ-es.

Refrain

And ho - ly is your name through all gen - er-

a - tions! Ev - er - last - ing is your mer-cy to the

peo - ple you have cho-sen, and ho - ly is your

name.

(⌢ last time)

4 To the hungry you give food,
  send the rich away__ empty.
  In your mercy you are mindful
  of the people you have chosen.
  Refrain

5 In your love you now fulfill
  what you promised to your people.
  I will praise you Lord, my Savior,
  everlasting is your mercy.
  Refrain

Words: Luke 1:46-55; David Haas (b. 1957) © 1989 GIA Publications, Inc.
Music (WILD MOUNTAIN THYME): Irish traditional; arr. David Haas (b. 1957) © 1989 GIA Publications, Inc.

My Soul Rejoices in the Lord

My soul re-joic-es in the Lord; I glo-ri-fy the ho-ly name of God.

1 My soul proclaims the greatness of the Lord,
2 For you, Lord, have looked with favor on your low - ly servant;

3 You, the Almighty, have done great things for me,
4 You have mercy on those who fear you,

5 You have shown strength with your arm
6 Casting down the mighty from their thrones,
7 You have filled the hungry with good things,

8 You have come to the help of your ser - vant Israel,
9 the promise made to our forbears,

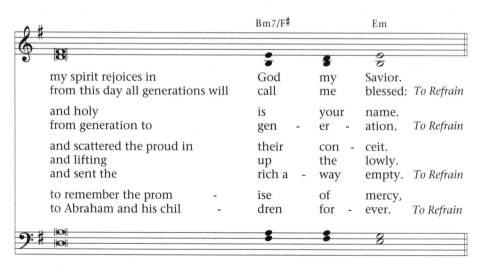

my spirit rejoices in God my Savior.
from this day all generations will call me blessed: *To Refrain*

and holy is your name.
from generation to gen - er - ation. *To Refrain*

and scattered the proud in their con - ceit.
and lifting up the lowly.
and sent the rich a - way empty. *To Refrain*

to remember the prom - ise of mercy,
to Abraham and his chil - dren for - ever. *To Refrain*

Words: Luke 1:46-55, English Language Liturgical Consultation (ELLC), 1988; 'Sanctum nomen Domini,' *Graduale Simplex*; ref. tr. Charles Thatcher © 2007 World Library Publications
Music: Charles Thatcher © 2007 World Library Publications

Luke 2:29-32
The Song of Simeon

²⁹ Master, now you are dismissing your servant in peace, *

    according to your word;

³⁰ for my eyes have seen your salvation, *

    ³¹ **which you have prepared in the presence of all peoples,**

³² a light for revelation to the Gentiles *

    and for glory to your people Israel.

O Lord, support us all the day long,
until the shadows lengthen and the evening comes,
the busy world is hushed, the fever of life is over, and our work is done.
Then, Lord, in your mercy grant us a safe lodging,
a holy rest, and peace at the last, through Christ our Lord. **Amen.**

The Song of Simeon is often called the *Nunc Dimittis* (the first words in its Latin text). The text has a missiological focus, emphasizing that God's work through the people of Israel, and especially through Israel's Messiah, offers illumination to all the peoples of the world. The imagery of light and illumination echoes several OT prophecies, and is evocative of a picture of Jesus as the Star of Jacob (Num. 24:17) and the Sun of Righteousness (Mal. 4:2). *Use in Worship: regular canticle in evening prayer services; a regular response to the reading of Scripture.*

For an additional setting of the Song of Simeon see p. 1051.

Now, Lord, You Let
Your Servant Go in Peace

Now, Lord, you let your ser - vant go in

peace; your word has been ful-filled. My

own eyes have seen the sal - va - tion which you have pre -

pared in the sight of all peo-ple: a light to re -

veal you to the na-tions and the glo-ry of your

peo-ple Is - ra - el. Glo - ry to the
Fa - ther, and to the Son, and to the Ho - ly Spir - it,
as it was in the be - gin - ning, is now, and
will be for - ev - er. A - men.

Guitar chords do not correspond with keyboard harmony.

Words: Luke 2:29-32; Nunc dimittis © 1988 English Language Liturgical Consultation (ELLC)
Music: James H. Harris and Tillis Butler © 1996 Augsburg Fortress Publishers

Guide Us Waking, O Lord

Introduction

Guide us wak-ing, O Lord, and guard us sleep-ing; that, a-wake, we may watch with Christ and, a-sleep, rest in his peace. peace.

First time to verses

Fine

Solo Voice *All*

Now, Lord, you let your ser-vant go in peace; your word has been ful-filled.

Solo Voice *All*

My own eyes have seen the sal-va-tion which you have prepared in the sight of

Guitar chords do not correspond with keyboard harmony.

THE SONG OF SIMEON

Go Now in Peace

Words: Luke 2:29-32; Hal H. Hopson © 1983 Hope Publishing Company
Music: Hal H. Hopson © 1983 Hope Publishing Company

Now May Your Servant, Lord

1 Now may your ser - vant, Lord, ac - cord-ing to your word,
2 You did for all pre - pare this gift so great, so rare,

de - part in ex - ul - ta - tion. My peace shall be se - rene,
ful - fill-ing proph-ets's sto - ry— a light to show the way

for now my eyes have seen your won-der-ful sal - va - tion.
to Gen-tiles gone a - stray, and un - to Is-rael's glo - ry.

Words: Luke 2:29-32; vers. Dewey Westra, 1931, alt., P.D.
Music (NUNC DIMITTIS 6.6.7.6.6.7): Louis Bourgeois (ca. 1510-1561), 1551; harm. Claude Goudimel (ca. 1505-1572), 1564, P.D.

A Service of

Morning Prayer

Opening Sentences

Our help is in the name of the Lord,
who made heaven and earth.
O Lord, open my lips.
And my mouth shall declare your praise.
The Lord's unfailing love and mercy never cease,
fresh as the morning and sure as the sunrise.

Morning Hymn

This or another morning hymn may be sung:

O Splendor of God's Glory Bright

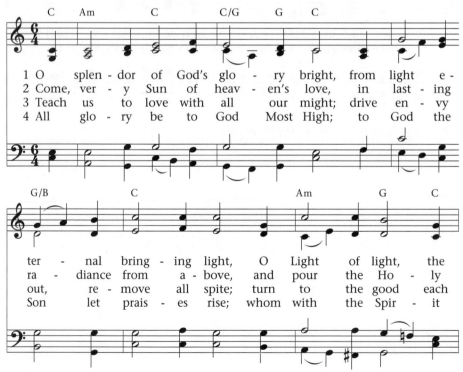

1 O splen - dor of God's glo - ry bright, from light e-
2 Come, ver - y Sun of heav - en's love, in last - ing
3 Teach us to love with all our might; drive en - vy
4 All glo - ry be to God Most High; to God the

ter - nal bring - ing light, O Light of light, the
ra - diance from a - bove, and pour the Ho - ly
out, re - move all spite; turn to the good each
Son let prais - es rise; whom with the Spir - it

	F	C	G/B	G	F	G	C
foun - tain spring,	O	Day,	all	days	il - lu -	mi -	ning.
Spir - it's ray	on	all	we	think	or do	to -	day.
trou - bling care,	and	give	us	grace	your name	to	bear.
we	a - dore	for - ev -	er	and	for - ev -	er -	more.

This tune in a higher key: p. 430.

Words: Ambrose of Milan, 4th c., tr. composite, P.D.
Music (PUER NOBIS 8.8.8.8): *Trier manuscript*, 15th c., Michael Praetorius, adapt.; harm. George Ratcliffe
Woodward, P.D.

Psalm(s)

One or more psalms may be sung or spoken. Silence for reflection may follow each psalm.
Psalms often used at morning prayer: 3, 5, 19, 34, 36, 51, 63, 90, 95, 100, and 119.

O come, let us sing to the LORD;

let us make a joyful noise to the rock of our salvation!

Let us come into his presence with thanksgiving;

let us make a joyful noise to him with songs of praise!

For the LORD is a great God,

and a great King above all gods.

In his hand are the depths of the earth;

the heights of the mountains are his also.

The sea is his, for he made it,

and the dry land, which his hands have formed.

O come, let us worship and bow down,

let us kneel before the LORD, our Maker!

For he is our God, and we are the people of his pasture,

and the sheep of his hand.

O that today you would listen to his voice!   *Psalm 95:1-7* (NRSV)

Scripture Reading

Silence for reflection may follow the reading or a meditation may be offered.

Canticle

This or another setting of the Song of Zechariah (Luke 1:68-79) may be sung or spoken:

Blessed Be the God of Israel

1 Blessed be the God of Is - ra - el, who comes to set us free
2 With prom-ised mer - cy will God still the cov - e - nant re - call,
3 My child, as proph-et of the Lord, you will pre - pare the way

and rais - es up new hope for us: a Branch from Da-vid's tree.
the oath once sworn to A - bra - ham, from foes to save us all,
to tell God's peo - ple they are saved from sin's e - ter - nal sway.

So have the proph-ets long de-clared that with a might-y arm
that we might wor-ship with-out fear and of - fer lives of praise,
Then shall God's mer - cy from on high shine forth and nev - er cease

God would turn back our en - e - mies and all who wish us harm.
in ho - li - ness and right-eous-ness to serve God all our days.
to drive a - way the gloom of death and lead us in - to peace.

Words: Carl P. Daw Jr. (b. 1944) © 1989 Hope Publishing Company
Music (FOREST GREEN 8.6.8.6 D): English folk tune; adapt. and harm. Ralph Vaughan Williams (1872-1958), 1906, P.D.

Prayers of the People

There may be a brief time of spoken and/or silent prayer. A litany such as the following may also be used:

The Lord be with you.
And also with you.
Let us pray.

Gracious God,
rejoicing in your blessings,
trusting in your loving care for all,
we bring you our prayers for the world.

We pray for the created world:
for those who rebuild where things have been destroyed;
for those who fight hunger, poverty, and disease;
for those who have power to bring change for the better and to renew hope.
In the life of our world
your kingdom come, O Lord, your will be done.

We pray for our country:
for those who frame our laws and shape our common life;
for those who keep the peace and administer justice;
for those who teach, those who heal, and all who serve the community.
In the life of our land
your kingdom come, O Lord, your will be done.

We pray for people in need:
those for whom life is a bitter struggle;
those whose lives are clouded by death or loss, by pain or disability,
by discouragement or fear, by shame or rejection.
In the lives of those in need
your kingdom come, O Lord, your will be done.

We pray for those in the circle of friendship and love around us:
children and parents; sisters and brothers; friends and neighbors;
and for those especially in our thoughts today.
In the lives of those we love
your kingdom come, O Lord, your will be done.

We pray for the church
in its stand with the poor,
in its love for the outcast and the ashamed,
in its service to the sick and neglected,
in its proclamation of the gospel,
in this land, in this place.
In the life of your church
your kingdom come, O Lord, your will be done.

Almighty and everlasting God,
We thank you that you have brought us safely
to the beginning of this new day.
Keep us from falling into sin or running into danger.
Order us in all our doings
and guide us to do always what is righteous in your sight.
Through Jesus Christ our Lord.
Amen.

The Lord's Prayer

This or another setting of the Lord's Prayer may be sung or spoken:

Our Fa - ther in heaven,   hal-lowed be your name.

Your king-dom come.   Your will be done, on earth   as in heaven.

Give us to-day our dai-ly bread.   For-give us our sins

as we for-give those   who sin   a-gainst   us.

Save us from the time of trial, and de-liv-er us from e-vil.

For the king-dom, the power, and the glo-ry are yours,

now and for-ev-er. A-men.

For additional settings of the Lord's Prayer see pp. 1038, 1044, 1045, and 1049.

Words: Matthew 6:9-13; tr. © 1988 English Language Liturgical Consultation (ELLC)
Music: Nikolai Rimsky-Korsakov (1844-1908); arr. George A. Black (b. 1931) © George A. Black

A closing hymn or psalm may be sung.

Closing Sentences

> May we continue to grow in the grace and knowledge of Jesus Christ,
> our Lord and Savior.
> **Amen.**
> Let us bless the Lord.
> **Thanks be to God.**

A sign of peace may be exchanged by all.

Prayers of the People: adapt. from the *Book of Common Order*, Church of Scotland, St. Andrews Press and
Celebrating Common Prayer. Reprinted by permission.

A Service of
Noon Prayer

Opening Sentences

Our help is in the name of the Lord,
who made heaven and earth.
Those who trust in the Lord for help
will find their strength renewed.
They will rise on wings like eagles;
they will run and not get weary;
they will walk and not grow weak.
Praise the Lord.
The Lord's name be praised.

Midday Hymn

This or another midday hymn may be sung:

Lord of All Hopefulness

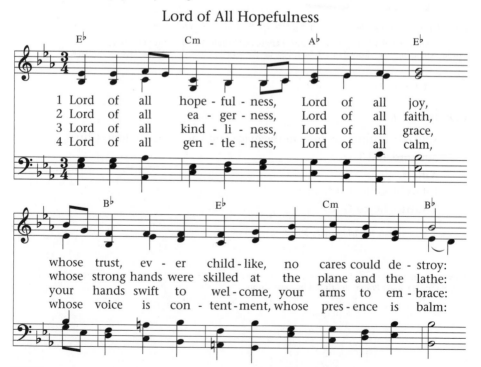

1 Lord of all hope - ful - ness, Lord of all joy,
2 Lord of all ea - ger - ness, Lord of all faith,
3 Lord of all kind - li - ness, Lord of all grace,
4 Lord of all gen - tle - ness, Lord of all calm,

whose trust, ev - er child - like, no cares could de - stroy:
whose strong hands were skilled at the plane and the lathe:
your hands swift to wel - come, your arms to em - brace:
whose voice is con - tent - ment, whose pres - ence is balm:

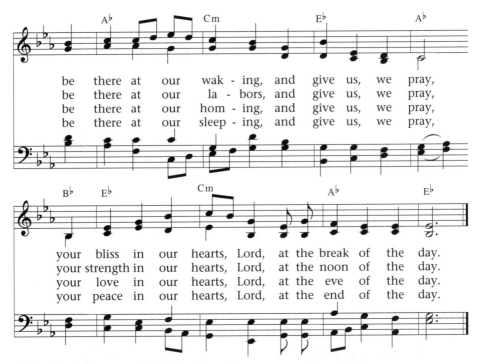

be there at our wak - ing, and give us, we pray,
be there at our la - bors, and give us, we pray,
be there at our hom - ing, and give us, we pray,
be there at our sleep - ing, and give us, we pray,

your bliss in our hearts, Lord, at the break of the day.
your strength in our hearts, Lord, at the noon of the day.
your love in our hearts, Lord, at the eve of the day.
your peace in our hearts, Lord, at the end of the day.

Psalm(s)

One or more psalms may be sung or spoken. Silence for reflection may follow each psalm.
Psalms often used at midday prayer: 19, 67, 113, 119:97-104, 119:129-136, 121, 122, 124, 126, 127, 128, and 130.

Scripture Reading

Silence for reflection may follow the reading, or a meditation may be offered.

Prayers of the People

There may be a brief time of spoken and/or silent prayer concluding with this or a similar prayer:

God, our Creator,

you have given us work to do

and call us to use our talents for the good of all.

Guide us as we work,

and teach us to live in the Spirit who made us your sons and daughters,

in the love that made us sisters and brothers,

through Jesus Christ our Lord. **Amen.**

The Lord's Prayer

This or another setting of the Lord's Prayer may be sung or spoken:

e - vil, for the king - dom, the power and the glo - ry are

yours now and for - ev - er. A-men. For - ev - er. A-men.

For additional settings of the Lord's Prayer see pp. 1034, 1044, 1045, and 1049.

Words: traditional, from *Praying Together* © 1988 English Language Liturgical Consultation (ELLC)
Music: Swee Hong Lim © 2010 Swee Hong Lim, admin. Faith Alive Christian Resources

A closing hymn or psalm may be sung.

Closing Sentences

The God of peace be with us.
Amen.
Let us bless the Lord.
Thanks be to God.

A sign of peace may be exchanged by all.

A Service of
Evening Prayer

Opening Sentences

Our help is in the name of the Lord,
who made heaven and earth.
Jesus Christ is the light of the world,
the light no darkness can overcome.
Stay with us, Lord, for it is evening
and the day is almost over.
Let your light scatter the darkness
and illumine your church.

Evening Hymn

This or another evening hymn may be sung:

Joyous Light of Heavenly Glory

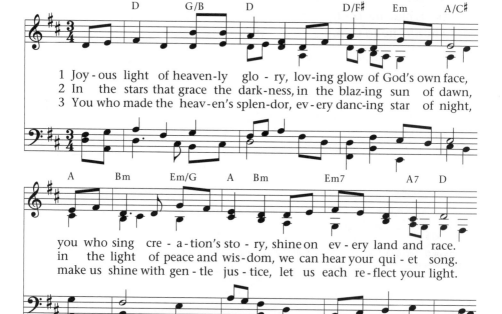

1 Joy-ous light of heaven-ly glo - ry, lov-ing glow of God's own face,
2 In the stars that grace the dark-ness, in the blaz-ing sun of dawn,
3 You who made the heav-en's splen-dor, ev-ery danc-ing star of night,

you who sing cre - a-tion's sto - ry, shine on ev - ery land and race.
in the light of peace and wis-dom, we can hear your qui - et song.
make us shine with gen - tle jus - tice, let us each re - flect your light.

Now as eve-ning falls a-round us, we shall raise our songs to you.
Love that fills the night with won-der, love that warms the wear-y soul,
Might-y God of all cre-a-tion, gen-tle Christ who lights our way,

God of day-break, God of shad-ows, come and light our hearts a-new.
love that bursts all chains a-sun-der, set us free and make us whole.
lov-ing Spir-it of sal-va-tion, lead us on to end-less day.

Words: Greek hymn, 3rd c.; para. Marty Haugen (b. 1950) © 1987 GIA Publications, Inc.
Music (JOYOUS LIGHT 8.7.8.7 D): Marty Haugen (b. 1950) © 1987 GIA Publications, Inc.

A prayer of thanksgiving may be spoken.

Psalm(s)

One or more psalms may be sung or spoken. Silence for reflection may follow each psalm.
Psalms often used at evening prayer: 4, 5, 8, 23, 36, 46, 66, 81, 93, 113, 117, 121, 134, 139, and 141.

I call upon you, O LORD; come quickly to me;

give ear to my voice when I call to you.

Let my prayer be counted as incense before you,

and the lifting up of my hands as an evening sacrifice.

Set a guard over my mouth, O LORD;

keep watch over the door of my lips.

Do not turn my heart to any evil, to busy myself

with wicked deeds in company with those who work iniquity;

do not let me eat of their delicacies.

But my eyes are turned toward you, O GOD, my Lord;

in you I seek refuge; do not leave me defenseless.

Let my prayer be counted as incense before you,

and the lifting up of my hands as an evening sacrifice.

from Psalm 141 (NRSV)

Scripture Reading

Silence for reflection may follow the reading or a meditation may be offered.

Canticle

This or another setting of the Song of Mary (Luke 1:46-55) may be sung or spoken:

My Soul Gives Glory to My God

1 My soul gives glo - ry to my God. My
2 My God has done great things for me: yes,
3 From age to age, to all who fear, such

heart pours out its praise. God lift - ed up my
ho - ly is this name. All peo - ple will de -
mer - cy love im - parts, dis - pens - ing jus - tice

low - li - ness in man - y mar - velous ways.
clare me blessed, and bless - ings they shall claim.
far and near, dis - miss - ing self - ish hearts.

4 Love casts the mighty from their thrones,
  promotes the insecure,
  leaves hungry spirits satisfied;
  the rich seem suddenly poor.

5 Praise God, whose loving covenant
  supports those in distress,
  remembering past promises
  with present faithfulness.

Words: Luke 1:46b-55; vers. Miriam Therese Winter © 1978, 1987 Medical Mission Sisters
Music (MORNING SONG/CONSOLATION 8.6.8.6): J. Wyeth's *Repository of Sacred Music,* 1813; harm. Kevin
Hildebrand (b. 1973) © 2006 Concordia Publishing House

Prayers of the People

There may be a brief time of spoken and/or silent prayer. A litany such as the following may also be sung or spoken:

Let us pray to the Lord. Lord, hear our prayer.

For the peace from above, and for our salvation, let us pray to the Lord.
Lord, hear our prayer.

For the peace of the whole world, for the well-being of the church of God,
and for the unity of all, let us pray to the Lord.
Lord, hear our prayer.

For this holy house, and for all who offer here their worship and praise,
let us pray to the Lord.
Lord, hear our prayer.

For the health of the creation, for abundant harvests that all may share,
and for peaceful times, let us pray to the Lord.
Lord, hear our prayer.

For public servants, the government, and those who protect us;
for those who work to bring peace, justice, healing, and protection in this and
every place, let us pray to the Lord.
Lord, hear our prayer.

For those who travel, for those who are sick and suffering, and for those who
are in captivity, let us pray to the Lord.
Lord, hear our prayer.

For deliverance in the time of affliction, wrath, danger, and need,
let us pray to the Lord.
Lord, hear our prayer.

For all servants of the church, for this gathering, and for all people who await
from the Lord great and abundant mercy, let us pray to the Lord.
Lord, hear our prayer.

Other petitions may be added. After a brief silence, the leader concludes the prayers with the following prayer or another prayer. This prayer may be spoken, even if the litany itself is sung.

God of all who fear you,
make us one with all your saints
and with any who are in need.
Teach us to befriend the weak,
and welcome the outcast,
that we may serve the Lord Jesus Christ
and live to offer him glory.
In his holy name we pray. **Amen.**

The Lord's Prayer

One of these options or another setting of the Lord's Prayer is sung or spoken:

Option 1

1 Our Fa-ther, Lord of heaven and earth, let praise and hon-or
2 For-give us, Lord, our sins and debts as we to debt-ors

clothe your name. Your king-dom come, your will be done;
show your grace. Re-move us from all tempt-ing paths,

through-out the world com-plete your reign. Teach us, O Lord,
and guard us from the dev-il's ways; for glo-ry, strength,

to trust in you for bread and breath each day a-new.
and heav-en's throne be-long to you, and you a-lone. A-men.

Guitar chords do not correspond with keyboard harmony.
Alternate harmonization on p. 727.
For additional settings of the Lord's Prayer see pp. 1034, 1038, and 1049.

Words: Matthew 6:9-13; vers. Henry J. deJong, 1982, © 1987 Faith Alive Christian Resources
Music (VATER UNSER 8.8.8.8.8.8): V. Schumann's *Geistliche Lieder*, 1539; harm. Johann S. Bach (1685-1750), in the *St. John Passion*, 1723, P.D.

1044

Option 2

> Our Father, who art in heaven, hallowed be thy name;
> thy kingdom come, thy will be done, on earth as it is in heaven.
> Give us this day our daily bread;
> and forgive us our debts, as we forgive our debtors;
> and lead us not into temptation, but deliver us from evil.
> For thine is the kingdom, and the power, and the glory, forever. Amen.

Option 3

> Our Father, who art in heaven, hallowed be thy name,
> thy kingdom come, thy will be done, on earth as it is in heaven.
> Give us this day our daily bread;
> and forgive us our trespasses, as we forgive those who trespass against us;
> and lead us not into temptation, but deliver us from evil.
> For thine is the kingdom, and the power, and the glory, forever and ever. Amen.

Option 4

> Our Father in heaven, hallowed be your name,
> your kingdom come, your will be done, on earth as in heaven.
> Give us today our daily bread.
> Forgive us our sins as we forgive those who sin against us.
> Save us from the time of trial and deliver us from evil.
> For the kingdom, the power, and the glory are yours, now and forever. Amen.

A closing hymn or psalm may be sung.

Closing Sentences

> May the peace of God, which surpasses all understanding,
> guard our hearts and minds in Christ Jesus.
> **Amen.**
> Let us bless the Lord.
> **Thanks be to God.**

A sign of peace may be exchanged by all.

Prayers of the People: taken from Eastern Liturgies of St. Basil and St. Chrysostom, P.D.; concluding prayer adapt. from the *Book of Common Worship* © 1993 Westminster John Knox Press. Reprinted by permission. Prayer Words and Music: Byzantine chant, P.D.

The options for the Lord's Prayer above (2, 3, and 4) come from the gospel account of Matthew, chapter 6. Variants of options 2 and 3 have been used by English-speaking Christians for centuries. Option 2 is derived from the Authorized Version of the Bible (King James' Version, 1611). Option 3 is derived from the *Book of Common Prayer* (1662). Option 4 uses contemporary language and is widely used in local congregations as well as ecumenical gatherings. It was prepared by the English Language Liturgical Consultation (*Praying Together*, 1988). (See Copyright Holders Index for publisher information.)

A Service of

Night Prayer

Opening Sentences

Our help is in the name of the Lord,
who made heaven and earth.
It is good to give thanks to the Lord,
to sing your praise, O Most High;
to declare your steadfast love in the morning,
and your faithfulness at night.

Night Hymn

This or another night hymn may be sung:

All Praise to You, My God, This Night

May be sung in canon

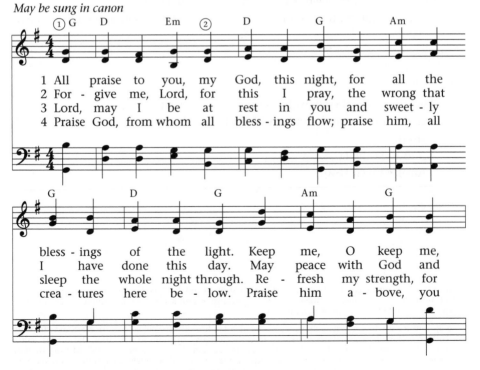

1 All praise to you, my God, this night, for all the
2 For-give me, Lord, for this I pray, the wrong that
3 Lord, may I be at rest in you and sweet-ly
4 Praise God, from whom all bless-ings flow; praise him, all

bless-ings of the light. Keep me, O keep me,
I have done this day. May peace with God and
sleep the whole night through. Re-fresh my strength, for
crea-tures here be-low. Praise him a-bove, you

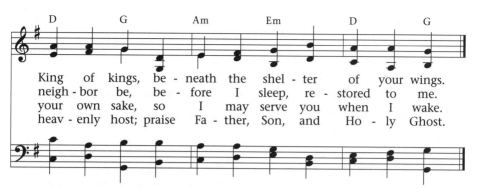

King of kings, be-neath the shel-ter of your wings.
neigh-bor be, be-fore I sleep, re-stored to me.
your own sake, so I may serve you when I wake.
heav-enly host; praise Fa-ther, Son, and Ho-ly Ghost.

Guitar chords do not correspond with keyboard harmony.
Words: Thomas Ken, 1709, alt., P.D.
Music (TALLIS CANON 8.8.8.8): Thomas Tallis, ca. 1561, P.D.

Prayer of Confession

This or another prayer of confession may be spoken:

Let us confess our sins to God.

Almighty God, our heavenly Father:
we have sinned against you, through our own fault,
in thought, and word, and deed,
and in what we have left undone.
For the sake of your Son, our Lord Jesus Christ,
forgive us all our offenses;
and grant that we may serve you in newness of life,
to the glory of your name. Amen.

May the Almighty God grant us forgiveness for all our sins,
and the grace and comfort of the Holy Spirit.
Amen.

Psalm(s)

One or more psalms may be sung or spoken. Silence for reflection may follow each psalm.
Psalms often used at night prayer: 3, 4, 16, 17, 23, 33, 34, 63, 91, 121, 134, 136, and 139.

You, O LORD, are a shield around me,

my glory, and the one who lifts up my head.

I cry aloud to the LORD,

and he answers me from his holy hill.

I lie down and sleep;

I wake again, for the LORD sustains me. *from Psalm 3 (NRSV)*

Scripture Reading

The following or another brief lesson is read. Other suggested readings: Deut. 6:4-7, Jer. 14:9, Matt. 6:31-34, Rom. 8:38-39, 2 Cor. 4:6-10, 1 Thess. 5:23, 1 Pet. 5:6-9a, 1 John 4:18-20, and Rev. 22:3c-5.

[Jesus said:] "Peace I leave with you; my peace I give to you. I do not give to you as the world gives. Do not let your hearts be troubled, and do not let them be afraid."   *John 14:27* (NRSV)

Silence for reflection may follow the reading.

Prayer

There may be a brief time of spoken and/or silent prayer. A litany such as the following may also be used:

I call upon you, for you will answer me, O God;
incline your ear to me, hear my words.
Guard me as the apple of the eye;
hide me in the shadow of your wings.
I shall behold your face in righteousness;
when I awake I shall be satisfied,
beholding your likeness.   *from Psalm 17* (NRSV)

O God our Creator,
by whose mercy and might
the world turns safely into darkness
and returns again to light:
We give into your hands our unfinished tasks,
our unsolved problems,
and our unfulfilled hopes,
knowing that only those things which you bless will prosper.
To your great love and protection
we commit each other
and all for whom we have prayed,
knowing that you alone are our sure defender,
through Jesus Christ our Lord.
Amen.

The Lord's Prayer

This or another setting of the Lord's Prayer is sung or spoken:

(continues)

For additional settings of the Lord's Prayer see pp. 1034, 1038, 1044, and 1045.

Words: Laila Constantine, Lebanon © 2002 *Songs of the Evangelical Presbyterian Church of Egypt*, Council of Pastoral Work and Evangelism, admin. Faith Alive Christian Resources; tr. and adapt. Anne Emile Zaki, Emily R. Brink (b. 1940), and Greg Scheer © 2008 Faith Alive Christian Resources
Music: Laila Constantine, Lebanon © 2002 *Songs of the Evangelical Presbyterian Church of Egypt*, Council of Pastoral Work and Evangelism, admin. Faith Alive Christian Resources; arr. Greg Scheer © 2008 Greg Scheer

Canticle

This or another setting of the Song of Simeon (Luke 2:29-32) may be sung or spoken:

Lord, Bid Your Servant Go in Peace

1 Lord, bid your ser - vant go in peace; your
word is now ful - filled. These eyes have seen sal -
va - tion's dawn, this child so long fore - told.

2 This is the Sav - ior of the world, the
Gen - tile's prom - ised light, God's glo - ry dwell - ing
in our midst, the joy of Is - ra - el.

Words: Luke 2:29-32; Nunc dimittis; James Quinn, S. J. (b. 1919), 1969, 1989, © 1969 James Quinn, S. J., admin. Selah Publishing Company, Inc., exclusive North American agent
Music (LAND OF REST 8.6.8.6): American folk melody; harm. Annabel Morris Buchanan (1889-1983), P.D.

Closing Sentences

Guide us waking, O Lord, and guard us sleeping,

that awake we may watch with Christ, and asleep rest in his peace.

May Almighty God bless, preserve, and keep us, this night and forevermore.

Amen.

Let us bless the Lord.

Thanks be to God.

A sign of peace may be exchanged by all.

Service of Prayer for a
Meeting, Class, or Conference

Opening Sentences

Our help is in the name of the Lord
who made the heaven and the earth.

Psalm(s)

One or more psalms may be sung or spoken. Silence for reflection may follow each psalm.

Psalms especially appropriate for meetings related to the mission of God's people: 15, 24, 67, 87, 133.

Psalms especially appropriate for class sessions or other learning opportunities: 1, 19, 78, 119.

Psalm especially appropriate for reflecting on human labor and daily discipleship: 1, 26, 90, 112, 121, 127.

Scripture Reading(s)

Readings may be followed by a time for silent reflection, a brief meditation, or prayerful discussion.

Readings especially appropriate for meetings related to the work and mission of God's people:
Gen. 12:1-3; Isa. 61:1-4; Matt. 5:13-16; Matt. 28:16-20; John 17:20-26; Rom. 12:1-8, 9-21;
1 Cor. 12:1-11, 12-31; 2 Cor. 4:1-15; Eph. 4:1-16.

Readings especially appropriate for class sessions or other learning opportunities:
Prov. 3:5-6; Prov. 8:1-21; Phil. 1:9-10; Heb. 6:1-12.

Readings especially appropriate for reflecting on human labor and daily discipleship:
Ex. 20:1-21; Eccl. 3:1-8; Eccl. 12:1-14; Mic. 6:6-8; Matt. 6:19-34 Col. 3:1-17; Gal. 5:22-26;
Heb. 12:1-13; James 1:19-27.

Prayers

Our Father in heaven, hallowed be your name. . .

[prayers of adoration and thanksgiving]

Your kingdom come. Your will be done, on earth as it is in heaven. . .

[prayers of longing for God's shalom]

Give us this day our daily bread. . .

[prayers for the needs of the community]

Forgive us our debts, as we also have forgiven our debtors. . .

[prayers for interpersonal reconciliation]

And do not bring us to the time of trial, but rescue us from the evil one. . .

[prayers for the world and for personal struggles with temptation and evil]

For the kingdom and the power and the glory are yours forever. **Amen.**

from Matthew 6 (NRSV)

For an alternate form for prayer, see p. 1043.

Closing

Grow in the grace and knowledge of our Lord and Savior Jesus Christ.
To him be glory both now and forever! Amen. *based on 2 Peter 3:18*

Appendixes

General Refrains

The six general refrains presented on this page may be reproduced in a format that is conducive for projection or reproduction in printed liturgies with the proper credit line and use of your copyright license. Refrains 1-6 are covered by OneLicense.net; refrains 3 and 5 are also covered by CCLI. If you do not own a copyright license, please contact the publisher for permission. (See Copyright Holders Index for contact information.)

1.

Al - le - lu - ia, al - le - lu - ia, al - le - lu - ia.

Words and Music: Plainsong, mode VI; arr. © Augsburg Fortress Publishers
See p. 991 for accompaniment and chant tone.

2.

Let the giv - ing of thanks be our sac - ri - fice to God.

Words and Music (GREYFRIARS refrain): The Iona Community © 1993 Wild Goose Resource Group, Iona Community, Scotland, GIA Publications, Inc., exclusive North American agent
See p. 319 for accompaniment and chant tone.

3.

O Lord, my de - light, my de - light is in your law.

Words and Music: Hal H. Hopson © 1987 Hope Publishing Company
See p. 778 for accompaniment and chant tone.

4.

To you, O Lord, I lift my soul, to you, I lift my soul.

Words and Music: Marty Haugen (b. 1950) © 1982 GIA Publications, Inc.
See p. 153 for accompaniment and chant tone.

5.
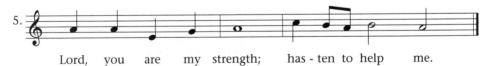

Lord, you are my strength; has - ten to help me.

Words and Music: Hal H. Hopson © 1986 Hope Publishing Company
See p. 353 for accompaniment and chant tone.

6.

Have mer - cy on us, Lord, have mer - cy on us.

Words and Music (KHUDAAYAA fragment): traditional Urdhu; trans. © 1990 GIA Publications, Inc.
See p. 335 for accompaniment and chant tone.

Guitar Capo Charts

The capo charts on this page are meant for use with songs whose key requires the guitarist to use an abundance of barre chords. By putting a capo on the appropriate fret—represented by the roman numerals on the left-hand side of each chart—the songs may be played more easily with fewer barre chords. To use the chart, first locate the song's key signature. Then find the chords needed for the song as listed in the gray row along the top. Easier chords are listed below the chords they replace in rows that correspond to the fret upon which the capo can be placed. For the Key of F or Dm and the Key of E♭ or Cm, the lesser capo should generally be utilized when the song is major (III for F, I for E♭) and the greater capo when the song is minor (V for Dm, III for Cm). Songs in the keys of D, A, E and B can usually be played without using a capo. Some, however, require a greater use of barre chords. These songs can be played more easily with a capo on the second fret, using the chords listed in the appropriate charts. For the sake of simplicity, only the basic chord forms (without added tones or bass notes) have been included in these charts.

Key of F or Dm

	F	G	Gm	G♯	A	Am	B♭	C	Cm	D	Dm	E♭	Em
III	D	E	Em	F	F♯	F♯m	G	A	Am	B	Bm	C	C♯m
V	C	D	Dm	E♭	E	Em	F	G	Gm	A	Am	B♭	Bm

Key of B♭ or Gm

	B♭	C	Cm	D	Dm	E♭	F	Fm	G♭	G	Gm
III	G	A	Am	B	Bm	C	D	Dm	E♭	E	Em

Key of E♭ or Cm

	E♭	E♭m	F	Fm	G♭	G	Gm	A♭	B♭	B♭m	C	Cm	D♭
I	D	Dm	E	Em	F	F♯	F♯m	G	A	Am	B	Bm	C
III	C	Cm	D	Dm	E♭	E	Em	F	G	Gm	A	Am	B

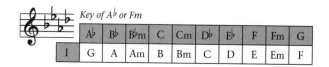

Key of A♭ or Fm

	A♭	B♭	B♭m	C	Cm	D♭	E♭	F	Fm	G
I	G	A	Am	B	Bm	C	D	E	Em	F

Key of D♭ or B♭m

	D♭	G♭	A♭	B♭m
I	C	F	G	Am

(continues)

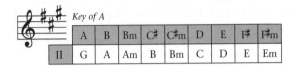

Key of D

	D	Em	F#	F#m	G	A	Am	B♭	B	Bm	C	C#
II	C	Dm	E	Em	F	G	Gm	G#	A	Am	B♭	B

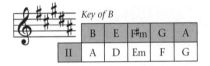

Key of A

	A	B	Bm	C#	C#m	D	E	F#	F#m
II	G	A	Am	B	Bm	C	D	E	Em

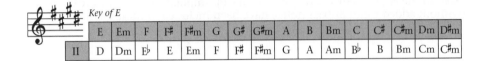

Key of E

	E	Em	F	F#	F#m	G	G#	G#m	A	B	Bm	C	C#	C#m	Dm	D#m
II	D	Dm	E♭	E	Em	F	F#	F#m	G	A	Am	B♭	B	Bm	Cm	C#m

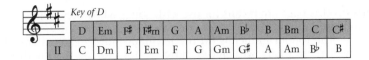

Key of B

	B	E	F#m	G	A
II	A	D	Em	F	G

Explanation of Chord Symbols

A chord without a symbol is a major chord. An 'm' indicates a minor chord. The ° indicates a diminished chord, the °7 indicates a diminished 7th chord, and the ᵒ7 indicates a half-diminished 7th chord. The 'aug' indicates an augmented chord, and the '(no3)' indicates a chord played without the 3rd (a power chord). (See examples below.)

In the key of D

D	Dm	D°	D aug	D°7	Dᵒ7	D(no3)
Major	*Minor*	*Diminished*	*Augmented*	*Diminished 7th*	*Half-Dim. 7th*	*(power chord)*

Guitar Chord Diagrams

A	Am	A°	A aug	A°7	Aø7	A(no3)

B♭	B♭m	B♭°	B♭aug	B♭°7	B♭ø7	B♭(no3)

B	Bm	B°	B aug	B°7	Bø7	B(no3)

C	Cm	C°	C aug	C°7	Cø7	C(no3)

C♯/D♭	C♯m	C♯°	C♯aug	C♯°7	C♯ø7	C♯(no3)

D	Dm	D°	D aug	D°7	Dø7	D(no3)

E♭	E♭m	E♭°	E♭aug	E♭°7	E♭ø7	E♭(no3)

E	Em	E°	E aug	E°7	Eø7	E(no3)

F	Fm	F°	F aug	F°7	Fø7	F(no3)

F♯/G♭	F♯m	F♯°	F♯aug	F♯°7	F♯ø7	F♯(no3)

G	Gm	G°	G aug	G°7	Gø7	G(no3)

A♭	A♭m	A♭°	A♭aug	A♭°7	A♭ø7	A♭(no3)

The *Revised Common Lectionary*

A lectionary is a schedule of Scripture readings arranged and intended for proclamation during worship. The *Revised Common Lectionary* is a three-year schedule prepared by the Consultation on Common Texts (*www.commontexts.org*), an ecumenical consultation of liturgical scholars and denominational representatives from the United States and Canada who produce liturgical texts for use in common by North American Christian churches. The lectionary presented here is adapted from the *Revised Common Lectionary*, © 1992 by the Consultation on Common Texts and used with permission.

The three years (designated A, B, and C) include several Scripture readings for each Sunday: an Old Testament reading; a psalm, preferably sung, which serves as a congregational response to the Old Testament reading; a reading from one of the New Testament epistles; and, finally, a reading from one of the four gospels—Matthew in Year A, Mark in Year B, and Luke in Year C. Readings from the Gospel of John are included in all three years. Over the three years, at least one reading from each book of the Bible is included.

For the Sundays following Pentecost, there are two suggested readings from the Old Testament: one that is chosen to set up a semicontinuous set of readings through the Old Testament over several weeks, and one (listed below in italics) that continues the pattern of offering Old Testament readings that are complementary to the New Testament readings. The term *complementary* here means that the juxtaposition of the Old Testament and New Testament readings is theologically significant in some way. However, it is important to understand that the inter-relationships among texts throughout the lectionary come in several forms: some combinations of Old Testament and New Testament readings explore contrasting themes, while others explore the same theme or image; some feature an Old Testament prophecy and its New Testament fulfillment, while others feature an Old Testament narrative that is a type or pattern echoed in a New Testament narrative or parable.

Sunday or Festival	Year A	Year B	Year C
Season of Advent			
1st Sunday of Advent	Isa. 2:1-5 Ps. 122 Rom. 13:11-14 Matt. 24:36-44	Isa. 64:1-9 Ps. 80:1-7, 17-19 1 Cor. 1:3-9 Mark 13:24-37	Jer. 33:14-16 Ps. 25:1-10 1 Thess. 3:9-13 Luke 21:25-36
2nd Sunday of Advent	Isa. 11:1-10 Ps. 72:1-7, 18-19 Rom. 15:4-13 Matt. 3:1-12	Isa. 40: 1-11 Ps. 85:1-2, 8-13 2 Pet. 3:8-15a Mark 1:1-8	Mal. 3:1-4 Luke 1:68-79 Phil. 1:3-11 Luke 3:1-6
3rd Sunday of Advent	Isa. 35:1-10 Ps. 146:5-10 or Luke 1:46b-55 James 5:7-10 Matt. 11:2-11	Isa. 61:1-4, 8-11 Ps. 126 or Luke 1:46b-55 1 Thess. 5:16-24 John 1:6-8, 19-28	Zeph. 3:14-20 Isa. 12:2-6 Phil. 4:4-7 Luke 3:7-18
4th Sunday of Advent	Isa. 7:1-16 Ps. 80:1-7, 17-19 Rom. 1:1-7 Matt. 1:18-25	2 Sam. 7:1-11, 16 Luke 1:46b-55 or Ps. 89:1-4, 19-26 Rom. 16:25-27 Luke 1:26-38	Mic. 5:2-5a Luke 1:46b-55 or Ps. 80:1-7 Heb. 10:5-10 Luke 1:39-45 (46-55)
Season of Christmas			
Christmas I (December 24 or 25)	Isa. 9:2-7 Ps. 96 Titus 2:11-14 Luke 2:1-14 (15-20)	Isa. 9:2-7 Ps. 96 Titus 2:11-14 Luke 2:1-14 (15-20)	Isa. 9:2-7 Ps. 96 Titus 2:11-14 Luke 2:1-14 (15-20)

Christmas II (December 24 or 25)	Isa. 62:6-12 Ps. 97 Titus 3:4-7 Luke 2:(1-7) 8-20	Isa. 62:6-12 Ps. 97 Titus 3:4-7 Luke 2:(1-7) 8-20	Isa. 62:6-12 Ps. 97 Titus 3:4-7 Luke 2:(1-7) 8-20
Christmas III (December 24 or 25)	Isa. 52:7-10 Ps. 98 Heb. 1:1-4 (5-12) John 1:1-14	Isa. 52:7-10 Ps. 98 Heb 1:1-4 (5-12) John 1:1-14	Isa. 52:7-10 Ps. 98 Heb. 1:1-4 (5-12) John 1:1-14
1st Sunday after Christmas Day	Isa. 63:7-9 Ps. 148 Heb. 2:10-18 Matt. 2:13-23	Isa. 61:10-62:3 Ps. 148 Gal. 4:4-7 Luke 2:22-40	1 Sam. 2:18-20, 26 Ps. 148 Col. 3:12-17 Luke 2:41-52
2nd Sunday after Christmas Day	Jer. 31:7-14 Ps. 147:12-20 Eph. 1:3-14 John 1:(1-9) 10-18	Jer. 31:7-14 Ps. 147:12-20 Eph. 1:3-14 John 1:(1-9) 10-18	Jer. 31:7-14 Ps. 147:12-20 Eph. 1:3-14 John 1:(1-9) 10-18
Epiphany (January 6 or Sunday before Epiphany)	Isa. 60:1-6 Ps. 72:1-7, 10-14 Eph. 3:1-12 Matt. 2:1-12	Isa. 60:1-6 Ps. 72:1-7, 10-14 Eph. 3:1-12 Matt. 2:1-12	Isa. 60:1-6 Ps. 72:1-7, 10-14 Eph. 3:1-12 Matt. 2:2-12

Season of Epiphany/Ordinary Time

Baptism of the Lord (January 7-13)	Isa. 42:1-9 Ps. 29 Acts 10:34-43 Matt. 3:13-17	Gen. 1:1-5 Ps. 29 Acts 19:1-17 Mark 1:4-11	Isa. 43:1-7 Ps. 29 Acts 8:14-17 Luke 3:15-17, 21-22
2nd Sunday in Ordinary Time (January 14-20)	Isa. 49:1-7 Ps. 40:1-11 1 Cor. 1:1-9 John 1:29-42	1 Sam. 3:1-10 (11-20) Ps. 139:1-6, 13-18 1 Cor. 6:12-20 John 1:43-51	Isa. 62:1-5 Ps. 36:5-10 1 Cor. 12:1-11 John 2:1-11
3rd Sunday in Ordinary Time (January 21-27)	Isa. 9:1-4 Ps. 27:1, 4-9 1 Cor. 1:10-18 Matt. 4:12-23	Jon. 3:1-5, 10 Ps. 62:5-12 1 Cor. 7:29-31 Mark 1:14-20	Neh. 8:1-3, 5-6, 8-10 Ps. 19 1 Cor. 12:12-31a Luke 4:14-21
4th Sunday in Ordinary Time (January 28- February 3)	Mic. 6:1-8 Ps. 15 1 Cor. 1:18-31 Matt. 5:1-12	Deut. 18:15-20 Ps. 111 1 Cor. 8:1-13 Mark 1:21-28	Jer. 1:4-10 Ps. 71:1-6 1 Cor. 13:1-13 Luke 4:21-30
5th Sunday in Ordinary Time (February 4-10)	Isa. 58:1-9a (9b-12) Ps. 112:1-9 (10) 1 Cor. 2:1-12 (13-16) Matt. 5:13-20	Isa. 40:21-31 Ps. 147:1-11, 20c 1 Cor. 9:16-23 Mark 1:29-39	Isa. 6:1-8 (9-13) Ps. 138 1 Cor. 15:1-11 Luke 5:1-11
6th Sunday in Ordinary Time (February 11-17)	Deut. 30:15-20 Ps. 119:1-8 1 Cor. 3:1-9 Matt. 5:21-37	2 Kings 5:1-14 Ps. 30 1 Cor. 9:24-27 Mark 1:40-45	Jer. 17:5-10 Ps. 1 1 Cor. 15:12-20 Luke 6:17-26
7th Sunday in Ordinary Time (February 18-24)	Lev. 19:1-2, 9-18 Ps. 119:33-40 1 Cor. 3:10-11, 16-23 Matt. 5:38-48	Isa. 43:18-25 Ps. 41 2 Cor. 1:18-22 Mark 2:1-12	Gen. 45:3-11, 15 Ps. 37:1-11, 39-40 1 Cor. 15:35-38, 42-50 Luke 6:27-38

8th Sunday in Ordinary Time (February 25-29)	Isa. 49:8-16a Ps. 131 1 Cor. 4:1-5 Matt. 6:24-34	Hos. 2:14-20 Ps. 103:1-13, 22 2 Cor. 3:1-6 Mark 2:13-22	Isa. 55:10-13 Ps. 92:1-4, 12-15 1 Cor. 15:51-58 Luke 6:39-49
9th Sunday in Ordinary Time (when required)	Deut. 11:18-21, 26-28 Ps. 31:1-5, 19-24 Rom. 1:16-17; 3:22b-28 (29-13) Matt. 7:21-29	Deut. 5:12-15 Ps. 81:1-10 2 Cor. 4:5-12 Mark 2:23-3:6	1 Kings 8:22-23, 41-43 Ps. 96:1-9 Gal. 1:1-12 Luke 7:1-10
Transfiguration of the Lord (Sunday preceding Lent)	Ex. 24:12-18 Ps. 2 or Ps. 99 2 Pet. 1:16-21 Matt. 17:1-9	2 Kings 2:1-12 Ps. 50:1-6 2 Cor. 4:3-6 Mark 9:2-9	Ex. 34:29-35 Ps. 99 2 Cor. 3:12-4:2 Luke 9:28-36 (37-43)

Season of Lent

Ash Wednesday	Joel 2:1-2, 12-17 or Isa. 58:1-12 Ps. 51:1-17 2 Cor. 5:20b-6:10 Matt 6:1-6, 16-21	Joel 2:1-2, 12-17 or Isa. 58:1-12 Ps. 51:1-17 2 Cor. 5:20b-6:10 Matt 6:1-6, 16-21	Joel 2:1-2, 12-17 or Isa. 58:1-12 Ps. 51:1-17 2 Cor. 5:20b-6:10 Matt 6:1-6, 16-21
1st Sunday in Lent	Gen 2:15-17, 3:1-7 Ps. 32 Rom. 5:12-19 Matt. 4:1-11	Gen 9:8-17 Ps. 25:1-10 1 Pet. 3:18-22 Mark 1:9-15	Deut. 26:1-11 Ps. 91:1-2, 9-16 Rom. 10:8b-13 Luke 4:1-13
2nd Sunday in Lent	Gen 12:1-4a Ps. 121 Rom. 4:1-5, 13-17 John 3:1-17 or Matt. 17:1-9	Gen. 17:1-7, 15-16 Ps. 22:23-31 Rom. 4:13-25 Mark 8:31-38 or Mark 9:2-9	Gen. 15:1-12, 17-18 Ps. 27 Phil. 3:17-4:1 Luke 13:31-35 or Luke 9:28-36 (37-43)
3rd Sunday in Lent	Ex. 17:1-7 Ps. 95 Rom. 5:1-11 John 4:5-42	Ex. 20:1-17 Ps. 19 1 Cor. 1:18-25 John 2:13-22	Isa. 55:1-9 Ps. 63:1-8 1 Cor. 10:1-13 Luke 13:1-9
4th Sunday in Lent	1 Sam. 16:1-13 Ps. 23 Eph. 5:8-14 John 9:1-41	Num. 21:4-9 Ps. 107:1-3, 17-22 Eph. 2:1-10 John 3:14-21	Josh. 5:9-12 Ps. 32 2 Cor. 5:16-21 Luke 15:1-3, 11b-32
5th Sunday in Lent	Ezek. 37:1-14 Ps. 130 Rom. 8:6-11 John 11:1-45	Jer. 31:31-34 Ps. 51:1-12 or Ps. 119:9-16 Heb. 5:5-10 John 12:20-33	Isa. 43:16-21 Ps. 126 Phil. 3:4b-14 John 12:1-8

Holy Week

Passion/Palm Sunday (6th Sunday in Lent)	*Liturgy of the Palms:* Ps. 118:1-2, 19-29 Matt. 21:1-11	Ps. 118:1-2, 19-29 Mark 11:1-11 or John 12:12-26	Ps. 118:1-2, 19-29 Luke 19:28-40
	Liturgy of the Passion: Isa. 50:4-9a Ps. 31:9-16 Phil. 2:5-11 Matt. 26:14-27:66 or Matt. 27:11-54	Isa. 50:4-9a Ps. 31:9-16 Phil. 2:5-11 Mark 14:1-15:47 or Mark 15:1-39 (40-47)	Isa. 50:4-9a Ps. 31:9-16 Phil. 2:5-11 Luke 22:14-23:56 or Luke 23:1-49

Monday of Holy Week	Isa. 42:1-9 Ps. 36:5-11 Heb. 9:11-15 John 12:1-11	Isa. 42:1-9 Ps. 36:5-11 Heb. 9:11-15 John 12:1-11	Isa. 42:1-9 Ps. 36:5-11 Heb. 9:11-15 John 12:1-11
Tuesday of Holy Week	Isa. 49:1-7 Ps. 71:1-14 1 Cor. 1:18-31 John 12:20-36	Isa. 49:1-7 Ps. 71:1-14 1 Cor. 1:18-31 John 12:20-36	Isa. 49:1-7 Ps. 71:1-14 1 Cor. 1:18-31 John 12:20-36
Wednesday of Holy Week	Isa. 50:4-9a Ps. 70 Heb. 12:1-3 John 13:21-32	Isa. 50:4-9a Ps. 70 Heb. 12:1-3 John 13:21-32	Isa. 50:4-9a Ps. 70 Heb. 12:1-3 John 13:21-32
Maundy Thursday	Ex. 12:1-4 (5-10) 11-14 Ps. 116:1-2, 12-19 1 Cor. 11:23-26 John 13:1-17, 31b-35	Ex. 12:1-4 (5-10) 11-14 Ps. 116:1-2, 12-19 1 Cor. 11:23-26 John 13:1-17, 31b-35	Ex. 12:1-4 (5-10) 11-14 Ps. 116:1-2, 12-19 1 Cor. 11:23-26 John 13:1-17, 31b-35
Good Friday	Isa. 52:13-53:12 Ps. 22 Heb. 10:16-25 or Heb. 4:14-16; 5:7-9 John 18:1-19:42	Isa. 52:13-53:12 Ps. 22 Heb. 10:16-25 or Heb. 4:14-16; 5:7-9 John 18:1-19:42	Isa. 52:13-53:12 Ps. 22 Heb. 10:16-25 or Heb. 4:14-16; 5:7-9 John 18:1-19:42
Holy Saturday	Job 14:1-14 or Lam. 3:1-9, 19-24 Ps. 31:1-4, 15-16 1 Pet. 4:1-8 Matt. 27:57-66 or John 19:38-42	Job 14:1-14 or Lam. 3:1-9, 19-24 Ps. 31:1-4, 15-16 1 Pet. 4:1-8 Matt. 27:57-66 or John 19:38-42	Job 14:1-14 or Lam. 3:1-9, 19-24 Ps. 31:1-4, 15-16 1 Pet. 4:1-8 Matt. 27:57-66 or John 19:38-42

Season of Easter

Easter Vigil (First service of Easter)	Gen. 1:1-2:4a Ps. 136:1-9, 23-26	Gen. 1:1-2:4a Ps. 136:1-9, 23-26	Gen. 1:1-2:4a Ps. 136:1-9, 23-26
	Gen. 7:1-5, 11-18; 8:6-18; 9:8-13 Ps. 46	Gen. 7:1-5, 11-18; 8:6-18; 9:8-13 Ps. 46	Gen. 7:1-5, 11-18; 8:6-18; 9:8-13 Ps. 46
	Gen. 22:1-18 Ps. 16	Gen. 22:1-18 Ps. 16	Gen. 22:1-18 Ps. 16
	Ex. 14:10-31; 15:20-21 Ex. 15:1b-13, 17-18	Ex. 14:10-31; 15:20-21 Ex. 15:1b-13, 17-18	Ex. 14:10-31; 15:20-21 Ex. 15:1b-13, 17-18
	Isa. 55:1-11 Isa. 12:2-6	Isa. 55:1-11 Isa. 12:2-6	Isa. 55:1-11 Isa. 12:2-6
	Prov. 8:1-8, 19-21; 9:4b-6 Ps. 19	Prov. 8:1-8, 19-21; 9:4b-6 Ps. 19	Prov. 8:1-8, 19-21; 9:4b-6 Ps. 19
	Ezek. 36:24-28 Pss. 42 and 43	Ezek. 36:24-28 Pss. 42 and 43	Ezek. 36:24-28 Pss. 42 and 43
	Ezek. 37:1-14 Ps. 143 Zeph. 3:14-20 Ps. 98	Ezek. 37:1-14 Ps. 143 Zeph. 3:14-20 Ps. 98	Ezek. 37:1-14 Ps. 143 Zeph. 3:14-20 Ps. 98

	Rom. 6:3-11 Ps. 114 Matt. 28:1-10	Rom. 6:3-11 Ps. 114 Mark 16:1-8	Rom. 6:3-11 Ps. 114 Luke 24:1-12
Easter/ Resurrection of the Lord	Acts 10:34-43 or Jer. 31:1-6 Ps. 118:1-2, 14-24 Col. 3:1-4 or Acts 10:34-43 John 20:1-18 or Matt. 28:1-10	Acts 10:34-43 or Isa. 25:6-9 Ps. 118:1-2, 14-24 1 Cor. 15:1-11 or Acts 10:34-43 John 20:1-18 or Mark 16:1-8	Acts 10:34-43 or Isa. 65:17-25 Ps. 118:1-2, 14-24 1 Cor. 15:19-26 or Acts 10:34-43 John 20:1-18 or Luke 24:1-12
Easter Evening	Isa. 25:6-9 Ps. 114 1 Cor. 5: 6b-8 Luke 24:13-49	Isa. 25:6-9 Ps. 114 1 Cor. 5:6b-8 Luke 24:13-49	Isa. 25:6-9 Ps. 114 1 Cor. 5:6b-8 Luke 24:13-49
2nd Sunday of Easter	Acts 2:14a, 22-32 Ps. 16 1 Pet. 1:3-9 John 20:19-31	Acts 4:32-35 Ps. 133 1 John 1:1-2:2 John 20:19-31	Acts 5:27-32 Ps. 118:14-29 or Ps. 150 Rev. 1:4-8 John 20:19-31
3rd Sunday of Easter	Acts 2:14a, 36-41 Ps. 116:1-4, 12-19 1 Pet. 1:17-23 Luke 24:13-25	Acts 3:12-19 Ps. 4 1 John 3:1-7 Luke 24:36b-48	Acts 9:1-6 (7-20) Ps. 30 Rev. 5:11-14 John 21:1-19
4th Sunday of Easter	Acts 2:42-47 Ps. 23 1 Pet. 2:19-25 John 10:1-10	Acts 4:5-12 Ps. 23 1 John 3:16-24 John 10:11-18	Acts 9:36-43 Ps. 23 Rev. 7:9-17 John 20:22-30
5th Sunday of Easter	Acts 7:55-60 Ps. 31:1-5, 15-15 1 Pet. 2:2-10 John 14:1-14	Acts 8:26-40 Ps. 22:25-31 1 John 4:7-21 John 15:1-8	Acts 11:1-18 Ps. 148 Rev. 21:1-6 John 13:31-35
6th Sunday of Easter	Acts 17:22-31 Ps. 66:8-20 1 Pet. 3:13-22 John 14:15-21	Acts 10:44-48 Ps. 98 1 John 5:1-6 John 15:9-17	Acts 16:9-15 Ps. 67 Rev. 21:10, 22-22:5 John 14:23-29 or John 5:1-9
Ascension of the Lord (for Thursday or 7th Sunday of Easter)	Acts 1:1-11 Ps. 47 or Ps. 93 Eph. 1:15-23 Luke 24:44-53	Acts 1:1-11 Ps. 47 or Ps. 93 Eph. 1:15-23 Luke 24:44-53	Acts 1:1-11 Ps. 47 or Ps. 93 Eph. 1:15-23 Luke 24:44-53

7th Sunday
of Easter
	Acts 1:6-14
	Ps. 68:1-10, 32-35
	1 Pet. 4:12-14;
	  5:6-11
	John 17:1-11
		Acts 1:15-17, 21-26
		Ps. 1
		1 John 5:9-13
		
		John 17:6-19
			Acts 16:16-34
			Ps. 97
			Rev. 22:12-14, 16-17,
			  20-21
			John 17:20-26

Day of Pentecost	Acts 2:1-21 or Num. 11:24-30 Ps. 104:24-34, 35b 1 Cor. 12:3b-13 or Acts 2:1-21 John 20:19-23 or John 7:37-39	Acts 2:1-21 or Ezek. 37:1-14 Ps. 104:24-34, 35b Rom. 8:22-27 or Acts 2:1-21 John 15:26-27; 16:4b-15	Acts 2:1-21 or Gen. 11:1-9 Ps. 104:24-34, 35b Rom. 8:14-17 or Acts 2:1-21 John 14:8-17 (25-27)

Season After Pentecost/Ordinary Time

Trinity Sunday	Gen. 1:1-2:4a Ps. 8 2 Cor. 13:11-13 Matt. 28:16-20	Isa. 6:1-8 Ps. 29 Rom. 8:12-17 John 3:1-17	Prov. 8:1-4, 22-31 Ps. 8 Rom. 5:1-5 John 16:12-15
Sunday between May 24-28 (if after Trinity Sunday)	Isa. 26:1-6 Ps. 131 1 Cor. 4:1-5 Matt. 6:24-34	Hos. 2:14-20 Ps. 103:1-13, 22 2 Cor. 3:1-6 Mark 2:13-22	Isa. 55:10-13 Ps. 92:1-4, 12-15 1 Cor. 15:51-58 Luke 6:39-49

Semicontinuous Readings/*Complementary Readings*

Sunday between May 29 - June 4 (if after Trinity Sunday)	Gen. 6:9-22; 7:24; 8:14-19 Ps. 46 *Deut. 11:18-21, 26-28* *Ps. 31:1-5, 19-24* Rom. 1:16-17; 3:22b-28 (29-31) Matt. 7:21-29	1 Sam. 3:1-10 (11-20) Ps. 139:1-6, 13-18 *Deut. 5:12-15* *Ps. 81:1-10* 2 Cor. 4:5-12 Mark 2:23-3:6	1 Kings 18:20-21 (22-29), 30-39 Ps. 96 *1 Kings 8:22-23, 41-43* *Ps. 69:1-9* Gal. 1:1-12 Luke 7:1-10
Sunday between June 5-11 (if after Trinity Sunday)	Gen. 12:1-9 Ps. 33:1-12 *Hos. 5:15-6:6* *Ps. 50:7-15* Rom. 4:13-25 Matt. 9:9-13, 18-26	1 Sam. 8:4-11 (12-15) 16-20 (11:14-15) Ps. 138 *Gen. 3:8-15* *Ps. 130* 2 Cor. 4:13-5:1 Mark 3:20-35	1 Kings 17:8-16 (17-24) Ps. 146 *1 Kings 17:17-24* *Ps. 30* Gal. 1:11-24 Luke 7:11-17
Sunday between June 12-18 (if after Trinity Sunday)	Gen. 18:1-15 (21:1-7) Ps. 116:1-2, 12-19 *Ex. 19:2-8a* *Ps. 100* Rom. 5:1-8 Matt. 9:35-10:8 (9-23)	1 Sam. 15:34-16:13 Ps. 20 *Ezek. 17:22-4* *Ps. 92:1-4, 12-15* 2 Cor. 5:6-10 (11-13), 14-17 Mark 4:26-34	1 Kings 21:1-10 (11-14) 15-21a Ps. 5:1-8 *2 Sam. 11:26-12:10, 13-15* Gal. 2:15-21 Luke 7:36-8:3
Sunday between June 19-25 (if after Trinity Sunday)	Gen. 21:8-21 Ps. 86:1-10, 16-17 *Jer. 20:7-13* *Ps. 69:7-10 (11-15) 16-18* Rom. 6:1b-11 Matt. 10:24-39	1 Sam. 17:(1a, 4-11, 19-23) 32-39 and Ps. 9:9-20 or 1 Sam. 17:57-18:5 10-16 and Ps. 133 *Job 38:1-11* *Ps. 107:1-3, 23-32* 2 Cor. 6:1-13 Mark 4:35-41	1 Kings 19:1-4 (5-7) 8-15a Pss. 42-43 *Isa. 65:1-9* *Ps. 22:19-28* Gal. 3:23-29 Luke 8:26-39
Sunday between June 26 - July 2	Gen. 22:1-14 Ps. 13 *Jer. 28:5-9* *Ps. 89:1-4, 15-18* Rom. 6:12-23 Matt. 10:40-42	2 Sam. 1:1, 17-27 Ps. 130 *Lam. 3:23-33* *Ps. 30* 2 Cor. 8:7-15 Mark 5:21-43	2 Kings 2:1-2, 6-14 Ps. 77:1-2, 11-20 *1 Kings 19:15-16, 19-21* *Ps. 16* Gal. 5:1, 13-25 Luke 9:51-62

Sunday between July 3-9	Gen. 24:34-38, 42-49, 58-67	2 Sam. 5:1-5, 9-10	2 Kings 5:1-14
	Ps. 45:10-17 or Song of Songs 2:8-13	Ps. 48	Ps. 30
	Zech. 9:9-12	*Ezek. 2:1-5*	*Isa. 66:10-14*
	Ps. 145:8-14	*Ps. 123*	*Ps. 66:1-9*
	Rom. 7:15-25a	2 Cor. 12:2-10	Gal. 6:(1-6) 7-16
	Matt. 11:16-19, 25-30	Mark 6:1-13	Luke 10:1-11, 16-20

Sunday between July 10-16	Gen. 25:19-34	2 Sam. 6:1-5, 12b-19	Amos 7:7-17
	Ps. 119:105-112	Ps. 24	Ps. 82
	Isa. 55:10-13	*Amos 7:7-15*	*Deut. 30:9-14*
	Ps. 65:(1-8) 9-13	*Ps. 85:8-13*	*Ps. 25:1-10*
	Rom. 8:1-11	Eph. 1:3-14	Col. 1:1-14
	Matt. 13:1-9, 18-23	Mark 6:14-29	Luke 10:25-37

Sunday between July 17-23	Gen. 28:10-19a	2 Sam. 7:1-14a	Amos 8:1-12
	Ps. 139:1-12, 23-24	Ps. 89:20-37	Ps. 52
	Isa. 44:6-8	*Jer. 23:1-6*	*Gen. 18:1-10a*
	Ps. 86:11-17	*Ps. 23*	*Ps. 15*
	Rom. 8:12-25	Eph. 2:11-22	Col. 1:15-28
	Matt. 13:24-30, 36-43	Mark 6:30-34, 53-56	Luke 10:38-42

Sunday between July 24-30	Gen. 29:15-28	2 Sam. 11:1-5	Hos. 1:2-10
	Ps. 105:1-11, 45b or Ps. 128	Ps. 14	Ps. 85
	1 Kings 3:5-12	*2 Kings 4:42-44*	*Gen. 18:20-32*
	Ps. 119:129-136	*Ps. 145:10-18*	*Ps. 138*
	Rom. 8:26-39	Eph. 3:14-21	Col. 2:6-15 (16-19)
	Matt. 13:31-33, 44-52	John 6:1-21	Luke 11:1-3

Sunday between July 31 - August 6	Gen. 33:22-31	2 Sam. 11:26-12:13a	Hos. 11:1-11
	Ps. 17:1-7, 15	Ps. 51:1-12	Ps. 107:1-9, 43
	Isa. 55:1-5	*Ex. 16:2-4, 9-15*	*Eccl. 1:2, 12-14; 2:18-23*
	Ps. 145:8-9, 14-21	*Ps. 78:23-29*	*Ps. 49:1-12*
	Rom. 9:1-5	Eph. 4:1-16	Col. 3:1-11
	Matt. 14:13-21	John 6:24-35	Luke 12:12-21

Sunday between August 7-13	Gen. 37:1-4, 12-28	2 Sam. 18:5-9, 15, 31-33	Isa. 1:1, 10-20
	Ps. 105:1-6, 16-22, 45b	Ps. 130	Ps. 50:1-8, 22-23
	1 Kings 19:9-18	*1 Kings 19:4-8*	*Gen. 15:1-6*
	Ps. 85:8-13	*Ps. 34:1-8*	*Ps. 33:12-22*
	Rom. 10:5-15	Eph. 4:25-5:2	Heb. 11:1-3, 8-16
	Matt. 14:22-33	John 6:35, 41-51	Luke 12:32-40

Sunday between August 14-20	Gen. 45:1-15	1 Kings 2:10-12; 3:3-14	Isa. 5:1-7
	Ps. 133	Ps. 111	Ps. 80:1-2, 8-19
	Isa. 56:1, 6-8	*Prov. 9:1-6*	*Jer. 23:23-29*
	Ps. 67	*Ps. 34:9-14*	*Ps. 82*
	Rom. 11:1-2a, 29-32	Eph. 5:15-20	Heb. 11:29-12:2
	Matt. 15:(10-20) 21-28	John 6:51-58	Luke 12:49-56

Sunday between August 21-27	Ex. 1:8-20 Ps. 124 *Isa. 51:1-6* *Ps. 138* Rom. 12:1-8 Matt. 16:13-20	1 Kings 8:(1, 6, 10-11) 22-30, 41-43 Ps. 84 *Josh. 24:1-2a, 14-18* *Ps. 34:15-22* Eph. 6:10-20 John 6:59-69	Jer. 1:4-10 Ps. 71:1-6 *Isa. 58:9b-14* *Ps. 103:1-8* Heb. 12:18-29 Luke 13:10-17
Sunday between August 28 - September 3	Ex. 3:1-15 Ps. 105:1-6, 23-26, 45b *Jer. 15:15-21* *Ps. 26:1-8* Rom. 12:9-21 Matt. 16:21-28	Song of Songs 2:8-13 Ps. 45:1-2, 6-9 *Deut. 4:1-2, 6-9* *Ps. 15* James 1:17-27 Mark 7:1-8, 14-15 21-23	Jer. 2:4-13 Ps. 81:1, 10-16 *Prov. 25:6-7* *Ps. 112* Heb. 13:1-8, 15-16 Luke 14:1, 7-14
Sunday between September 4-10	Ex. 12:1-14 Ps. 149 *Ezek. 33:7-11* *Ps. 119:33-40* Rom. 13:8-14 Matt. 18:15-20	Prov. 22:1-2, 8-9, 22-23 Ps. 125 *Isa. 35:4-7a* *Ps. 146* James 2:1-10 (11-13) 14-17 Mark 7:24-37	Jer. 18:1-11 Ps. 139:1-6, 13-18 *Deut. 30:15-20* *Ps. 1* Philem. 1-21 Luke 14:25-33
Sunday between September 11-17	Ex. 14:19-31 Ps. 114 or Ex. 15:1b-11, 20-21 *Gen. 50:15-21* *Ps. 103:(1-7) 8-13* Rom. 14:1-12 Matt. 18:21-25	Prov. 1:20-33 Ps. 19 *Isa. 50:4-9a* *Ps. 116:1-9* James 3:1-12 Mark 8:27-38	Jer. 4:11-12, 22-28 Ps. 14 *Ex. 32:7-14* *Ps. 51:1-10* 1 Tim. 1:12-17 Luke 15:1-10
Sunday between September 18-24	Ex. 16:2-15 Ps. 105:1-6, 37-45 *Jon. 3:10-4:11* *Ps. 145:1-8* Phil. 1:21-30 Matt. 20:1-16	Prov. 31:10-31 Ps. 1 *Jer. 11:18-20* *Ps. 54* James 3:13-4:3, 7-8a Mark 9:30-37	Jer. 8:18-9:1 Ps. 79:1-9 *Amos 8:4-7* *Ps. 113* 1 Tim. 2:1-7 Luke 16:1-13
Sunday between September 25 - October 1	Ex. 17:1-7 Ps. 78:1-4, 12-16 *Ezek. 18:1-4, 25-32* *Ps. 25:1-9* Phil. 2:1-13 Matt. 21:23-32	Esther 7:1-6, 9-10; 9:20-22 Ps. 124 *Num. 11:406, 10-16 24-29* *Ps. 19:7-14* James 5:13-20 Mark 9:38-50	Jer. 32:1-3a, 6-15 Ps. 91:1-6, 14-16 *Amos 6:1a, 4-7* *Ps. 146* 1 Tim. 6:6-19 Luke 16:19-31
Sunday between October 2-8	Ex. 20:1-4, 7-9, 12-20 Ps. 19 *Isa. 5:1-7* *Ps. 80:7-15* Phil. 3:4b-14 Matt. 21:33-46	Job 1:1; 2:1-10 Ps. 26 *Gen. 2:18-24* *Ps. 8* Heb. 1:1-4; 2:5-12 Mark 10:2-16	Lam. 1:1-6 Lam. 3:19-26 or Ps. 137 *Hab. 1:1-4; 2:1-4* *Ps. 37:1-9* 2 Tim. 1:1-14 Luke 17:5-10

Sunday between October 9-15	Ex. 32:1-14 Ps. 106:1-6, 19-23 *Isa. 25:1-9* *Ps. 23* Phil. 4:1-9 Matt. 22:1-14	Job 23:1-9, 16-17 Ps. 22:1-15 *Amos 5:6-7, 10-15* *Ps. 90:12-17* Heb. 4:12-16 Mark 10:17-31	Jer. 29:1, 4-7 Ps. 66:1-12 *2 Kings 5:1-3, 7-15c* *Ps. 111* 2 Tim. 2:8-15 Luke 17:11-19
Sunday between October 16-22	Ex. 33:12-23 Ps. 99 *Isa. 45:1-7* *Ps. 96:1-9 (10-13)* 1 Thess. 1:1-10 Matt. 22:15-22	Job 38:1-7 (34-41) Ps. 104:1-9, 24, 35c *Isa. 53:4-12* *Ps. 91:9-16* Heb. 5:1-10 Mark 10:35-45	Jer. 31:27-34 Ps. 119:97-104 *Gen. 32:22-31* *Ps. 121* 2 Tim. 3:14-4:5 Luke 18:1-8
Sunday between October 23-29	Deut. 34:1-12 Ps. 90:1-6, 13-17 *Lev. 19:1-2, 15-18* *Ps. 1* 1 Thess. 2:1-8 Matt. 22:34-46	Job 42:1-6, 10-17 Ps. 34:1-8 (19-22) *Jer. 31:7-9* *Ps. 126* Heb. 7:23-28 Mark 10:46-52	Joel 2:23-32 Ps. 65 *Jer. 14:7-10, 19-22* *Ps. 84:1-7* 2 Tim. 4:6-8, 16-18 Luke 18:9-14
Sunday between October 30 - November 5	Josh. 3:7-17 Ps. 107:1-7, 33-37 *Mic. 3:5-12* *Ps. 43* 1 Thess. 2:9-13 Matt. 23:1-12	Ruth 1:1-18 Ps. 146 *Deut. 6:1-9* *Ps. 119:1-8* Heb. 9:11-14 Mark 12:28-34	Hab. 1:1-4; 2:1-4 Ps. 119:137-144 *Isa. 1:10-18* *Ps. 32:1-7* 2 Thess. 1:1-4, 11-12 Luke 19:1-10
All Saints' Day (November 1 or 1st Sunday in November)	Rev. 7:9-17 Ps. 34:1-10, 22 1 John 3:1-3 Matt. 5:1-12	Isa. 25:6-9 Ps. 24 Rev. 21:1-6a John 11:32-44	Dan. 7:1-3, 15-18 Ps. 149 Eph. 1:11-23 Luke 6:20-31
Sunday between November 6-12	Josh. 24:1-3a, 14-25 Ps. 78:1-7 *Amos 5:18-24* *Ps. 70* 1 Thess. 4:13-18 Matt. 25:1-13	Ruth 3:1-5; 4:13-17 Ps. 127 *1 Kings 17:8-16* *Ps. 146* Heb. 9:24-28 Mark 12:38-44	Hag. 1:15b-2:9 Ps. 145:1-5, 17-21 or Ps. 98 *Job 19:23-27a* *Ps. 17:1-9* 2 Thess. 2:1-5, 13-17 Luke 20:27-38
Sunday between November 13-19	Judg. 4:1-7 Ps. 123 *Zeph. 1:7, 12-18* *Ps. 90:1-8 (9-11) 12* 1 Thess. 5:1-11 Matt. 25:14-30	1 Sam. 1:4-20 1 Sam. 2:1-10 *Dan. 12:1-3* *Ps. 16* Heb. 10:11-14 (15-18) 19-25 Mark 13:1-8	Isa. 65:17-25 Isa. 12 *Mal. 4:1-2a* *Ps. 98* 2 Thess. 3:6-13 Luke 25:5-19
Christ the King/ Reign of Christ (Sunday between November 20-26)	Ezek. 34:11-16, 20-24 Ps. 100 *Ezek. 34:11-16, 20-24* *Ps. 95:1-7a* Eph. 1:15-23 Matt. 25:31-46	2 Sam. 23:1-7 Ps. 132:1-12 (13-18) *Dan. 7:9-10, 13-14* *Ps. 93* Rev. 1:4b-8 John 18:33-37	Jer. 23:1-6 Luke 1:68-79 *Jer. 23:1-6* *Ps. 46* Col. 1:11-20 Luke 23:33-43

Special Days
New Year's Day
January 1

Eccl. 3:1-13	Eccl. 3:1-13	Eccl. 3:1-13
Ps. 8	Ps. 8	Ps. 8
Rev. 21:1-6a	Rev. 21:1-6a	Rev. 21:1-6a
Matt. 25:31-46	Matt. 25:31-46	Matt. 25:31-46

Holy Name of Jesus
January 1

Num. 6:22-27	Num. 6:22-27	Num. 6:22-27
Ps. 8	Ps. 8	Ps. 8
Gal. 4:4-7 or	Gal. 4:4-7 or	Gal. 4:4-7 or
Phil. 2:5-11	Phil. 2:5-11	Phil. 2:5-11
Luke 2:15-21	Luke 2:15-21	Luke 2:15-21

Presentation of the Lord
February 2

Mal. 3:1-4	Mal. 3:1-4	Mal. 3:1-4
Ps. 84	Ps. 84	Ps. 84
Heb. 2:14-18	Heb. 2:14-18	Heb. 2:14-18
Luke 2:22-40	Luke 2:22-40	Luke 2:22-40

Annunciation of the Lord
March 25

Isa. 7:10-14	Isa. 7:10-14	Isa. 7:10-14
Ps. 45 or	Ps. 45 or	Ps. 45 or
Ps. 40:5-10	Ps. 40:5-10	Ps. 40:5-10
Heb. 10:4-10	Heb. 10:4-10	Heb. 10:4-10
Luke 1:26-38	Luke 1:26-38	Luke 1:26-38

Visitation of Mary to Elizabeth
May 31

1 Sam. 2:1-10	1 Sam. 2:1-10	1 Sam. 2:1-10
Ps. 113	Ps. 113	Ps. 113
Rom. 12:9-16b	Rom. 12:9-16b	Rom. 12:9-16b
Luke 1:39-57	Luke 1:39-57	Luke 1:39-57

Holy Cross
September 14

Num. 21:4b-9	Num. 21:4b-9	Num. 21:4b-9
Ps. 98:1-5 or	Ps. 98:1-5 or	Ps. 98:1-5 or
Ps. 78:1-2, 34-38	Ps. 78:1-2, 34-38	Ps. 78:1-2, 34-38
1 Cor. 1:18-24	1 Cor. 1:18-24	1 Cor. 1:18-24
John 3:13-17	John 3:13-17	John 3:13-17

Thanksgiving Day
October, Canada
November, USA

Deut. 8:7-18	Joel 2:21-27	Deut. 26:1-11
Ps. 65	Ps. 126	Ps. 100
2 Cor. 9:6-15	1 Tim. 2:1-7	Phil. 4:4-9
Luke 17:11-19	Matt. 6:25-33	John 6:25-35

Psalms in the *Revised Common Lectionary*

The psalm and psalm portions that appear as Sunday or Festival readings in the *Revised Common Lectionary* are listed below in biblical order. Each psalm is organized by year, season, and the day on which the reading occurs. Psalms designated as complementary readings during Ordinary Time after Pentecost are shown in italics.

Psalm	Year	Season or Festival	Day or Sunday between
Ps. 1	A	*Ordinary Time after Pentecost*	*October 23-29*
Ps. 1	B	Easter	7th Sunday
Ps. 1	B	Ordinary Time after Pentecost	September 18-24
Ps. 1	C	Ordinary Time after Epiphany	6th Sunday
Ps. 1	C	*Ordinary Time after Pentecost*	*September 4-10*
Ps. 2	A	Ordinary Time after Epiphany	Transfiguration Sunday
Ps. 4	B	Easter	3rd Sunday
Ps. 5:1-8	C	Ordinary Time after Pentecost	June 12-18 (if after Trinity Sunday)
Ps. 8	A	Christmas	New Year's Day
Ps. 8	A	Holy Name of Jesus	January 1
Ps. 8	A	Ordinary Time after Pentecost	Trinity Sunday
Ps. 8	B	Christmas	New Year's Day
Ps. 8	B	Holy Name of Jesus	January 1
Ps. 8	B	*Ordinary Time after Pentecost*	*October 2-8*
Ps. 8	C	Christmas	New Year's Day
Ps. 8	C	Holy Name of Jesus	January 1
Ps. 8	C	Ordinary Time after Pentecost	Trinity Sunday
Ps. 9:9-20	B	Ordinary Time after Pentecost	June 19-25 (if after Trinity Sunday)
Ps. 13	A	Ordinary Time after Pentecost	June 26 - July 2
Ps. 14	B	Ordinary Time after Pentecost	July 24-30
Ps. 14	C	Ordinary Time after Pentecost	September 11-17
Ps. 15	A	Ordinary Time after Epiphany	4th Sunday
Ps. 15	B	*Ordinary Time after Pentecost*	*August 28 - September 3*
Ps. 15	C	*Ordinary Time after Pentecost*	*July 17-23*
Ps. 16	A	Easter	2nd Sunday
Ps. 16	A	Easter	Easter Vigil
Ps. 16	B	Easter	Easter Vigil
Ps. 16	B	*Ordinary Time after Pentecost*	*November 13-19*
Ps. 16	C	Easter	Easter Vigil
Ps. 16	C	*Ordinary Time after Pentecost*	*June 26 - July 2*
Ps. 17:1-7, 15	A	Ordinary Time after Pentecost	July 31 - August 6
Ps. 17:1-9	C	*Ordinary Time after Pentecost*	*November 6-12*
Ps. 19	A	Easter	Easter Vigil
Ps. 19	A	Ordinary Time after Pentecost	October 2-8
Ps. 19	B	Lent	3rd Sunday
Ps. 19	B	Easter	Easter Vigil
Ps. 19	B	Ordinary Time after Pentecost	September 11-17

Ps. 19:7-14	*B*	*Ordinary Time after Pentecost*	*September 25 - October 1*
Ps. 19	C	Ordinary Time after Epiphany	3rd Sunday
Ps. 19	C	Easter	Easter Vigil
Ps. 20	B	Ordinary Time after Pentecost	June 12-18 (if after Trinity Sunday)
Ps. 22	A	Holy Week	Good Friday
Ps. 22:23-31	B	Lent	2nd Sunday
Ps. 22	B	Holy Week	Good Friday
Ps. 22:25-31	B	Easter	5th Sunday
Ps. 22:1-15	B	Ordinary Time after Pentecost	October 9-15
Ps. 22	C	Holy Week	Good Friday
Ps. 22:19-28	*C*	*Ordinary Time after Pentecost*	*June 19-25* (if after Trinity Sunday)
Ps. 23	A	Lent	4th Sunday
Ps. 23	A	Easter	4th Sunday
Ps. 23	*A*	*Ordinary Time after Pentecost*	*October 9-15*
Ps. 23	B	Easter	4th Sunday
Ps. 23	*B*	*Ordinary Time after Pentecost*	*July 17-23*
Ps. 23	C	Easter	4th Sunday
Ps. 24:7-10	A	Presentation of the Lord	February 2
Ps. 24:7-10	B	Presentation of the Lord	February 2
Ps. 24	B	Ordinary Time after Pentecost	July 10-16
Ps. 24	B	All Saints' Day	November 1
Ps. 24:7-10	C	Presentation of the Lord	February 2
Ps. 25:1-9	*A*	*Ordinary Time after Pentecost*	*September 25 - October 1*
Ps. 25:1-10	B	Lent	1st Sunday
Ps. 25:1-10	C	Advent	1st Sunday
Ps. 25:1-10	*C*	*Ordinary Time after Pentecost*	*July 10-16*
Ps. 26:1-8	*A*	*Ordinary Time after Pentecost*	*August 28 - September 3*
Ps. 26	B	Ordinary Time after Pentecost	October 2-8
Ps. 27:1, 4-9	A	Ordinary Time after Epiphany	3rd Sunday
Ps. 27	C	Lent	2nd Sunday
Ps. 29	A	Ordinary Time after Epiphany	Baptism of the Lord
Ps. 29	B	Ordinary Time after Epiphany	Baptism of the Lord
Ps. 29	B	Ordinary Time after Pentecost	Trinity Sunday
Ps. 29	C	Ordinary Time after Epiphany	Baptism of the Lord
Ps. 30	B	Ordinary Time after Epiphany	6th Sunday
Ps. 30	*B*	*Ordinary Time after Pentecost*	*June 26 - July 2*
Ps. 30	C	Easter	3rd Sunday
Ps. 30	*C*	*Ordinary Time after Pentecost*	*June 5-11* (if after Trinity Sunday)
Ps. 30	C	Ordinary Time after Pentecost	July 3-9
Ps. 31:9-16	A	Lent	Liturgy of the Passion
Ps. 31:1-4, 15-16	A	Holy Week	Holy Saturday
Ps. 31:1-5, 15-16	A	Easter	5th Sunday
Ps. 31:1-5, 19-24	A	Ordinary Time after Epiphany	9th Sunday
Ps. 31:1-5, 19-24	*A*	*Ordinary Time after Pentecost*	*May 29 - June 4* (if after Trinity Sunday)
Ps. 31:9-16	B	Lent	Liturgy of the Passion

Ps. 31:1-4, 15-16	B	Holy Week	Holy Saturday
Ps. 31:9-16	C	Lent	Liturgy of the Passion
Ps. 31:1-4, 15-16	C	Holy Week	Holy Saturday
Ps. 32	A	Lent	1st Sunday
Ps. 32	C	Lent	4th Sunday
Ps. 32	*C*	*Ordinary Time after Pentecost*	*June 12-18* (if after Trinity Sunday)
Ps. 32:1-7	*C*	*Ordinary Time after Pentecost*	*October 30 - November 5*
Ps. 33:1-12	A	Ordinary Time after Pentecost	June 5-11 (if after Trinity Sunday)
Ps. 33:12-22	*C*	*Ordinary Time after Pentecost*	*August 7-13*
Ps. 34:1-10, 22	A	All Saints' Day	November 1
Ps. 34:1-8	*B*	*Ordinary Time after Pentecost*	*August 7-13*
Ps. 34:9-14	*B*	*Ordinary Time after Pentecost*	*August 14-20*
Ps. 34:15-22	*B*	*Ordinary Time after Pentecost*	*August 21-27*
Ps. 34:1-8 (19-22)	B	Ordinary Time after Pentecost	October 23-29
Ps. 36:5-11	A	Holy Week	Monday of Holy Week
Ps. 36:5-11	B	Holy Week	Monday of Holy Week
Ps. 36:5-10	C	Ordinary Time after Epiphany	2nd Sunday
Ps. 36:5-11	C	Holy Week	Monday of Holy Week
Ps. 37:1-11, 39-40	C	Ordinary Time after Epiphany	7th Sunday
Ps. 37:1-9	*C*	*Ordinary Time after Pentecost*	*October 2-8*
Ps. 40:1-11	A	Ordinary Time after Epiphany	2nd Sunday
Ps. 40:5-10	A	Annunciation of the Lord	March 25
Ps. 40:5-10	B	Annunciation of the Lord	March 25
Ps. 40:5-10	C	Annunciation of the Lord	March 25
Ps. 41	B	Ordinary Time after Epiphany	7th Sunday
Pss. 42 and 43	A	Easter	Easter Vigil
Pss. 42 and 43	B	Easter	Easter Vigil
Pss. 42 and 43	C	Easter	Easter Vigil
Pss. 42 and 43	C	Ordinary Time after Pentecost	June 19-25 (if after Trinity Sunday)
Ps. 43	*A*	*Ordinary Time after Pentecost*	*October 30 - November 5*
Ps. 45	A	Annunciation of the Lord	March 25
Ps. 45:10-17	A	Ordinary Time after Pentecost	July 3-9
Ps. 45	B	Annunciation of the Lord	March 25
Ps. 45:1-2, 6-9	B	Ordinary Time after Pentecost	August 28 - September 3
Ps. 45	C	Annunciation of the Lord	March 25
Ps. 46	A	Easter	Easter Vigil
Ps. 46	*A*	*Ordinary Time after Pentecost*	*May 29 - June 4* (if after Trinity Sunday)
Ps. 46	B	Easter	Easter Vigil
Ps. 46	C	Easter	Easter Vigil
Ps. 46	*C*	*Reign of Christ*	*November 20-26*
Ps. 47	A	Easter, Ascension of the Lord	Ascension Day (Thursday or 7th Sunday of Easter)
Ps. 47	B	Easter, Ascension of the Lord	Ascension Day (Thursday or 7th Sunday of Easter)

Ps. 47	C	Easter, Ascension of the Lord	Ascension Day (Thursday or 7th Sunday of Easter)
Ps. 48	B	Ordinary Time after Pentecost	July 3-9
Ps. 49:1-12	*C*	*Ordinary Time after Pentecost*	*July 31 - August 6*
Ps. 50:7-15	*A*	*Ordinary Time after Pentecost*	*June 5-11* (if after Trinity Sunday)
Ps. 50:1-6	B	Ordinary Time after Epiphany	Transfiguration Sunday
Ps. 50:1-8, 22-23	C	Ordinary Time after Pentecost	August 7-13
Ps. 51:1-17	A	Lent	Ash Wednesday
Ps. 51:1-12	B	Lent	5th Sunday
Ps. 51:1-17	B	Lent	Ash Wednesday
Ps. 51:1-12	B	Ordinary Time after Pentecost	July 31 - August 6
Ps. 51:1-17	C	Lent	Ash Wednesday
Ps. 51:1-10	*C*	*Ordinary Time after Pentecost*	*September 11-17*
Ps. 52	C	Ordinary Time after Pentecost	July 17-23
Ps. 54	*B*	*Ordinary Time after Pentecost*	*September 18-24*
Ps. 62:5-12	B	Ordinary Time after Epiphany	3rd Sunday
Ps. 63:1-8	C	Lent	3rd Sunday
Ps. 65:(1-8) 9-13	*A*	*Ordinary Time after Pentecost*	*July 10-16*
Ps. 65	A	Thanksgiving Day, Canada	2nd Monday in October
Ps. 65	A	Thanksgiving Day, USA	4th Thursday in November
Ps. 65	C	Ordinary Time after Pentecost	October 23-29
Ps. 66:8-20	A	Easter	6th Sunday
Ps. 66:1-9	*C*	*Ordinary Time after Pentecost*	*July 3-9*
Ps. 66:1-12	C	Ordinary Time after Pentecost	October 9-15
Ps. 67	*A*	*Ordinary Time after Pentecost*	*August 14-20*
Ps. 67	C	Easter	6th Sunday
Ps. 68:1-10, 32-35	A	Easter	7th Sunday
Ps. 69:7-10 *(11-15) 16-18*	*A*	*Ordinary Time after Pentecost*	*June 19-25* (if after Trinity Sunday)
Ps. 70	A	Holy Week	Wednesday of Holy Week
Ps. 70	*A*	*Ordinary Time after Pentecost*	*November 6-12*
Ps. 70	B	Holy Week	Wednesday of Holy Week
Ps. 70	C	Holy Week	Wednesday of Holy Week
Ps. 71:1-14	A	Holy Week	Tuesday of Holy Week
Ps. 71:1-14	B	Holy Week	Tuesday of Holy Week
Ps. 71:1-6	C	Ordinary Time after Epiphany	4th Sunday
Ps. 71:1-14	C	Holy Week	Tuesday of Holy Week
Ps. 71:1-6	C	Ordinary Time after Pentecost	August 21-27

Ps. 72:1-7, 18-19	A	Advent	2nd Sunday
Ps. 72:1-7, 10-14	A	Epiphany	Epiphany of the Lord (January 6 or Sunday before Epiphany)
Ps. 72:1-7, 10-14	B	Epiphany	Epiphany of the Lord (January 6 or Sunday before Epiphany)
Ps. 72:1-7, 10-14	C	Epiphany	Epiphany of the Lord (January 6 or Sunday before Epiphany)
Ps. 77:1-2, 11-20	C	Ordinary Time after Pentecost	June 26 - July 2
Ps. 78:1-2, 34-38	A	Holy Cross	September 14
Ps. 78:1-4, 12-16	A	Ordinary Time after Pentecost	September 25 - October 1
Ps. 78:1-7	A	Ordinary Time after Pentecost	November 6-12
Ps. 78:23-29	B	*Ordinary Time after Pentecost*	*July 31 - August 6*
Ps. 78:1-2, 34-38	B	Holy Cross	September 14
Ps. 78:1-2, 34-38	C	Holy Cross	September 14
Ps. 79:1-9	C	Ordinary Time after Pentecost	September 18-24
Ps. 80:1-7, 17-19	A	Advent	4th Sunday
Ps. 80:1-7, 17-19	B	Advent	1st Sunday
Ps. 80:1-7	C	Advent	4th Sunday
Ps. 80:1-2, 8-19	C	Ordinary Time after Pentecost	August 14-20
Ps. 80:7-15	C	*Ordinary Time after Pentecost*	*October 2-8*
Ps. 81:1-10	B	Ordinary Time after Epiphany	9th Sunday
Ps. 81:1-10	B	*Ordinary Time after Pentecost*	*May 29 - June 4* (if after Trinity Sunday)
Ps. 81:1, 10-16	C	Ordinary Time after Pentecost	August 28 - September 3
Ps. 82	C	Ordinary Time after Pentecost	July 10-16
Ps. 82	C	*Ordinary Time after Pentecost*	*August 14-20*
Ps. 84	A	Presentation of the Lord	February 2
Ps. 84	B	Presentation of the Lord	February 2
Ps. 84	B	Ordinary Time after Pentecost	August 21-27
Ps. 84	C	Presentation of the Lord	February 2
Ps. 84:1-7	C	*Ordinary Time after Pentecost*	*October 23-29*
Ps. 85:8-13	A	*Ordinary Time after Pentecost*	*August 7-13*
Ps. 85:1-2, 8-13	B	Advent	2nd Sunday
Ps. 85:8-13	B	*Ordinary Time after Pentecost*	*July 10-16*
Ps. 85	C	Ordinary Time after Pentecost	July 24-30
Ps. 86:1-10, 16-17	A	Ordinary Time after Pentecost	June 19-25 (if after Trinity Sunday)
Ps. 86:11-17	A	*Ordinary Time after Pentecost*	*July 17-23*
Ps. 89:1-4, 15-18	A	*Ordinary Time after Pentecost*	*June 26 - July 2*
Ps. 89:1-4, 19-26	B	Advent	4th Sunday
Ps. 89:20-37	B	Ordinary Time after Pentecost	July 17-23
Ps. 90:1-6, 13-17	A	Ordinary Time after Pentecost	October 23-29
Ps. 90:1-8 (9-11) 12	A	*Ordinary Time after Pentecost*	*November 13-19*
Ps. 90:12-17	B	*Ordinary Time after Pentecost*	*October 9-15*
Ps. 91:9-16	B	*Ordinary Time after Pentecost*	*October 16-22*
Ps. 91:1-2, 9-16	C	Lent	1st Sunday

Ps. 91:1-6, 14-16	C	Ordinary Time after Pentecost	September 25 - October 1
Ps. 92:1-4, 12-15	*B*	*Ordinary Time after Pentecost*	*June 12-18* (if after Trinity Sunday)
Ps. 92:1-4, 12-15	C	Ordinary Time after Epiphany	8th Sunday
Ps. 92:1-4, 12-15	C	Ordinary Time after Pentecost	May 24-28 (if after Trinity Sunday)
Ps. 93	A	Easter, Ascension of the Lord	Ascension Day (Thursday or 7th Sunday of Easter)
Ps. 93	B	Easter, Ascension of the Lord	Ascension Day (Thursday or 7th Sunday of Easter)
Ps. 93	*B*	*Reign of Christ*	*November 20-26*
Ps. 93	C	Easter, Ascension of the Lord	Ascension Day (Thursday or 7th Sunday of Easter)
Ps. 95	A	Lent	3rd Sunday
Ps. 95:1-7a	*A*	*Reign of Christ*	*November 20-26*
Ps. 96	A	Christmas I	December 24 or 25
Ps. 96:1-9 (10-13)	*A*	*Ordinary Time after Pentecost*	*October 16-22*
Ps. 96	B	Christmas I	December 24 or 25
Ps. 96	C	Christmas I	December 24 or 25
Ps. 96:1-9	C	Ordinary Time after Epiphany	9th Sunday
Ps. 96	C	Ordinary Time after Pentecost	May 29 - June 4 (if after Trinity Sunday)
Ps. 96:1-9	*C*	*Ordinary Time after Pentecost*	*May 29 - June 4* (if after Trinity Sunday)
Ps. 97	A	Christmas II	December 24 or 25
Ps. 97	B	Christmas II	December 24 or 25
Ps. 97	C	Christmas II	December 24 or 25
Ps. 97	C	Easter	7th Sunday
Ps. 98	A	Christmas III	December 24 or 25
Ps. 98	A	Easter	Easter Vigil
Ps. 98:1-5	A	Holy Cross	September 14
Ps. 98	B	Christmas III	December 24 or 25
Ps. 98	B	Easter	Easter Vigil
Ps. 98	B	Easter	6th Sunday
Ps. 98:1-5	B	Holy Cross	September 14
Ps. 98	C	Christmas III	December 24 or 25
Ps. 98	C	Easter	Easter Vigil
Ps. 98:1-5	C	Holy Cross	September 14
Ps. 98	C	Ordinary Time after Pentecost	November 6-12
Ps. 98	*C*	*Ordinary Time after Pentecost*	*November 13-19*
Ps. 99	A	Ordinary Time after Epiphany	Transfiguration Sunday
Ps. 99	A	Ordinary Time after Pentecost	October 16-22
Ps. 99	C	Ordinary Time after Epiphany	Transfiguration Sunday
Ps. 100	*A*	*Ordinary Time after Pentecost*	*June 12-18* (if after Trinity Sunday)
Ps. 100	A	Reign of Christ	November 20-26
Ps. 100	C	Thanksgiving Day, Canada	2nd Monday in October
Ps. 100	C	Thanksgiving Day, USA	4th Thursday in November
Ps. 103:(1-7) 8-13	*A*	*Ordinary Time after Pentecost*	*September 11-17*
Ps. 103:1-13, 22	B	Ordinary Time after Epiphany	8th Sunday
Ps. 103:1-13, 22	B	Ordinary Time after Pentecost	May 24-28 (if after Trinity Sunday)

Ps. 103:1-8	C	*Ordinary Time after Pentecost*	*August 21-27*
Ps. 104:24-34, 35b	A	Easter	Day of Pentecost
Ps. 104:24-34, 35b	B	Easter	Day of Pentecost
Ps. 104:1-9, 24, 35c	B	Ordinary Time after Pentecost	October 16-22
Ps. 104:24-34, 35b	C	Easter	Day of Pentecost
Ps. 105:1-11, 45b	A	Ordinary Time after Pentecost	July 24-30
Ps. 105:1-6, 16-22, 45b	A	Ordinary Time after Pentecost	August 7-13
Ps. 105:1-6, 23-26, 45b	A	Ordinary Time after Pentecost	August 28 - September 3
Ps. 105:1-6, 37-45	A	Ordinary Time after Pentecost	September 18-24
Ps. 106:1-6, 19-23	A	Ordinary Time after Pentecost	October 9-15
Ps. 107:1-7, 33-37	A	Ordinary Time after Pentecost	October 30 - November 5
Ps. 107:1-3, 17-22	B	Lent	4th Sunday
Ps. 107:1-3, 23-32	B	*Ordinary Time after Pentecost*	*June 19-25* (if after Trinity Sunday)
Ps. 107:1-9, 43	C	Ordinary Time after Pentecost	July 31 - August 6
Ps. 111	B	Ordinary Time after Epiphany	4th Sunday
Ps. 111	B	Ordinary Time after Pentecost	August 14-20
Ps. 111	C	*Ordinary Time after Pentecost*	*October 9-15*
Ps. 112:1-9 (10)	A	Ordinary Time after Epiphany	5th Sunday
Ps. 112	C	*Ordinary Time after Pentecost*	*August 28 - September 3*
Ps. 113	A	Visitation of Mary to Elizabeth	May 31
Ps. 113	B	Visitation of Mary to Elizabeth	May 31
Ps. 113	C	Visitation of Mary to Elizabeth	May 31
Ps. 113	C	*Ordinary Time after Pentecost*	*September 18-24*
Ps. 114	A	Easter	Easter Vigil
Ps. 114	A	Easter	Easter Evening
Ps. 114	A	Ordinary Time after Pentecost	September 11-17
Ps. 114	B	Easter	Easter Vigil
Ps. 114	B	Easter	Easter Evening
Ps. 114	C	Easter	Easter Vigil
Ps. 114	C	Easter	Easter Evening
Ps. 116:1-2, 12-19	A	Holy Week	Maundy Thursday
Ps. 116:1-4, 12-19	A	Easter	3rd Sunday
Ps. 116:1-2, 12-19	A	Ordinary Time after Pentecost	June 12-18 (if after Trinity Sunday)
Ps. 116:1-2, 12-19	B	Holy Week	Maundy Thursday
Ps. 116:1-9	B	*Ordinary Time after Pentecost*	*September 11-17*
Ps. 116:1-2, 12-19	C	Holy Week	Maundy Thursday
Ps. 118:1-2, 19-29	A	Lent	Liturgy of the Palms
Ps. 118:1-2, 14-24	A	Easter	Resurrection of the Lord
Ps. 118:1-2, 19-29	B	Lent	Liturgy of the Palms
Ps. 118:1-2, 14-24	B	Easter	Resurrection of the Lord
Ps. 118:1-2, 19-29	C	Lent	Liturgy of the Palms
Ps. 118:1-2, 14-24	C	Easter	Resurrection of the Lord
Ps. 118:14-29	C	Easter	2nd Sunday
Ps. 119:1-8	A	Ordinary Time after Epiphany	6th Sunday
Ps. 119:33-40	A	Ordinary Time after Epiphany	7th Sunday
Ps. 119:33-40	A	*Ordinary Time after Pentecost*	*September 4-10*

Ps. 119:105-112	A	Ordinary Time after Pentecost	July 10-16
Ps. 119:129-136	*A*	*Ordinary Time after Pentecost*	*July 24-30*
Ps. 119:9-16	B	Lent	5th Sunday
Ps. 119:1-8	*B*	*Ordinary Time after Pentecost*	*October 30 - November 5*
Ps. 119:97-104	C	Ordinary Time after Pentecost	October 16-22
Ps. 119:137-144	C	Ordinary Time after Pentecost	October 30 - November 5
Ps. 121	A	Lent	2nd Sunday
Ps. 121	*C*	*Ordinary Time after Pentecost*	*October 16-22*
Ps. 122	A	Advent	1st Sunday
Ps. 123	A	Ordinary Time after Pentecost	November 13-19
Ps. 123	*B*	*Ordinary Time after Pentecost*	*July 3-9*
Ps. 124	A	Ordinary Time after Pentecost	August 21-27
Ps. 124	B	Ordinary Time after Pentecost	September 25 - October 1
Ps. 125	B	Ordinary Time after Pentecost	September 4-10
Ps. 126	B	Advent	3rd Sunday
Ps. 126	*B*	*Ordinary Time after Pentecost*	*October 23-29*
Ps. 126	B	Thanksgiving Day, Canada	2nd Monday in October
Ps. 126	B	Thanksgiving Day, USA	4th Thursday in November
Ps. 126	C	Lent	5th Sunday
Ps. 127	B	Ordinary Time after Pentecost	November 6-12
Ps. 128	A	Ordinary Time after Pentecost	July 24-30
Ps. 130	A	Lent	5th Sunday
Ps. 130	*B*	*Ordinary Time after Pentecost*	*June 5-11* (if after Trinity Sunday)
Ps. 130	B	Ordinary Time after Pentecost	June 26 - July 2
Ps. 130	B	Ordinary Time after Pentecost	August 7-13
Ps. 131	A	Ordinary Time after Epiphany	8th Sunday
Ps. 131	A	Ordinary Time after Pentecost	May 24-28 (if after Trinity Sunday)
Ps. 132:1-12 (13-18)	*B*	*Reign of Christ*	*November 20-26*
Ps. 133	A	Ordinary Time after Pentecost	August 14-20
Ps. 133	B	Easter	2nd Sunday
Ps. 133	B	Ordinary Time after Pentecost	June 19-25 (if after Trinity Sunday)
Ps. 136:1-9, 23-26	A	Easter	Easter Vigil
Ps. 136:1-9, 23-26	B	Easter	Easter Vigil
Ps. 136:1-9, 23-26	C	Easter	Easter Vigil
Ps. 137	C	Ordinary Time after Pentecost	October 2-8
Ps. 138	*A*	*Ordinary Time after Pentecost*	*August 21-27*
Ps. 138	B	Ordinary Time after Pentecost	June 5-11 (if after Trinity Sunday)
Ps. 138	C	Ordinary Time after Epiphany	5th Sunday
Ps. 138	*C*	*Ordinary Time after Pentecost*	*July 24-30*

Ps. 139:1-12, 23-24	A	Ordinary Time after Pentecost	July 17-23
Ps. 139:1-6, 13-18	B	Ordinary Time after Epiphany	2nd Sunday
Ps. 139:1-6, 13-18	B	Ordinary Time after Pentecost	May 29 - June 4
			(if after Trinity Sunday)
Ps. 139:1-6, 13-18	C	Ordinary Time after Pentecost	September 4-10
Ps. 143	A	Easter	Easter Vigil
Ps. 143	B	Easter	Easter Vigil
Ps. 143	C	Easter	Easter Vigil
Ps. 145:1-8	*A*	*Ordinary Time after Pentecost*	*September 18-24*
Ps. 145:8-9, 14-21	*A*	*Ordinary Time after Pentecost*	*July 31 - August 6*
Ps. 145:8-14	*A*	*Ordinary Time after Pentecost*	*July 3-9*
Ps. 145:10-18	*B*	*Ordinary Time after Pentecost*	*July 24-30*
Ps. 145:1-5, 17-21	C	Ordinary Time after Pentecost	November 6-12
Ps. 146:5-10	A	Advent	3rd Sunday
Ps. 146	*B*	*Ordinary Time after Pentecost*	*September 4-10*
Ps. 146	B	Ordinary Time after Pentecost	October 30 - November 5
Ps. 146	*B*	*Ordinary Time after Pentecost*	*November 6-12*
Ps. 146	C	Ordinary Time after Pentecost	June 5-11 (if after Trinity Sunday)
Ps. 146	*C*	*Ordinary Time after Pentecost*	*September 25 - October 1*
Ps. 147:12-20	A	Christmas	2nd Sunday
Ps. 147:12-20	B	Christmas	2nd Sunday
Ps. 147:1-11, 20c	B	Ordinary Time after Epiphany	5th Sunday
Ps. 147:12-20	C	Christmas	2nd Sunday
Ps. 148	A	Christmas	1st Sunday
Ps. 148	B	Christmas	1st Sunday
Ps. 148	C	Christmas	1st Sunday
Ps. 148	C	Easter	5th Sunday
Ps. 149	A	Ordinary Time after Pentecost	September 4-10
Ps. 149	C	All Saints' Day	November 1
Ps. 150	C	Easter	2nd Sunday

Performance Notes

1B: The refrain should be sung simply and unhurriedly, feeling each bar as one. Accompaniment should be sparse. Bells or chimes can be used by playing F and C together or alternating F and C on the first beats of every measure. This pattern can continue under the reading of the psalm. At the conclusion of the psalm the refrain may be sung several times in two or three part canon.

1C: This Thai melody should be sung unhurriedly and with a light voice. It may be accompanied by some voices or soft instruments droning on G and D throughout. A light wind or string instrument may double the melody. Soft hand drum and finger cymbals or triangle may also be added. The Thai pattern for accompanying with finger cymbals is to begin with a closed strike (short *chap* sound) followed by an open strike (ringing *ching* sound).

1E: The first four stanzas flesh out Ps. 1:1, elaborating on the sorts of paths that should be avoided. In contrast, st. 5 describes the fruits of the righteous path. Even when sung by English-speaking congregations, the refrain is best sung in Spanish. There is a playful, rhythmic interplay between the steady eighth-note pattern in the bass of the accompaniment and the driving 3+3+2 rhythm of the melody. These counter-rhythms can be heightened by percussion instruments such as shakers and woodblock.

1F: This setting should be sung confidently but gently, as an affirmation rather than a boast.

2B: This dramatic reading could conclude with a prayer of confession and/or a hymn or psalm of trust, such as "You Are My Hiding Place" (p. 208).

2C: This overt Christological paraphrase coupled with the Easter tune CHRIST IST ERSTANDEN (Christ Is Arisen) commends its use in the season of Easter and/or Ascension.

3A: Note in the first measure that the D-natural in the melody is sung against the D-sharp in the chord. If a solo voice sings this line first, the congregation will easily pick up on this "blue" note. At each return of the refrain, singers and percussionists should crescendo into the word *"glory."* The chanted verses may be accompanied simply by soft arpeggiated chords played on keyboard or guitar with improvised percussion played on djembe and shakers. The text should move ahead in a natural way, without dragging. A cantor or an ensemble may sing these verses with the congregation joining on the refrain. With leadership, the entire congregation should be able to sing the chant.

3B: This song, a setting of v. 3, may be used as a frame or as a refrain for the reading of the entire psalm. One possibility would be to sing the first half of the song before v. 1 after v. 4 and then to sing it in its entirety (with the *"hallelujahs"*) after v. 8. Keyboard or guitar should vamp softly under the reading.

4A: The tune BROTHER JAMES' AIR is often associated with Ps. 23. Consider singing Pss. 4 and 23 together with this tune (see 23C), noting both the stark contrasts and common themes, especially in the last stanza of each setting.

4B: The alternate refrain is a song from Malawi. It should be sung gently, ideally without accompaniment. It is particularly suitable for evening services. When using this song alone, additional stanzas may be improvised. *(Darkness now has come . . . See your children, Lord . . . We are with you, Lord . . . Soon we go to rest . . .)*

5B: This refrain comes from a larger composition by Luke Hyder titled "Psalm 5."

6B: The second refrain, "Healer of Our Every Ill," comes from a larger composition by Marty Haugen. The full composition is published in several hymnals (see www.hymnary.org) and is available from GIA Publications.

6C: Psalm 6 is appropriate not only when the gathered community faces pain and anguish, but also as way of praying in solidarity with others. To emphasize this latter use, consider singing the entirety of Ps. 6, as found on p. 31, or reading or chanting the entire psalm and then continuing in prayer using the refrains and texts on this page.

8C: Richard Smallwood's chorus makes use of the beloved language of the King James Version of the Bible. The rich language of this version still resonates in many communities. The chorus may be used to frame the reading of the psalm, or it may be used as a refrain within the reading.

8E: In some traditions Ps. 8 is sung on January 1, the Feast of the Holy Name of Jesus, commemorating the presentation of the infant in the temple (see Luke 2:21). The refrain is derived from an anthem for cantor, choir, and congregation by Alfred V. Fedak titled "Psalm 8" (GIA Publications, G-4511).

8F: This chorus comes from a larger work by Brenda Joyce Moore titled "Perfect Praise." A full arrangement by Nolan Williams can be found in the *African American Heritage Hymnal* (GIA Publications). It is best led by a choir with congregation joining on the melody. It may be used to frame the reading of the psalm.

9A: The refrain, commonly referred to as *Kyrie Guarany*, comes from an indigenous people on the east coast of South America. The plaintive song arises from their particular experience of oppression and suffering. It reflects both the frustration and hope of the psalmist. A second stanza may be added that would allow the song to be used as a traditional Kyrie: *"On the poor, on the poor, show your mercy, O Christ"/"Oré mboriajú verekó Jesucristo."* The chanting tone is very simple. An ensemble or congregation can easily sing the psalm in improvised harmony.

9C: Psalms 9 and 10 taken together form an acrostic poem. These paraphrases by Ruth Duck maintain the connection between these two psalms. They may be taken separately or sung consecutively.

10A: The tune JESU DULCIS MEMORIA, which for some evokes associations with Jesus' life and passion, is an unusual choice for a psalm about looming trouble. Nevertheless, it allows for a hushed, contemplative approach to this poignant text, and its associations remind us that healing and resolution to trouble come through Jesus. Instead of the accompaniment provided, the plainsong melody may be accompanied by a sustained hum on the pitches C and G.

12A: Both the text and tune can suggest quite different moods. The leader should set a clear context for singing with indignation, defiance, or weariness. When taking the latter approach, consider the alternate accompaniment at 137A.

13B: Consider adding an instrumental interlude between sts. 3 and 4. The tune MARTYRDOM, often associated with the hymn "Alas, and Did My Savior Bleed," helps to make a connection to Good Friday and Christ's suffering.

13E: When reading the psalm, consider singing the first stanza of the Taizé refrain several times before the reading, singing softly or humming under the reading of vv. 1-4. After reading v. 4, move to st. 2 of the refrain, singing several times before the final reading, again undergirding the reading with soft singing or humming. The singing of st. 2 may continue for some time after the reading concludes. When chanting the psalm, allow some silence or repeated singing of the Taizé refrain between vv. 4 and 5.

14A: The tune is based on the Advent plainchant RORATE CAELI ("Drop Down, Ye Heavens, from Above"). Though set here in rhythm (2+3), this should not be interpreted with rigidity. The stanzas may be sung by a solo voice or an ensemble with the congregation joining on the refrain. With leadership, the entire congregation should be able to sing the stanzas.

14B: The choice of refrain will reflect a particular appropriation of the psalm. The refrain provided here resists the inclination to hear the psalm as a reference to other people, owning up to the fact that all of us struggle with tendencies to deny God. The refrain of 14A is a cry for help and deliverance on behalf of oppressed people.

14C: This litany of confession should follow either the reading or singing of Ps. 14. In the passages quoted in the assurance of pardon, the apostle Paul quotes from both Pss. 14 and 32 in order to teach concerning justification and redemption in Christ Jesus. The hymn stanza provided may be sung either to the tune BEACH SPRING or NETTLETON. Alternately, the entire hymn "Come, Thou Fount of Every Blessing" or another hymn of praise may be sung as a response to the assurance of pardon.

15B: The refrain may be sung in harmony. The stanzas are sung in unison and may be sung by a solo voice or an ensemble with all joining on the refrain.

15C: The spiritual "I'm Gonna Live So God Can Use Me" is an affirmative response of commitment. Additional stanzas (*I'm gonna speak . . . I'm gonna share . . . I'm gonna pray . . . I'm gonna sing . . .*) may be improvised throughout the chanting or speaking of the psalm or as a conclusion. Selection 15B, "Lord, Who Shall Be Welcome," provides an alternate refrain that is less affirmative and more introspective.

15D: The use of the tune CRIMOND may help to create a link to Ps. 23 (see 23B). When used with the prayer from 15E, the psalm functions as a call to repentance.

15E: This prayer of confession may also function as an entrance prayer at the beginning of worship. Begin with singing or speaking Ps. 15. Conclude with singing the stanza provided from Ps. 23 to the tune CRIMOND (p. 74), or sing Ps. 23 in its entirety or another psalm or hymn of trust.

16B: The refrain may be sung in harmony. The stanzas are sung by all in unison or by a solo voice or an ensemble with all joining on the refrain.

17C: This setting lifts up Ps. 17:1, 8, and 15, the traditional verses recited in the service of night prayer. It is appropriate to sing and meditate on these verses at times when we must put our trust in God. In fact, each night when we go to sleep we place our lives in God's care, confident that we will awaken in God's presence, whether in this world or another. These three stanzas may be sung in conjunction with a full reading of the psalm. Sing st. 1; read Ps. 17:1-7; sing st. 2; read Ps. 17:8-15; sing st. 3.

18B: These two stanzas may be used as a frame for the reading of the psalm or a portion of the psalm.

19A, 19B, 19F: These metrical settings reflect the profound significance of the structure of Ps. 19: a testimony to both the beauty of creation (part 1) and the beauty of God's law (part 2), leading to a reflective expression of desire to serve God faithfully (part 3).

19B: See above note for 19A, 19B, and 19F.

19C: The alternate refrain, "Lord, You Have the Words," comes from a larger composition by Ann Celeen Dohms. The full composition is published in *Sing Out! A Children's Psalter* (World Library Publications).

19F: See above note for 19A, 19B, and 19F.

20A: Although notated as 6/8, the rhythm here is a combination of 6/8 and 3/4. With the exception of one measure, the accompaniment needs to keep a consistent 3/4 feel throughout. The melody is primarily in 6/8 but playfully slips into 3/4 here and there. (The beaming of the eighth notes marks these shifts.) It would be helpful to the singers to have some percussion instrument, such as a woodblock, keep the 3/4 pulse, with other percussion instruments, such as shakers or triangle, marking the 6/8 rhythm.

20B: The first refrain allows for a prayer for God's blessing or a blessing on an individual or on one another in the Lord's name. The latter would be particularly appropriate at a service of baptism, ordination, or any time when members of congregation profess their faith publicly. The traditional Byzantine chant tone allows for both the refrain and the psalm to be sung in harmony. The alternate refrain is an Afro-American Spiritual that invites the entire congregation to profess with the psalmist their trust in the Lord. Additional stanzas may be improvised. (*I will stay on bended knee . . . till I die; I will stay on the battlefield . . . till I die; I will treat everybody right . . . till I die; Sister/Brother/People, will you trust in the Lord . . . till you die?*)

22A: The paraphrase here offers a compelling interpretation of the psalm in the voice of Christ, making it ideal for use on Good Friday.

22B: This musical setting helps us experience the profound shift in the middle of the psalm: a turn from lament to praise, from scorn to wonder. Musically, we move from unison singing in the minor mode to four-part harmony in the major mode. Between sts. 4 and 5 the keyboard or guitar should play through the new harmony of the second page. This interlude will not only establish the new major mode but also allow for some space between these two contrasting sections of the psalm. This setting may be followed by a setting of Ps. 23. (Close key relationships make 23A, 23D, or 23H ideal). Some biblical scholars suggest that Pss. 22 and 23 have been placed together intentionally, with the lament and praise of Ps. 22 leading toward the expression of trust in Ps. 23.

22C: The opening words of each stanza of the hymn "What Wondrous Love Is This" help to guide us through the shifts in the psalm. To introduce the psalm, a soloist, ensemble, or the entire congregation can hum the opening phrases of the song, preferably unaccompanied. The congregation may also hum a low D under the reading. Random handbell ringing can also enliven the reading. Play only low D's through the first half. At v. 22, gradually begin adding upper bells (D's, A's, even some high E's and B's). Crescendo through the singing of the final refrain, taking care that the readers' voices are still clearly heard.

22D: The first refrain is especially appropriate when focusing on the first half of the psalm, particularly in conjunction with Christ's passion. It comes from a larger composition by Val Parker titled "My God, My God, Why Have You Abandoned Me." The full composition can be found in *Psalms from the Soul, Vol. 2* (Oregon Catholic Press). The alternate refrain is appropriate when focusing on the second part of the psalm. See 88A and 88B for other refrains appropriate for lament and Good Friday uses of vv. 1-21. See 150B and 150G for other refrains appropriate for praise or Easter uses of vv. 22-31.

22F: This song can start at a slow tempo and gradually increase through the singing of the stanzas. Add the descant after the first stanza. The song works well with tambourine and a simple grapevine step for a ring dance.

23H: The stanzas may be sung by a solo voice or an ensemble, with the congregation joining in singing the refrain. The refrain may also be taken separately to frame the reading of the psalm. See p. 137 for a two-part setting of the refrain.

24C: Sing at a brisk tempo so that the eighth notes *snap* on the downbeats. The antiphonal singing of the opening chorus can heighten the sense of joy. The composer recommends men for group 1 and women for group 2, but any combination of singers for the groups will work.

24E: Add drums, tambourine, and other percussion instruments. Increase the tempo at each return of the refrain. To extend the psalm, the refrain may be sung after each stanza. The assembly may be invited to join in a ring dance around the perimeter of the assembly, using a simple grapevine step. When dancing, it may be helpful to have a solo voice sing the stanzas, with the dancers joining in singing the refrain.

25A: The refrain "To You, O Lord" comes from a larger composition by Marty Haugen. The full composition is published in several hymnals (see www.hymnary.org) and is available from GIA Publications.

25D: A setting of this psalm composed by Eelco Vos for leadership by a contemporary worship band is available from *The Psalm Project* (see www.thepsalmproject.com).

27A: Each of the two themes can be sung separately, either in unison or as a round. The two themes can also be sung together, preferably with theme A for treble voices and theme B for lower voices.

27B: This setting of Ps. 27 by Lillian Bouknight should be accompanied by keyboard in a gospel style. When singing the refrain the last time, stretch each note of "*Whom shall I fear.*" Bring it back into tempo for "*The Lord is the strength,*" repeating this several times before concluding the refrain with a generous ritard.

27C: Since its appearance in the *Psalter*, 1912, to the tune ARTHUR'S SEAT, this versification has often been sung in a confident, even triumphalistic tone of voice. The coupling with the tune RHOSYMEDRE allows for a more nuanced rendering of the different emotions of this text. St. 1 can be sung with a sense of quiet trust. Sing st. 2 in harmony with a sense of earnestness. St. 3 might begin with a sense of anxiety, accompanying the opening phrases with D-minor and G-minor chords. This stanza grows in confidence and intensity, leading to a joyful, harmonious, and resounding singing of the final stanza.

27E: Selected verses of the psalm may be spoken during the vocal vamp. The vamp is particularly suitable for children and beginning musicians. Orff instruments, bells, or chimes may double the ostinato patterns. The bass line may be played by open strings on a cello.

27F: With vocal leadership, the accompaniment need not double the melody line of the refrain. The strong pulse of the accompaniment allows for a natural syncopation in the melody line. The timing of the accompaniment with the spoken verses is approximate. Instrumentalists and readers should work this out, adjusting as necessary.

27H: The first refrain, "The Lord Is My Light," comes from a larger composition by David Haas. The full composition is published in several hymnals (see *www.hymnary.org*) and is available from GIA Publications. The alternate refrain comes from the Orthodox tradition. Sing unaccompanied with forward motion, doubling the harmony parts in the bass and tenor range. The psalm verses may also be chanted in harmony by an ensemble or even by the entire congregation. Take care that the singing does not drag.

27 I : These two simple stanzas may form a frame around an intercessory prayer.

27 J : The Czech tune comes from the post-Reformation 17th-Century. Accompany with strong, sustained organ or piano, but consider unaccompanied singing for at least one inner stanza.

28A: Consider using st. 1 as a call to prayer and st. 3 as a conclusion to prayer.

28B: This combination of Pss. 1 and 28 highlights how Ps. 28 offers a faithful way of responding to the call of Ps. 1, much like the way in which a creed, acclamation, or prayer of dedication is a fitting response to a sermon.

28C: Consider using these two stanzas as a frame for prayer.

29A: Sing with increasing volume and intensity through the first half of stanza 2. At the text *"But the Word which sets in motion . . .,"* allow the singing and accompaniment to diminish until the final measure, ending in a gentle whisper.

29B: Maintain a strong sense of the 3+3+2 pulse in the accompaniment (guitar, keyboard, and/or percussion).

29D: When celebrating the power and majesty of God throughout this psalm, use the first refrain. When considering the voice of peace and blessing, use the alternate refrain. It is possible to use both refrains by singing the first refrain at the beginning, after v. 2, after v. 6, and after v. 9, and the alternate refrain before v. 10 and again after v. 11.

30A: Consider having st. 4 sung by a solo voice. An instrumental interlude before st. 5 will help people grasp the turn in the psalm.

30B: This refrain is taken from a bilingual choral anthem composed by John L. Bell (GIA Publications, G-5156).

30C: To heighten the sense of the dance, steadily increase the tempo throughout the singing of the psalm.

30D: While this song may appear intimidating, a well planned introduction will make it immediately accessible. Introduce the refrain with a solo voice or an ensemble. Have the congregation join in singing this several times, adding percussion instruments, until all is firmly established. The rhythm comes to a halt at the singing of the stanzas. Introduce each phrase with a rolled chord on the keyboard, and accompany with improvisation on shakers and cymbals. A solo voice could sing all of the stanzas, or the congregation may be invited to join beginning on st. 2. It is not necessary that the syllables move precisely together for the stanzas. At the final measure of the stanzas, the percussion should fall into place, establishing the pulsing rhythm of the refrain.

31B: This song comes from the collection *Sing for Joy: Psalm Settings for God's Children* (The Liturgical Press). It allows for improvisation and simple layering of textures. One group may sing an echo on the refrain by delaying their entrance by two beats, joining with the other singers on the last *"I trust in you."* The bell part for the refrain can also be played on chimes or Orff instruments. The verses are like a simple chant melody and may be accompanied by some voices singing the counter melody.

31C: When v. 5 is not part of the lection, the refrain should be sung after v. 4.

32C: Accompany with soft instruments or humming voices, sustaining the pitches E and B. The melody line may be doubled by a flute or stringed instrument, an organ stop, or down an octave by the cello. The singing should be flexible.

33A: When using the lection beginning at v. 12, the refrain after v. 12 should be omitted. The alternate refrain, "Happy the People," comes from a larger composition by James V. Marchionda. The full composition can be found in the collection *Sing Out! A Children's Psalter* (World Library Publications).

34A: The alternate refrain comes from a larger composition by Rawn Harbor titled "Psalm 34: Taste and See the Goodness of the Lord/I Will Bless the Lord." The full composition can be found in *Psalms from the Soul, Vol. 2* (Oregon Catholic Press).

34B: The stanzas may be sung by a solo voice or an ensemble, with all joining in the singing of the refrain, which may be sung in harmony. The bass rhythm in the bass of the stanzas should be carried into the refrain. Accompany in a gospel style, feeling in a slow 2.

34C: This anonymous folksong may be sung simply, in harmony, with light keyboard or plucked guitar accompaniment. Do not sing too fast.

35A: The closing prayer of the litany may continue with a specific prayer for a member of the community or other people who have been slandered. Or the prayer may be followed by a prayer of confession, acknowledging our own sin of slander and gossip. Conclude with the singing of a hymn of assurance, such as "What a Friend We Have in Jesus" or "O Lord, Hear Our Prayer" or a hymn of commitment, such as "O God, My Faithful God."

36A: When the lection ends at v. 10, sing refrain after v. 10. The refrain "How Precious Is Your Unfailing Love, O God," comes from a larger composition by David Lee.

36B: To perform the entire psalm, read Ps. 36:1-4; sing all 4 stanzas of the hymn; read Ps. 36:10-12; sing st. 1 of the hymn.

38A: Stanzas 3, 4, and/or 6 of this setting may be interlaced with readings of the gospel passion narratives or with the singing of Henry H. Milman's hymn "Ride On, Ride On in Majesty."

40A: The refrain "Here I Am" comes from a larger composition by Rory Cooney (Oregon Catholic Press).

40B: Approach this setting with a slower tempo. The tune can carry the profundity of the psalm, but because it is so well known there is a danger of it being sung superficially and too quickly. The triplets can help to keep the tempo in check, but they may be left out according to the context. To signal the change in character at st. 3, consider singing it in canon at the measure, moving into harmony for st. 4.

41B: This psalm may be spoken or chanted with a single refrain or with a series of phrases from the hymn "What a Friend We Have in Jesus." The final verse of doxology is a conclusion not only of this psalm, but, more significantly, also marks the end of Book 1 of the Psalter. The double amen should be the final word.

42B: This psalm setting is derived from a choral setting by Greg Scheer and can be found in the collection *GladSong Choirbook, Vol. 1* (Augsburg Fortress Press).

42C: There is nothing to add to this two-part masterpiece in miniature. If necessary, two flutes (preferably the Korean *taegum*, a long transverse flute) may double the parts. The unresolved dissonance in the final measure is intentional.

42E: The refrain built right into Pss. 42/43 may serve as a framing for the reading of the psalm verses. Any of the three sections of the psalm may be sung alone. When singing the entire psalm, alternate stanzas may be sung antiphonally by different groups, with all joining on the refrain. The refrain may be sung after the final stanza only.

42F: Observe that the final note of the melody and the chord of the accompaniment should not resolve. This is intentional, reflecting the questions that pervade this psalm.

42G: Do not sing too quickly. The echo of the refrain may be sung by an ensemble, perhaps softer and sounding far off, like the distant memory of the psalmist. Singing the refrain twice after both sts. 1 and 2 will allow for this haunting refrain to take root.

43A: This setting of Ps. 43:3 functions well as a sung prayer before the reading of Scripture.

43B: This setting may be sung with or without the bridge. When not using the bridge, the singing may conclude after the second singing of the refrain. When using the bridge, repeat as desired, building in intensity before returning to the refrain.

44A: These two stanzas form a frame for the reading of Ps. 44. St. 1 may be sung confidently. St. 2, particularly if sung after the reading of the psalm, should be sung softly, humbly. Lower voices can accompany the melody (sung in parallel fourths) by singing the drone (with a slight scoop and guttural attack), or they may double the treble parts an octave lower.

45B: When using this psalm in the context of the Annunciation (see Luke 1:26-38), or when celebrating the everlasting reign of God and the lordship of Christ, use the first refrain. When the psalm is used as a love poem or interpreted allegorically as marriage imagery between Christ and the Church, use the alternate refrain.

46A: Consider assigning stanzas to different groups. For example, all sing sts. 1-2; men sing st. 3; women sing st. 4; a soloist sings the first half of st. 5, with all joining in the singing of the final two lines, perhaps in a quieter, humbler voice.

46B: This lively song should be sung in the style of a modern *corrido,* with a strong bass rhythm on the beats and hand clapping or tambourines on the off-beats.

46D: When using the first refrain it is not necessary to read or chant vv. 7 and 11. Consider having the congregation hum an E throughout the reading or chanting of the psalm text. Alternate refrain 1 may be sung in canon. After the final verse it may be repeated several times. (When repeating, do not sing the last measure until the final time.) Alternate refrain 2 is particularly mindful of children.

46E: Those unfamiliar with four-part chant (commonly referred to as "Anglican chant") may find this setting a good entry point for the genre, particularly if they are familiar with the Lutheran chorale EIN FESTE BURG ("A Mighty Fortress Is Our God"). The harmonic movement is intuitive. It is important when singing four-part chant that the rhythm follow the pattern of speech and that it not drag.

47B: If adding hand claps on the off-beats, at each fourth measure add an extra clap on beat 3. During the interlude, clap on each beat (or even each eighth note) to heighten to the return to the refrain. St. 3 is overtly Christological in its interpretation, making the song particularly appropriate for festivals celebrating Christ's resurrection, ascension, and/or reign.

47D: Sing in a call and response manner. The folksong is best sung without keyboard or guitar. Accompany with percussion and hand claps.

47F: Clap on beats two and three of the refrain. The clapping pattern could continue under the reading of the text. The leader should take care to ensure that the refrain begins on beat one. (The temptation for the congregation will be to enter with the hand clap on beat 2.) Alternatively, an ensemble may prepare a clapping accompaniment for the reading or chanting of the psalm, or all may be invited to improvise their own clapping rhythms with a percussive crescendo leading into the singing of each refrain. The refrain comes from a larger composition by John Bell. The full composition is published in several hymnals (see *www.hymnary.org*) and is available from GIA Publications.

48A: This versification originally began with the words found in stanza 3, "*Within in your temple, Lord.*" This single stanza functions well as an introit or opening verse for the worship service. It could be sung by an ensemble and lead into the singing of a psalm or hymn of praise.

49B: The Asian melody carries well the text of this psalm. It should not be sung forcefully, but gently, as a wise bard sharing ancient proverbs. The melody line may be doubled by flute or violin. A second instrument could play in canon at the measure. The bass line should be played by a pitched percussion instrument or may be plucked on a cello or bass. The ostinato pattern may be varied rhythmically.

51A: As a prayer of confession, read together Ps. 51:1-10, sing this song, read Ps. 51:15-17, and sing this song again. Soft instrumental music under the reading will help to tie this prayer together.

51B: This 16th-Century psalm is often accompanied on the organ, but it could be performed in many different ways. It is very close to chant and could be sung unaccompanied and in unison with a rather free, plainchant feel. This would have been how it was originally conceived for singing in the church (hence the designation *a capella,* Latin for "as in church"). But outside the church these psalms were often accompanied by the lute, so accompanying with guitars today may also be recommended. One might select particular stanzas as a call or response to confession. If all the stanzas are sung, consider having different voices sing in alternation.

51C: The way this song is sung varies from community to community. Once the song is known, the leader may improvise other harmonies. It is customary for the stanzas to be sung by a solo voice. It is not necessary to sing the refrain between the two stanzas.

51G: Alternate refrain 1 is a single line from a longer Urdhu (Pakistani) song. The full song can be found in the collection *Sound the Bamboo* (Christian Conference of Asia, administered North America by GIA Publications). A solo voice should demonstrate for the congregation the slides and ornaments in the melody. When singing in Urdhu, close to a humming *m* on "*raeham.*" Likewise, alternate refrain 2 is drawn from a longer Xhosa (South African) song. The full song can be found in the collection *Freedom Is Coming* (Walton Music Corporation). A soft drum may accompany this plaintive cry for mercy. (If reading the psalm, the drum can continue playing under the reading between entrances of the refrain.) The letter *c* in "*nenceba*" is pronounced with a gentle smack by the tip of the tongue against the upper row of teeth.

51M: The verses may be sung by a solo voice or an ensemble, with all joining in singing the refrain. It can be quite satisfying for congregations to sing the chanted verses. Take care not to slow down when moving from the reciting tone (the long note with multiple syllables under it) to the cadence. The music leaders should make sure that the singing does not drag but progresses naturally, as in speech.

52A: Sing slowly and softly. Sts. 1-2 in particular should be sung with a sense of weariness or exhaustion. It would also be effective to use st. 3 alone as a frame for the reading of the psalm. Or sts. 1-2 could be spoken, concluding with the singing of st. 3.

53A: The stanzas may be sung by a solo voice. When all sing the refrain (*"All have sinned . . ."*), it is a reminder that we also are indicted by the psalmist's words. (See Rom. 3:10. See also p. 69.)

55A: These two stanzas are drawn primarily from the opening and closing verses of the psalm. As such, they form a suitable frame for the reading of the psalm. The tune RESTING PLACE is associated with the hymn "I Heard the Voice of Jesus Say," a text that resonates well with the psalm. If the hymn is familiar to the congregation, consider having a soloist or choir sing the psalm stanzas to whatever tune the congregation associates with the hymn, with some or all of the psalm read between the stanzas. This can be followed by the reading of some words of Jesus, such as Matt. 11:28-30. The congregation can then respond by singing the assuring words of the hymn "I Heard the Voice of Jesus Say."

55B: This serene chorale from Mendelssohn's oratorio *Elijah*, though scored for choir, is easily managed by the congregation and appropriate as a call or conclusion to prayer. The text draws from Ps. 55:22, as well as Ps. 16:8.

56A: Typically refrains are rousing and climactic. This refrain is different. It may be sung in a subdued voice. A solo voice might sing the stanzas; sts. 1 and 3 in particular may be sung stridently. If possible, the refrain should be sung in harmony.

56B: Though the outlay of this song may look intimidating on the page, after a quick review one discovers that it is quite simple. Here is the sequence: introduction (same as interlude)/st. 1/interlude/st. 2/interlude/ refrain/interlude/st. 3/interlude/refrain with repeated last line. (The refrain can be repeated an additional time, with a generous ritard.)

57B: This vocal framing and accompaniment for psalm reading comes from a children's Psalter, but the entire congregation should enjoy its simple form. Allow the sung ostinato (vocal vamp under the spoken verses) to be sung several times before beginning the reading. Be sure that the verses are read at a relaxed pace. Use enough amplification so that the reader can speak with a natural tone and still be heard by the singing congregation.

60A: Each stanza may function as a refrain for the individual psalm. The stanzas may also be sung together, each culminating in the singing of the refrain, which is drawn from Ps. 61. The refrain may also be a conclusion to the setting, sung only after the final stanza.

60B: The imprecatory stanzas by James Hart Brumm are not intended to represent any particular psalm; rather, they reflect the tone of Pss. 58-60 (and many others like them), with honest expressions of hurt, anger, bitterness, and desires for vengeance. The strident nature of the stanzas is matched by the tonal dissonance of the musical setting. This dissonance is most pronounced in the accompaniment, allowing the melody to be straightforward and accessible for congregational singing. However, care should be taken when choosing to sing this setting. Congregations are not accustomed to singing stinging words like this, and without intentional preparation they may be bewildered or resentful. The first half of each stanza presents the most biting text and should be sung with vehemence. The second half takes a step back; it is more pleading. If the congregation cannot sing the first half of the stanza with integrity, a representative solo voice may sing this on behalf of the congregation or particular people who need to cry out to God in this way. The congregation can then join in singing the petitions in the second half of each stanza.

61A: This verification may conclude well at st. 5. When singing all stanzas, consider alternating the singing among different groups. For example, st. 1, solo voice; st. 2, all; st. 3, women; st. 4, men; st. 5, women; st. 6, men; st. 7, all.

62A: Each stanza builds in strength to the refrain. Accompany with jazzy piano, bass, and drum set. Take care in the refrain not to hold out the singing on *"rock," "strength,"* and *"not."* Land firmly on these words and then get out of the way, allowing the piano accompaniment to fill in the gap.

62B: Typically 5/4 time signatures signal driving rhythms of 3+2. Here it does something quite different. Think of these stanzas as being in a very relaxed, common time rhythm, with a built-in repose at the end of each measure—an extra beat to catch one's breath before moving on.

62C: When led well, the tune THIRD MODE MELODY captures the sentiment of this text perfectly. Perhaps the best way to introduce this melody to a group of singers is to have them listen to the stirring orchestral setting of the tune by Ralph Vaughan Williams (*Fantasia on a Theme* by Thomas Tallis). It would be good to have a solo voice sing st.1, with all joining at st. 2, which textually is a sort of reboot of the psalm. A good alternate tune is RESIGNATION. In either case, give care that the singing does not drag. It should be gentle but buoyant.

63A: The vamp may be played during the speaking of the psalm. From the refrain proceed directly to the vamp or chant tone, using the final ending only at the last singing of the refrain. The vamp may be shortened or lengthened as necessary.

64B: This setting combines elements of jazz with plainsong chant. The tone for the chanted text has four cadences. Roll the chord before the singing of each phrase. The keyboard punctuates the phrases of the chant with a couple of beats of interlude. The soloist singing the stanzas may improvise the chanted text within the chord structure provided in the tone. The three eighth notes leading out of the tone accompaniment (played by keyboard and/or bass) are all that is needed to reestablish the rhythm of the refrain.

65E: The association of ST. GEORGE'S WINDSOR with the hymn "Come, Ye Thankful People" creates natural associations with thanksgiving, particularly at the time of harvest.

66A: The stanzas may be sung by a solo voice, with all joining in singing the refrain. For trumpet descant see *Psalms of the Notre Dame Folk Choir* (World Library Publications).

66B: This song functions well as a processional or an entrance into worship. Once it is known by a community, it is not necessary to sing from the page. A leader can sing out the text for the next stanza while the congregation sings the final syllable (e.g., singing *"Come praise the Savior!"*). Accompany with djembes, shakers, triangle, cowbell, hand claps—anything that will enliven the singing without overwhelming it. When used as a frame for the psalm, keep a soft drum pattern going under the reading.

67C: The refrain is derived from an anthem for cantor, choir, and congregation by John McCann titled "Let the People Praise You" (GIA Publications, G-4696).

68A: The grand procession of God presented in Ps. 68 should be evident in the way this instance is enacted in worship. For example, the leader parts of the reading may be read by different voices, beginning at the back of the sanctuary. At each singing of the refrain, the readers move forward so that by the end of the reading they are at the front of the sanctuary. At this point the congregation may sing in response "Approach Our God with Songs of Praise." A short instrumental interlude between the responsive reading and the singing of the metrical psalm will help to bridge the two pieces together. The triumphant refrain makes this especially appropriate for Easter or Ascension celebrations, and in conjunction with sermons dealing with the Second Advent.

68C: The indications for singing sts. 2-9 antiphonally are merely suggestions. The division of the stanzas for responsive or antiphonal singing can be done in any number of ways (e.g., solo voice, choir, or different sections of the congregation). The stanzas are short and sing quickly. The fact that there are 10 stanzas should not be an impediment for singing the selection in its entirety.

70A: Do not sing too quickly. The last stanza may be sung quietly.

70B: The refrain "God, Make Speed to Save Me" comes from a larger composition by David Lee.

71C: The alternate refrain is particularly appropriate during Holy Week, when we "turn our eyes" to Christ and his suffering, or for any time when we pray to Christ in our own suffering.

72C: Use the first refrain, "In His Days," for Advent. Use the alternate refrain, "Lord, Every Nation," for Epiphany. For the alternate refrain, a solo voice may sing the first half of the refrain each time. The first refrain comes from a larger composition by Michael Joncas. The full composition is published in several hymnals (see *www.hymnary.org*) and is available from GIA Publications. The alternate refrain comes from a larger composition by Val Parker. The full composition can be found in *Psalms from the Soul, Vol. 1* (Oregon Catholic Press).

73A: Ken Medema's song captures well the twists and turns in the psalm. The opening stanzas should be sung with a touch of resentment and frustration. The second page corresponds to the turn in the psalm. Although it is through-composed, it is created by a string of rising motifs. It is intuitive and could be sung by the congregation, or it may be sung by a solo voice. The pseudo-chorale (beginning with the text *"You draw me near to you . . ."*) is a response that should be sung by all. If necessary, it could be sung first by a solo voice and repeated by the congregation. On the last page (beginning with the text *"Now my song . . ."*) we have come full circle with a return to the folk song that has been transformed into a song of trust. It should be experienced differently from the opening stanzas. Sing with joy, but more quietly and slowly.

73B: When using the optional text as a lead-in to the singing of "In Sweet Communion," consider having a keyboard player improvise under the reading. Toward the end of the reading, begin the introduction of the melody, creating a seamless transition between the reading and the congregational singing.

73C: Andrew Donaldson's setting uses rhythmic speech (in a quasi hip-hop style) with evolving vamps and refrains to capture the transformation within the psalm. Though it requires some preparation on the part of the reader and lead musicians, it is completely accessible to the congregation, which simply repeats the refrains at each occurrence. The vamp musician and reader will need to rehearse the timing of the spoken portions. The reader casts the text into rhythmic units that correspond to the vamp patterns. The red [|] markings serve to make these clear. Note that sometimes the reader is silent at the second half of the vamp pattern. There is no need to rush the transition between the refrains and the spoken portions. The musician can reestablish the vamp with a riff or two before the speaker begins. Note that although the tempo does not change, the second refrain feels twice as slow because of the notation (shifting to quarter and eighth notes). At the end, all should speak *"God is good . . . it's true . . ."* in hushed tones. This should not be done in unison speech but with random entrances. A few "plants" in the congregation can help get this going.

74A: The combination of this quintessential Advent hymn and Ps. 74 can transform our understanding of both the psalm and the hymn. The psalm offers jolting imagery of what we often glibly sing in the hymn: *"mourning in exile," "depths of hell,"* and *"shadows of night."* The hymn helps us to imagine the pathos with which the psalmist's community longed for the coming of the Messiah. It also opens us up to the pain that persecuted Christian communities feel today as they desperately cry out for liberation. The congregation or an ensemble can softly hum a drone on the pitches E and B under the reading. The scripture can also be chanted on an unadorned E tone.

75A: It is dangerous to sing a psalm calling for God to judge the powerful or to pour a draught of bitter wine down the throats of the proud when the singers themselves may in fact be the powerful and the proud. Rather than representing the psalm as a call for judgment on others, this versification imagines that we may be the ones in danger of being judged as insolent. The psalm could first be read, after which the worship leader might ask, "Is it possible that some may be able to pray this psalm against us? Have we lifted ourselves up?" After a moment of silence for contemplation, the congregation can sing this song with humility and contrition.

75B: The themes of this psalm are echoed in Mary's song (the Magnificat), which is freely paraphrased in Cooney's "Canticle of the Turning." The canticle may be sung at the conclusion of the reading. In anticipation of the congregation's singing, a soloist could sing just the refrain at the beginning of the reading and after vv. 3, 5, and 8. Accompany the canticle with raucous keyboard accompaniment and djembe.

77A: There is a significant transformation between sts. 2 and 3. It would serve the psalm well to have some silence or an instrumental interlude between these stanzas. A solo voice or ensemble could sing the first two stanzas. A setting of this psalm composed by Eelco Vos for leadership by a contemporary worship band is available from *The Psalm Project* (see *www.thepsalmproject.com*).

77B: This song could effectively be sung in a blues style, with a soloist on the stanzas and all singing the refrain.

78A: Different sections of the congregation may alternate in the singing of the lead and the echo. Or a solo voice can sing the lead with all responding with the echo. This setting is distilled from a larger composition by Greg Scheer.

78D: When only chanting the lectionary portion for vv. 23-29, the alternate refrain of 81A, "You Satisfy the Hungry Heart" (p. 498) may be used.

79A: The same refrain text may be sung throughout the chanting or reading of the psalm, or various stanzas may be improvised (*Someone's praying . . . Someone's singing . . .*).

79B: Option for use with psalm reading: read Ps. 79:1-7; sing st. 1; read Ps. 79:8-10; sing st. 2; read Ps. 79:11-13; sing st. 3.

80A: The refrain "Restore Us Again" comes from a larger composition by David Lee.

80C: The association of the tune ST. LOUIS with the hymn "O Little Town of Bethlehem" has connections that may be used to good effect. (*Bethlehem* in Hebrew means "house of bread.") It would be effective to sing this setting during Advent, though it may be sung in any season.

81B: A reader may read selected psalm verses while the congregation or choir softly sings the ostinato *"Hear my voice."* For example: refrain; read Ps. 81:6-7; refrain; Ps. 81:8-10; refrain; read Ps. 81:13-16; refrain.

82B: The first refrain comes from a larger composition by John Foley titled "Psalm 34: The Cry of the Poor." The full composition is published in several hymnals (see *www.hymnary.org*) and is available from GIA Publications.

83A: John Bell commends this setting as a community lament—a protest song in which the people of God ask that those who are not merely political enemies but the enemies of heaven might be put down. The stanzas could be sung by a solo voice, but since this is a community lament, they should be sung by several people (e.g., men and women alternating). For the stanzas, the pulse is maintained and the text is chanted within these half-note pulses. The dissonance at the last chord of the verses is intentional.

84A: Selections 84A and 84B cover different sections of Ps. 84. While 84A ends at v. 7 of the psalm, 84B creates a refrain out of v. 10. Though the styles are different, it can be effective to follow the singing of 84A with the reading of Ps. 84:8-12, concluding with the singing of 84B.

84B: The final refrain on p. 513 may be sung several times and may also be layered with the singing of the original refrain on p. 511.

84D: Ps. 84 is usually associated with introspective and quiet strength. The association of the tune SINE NOMINE with the text "For All the Saints" suggests a different interpretation. In lofty tones we imagine the heavenly dwelling of God, our final home. This setting would be particularly appropriate at funerals or other celebrations of our hope of eternal life with God.

84E: The tune BROTHER JAMES' AIR is often associated with Ps. 23. There is a strong resonance between Pss. 23 and 84. One could conclude the singing of 84E with the final stanza of 23C.

85B: The congregation may repeat the ostinato refrain for some time before the solo voice begins singing the verses. It is intended that the singing of the ostinato refrain continues as the soloist sings the stanzas. The congregation may sing the ostinato alone a few times between stanzas.

86B: The piano accompaniment for this refrain is challenging. To simplify, one may play only the root of the chords in the left hand. This setting by Val Parker comes from a larger composition titled "Psalm 91: Be with Me, Lord." The full composition can be found in *Psalms from the Soul, Vol. 2* (Oregon Catholic Press).

87D: The tune associations for "Glorious Things of Thee Are Spoken" have long been a source of controversy. For some the association with AUSTRIAN HYMN is sacrosanct. For others, for whom that tune is too closely tied to German nationalism, particularly with the Third Reich, the singing of AUSTRIAN HYMN in worship is understandably problematic. Depending on context, congregations may choose this setting or the setting at 87E, set to the tune JEFFERSON, or may choose from any number of 8.7.8.7 D tunes. The setting at 87D reflects the original text by John Newton, with slight adaptation. The setting at 87E is an updated version of Newton's original. The texts are interchangeable.

87E: This Appalachian melody should be sung with a driving rhythm. It can be accompanied equally well by organ or piano, modern praise band, traditional blue grass band, or simply with hand percussion. See also note at 87D.

87F: This song may be used as a refrain with the reading of Ps. 87. Sing at the beginning and after vv. 3, 5, and 7.

88A: The ostinato refrain may be sung softly or hummed while a leader reads portions of the psalm. (Portions of the psalm as paraphrased in *The Message* are provided on p. 538.) This may conclude with the prayer on p. 538.

88B: The stanzas of this spiritual may be used as a framing of the psalm or as a refrain for portions of the psalm. The reading of the psalm may be accompanied by a solo voice, ensemble, or congregation humming the melody.

89C: This way of presenting Ps. 89 invites the congregation to experience the psalm as a memorial to the experience of Israel. It acknowledges the despair voiced in the second half of the psalm but also testifies to the ultimate redemption of God's people that comes through Christ.

89D: Although it begins as a hymn of confident praise, this psalm deteriorates into despair before ending with a doxological declaration of trust and praise. (The doxology also signals the conclusion of Book 3 of the Psalter as a whole.) The down side of the psalm is acknowledged in st. 3. It would be good to set off this stanza by having it sung by a solo voice or choir, with all rejoining on the final stanza. Note the melodic "swing" at the end of the melody. This syncopation gives the final phrase a playful lift, but it can come as a surprise to the uninitiated. This setting can be used in conjunction with the litany at 89C.

91A: Notice the shift in voices from first person in st. 1 ("*I trust*"), to an address of one another in sts. 2-4, to the voice of the Lord addressing the community in st. 5. This final stanza could be sung by a soloist or an ensemble in order to mark it as a distinct voice. The singing could end here, or the congregation could return to singing st. 1 as a concluding affirmation of trust.

91D: The first refrain comes from a larger composition by Val Parker titled "Psalm 91: Be with Me, Lord." The full composition can be found in *Psalms from the Soul, Vol. 2* (Oregon Catholic Press).

92B: This song may be sung by the congregation as a two-part canon. It is also effective to have the congregation sing only part 2 ("*Hallelujah*"), divided evenly between lead and echo, with a soloist or ensemble singing the text of part 1. This simple chant forms a wonderful meditative prayer that can frame the reading of this psalm or any Scripture reading.

92C: For an extension of the last singing of the refrain, instead of resolving to the tonic (F major) on the word "*Lord*," go to D minor, pass through B-flat major, and sing the final line one or two additional times.

94A: This song should be sung plaintively and is best accompanied by guitar. The setting is patterned after songs sung by Christians in Nicaragua and El Salvador, protesting the political and economic abuse of the poor. It may be sung in solidarity with those who continue to suffer such oppression.

95C: The singing of this four-part chant is surprisingly easy. For congregations unfamiliar with this style of singing, have the choir lead the singing with the support of the organ. Move according to the natural rhythm of speech, taking care not to let the pace drag.

95E: The first refrain comes from a larger composition by Susan Sayers and Andrew Moore titled "O That Today You Would Listen to His Voice" (Kevin Mayhew Ltd).

95F: Melodies from India can sometimes seem intimidating. For hesistant congregations, consider singing this responsively: solo voice sings first two phrases; all repeat; solo voice sings the next two phrases; and all sing the refrain (same music as the opening). This allows the congregation to learn by listening to the leader. The leader should sing with a lilting voice. Think of the ornaments as imitating the bending of the tone on a stringed instrument, such as the *veena*. A drone on the pitches A and E can be played on instruments or soft organ stops or can be hummed. The melody could be doubled by a flute or flute stop on the organ.

96A: When using the ostinato accompaniment, all should sing in unison. The ostinato pattern does not stop at the fermata. The singing of subsequent stanzas falls into place with the beginning of the next two-measure ostinato pattern.

96D: Sing buoyantly, with a little break after the first two syllables of each stanza. Take note of the rhythmic augmentation in the penultimate measure.

96E: Percussion is essential for this song. Every beat is equally strong, and the interlocking patterns of hand clapping, with or without the xylophone ostinato, establishes a platform for the singers. This clapping pattern is not meant for everyone. Have a rehearsed ensemble of hand clappers positioned with the music leadership. This song may be sung by a solo voice or an ensemble, with all coming in on the refrain "*ay, ay, salidummay.*"

96F: This setting to the chorale melody ES IST EIN' ROS' ENTSPRUNGEN ("Lo How a Rose E'er Blooming") solidifies its association with Christmas. It also allows a psalm that is otherwise assumed to be loud and boisterous to be rendered in a more contemplative, ethereal, peace-filled way.

96G: The melody and text of this setting are bold and brash. St. 1 can be seen as a call to sing. Particularly when this surprising text and melody are new to a congregation, the first stanza is best sung by a solo voice or an ensemble, with the entire congregation responding in singing sts. 2 and 3. The stanzas are dense with text and imagery. Take care that they are not sung too quickly.

96H: The singing of the chanted verses, in unison or harmony, is not difficult. If invited to join in singing on the even verses, most will pick it up rather intuitively. Move according to the natural rhythm of speech, taking care not to let the pace drag.

97A: The association of the tune NOËL NOUVELET with both Christmas ("Sing We Now of Christmas") and Easter ("Now the Green Blade Rises") might aid congregations to pick up on the connections of this psalm with these particularly festive seasons.

98A: This arrangement of Greg Scheer's "Sing to the Lord a New Song" is distilled from a larger composition.

98B: The first refrain comes from a larger composition by Timothy Dudley Smith and David G. Wilson. The full composition is published in several hymnals (see *www.hymnary.org*) and is available from Hope Publishing Company.

98C: A setting of this psalm composed by Eelco Vos for leadership by a contemporary worship band is available from *The Psalm Project* (see *www.thepsalmproject.com*).

100A: Although this tune from the Genevan Psalter is probably the most sung church melody throughout the world, it was in fact not composed for Ps. 100 but rather for Ps. 134. (See 100C for the original tune for Ps. 100 from the *Genevan Psalter*.) The 16th-Century text by William Kethe (with modern spelling) is perhaps the oldest English psalm versification that continues to be sung today. For an updated version of Kethe's text, see 100B.

100B: This song should be led in a slow, traditional gospel style. The triplet patterns must not feel rushed.

100D: Singers should elegantly glide into the notes preceded by grace notes. Ideally unaccompanied, it also works well to double the melody with a flute (or flute stop on the organ). For the finger cymbals or finger bells, (o) denotes an open, striking (ringing *ching* sound), while (+) denotes a stopped, striking (closed *chap* sound), in which the cymbals or bells are closed on one another.

100E: This song is based on a traditional Taiwanese tribal dance. The dance is similar to the grapevine step but slower. On each stronger beat (when the moving foot passes in front of the other foot) the dancers bow forward. On each weaker beat (when the moving foot passes behind the other foot) the dancers look up and lean back slightly. This makes for a jubilant processional or entrance into worship and can lead directly into a psalm or hymn of praise.

100F: The composer has provided many possible musical layers for this refrain. At each return of the refrain something new might be added. When the psalm text is read the Orff instruments (or xylophones) could continue as accompaniment for the reading. At the final singing of the refrain have all sing in 2-, 3- or 4-part canon, working through the music several times.

100G: In Latin the word *jubilate* is pronounced "yoo-bih-lah-teh."

101A: Instead of using the sung refrain, this reading may be framed by the singing of "O God, My Faithful God" (35A). For example: sing sts. 1-2; responsive reading; sing sts. 3-4.

102B: Although there is no lack of prayer for the dying in our worship, rarely do we find prayers of the dying as part of our liturgies. The litany can be used in either congregational or pastoral care settings. In a congregational setting a member of the congregation would be asked to speak voice 2 on behalf of the sufferer. The litany offers the opportunity for the dying person to be present as voice 2, as congregation members symbolically take their place at the bedside and enter into the prayers in a direct and personal way. Subsequently, the pastor and elders could bring the litany to the bedside of the sufferer. Voice 1 would be read by an elder, pastor, or other representative of the church. Voice 2 might be prayed by the sufferer or, when that is not possible, could be spoken by a family representative, preferably while making some kind of physical contact with the sufferer. There is a part of the psalm that relates to circumstances of an untimely serious illness. If this is the case, include the shaded portion of the litany. A litany such as this has the capacity to frame the setting of a deathbed and to respect its significance. By bringing in the soaring and searing language of the psalms, we avoid being banal in a situation that cries out for depth of meaning.

103B: See note for 104C below.

103G: The refrain by Peter M. Kolar comes from a larger composition titled "El Señor Es Compasivo/The Lord Is Rich in Kindness," which includes sung stanzas in both Spanish and English. It is published by World Library Publications in the collection ¡Aclama, Tierra Entera!/Sing, All You Lands!: Salmos Bilingües/Bilingual Psalms.

104A: This litany is particularly appropriate at Pentecost. It would be most effective if it could be repeated weekly for a season, allowing the congregation to sing these short responses from the heart. The litany can move directly into the singing of a psalm or hymn of praise.

104C: When singing all the stanzas, the refrain should be sung only after sts. 2, 4, and 6. Odd- and even-numbered stanzas may be sung antiphonally by two different groups, with all joining on the refrain. It is intentional that 104C and 103B are set to the same tune. There is a close connection between these two psalms, which are both framed by the exclamation "Bless the Lord, O my soul."

104E: Ps. 104 is sometimes referred to as the third OT account of creation. This versification leaves nothing out. Groups of stanzas can be selected to create shorter hymns of praise for creation and God's providential care. The optional refrain is inserted at several points to suggest stanza groupings. (When following the text of the psalm, the refrain text should come only after st. 10.) When preaching or teaching about creation, select stanzas that correspond to the particular facets of creation.

104G: The alternate refrain is based on a plainsong melody that has been associated with the Latin hymn "Veni Creator Spiritus" (Come, Creator Spirit) since the 9th-Century. Ideally it should be sung unaccompanied.

105A: Ps. 105 not only tells us to remember, tell, and make known the deeds of the Lord, but it also provides a model for how to do so. This prayer outline begins and ends with the framing words of Ps. 105, and allows for us to follow the model of the psalm, a joyful retelling of God's redemptive history. Ps. 105 focuses especially on God's works in the time of Joseph and Moses. Our improvisatory praise can include a wide variety of memories from both biblical history and our own lives. This outline for a doxological memorial could be used for nearly any occasion. It is especially fitting for celebrations of the festivals in the Christian year that mark particular actions of God in history.

105B: The "Hallelujah" (v. 45b) should conclude any of the spoken or chanted lections. This may be accomplished by using an Alleluia or Hallelujah refrain. (See the first refrain option and also the general refrains index for more options.) The text of the alternate refrain, "The Steadfast Love of the Lord," comes from Lam. 3:22-23. This chorus may be used as a frame for the reading of the psalm.

105C: Ps. 105 is one of the psalms included in the Easter Vigil service. The use of the tune GAUDEAMUS PARITER/VIRGO VIRGINUM is intentional as it brings to mind the Easter hymn "Come, Ye Faithful, Raise the Strain of Triumphant Gladness." Michael Morgan casts the psalm text in the light of resurrection. For congregations who associate the Easter hymn with another tune (e.g., ST. KEVIN), consider using that for the singing of this text.

106A: When accompanying on piano or finger picking on guitar, continue with an arpeggiated chord pattern under the part-singing of the refrain. Conversely, the accompaniment of the stanzas may be interpreted as sustained chords to match the harmony of the refrain. If a contrast is desired between the stanzas and the refrain, consider allowing the refrain to be sung unaccompanied. Another possibility would be to have the stanzas sung by different solo voices, with all joining on the refrain. This may be sung unaccompanied throughout.

106B: The refrain would be suitable as a frame for any of the sections of this psalm.

107A: Performance option: all sing st. 1; sts. 2-5 sung by solo voices, bringing the congregation in to sing each final phrase beginning on the word "then"; all sing st. 6.

107B: This chorus reflects the recurring refrain built into the psalm. We cry out for help and, having been heard, we declare the goodness of God. It may be used as a frame of the psalm, as a recurring refrain with a psalm reading, or as a response to the reading of the psalm. This may be followed by intercessory prayers and/or testimonies of God's goodness which may then conclude with a reprise of the chorus.

107C: There are two refrains that interweave throughout Ps. 107. In the first refrain, these have been put into musical counterpoint (top and middle voices), along with the concluding verse (bottom voice). Any of these voice parts can be taken alone, or they can be put together in any permutation. The congregation could focus on the bottom part, with solo voices interweaving the top and bottom parts. Take care in singing the D-natural in the penultimate measure. It is a "blue note" that is cast against the D-sharp in the accompaniment. The alternate refrain supplies two stanza possibilities. It is possible to choose either stanza as a consistent refrain, or to alternate between the two. This Afro-American spiritual should be sung slowly, feeling the inner pulses. When the psalm text is spoken, the harmony of the refrain may be hummed under the reading.

107D: Performance option: all sing st. 1; sts. 2-5, first half sung by solo voices with all joining at *"Then when they sought God's name . . ."*; all sing st. 6.

108A: St. 5 could be sung by a solo voice or an ensemble in order to set it off as God's address to the congregation. A different voice might sing the difficult questioning text of st. 6, perhaps switching to the minor mode for this one stanza (F-minor, 4 flats). A short interlude could reestablish the major mode before the singing of st. 7.

109A: Rather than re-presenting the content of the psalm, the hymn "Give to the Winds Your Fears" serves as a sounding board and conversation partner. The cursing of the psalmist is accompanied by a sense of tremorous anxiety and fear. The hymn whispers to the psalmist, and to us, to bring all cares to God. When using the hymn stanzas with the psalm text, introduce the reading by playing the hymn on an instrument. Continue with soft instrumental music under the reading so that there is not a break between the reading and the singing.

110B: This setting lifts up the three quotations of the psalm, each beginning with a punctuated *"The Lord . . . ."* These are among the most quoted psalm verses in the NT. The accompaniment for the verses is best sung by an ensemble, taking care to launch the verse together with the solo voice on *"The Lord."* The congregation joins in the singing of each refrain. Konstantin Zhigulin composes psalms and songs for the Church of Christ denomination in his native Russia. Just as in the Russian Orthodox Church, this music should be sung with full harmony, but without accompanying instruments.

111B: Pss. 111 and 112, both acrostic psalms, are cast as a pair. This free paraphrase by Michael Morgan holds the two psalms together. St. 1, based on Ps. 111, praises God's wonderful works and faithfulness. St. 2, based on Ps. 112, further recounts God's gifts to humanity and our obligation to reflect God's graciousness in how we live. The final stanza reflects both psalms together, emphasizing that it is the fear of the Lord that brings us to wisdom (Ps. 111:10).

113B: Regarding the tune AUSTRIAN HYMN, see note for 87D above.

114A: The tune ANDRE suggests a child-like telling of the story. Consider performing sts. 2 and 3 in canon to suggest the rolling of the waters and the skipping of the rams and lambs. The tune O HEILAND REISS (114B) interprets the psalm in a more awe-filled way. *O Heiland, reiss die Himmel auf* is an Advent chorale describing the rending of the heavens and the trembling of the earth at the coming of the Lord, an apt association for this psalm. (See 144A.)

114B: See note for 114A above.

114C: The refrain is particularly appropriate for use in the Easter Vigil service (where it is set in dialogue with Rom. 6:3-11), or in any situation that celebrates or anticipates freedom from slavery. This may be interpreted literally (e.g., remembering Israel's deliverance from bondage in Egypt or modern-day deliverances from oppression or servitude) or figuratively (e.g., liberation from death and sin). When using as a refrain within the psalm, sing only the first half, without the repeat. A leader calls (see top line) and all respond. At the conclusion, sing the entire song several times. As a second stanza the congregation may sing *"Jesus is coming . . . ,"* a theme particularly appropriate at Advent. Though djembe and hand clapping can be added, the song works equally well completely unaccompanied. Alternate refrain 2 includes a vocal vamp which may be used with Scripture reading. The number of repeats can be adapted to fit the timing of the Scripture reading.

115B: The tune VATER UNSER is quite close to plainchant. (For many the tune is closely associated with the words of the Lord's Prayer. See p. 1044.) Do not interpret the rhythm too rigidly, but allow the text to move forward at a natural pace. The tempo should not drag.

116B: This setting of vv. 12-19 is particularly appropriate when celebrating the Lord's Supper.

116C: It can be effective to sing this Afro-American spiritual very slowly, taking a generous breath at the end of every phrase and even before the final two words of each stanza (e.g., *"I'll hasten to . . .* [breath] *his throne").* The two stanzas can be used to frame a portion of the psalm or intercessory prayers.

116E: Stanzas may be sung by a solo voice, with all joining in singing the refrain.

117A: This setting could also be accompanied by a simple drum pattern with a hummed drone on D and A. Use this to frame the reading of Ps.117, continuing with the drum and humming during the reading. This short psalm could be read in several different languages, with the refrain inserted between the readings.

117B: This Taizé chant has a driving rhythm. Add djembe to the accompaniment and feel strong accents on all the sung quarter notes.

117D: This song is flexible and open to different interpretations. The accompaniment suggests a lilting, ballad-like rendering. Alternatively, it can be led with a driving, up-tempo rhythm with hand clapping on the off-beats and keyboard (and possibly other band instruments) improvising off the guitar chords.

118B: This setting is most appropriate when using the psalm in the context of a Palm Sunday celebration or during the season of Advent. At the final appearance of the refrain, sing several times in canon, using the accompaniment provided, either on keyboard or with handbells.

118D: This song is best accompanied in a brisk tempo, feeling each measure as a swinging 3+2+2. This rhythmic pattern can be marked by shakers, tambourine, or other rhythm instruments.

118F: When reading the psalm verses between the stanzas of the song, instrumentalists should vamp in the key of F, with percussion continuing the 3+3+2 pattern.

118H: A setting of this psalm composed by Eelco Vos for leadership by a contemporary worship band is available from *The Psalm Project* (see *www.thepsalmproject.com*).

119F: This refrain comes from a larger composition by Glenn Burleigh. The full composition is published in several hymnals (see *www.hymnary.org*). It is set here with selected verses from Ps. 119 that use the image of walking in the paths of God's Word.

119 O: Christopher Idle reflects the playfulness of the Hebrew acrostic by creating an English counterpart. Each full phrase begins with a subsequent letter of the alphabet. Consider dividing sts. 2-7 between two or more different groups, singing antiphonally.

120A: When using the accompanying text, the pattern in the opening measures of the bass can be used as a vamp under the reading. A leader should help the congregation enter into the singing of the appropriate stanzas through the course of the reading. When not using the accompanying text, conclude with a return to the singing of st. 1. Sing with a slow, "bluesy" feel, with a sense of woe.

120B: In this instance the congregation plays the role of accompanist. Although the ostinato is not difficult, care must be taken that the singers keep a steady 3+2+2 pulse. The drum and some leading singers can help with this. Before the solo voice's final phrase there may be a pause. The solo voice needs to give a clear pick-up to the next measure so that the congregation can fall into the final iteration of the ostinato. After each stanza, take time to reestablish the ostinato before beginning the next stanza. The congregation should sing softly. The solo voice should interpret the nuanced emotions of the psalm—longing, disdain, fear, exhaustion.

120C: The lead and echo arrangement of the refrain is an option and can be sung by any two groups. When the echo is not used, sing the entire text, with the exception of the repeated *"who lift."*

121B: Richard Smallwood's "Total Praise," here arranged by Stephen Kay, may be sung congregationally or as a four-part anthem. The accompaniment should be played in a gospel style, as suggested by the occasional cue notes. There are several choral arrangements available that offer a written-out piano accompaniment.

121C: There are wonderful cross-rhythms at play throughout this song. They should be gently marked by percussion instruments (e.g., claves playing a large 2 pattern (3+3), triangle playing a 3 pattern (2+2+2), and a soft shaker marking the incessant eighth notes.) The first eight measures of each stanza may be repeated.

121D: When using the vamp, each half verse is spoken over one measure. The refrain is then sung at the beginning, after v. 4, and at the end. When not using the vamp, sing the refrain as indicated in the psalm text. The first line of the refrain may be sung by a solo voice, with the congregation joining at the repeat of the text.

121E: This Appalachian tune should be sung warmly, with breadth, and not too quickly. Feel one very large pulse per measure.

121F: This beautifully spare song is better "caught than taught." If possible, have a soloist sing in Korean, with all repeating in English.

121H: The *Fine* on the G chord does not resolve. This is intentional, reflecting a sense of waiting and anticipation in the text.

122D: The first refrain, "I Was Glad," comes from a larger composition by David Haas. The full composition is published in several hymnals (see *www.hymnary.org*) and is available from GIA Publications. The alternate refrain can be sung in unison. At the conclusion of the psalm it should be sung in four-part canon. It is an unusual canon in that it is not rhythmic. Each measure settles on the last note. All breathe together and then commence with the next measure. Establish the pace for the fermata and the breath at the first singing of the refrain in unison.

123A: The refrain comes from a larger composition by David Haas. The full composition is published in several hymnals (see *www.hymnary.org*) and is available from GIA Publications.

124A: St. 1 is an elaboration of Ps. 124:8. For communities that regularly begin worship with this verse (often referred to as the *Votum*), the first stanza may be taken alone.

124B: The bridge material (p. 822) is composed in such a way that it can be superimposed on the refrain, as indicated in the cue notes on the last page of music. Note that there is no internal echo but that the phrases of the bridge material are sung in quick succession. For a fully realized score, contact the composer.

125C: Do not sing too quickly. Add tambourine on the off-beats.

126A: The use of the tune WAYFARING STRANGER, an Afro-American spiritual, creates resonance between this text and the Afro-American experience. Before singing this psalm setting, have an unaccompanied soloist sing the traditional, spiritual text (*I am a poor wayfaring stranger/While traveling through this world of woe./Yet there's no sickness, toil nor danger/In that bright world to which I go./I'm going there to see my father (mother/sister/brother/Jesus)/I'm going there no more to roam./I'm only going over Jordan,/I'm only going over home.*).

126E: St. 3 functions as a response to the psalm. This stanza could be sung alone after the reading of the psalm as the congregation's prayerful response.

128A: There is a nice interplay here between a Russian folk melody and Russian Orthodox chant. To enjoy the contrast between these two sections, encourage all to sing harmony at each return of the refrain.

128B: The refrain comes from a larger composition by Marty Haugen. The full composition is published in several hymnals (see *www.hymnary.org*) and is available from GIA Publications.

130G: This free paraphrase pulls together the texts of both Pss. 130 and 131. When using both texts, consider inserting an interlude between sts. 4 and 5 to mark the transition from one psalm to the next.

131A: This text may be used both as a personal, everyday prayer and liturgically as a prayer for illumination or at any time of prayer or testimony. As a prayer of surrender and trust, it is especially appropriate for intimate gatherings of prayer, encouragement, and discernment.

131B: Sing slowly, peacefully, even dreamily. The stanzas may be sung by a solo voice, with all joining in singing the refrain.

131C: As an introduction, build up the parts beginning with the bass and repeating only the first two measures. When the melody enters, sing through the entire refrain. This refrain is taken from an anthem for chorus with optional soloist or treble voices. The text of the anthem, "Like a Child," is based on Ps. 131:2 and Ps. 130:1 with words and music by Loretta Ellenberger and arr. by Rupert Lang (Hope Publishing Company, M-051-46984-0).

132B: The opening line (taken from a Christmas carol by Cecil F. Alexander) and the tune IRBY will make a solid connections with the Christmas carol "Once in Royal David's City." Although it may be associated with and sung in Christmastide, it should not be limited to such a use. At any time that the psalm is being preached or contemplated, the text will make a natural link for singers between God's promises to David and the fulfillment of these promises in Christ.

133B: Sing in a relaxed way, adding percussion to the accompaniment. A bass could add a Bolero rhythm. The unity of brothers and sisters can be embodied in the way the song is sung. The first two lines can be sung by women, with an echo sung by men beginning at the pick up to the third. (In the second line the echo will need to be adapted, singing all eighth notes on "*gift it is when*" and moving right into "*sisters and brothers*" together with the lead part.) The coming together at the text "*when sisters and brothers join hands . . .*" coincides wonderfully with the combining of the two voice parts. The treble parts may be sung as a simple two-part harmony, beginning on the third line.

133C: Accompany in a gospel style and sing exuberantly. Swing the paired eighth notes.

133D: Regardless of which language the stanzas are sung in, the refrain should be sung first in Spanish and then repeated in English.

134A: Accompany as a slow rock ballad, using the four bars of instrumental solo music as introduction, interlude, and coda. For traditional harmony and rhythm, see 100A.

134C: The verses could be sung by a solo voice but could also be chanted by the entire congregation. Take a slow tempo. Because the vocal part of the refrain is not doubled by the accompaniment, consider doubling this with an instrument or lead with an amplified voice, but not too loudly.

136A: This melody may be used with the four original stanzas by John Milton at 136B, ignoring the refrain.

136B: After singing the first two stanzas, sing the refrain four times. The refrain may be sung by two groups, the first one singing "*For God's mercies shall endure*" and the other group responding with "*ever faithful, ever* *sure."* Upon returning to sts. 3 and 4, the motifs of the refrain form a sort of descant to the melody line. The layering of the descant over the stanzas reflects the pervasiveness of the refrain that we find in the psalm. The interludes create space between each of these layered sections.

136C: Rather than having the stanzas sung by a leader, the entire song could be sung antiphonally by two or more groups. If the assembly could easily be divided into more groups, a leader could indicate which group is to take the lead at each stanza, with all the others responding with the refrain.

136D: The first refrain assumes that the psalm will be chanted and that the refrain will be sung by all at the second half of each verse. When using this option, observe the pointing of the psalm for the first half of each verse and sing the refrain for the second half. The refrain built into each verse of the psalm allows for a variety of interpretations. The psalm may be sung responsively between solo voice and congregation or antiphonally between two groups singing in harmony. The *Refrain* indications are disregarded when using this option. The alternate refrain should be used when speaking the psalm or when chanting the entire text to the alternate tone. Sing the refrain as indicated when using the alternate refrain/tone.

136F: This setting may be sung antiphonally, with one group singing the stanzas and the other group replying with the refrain.

136G: Prepare for the singing of this song by having music leaders go through each voice part of the refrain in turn, with the congregation echoing back these parts. This will not only serve to create confident harmonic singing but will also indicate which version of text will be used at the refrain. Then establish the *"Ahoms"* part by part, with strong attacks on each one. Make sure these are solid before beginning with the solo voice parts. Don't think of the *"Ahom"* as two syllables, but rather a guttural "ah" on the grace note, with a little slide up to the hum on the downbeat. Accompany with djembe and shakers.

136H: A solo voice or rehearsed ensemble sings the verses with all on the refrain. Although the refrain does not change, a gesture from the leader at each entrance will help the confidence of the singers. Keep the tempo steady to the very end. Note that the value of the notes doubles in the final ending, creating a built-in ritard.

137C: The refrain may be sung in canon. With each return of the refrain, sing more quietly. If vv. 7-9 are included as part of the lection, they may be chanted softly or whispered. The speaking of the psalm may be accompanied by soft humming of the melody.

137D: This is a wonderful three-part canon, but it may be a bit much to sing all the stanzas in canon. One option for singing all the stanzas is to have all sing st. 1 in unison; group 1 sing st. 2; group 2 sing st. 3; group 3 sing st. 4; sing st. 5 in canon several times, beginning with group 1 and adding groups 2 and 3, as indicated in the music. At the end, sing quietly.

137E: Alfred V. Fedak arranged EBENEZER for this particular text. Note the plaintive, mournful tone of the first half of each stanza and the infusion of some hope at each refrain. By using the tune AUTHORITY (p. 372), it is possible to sing this text with a sense of rage or defiance.

138A: When singing the text to the tune MELITA, ignore the repeat of the final line.

138B: Either or both of the stanzas of this spiritual may be used as the psalm refrain.

138C: A setting of this psalm composed by Eelco Vos for leadership by a contemporary worship band is available from *The Psalm Project* (see www.thepsalmproject.com).

139D: This beautiful piping tune, a favorite in Scotland, is often interpreted as a regal march for use at weddings and civic ceremonies. For the purposes of this psalm it should maintain a sense of solemnity, but rendered with sensitivity to the intimacy of the text. It should be sung as a folksong.

140A: The pairing of this text with the chorale tune PASSION CHORALE ("O Sacred Head Now Wounded") is intended to highlight the associations with Christ's suffering that can be found in the psalm.

141A: The first stanza can be used alone as the beginning of a prayer, particularly in the evening. When using only st. 1, it would be effective to sing this in canon, creating musically the sense of rising incense through the intertwining lines. This song is best sung unaccompanied, with instruments doubling the melody and a drone played or hummed on D and A if necessary. The text may also be sung to the tune FEDERAL STREET (see p. 909).

141B: Many will be drawn to the singing of this setting if they are familiar with the tune PICARDY ("Let All Mortal Flesh Keep Silence"). Although all the elements of the tune are quoted, be aware that the sequence and timing do not correspond to the hymn tune. This setting is a reduction from a fuller scoring by Lori True and Marshall Keating. It appears in several hymnals (see www.hymnary.org) and is published by GIA Publications.

141D: This Orthodox chant functions as a call to prayer, particularly in the context of evening services. Traditionally one group sings the first half and another group the second half. Sing in parts without accompaniment, leading with a vocal ensemble. Do not interpret the rhythm rigidly; a natural speech rhythm will help in setting the pace.

142A: The refrain *"I will arise and go to Jesus"* may be sung at the conclusion of the psalm or after each stanza. A solo voice could sing the stanzas, and the congregation could respond with the refrain.

144A: The stanzas of this Lutheran chorale O HEILAND, REISS have been reordered to reflect the development within the psalm. The stanzas may be sung together as a response to the reading of the entire psalm, or they may be interwoven with the chanting or reading of the selected verses presented below the hymn. This framing of the psalm is particularly fitting for celebrations of Advent or the Reign of Christ and in conjunction with sermons dealing with the Second Advent.

145B: Although seven stanzas are provided, it is possible to catch a sense of the psalm without singing the entire text. For example, as an opening psalm of praise addressed to God, sing sts. 1, 2, and 4. Or, as a response to the Word and in anticipation of the Lord's Supper, sing sts. 5 and 6.

145D: When following the varied lectionary apportions of the psalm, adjust the placement of the refrain as necessary. The refrain comes from a larger composition by Rawn Harbor titled "Psalm 145: I Will Praise Your Name Forever." The full composition can be found in *Psalms from the Soul, Vol. 2* (Oregon Catholic Press).

145F: The focus in st. 3 on *"manna"* and *"feeding"* makes this an appropriate setting to sing in preparation for the celebration of the Lord's Supper or as a communal thanksgiving after the meal, in anticipation of the benediction and sending.

146B: The alternate refrain is a very forceful Native American "Hallelujah." At the last return of the refrain, sing several times in canon. Add a bass drum sound or have the congregation firmly step with one foot on every down beat.

146E: This prayer, which may be prayed between stanzas 2 and 3 of 146A, C, or D, calls attention to the contrast between God's glory revealed in creation and God's glory revealed in the ordinary lives of those who struggle.

147A: Alternate refrain 2 can build up through the reading or chanting of the psalm. At the first indication of the refrain, the leader sings the first theme, which is then repeated by group 1. At the second singing of the refrain the leader sings the second theme, which is then repeated by group 2. The same pattern follows for the third theme with group 3. At the final singing of the refrain, bring in the three groups one at a time, each group repeating its theme.

147C: It works well to sing this setting and particularly the refrain in three parts. Begin the refrain with tenor/bass, then add the treble parts. Because the treble entrances are syncopated, the refrain feels contrapuntal. At the stanzas all of the voices move together. These can be more forceful and driving.

148D: The vamp on p. 980 is optional. When using the vamp, repeat it several times, alternating between the two texts and building in intensity. When breaking out of the vamp, go directly to the top of p. 979, singing st. 4 as a final refrain.

148E: The last phrase (after the *"Oh!"*) is a repeat of the previous line. Rather than singing the repeated English text, a refrain can be formed by singing the Indonesian text after each stanza. A simple quarter note percussion pattern (drums, hand claps, or foot stomps) is all that is necessary to keep a lively tempo.

148F: Regarding the tune AUSTRIAN HYMN, see note for 87D above.

148G: See also p. 755 for another refrain suitable for use in the Easter season.

148H: Take care that the timing is determined by the text and not by the apparent note values. Particularly when phrases have only one or two syllables under the initial reciting tone, do not stall but move immediately to the next word. In some of the cadences, some syllables do need to be stretched over two notes. To add variety, have a quartet sing in alternation with the congregation. The organ and/or choir can help to support the congregational singing and prevent the tempo from dragging.

149A: For the first refrain the text in italics may be used throughout, or the stanza segments of "Holy God We Praise Your Name" may be sung interspersed through the psalm, as indicated. The alternate refrain is best sung unaccompanied.

150A: This setting can be accompanied by just about any combination of instruments. If possible, add a "jazzy" drum set, one that does not overpower the singing but brings out the intricate cross rhythms with brush strokes. (See, for instance, the rhythm in the piano accompaniment at the refrain.) In obedience to the text, make room for brass, strings, and dancers to join too!

150C: This is an excellent setting to introduce to reticent congregations. There are only two musical lines the congregation needs to learn, both of them memorable and first sung by the leader. Notice that the opening introduction is sung the first time only. After each stanza, return to the refrain. The melody may be doubled by a flute or flute stop on the organ, if desired. The rhythm patterns may be improvised on finger cymbals, hand drums, tambourines, or other available instruments. The rhythmic accompaniment should be reduced or drop out entirely after the refrain, coming back in joyfully after the solo voice sings *"hallelujah!"*

150E: With strong leadership from a choir and organ, congregations can enjoy singing this glorious, English-style chant. It is different from other "Anglican chants" in that it does not use a repeated formula. Rather, it is through-composed, with variations in the texture, melody, and harmony throughout. Place the choir around the perimeter of the assembly as an encouragement and support to the congregation. A leader should conduct the entire assembly with a supporting gesture during the reciting tones; a fluid, quick two-beat pattern for all the cadences; and a generous ritard at the end.

p. 1013: The verses may be sung by a solo voice or an ensemble, with all joining in singing the refrain. The chanted verses can be sung antiphonally. For example, an ensemble could sing the odd-numbered verses, with all joining in singing the even-numbered verses. Let the text flow naturally, as in speech. When the verses are sung by all, it is not necessary to use the refrain

p. 1014: See note for p. 1013 above for chanting this canticle.

p. 1018: This Taizé chant should be sung in all possible permutations. First, teach both the melody and the descant. Once the congregation knows these parts, they are free to sing either part, staggering their entrances to form a double-layered canon. While it is possible to bring singers in section by section, it resonates more deeply if these parts are distributed freely throughout the assembly. The chant should be sung joyfully and should not be halted too early. The song needs time to develop. To conclude the singing, a lead musician should indicate a ritard. All end together at the end of the two-measure phrase, regardless of where they are in the canon.

p. 1022: See note for p. 1013 above for chanting this canticle.

p. 1024: This setting of the Song of Simeon is taken from a larger setting of Holy Communion titled *The Detroit Folk Mass*, composed by James Harris and Tillis Butler (Augsburg Fortress Press). It should be accompanied and sung in a gospel style. As an introduction, a solo voice could sing the text up to the *Gloria Patri* (through the word *"Israel"*), and then return to the beginning, inviting all to join. This will allow the congregation not only to hear the text and melody but also to catch the style. The song should be sung regularly at evening services or at the close of communion services so that the congregation can sing it from the heart.

p. 1026: This setting of the canticle for night prayer is best learned through repeated use. The refrain may be taken alone as a frame for the reading or chanting of the canticle. The use of the *Gloria Patri* is optional. This is also a wonderful setting for daily use in the home at bedtime. Children easily learn the responses in the verses, and the refrain is a wonderful prayer to be sung together before sleeping.

p. 1028: Firmly establish the soft singing of the ostinato by the congregation before the solo voice enters with the singing of the verses. Although best sung unaccompanied, soft arpeggios on a guitar or piano on the C and F/A chords can support the pitch of the ostinato, as well as keep the pulse. The leader could conduct the fermatas at the end.

p. 1034: Do not interpret the rhythm of this Russian Orthodox chant too rigidly. Allow the text to nuance the rhythm. Take care that the tempo does not drag. Ideally, this should be sung in parts, without accompaniment.

p. 1044: An alternate accompaniment for VATER UNSER can be found on p. 727. Regarding the singing of this melody, see note for 115B above.

p. 1046: When singing in canon, it works best to allow for a one-measure interval between the singing of the stanzas. When the trailing voice lands on the final syllable (beat 3), the lead voice launches into the next stanza on beat 4. Note that the tenor line of the accompaniment supports the trailing voice. Keep the pulse absolutely steady between stanzas.

p. 1049: *Abana* is Arabic for father. Ideally this Arabic chant should be chanted without accompaniment. It is also possible to sing in unison, supported by a low B-flat sustained on the organ or cello, or hummed.

Indexes

Index of Copyright Holders

We are grateful to all individuals and publishers who have granted us permission to print their copyrighted materials. If you wish to reproduce (or reprint) any copyrighted words or music contained in this book, please contact the copyright holder for permission or use an approved license.

Abingdon Press
See Copyright Company, The

Anderson, Fred
921 Madison Ave.
New York, NY 10021
Phone: 212-288-8920
Fax: 212-249-1466
Fra.mapc@mindspring.com

Archdiocese of Philadelphia
See International Liturgy Publications

Augsburg Fortress Publishers
100 South Fifth St., PO Box 1209
Minneapolis, MN 55440-1209
Phone: 800-421-0239
Fax: 800-722-7766
copyright@augsburgfortress.org
www.augsburgfortress.org

Bible, Ken
See Music Services

Birnamwood Publications
See MorningStar Music Publishers, Inc.

Black, George A. (the Estate of)
c/o Maragaret McLean Black
6-94 Crescent Rd.
Toronto, ON M4W 1T5
Canada
Phone: 416-920-9506
Fax: 416-920-9529
mcblack@sympatico.ca

Blenkinsop, Alison
64 Heron Wood Rd.
Aldershot GU12 4AL
United Kingdom
aliblenk@hotmail.com
www.linkable.biz

BMG Music Publishing/
Zomba Songs Inc.
BMI/T. Autumn Music, BMI
See Music Services

Boertje, Barbara
3939 Abel St. SW
Grandville, MI 49418
barbaraboertje@juno.com

Boyer, Horace Clarence
c/o Gloria Boyer
92 Grantwood Dr.
Amherst, MA 01002-1536
Phone: 413-549-5454
Fax: 413-253-5087

Brentwood-Benson Publishing
2555 Meridian Blvd., Ste 100
Franklin, TN 37067
Phone: 615-371-1320
Fax: 615-371-1351
brentwoodbenson@musicservices.org

Brentwood-Benson Songs
See Brentwood-Benson Publishing

Brummhart Publishing
708 Blooming Grove Dr.
Renselaer, NY 12144-9420
Kathleen@BrummhartPublishing.com
James@BrummhartPublishing.com

Burleigh Inspirations Music
c/o LaVonne Burleigh
5244 Parkview Dr.
Haltom City, TX 76148
Phone: 817-577-7570
bonnieburleigh@att.net

Bush, AnnaMae Meyer
850 Byerly SE
Ada, MI 49301
annamaebush@att.net

CanZion Producciones
Apdo. C-62 Durango Durango
34120 País, Mexico
Phone: 011-5218-17-24-64
Fax: 011-5218-18-07-79

Cárdenas, Casiodoro
Casilla 85-56 Quito
País: Ecuador

Cardiphonia Music
Bruce Benedict
2404 Stafford Ave.
Raleigh, NC 27607
brucebenedict@gmail.com

Caribbean Conference of Churches
PO Box 876
Port of Spain, Trinidad
trinidad-headoffice@ccc-caribe.org

Celebration
PO Box 309
809 Franklin Ave.
Aliquippa, PA 15001
Phone: 724-375-1510
Fax: 724-375-1138
mail@communityofcelebration.com

Celebremos/Libros Alianza
A.A. 100
Cucuta
Colombia
Phone: 57-7-574-2959
Fax: 57-7-574-4328

Century Oak Publishing Group
Richwood Music
See Conexion Media Group, Inc.

Chinese Christian Literature Council, Ltd.
14/F., Surson Commercial Building
140-142 Austin Rd.
Kowloon
Hong Kong
Phone: 011-852-2367-8031
Fax: 011-852-2739-6030
info@cclc.org.hk

Choristers Guild
2834 W. Kingsley Rd.
Garland, TX 75041
www.choristersguild.org

Christopher Miner Music
43 Diana St.
Memphis, TN 38104
christopherminer@hotmail.com

Church House Publishing
Great Smith St.
London SW 1P 3NZ
United Kingdom
www.chpublishing.co.uk
Phone: 011-44-20-7898-1451
Fax: 011-44-20-7898-1449

Church Pension Group/
Church Publishing, Inc.
445 Fifth Ave.
New York, NY 10016
copyrights@cpg.org
www.churchpublishing.org

Clemens, James
10605 Grapevine Ln.
Dayton, VA 22821
clemens@singtogether.net

Concordia Publishing House
3558 South Jefferson St.
St. Louis, MO 63118-3968
Phone: 314-268-1000
copyrights@cph.org
www.cph.org

Conexion Media Group, Inc.
1301 16th Ave. South
Nashville, TN 37212
Phone: 615-250-4602
Fax: 615-691-7140
info@conexion-media.com
www.conexion-media.com

Conferencia Episcopal Española
prensa@conferenciaepiscopal.es

Copyright Company, The
PO Box 128139
Nashville, TN 37212-8139
Phone: 615-244-9848
Fax: 615-244-9850
lynda.pearson@thecopyrightco.com

Covenant Publications
Evangelical Covenant Church
8303 W. Higgins Rd.
Chicago, IL 60631

Creative Commons
Attribution-NonCommercial-ShareAlike
444 Castro St., Suite 900
Mountain View, CA 94041
This license allows the indicated material to be remixed, tweaked, and built upon noncommercially, as long as the new creations are credited and licensed under identical terms.
www.creativecommons.org/licenses
by-nc-sa/3.0/

Darwin Jordan Music
PO Box 16307
Fort Worth, TX 76162
Fax: 817-294-5687

Digerness, Karl
837 27th Ave.
San Francisco, CA 94121
Phone: 415-726-4567
digerness2@gmail.com

Donaldson, Andrew
c/o Donald Anderson
170 Douglas Ave.
Toronto, ON M5M 1G6
Canada
Andrew.Donaldson@wcc-coe.org

Donnelly, Noel S.
3 Westfield
Dumbarton G82 4JR
Scotland
Phone: 011-44-01389-765-347
noeldonnelly@msn.com

Duba, Arlo D.
2 Birchwood Ct.
Princeton, NJ 08540
aduba@comcast.net

Dunn, John G.
125 Coolidge Ave. No. 404
Watertown, MA 02472
Phone: 339-368-1261

Earl Pleasant Publishing
Margaret Pleasant Douroux
CEO Heritage Music Foundation
PO Box 3247
Thousand Oaks, CA 91359
gospelmeg@aol.com

Eerdman's Publishing Company
2140 Oak Industrial Dr. NE
Grand Rapids, MI 49505
Phone: 616-234-0551
Fax: 616-742-6111
www.eerdmans.com

EMI CMG Publishing
PO Box 5085
Brentwood, TN 37024
emicmgpublishing.com

English Language Liturgical Consultation
Hugh F. Graham
97 Crofton Rd.
London, E13 8QT
United Kingdom
uisdean2@mac.com

Evangelisches Missionswerk in
Deutschland e.V.
Normannenweg 17-21
D - 20537 Hamburg
Germany
presse@emw-d.de

Faith Alive Christian Resources
2850 Kalamazoo Ave. SE
Grand Rapids, MI 49560
Phone: 866-823-0008
Fax: 616-726-1164
permissions@crcna.org

Feliciano, Francisco
kiko@sambalikhaan.org

Frey, Marvin V.
c/o Helen Frey
266 Merrimon Ave. Ste. 213
Asheville, NC 28801
Phone: 828-252-4753
hfrey@frontiernet.net

G. Schirmer, Inc.
The Music Sales Group
257 Park Ave. South, 20th Floor
New York, NY 10010
Phone: 212-254-2100
Fax: 212-254-2013
schirmer@schirmer.com
www.schirmer.com

General Board of Global Ministries
t/a GBG Musik
475 Riverside Dr.
New York, NY 10115
kdonato@gbgm-umc.org
Lorengo@gbgm-umc.org

GIA Publications, Inc.
7404 S. Mason Ave.
Chicago, IL 60638
Phone: 708-496-3858
Fax: 708-496-3828
www.giamusic.com

Gold, Rabbi Shefa
PO Box 430
Jemez Springs, MN 87025
Shefa@RabbiShefaGold.com

Goodmusic Publishing, Ltd.
David Good
PO Box 100
Tewkesbury GL20 7YQ
United Kingdom
Phone: 011-44-1684-773883
Fax: 011-44-1684-773884
sales@goodmusicpublishing.co.uk
www.goodmusicpublishing.co.uk

Hal Leonard Corporation
Attn: Copyright Department
7777 West Bluemound Rd.,
PO Box 13819
Milwaukee, WI 53213
Fax: 414-774-3259
hlcopyright@halleonard.com

HarperCollins Religious
See Music Services

Hinshaw Music, Inc.
PO Box 470
Chapel Hill, NC 27514-0470
Phone: 919-933-1691
Fax: 919-967-3399

Hope Publishing Company
380 South Main Place
Carol Stream, IL 60188
Phone: 800-323-1049
Fax: 630-665-2552
www.hopepublishing.com

Hopp, Roy
1676 Ridgemoore SE
Grand Rapids, MI 49506
royhopp@yahoo.com

Hughes, S. M., Howard L.
Marianist Center
22683 Alcalde Rd.
Cupertino, CA 95014-3903
Phone: 408-207-4849
Litmus2H@aol.com

Ian Pitt-Watson Trust
c/o The Fuller Foundation
135 N. Los Robles, Suite 660
Pasadena, CA 91101
Phone: 626-792-3232
Fax: 626-729-3456

Integrity Music, Inc.
See EMI CMG Publishing

Interkerkelijke Stichting
voor het Kerklied,
Leidschendam
The Netherlands
dpvdbosch@gmail.com

International Commission on English
in the Liturgy Corporation (ICEL)
1100 Connecticut Ave. NW, Suite 710
Washington, DC 20036-4101
Phone: 202-347-0800
Fax: 202-347-1839
permission@eliturgy.org
www.icelweb.org

International Liturgy Publications
PO Box 50476
Nashville, TN 37205
Phone: 888-898-SONG
www.ILPmusic.org

James Ward Music and Music A. D.
4106 Saint Elmo Ave.
Chattanooga, TN 37409
info@jameswardmusic.com

JASRAC
3-6-12 Vehara
Shibuya-ku
Tokyo 151-8540
Japan
intl-contact@pop02.jasrac.or.jp

Jesuit Communication Foundation, Inc.
Sonolux Building, Seminary Drive
Ateneo de Manila University
Katipunan Ave., Loyola Heights 1108
Quezon City, Philippines
corporate@jescom.ph

Filipino Society of Composers,
Authors and Publishers (FILSCAP)
mmvagustin@filscap.com.ph

Jones, Isaiah, Jr. (the Estate of)
c/o Covenant Presbyterian Church
670 East Meadow Dr.
Palo Alto, CA 94306
Phone: 650-494-1760
Fax: 650-494-7972

Ken Medema Music/Brier Patch Music
4324 Canal Ave. SW
Grandville, MI 49418
Phone: 888-536-5365
Fax: 616-534-1113
bevvmolen@aol.com
www.kenmedema.com

Kevin Mayhew Ltd.
Buxhall Stowmarket
Suffolk IP14 3BW
United Kingdom
Phone: 011-44-845-388-1634
info@kevinmayhewltd.com

Kingsway Music/
www.kingswaysongs.com
See EMI CMG Publishing

Landegent, David
502 South St.
Volga, SD 57071
egentdr@q.com

Lee, David
6 Reeds Ave.
Earley
Reading RG6 5SR
United Kingdom
Phone: 011-44-118-986-2911
t.d.lee@servicemusic.org.uk

Licensing Associates
Kathleen Karcher
935 Broad St. # 31
Bloomfield, NJ 07003
Phone: 973-743-6444
KathleenKarcher@hotmail.com

Liturgical Press
Saint John's Abbey
PO Box 7500
Collegeville, MN 56321-7500
Phone: 800-858-5458
Fax: 320-363-3278
www.litpress.org

Loh, I-to
23 Dong-Rong St. #4F
Tainan 701, Taiwan
Republic of China
Phone: 886-6-200-4414
ito@globalchurchmusic.org

Martínez, Raquel Mora
14710 Kinsem
San Antonio, TX 78248-0954
Fax: 210-493-6883
raqmart2003@yahoo.com

Medical Mission Sisters
Hartford Seminary
77 Sherman St.
Hartford, CT 06105-2260
mms@hartsem.edu
www.medicalmissionsisters.org

Metropolitan Andrey Sheptytsky
Institute of Eastern Christian Studies
Saint Paul University
223 Main St.
Ottawa, ON K1S 1C4
Canada
sheptytsky@ustpaul.ca

Moore, Brenda Joyce
15241 Chicago Rd., Apt. 2A
Dolton, IL 60419
Phone: 773-785-5483
imbren1@comcast.net

MorningStar Music Publishers
Birnamwood Publications, a division of
MorningStar Music Publishers, Inc.
1727 Larkin Williams Rd.
Fenton, MO 63026-2024
Fax: 636-305-0121
copyrights@morningstarmusic.com
www.morningstarmusic.com

Music A.D.
See James Ward Music

Music Services, Inc.
5409 Maryland Way, Suite 200
Brentwood, TN 37027
Phone: 615-371-1320
Fax: 615-371-1351
www.musicservices.org

New Spring Publishing
See Music Services

Obed Valencia Lozada
Fuego Fatuo Mz.3 Lote 13
Col. Valle de Luces
Iztapalapa 9800
México
lovoveja@hotmail.com

Olivétan Editions
contact@editions-Olivetan.com

Olivieri, Louis
Calle Colorado 1745
Urb. San Gerardo
San Juan
Puerto Rico 00926
Phone: 787-758-9014
louisolivieri@aol.com

OCP Publications
Oregon Catholic Press Publications
5536 NE Hassalo
Portland, OR 97213
Phone: 800-LITURGY
Fax: 503-535-8120
www.ocp.org

Oxford University Press
Music Department
Great Clarendon St.
Oxford OX2 6DP
United Kingdom
Phone: 800-445-9714
Fax: 919-677-1303
www.oup.com

Pandopo, H. A.
Harry van Dop
Schuilenburgerplein 1 B62
3816 TD Amersfoort
The Netherlands
hermanud@xs4all.nl

Parker, Alice
96 Middle Rd.
Hawley, MA 01339
aparker@melodiousaccord.org

Peermusic III, Ltd.
and Savgos Music, Inc.
See Hal Leonard Corporation

Pilgrim Press, The
700 Prospect Ave.
Cleveland, OH 44115-1100
frencht@ucc.org

Praise Trust
Mr. J. L. Ransome
PO Box 359
Darlington DL3 8YD
United Kingdom
Jing_ransome@hotmail.com

Re:Create Music
Gregg DeMey
147 E. Van Buren
Elmhurst, IL 60126
gregg.demey@elmhurstcrc.org

Reindorf, Dinah
c/o Myna Reindorf
2859 Strauss Terrace
Silver Spring, MD 20904
Phone: 301-890-3480
mreindorf@worldbank.org

Richard T. Proulx 1991 Trust
Attorney Doug Hoffman
PO Box 2593
Chicago, IL 60690
Phone: 312-845-3794
hoffman@chapman.com

Roberton Publications
See Goodmusic Publishing, Ltd.

Roberts, Leon C.
PO Box 9654
Washington, DC 20016-9654
info@leonroberts.org

Royal School of Church Music, The
19 The Close
Salisbury, Wiltshire SP1 2EB
United Kingdom
Phone: 011-44-1722-424855
Fax: 011-44-1722-424849
press@rscm.com
www.rscm.com

St. Andrews Press
www.standrewpress.org

Scheer, Greg
4364 Downing St. SE
Grand Rapids, MI 49546-3652
greg@gregscheer.com

Schmit, Clayton
135 N. Oakland Ave.
Pasadena, CA 91182
cjs@fuller.edu
Seerveld, Calvin
Toronto Tuppence Press
332 Senlac Rd.
Toronto, ON M2R 1R3
Canada
ttp@icscanada.edu
www.seerveld.com/tuppence.html

Selah Publishing Company, Inc.
4055 Cloverleaf St., PO Box 98066
Pittsburgh, PA 15227
licensing@selahpub.com
Phone: 412-886-1020
Fax: 412-886-1022

Sorge, Sheldon W., and Tammy Wiens
2153 Croghan Dr.
Carnegie, PA 15106
ssorge@alumni.duke.edu

Stainer & Bell Ltd.
PO Box 110
Victoria House
23 Gruneisen Rd.
London N3 1DZ
United Kingdom
post@stainer.co.uk

Tamaela, Christian
Fakultas Teologi UKIM
Komplaks Persekolahan Kristen YPPK
Dr. Sitanala
J1, Dr. Slwabessy, No. 2
PO Box 1914
Ambon, Indonesia

Thresholds Music Press
Ben Allaway
211 Zwart Rd.
Des Moines, IA 50312-5401
benlmnop@aol.com

Universal Music
See Brentwood Benson Publishing

Universal Music Publishing Group
(Germany)
Stralauer Allee 1
10245 Berlin
Germany
Phone: 011-49-30-52007-1218
Fax: 011-49-30-52007-31218
sylvie.franck@umusic.com
www.universal-music-publishing.de

United Church Press
See The Pilgrim Press

Walton Music Corporation
See Licensing Associates

Wayne Leupold Editions, Inc.
8510 Triad Dr.
Colfax, NC 27235
Phone: 1-800-765-3196
www.wayneleupold.com

Weaver, John
23 Rowell Rd.
West Glover, VT 05875

Webber, Christopher
80 Herb Road
Sharon, CT 06069
info@clwebber.com

Westminster John Knox Press
Presbyterian Publishing Corporation
100 Witherspoon St.
Louisville, KY 40202-1396
Fax: 502-569-5113
www.wjkbooks.com

Wilkey, Jay W.
30 Wildwood Dr., #14
Georgetown, TX 78633
jaywilkey@verizon.net

Word Music Group, Inc.
20 Music Square East
Nashville, TN 37203
Phone: 615-733-1885
Fax: 615-733-1880
www.wordmusic.com

World Council of Churches
PO Box 2100
CH-1211 Geneva 2
Switzerland
Phone: 011-41-22-791-6111
Fax: 011-41-22-791-0361
www.oikoumene.org

World Library Publications
3708 River Rd., Suite 400
Franklin Park, IL 60131-2158
www.wlp.jspaluch.com

Wright, David
510 S. Mattis, #104
Champaign, IL 61821
davidclarkwright@gmail.com

Wright, Helen
1966 Meadowbrook Way
Coshocton, OH 43812
Phone: 740-622-0641

Yale University Press
92A Yale Station
New Haven, CT 06520
Phone: 203-432-0960
Fax: 203-432-0948
www.yalepress.yale.edu/yupbooks/
home.asp

Yamuger Indonesian Institute
for Sacred Music
Mr. Sony Widyanto Utomo
Jalan Wisma Jaya 11
13220 Jakarta Timur
Indonesia
yamuger@bit.net.id

Zhigulin, Konstantin
6 line of Vasilevskiy Island
57 Neva Church of Christ
St. Petersburg, Russia
sestrannik@inbox.ru

Index of Authors, Composers, and Sources

Index of Genre and Musical Styles

The following index highlights the diversity of the major musical and textual traditions represented in this Psalter. Its aim is to help congregations and worship leaders identify those settings that are most accessible in their context, as well as particular settings that might stretch or challenge them. Whenever possible, this guide refers to an entry (name or publication) in the *Index of Authors, Composers, and Sources* (see pp. 1100-1104) rather than to specific instances. Any endeavor to distinguish unique traditions or genres is complicated by the fact that some individual composers or poets contribute to more than one tradition or genre, and some musical examples reflect multiple stylistic influences. Nevertheless, this guide offers a sketch of the primary traditions and styles included in this volume.

Genres and Traditions of Musical Settings

1. *Eastern Orthodox Chant*
   See 20B, 27H (Alt. Ref.), 51J; 141D, "You Have Come to Your People" (p. 1013), "The Lord's Prayer: Our Father in Heaven" (p. 1034), Prayers of the People (p. 1043).

2. *Gregorian Chant and other Medieval Traditions*
   See 10A, 74A, 104G (Alt. Ref.), 149A (Alt. Ref.), 150H, General Refrain 1 (p. 1054).

3. *16ᵗʰ-Century Genevan Psalter*
   See Genevan Psalter

4. *Lutheran Chorale Tradition*
   See contributions from Johann S. Bach, the 1524 *Enchiridia*, Freylinghausen's *Geistreiches Gesangbuch*, Severus Gastorius, the 1666 *Gesangbuch*, Hans Leo Hassler, Nikolaus Herman, Jakob Hintze, Martin Luther, Michael Praetorius, Melchoir Vulpius.

5. *17ᵗʰ-18ᵗʰ-Century American*
   See William Billings, William B. Bradbury, William H. Doane, Funk's *A Compilation of Genuine Church Music, Kentucky Harmony*, William J. Kirkpatrick, Lowell Mason, *The Sacred Harp*, Walkers's *Southern Harmony*, Wyeth's *Repository of Sacred Music*.

6. *Afro-American Spirituals*
   See Afro-American spirituals

7. *Traditional Hymn Tunes from England and Continental Europe*
   See contributions by George N. Allen, J. L. Macbeth Bain, Ludwig van Beethoven, William U. Butcher, Jeremiah Clarke, William Croft, Henry S. Cutler, John Darwall, John B. Dykes, John D. Edwards, George J. Elvey, Charles H. Gabriel, John Hatton, Franz Joseph Haydn, Johann Michael Haydn, Jessie Seymour Irvine, George Kirbye, Conrad Kocher, James Langran, William Lloyd, Charles Lockhart, Frederick Charles Maker, William H. Monk, Henry K. Oliver, Joseph Parry, Charles H. Purday, Richard Redhead, Lewis H. Redner, William F. Sherman, James Walch, Walter G. Whinfield, Thomas J. Williams.

8. *English and North American Cathedral Traditions*
   See contributions by William Boyce, Richard Dirksen, Henry J. Guantlet, Orlando Gibbons, John Goss, Charles F. Gounod, Gustav Holst, Herbert Howells, Gordon Jacob, Frederick A. Gore Ouseley, C. Hubert H. Parry, Charles Villiers Stanford, Arthur S. Sullivan, Thomas Tallis, Samuel S. Wesley, Ralph Vaughan Williams.

9. *Recently Written Responsorial Psalmody*
   See contributions by Ben Allaway, Mary Kay Beall, Lorraine Brugh, James Hart Brumm, AnnaMae Meyer Bush, Shannon Cerneka, Rory Cooney, Lucien Deiss, Gregg DeMey, Ann Celeen Dohms, Andrew Donaldson, Bernadette Farrell, Alfred V. Fedak, John Foley, Michael Guimont, David Haas, Rawn Harbor, Marty Haugen, Mike Hay, Robert Hobby, Jeffrey Honoré, Hal H. Hopson, Julie Howard, Bob Hurd, Orin Johnson, J. Michael Joncas, David Lee, James V. Marchionda, John Michaels, Andrew Moore, James E. Moore Jr., Fintan O'Carroll, Val Parker, Betty Carr Pulkingham, Susan Sayers, Daniel L. Schutte, Martin Tel, Robert J. Thompson, Christopher Walker, Steven C. Warner, Jay Wilkey.

10. *Recently Written Hymn-Like Tunes for Metrical Settings*
    See contributions by John Barnard, John L. Bell, James E. Clemens, Carol Doran, Alfred V. Fedak, Henry Bryan Hays O. S. B., Timothy Hoekman, Roy Hopp, David N. Johnson, Ken Medema, Christopher Norton, Iteke Prins, Clayton J. Schmit, Randall Sensmeier, Christian Strover, Larry Visser, James Ward, Norman L. Warren.

11. *Settings from Contemporary or Popular Worship Music from the 1970s and 1980s*
See contributions by Brent Chambers, Dave Doherty, Eddie Espinosa, Les Garrett, Graham Kendrick, Michael Ledner, Edith McNeill, Martin Nystrom, David Peacock, Donn Thomas, James Ward, Charles Williams, David G. Wilson.

12. *Settings from Contemporary or Popular Worship Music from the 1990s and 2000s*
See contributions by Bruce Benedict, Barbara Boertje, Karl Digerness, Brian Doerksen, Noel Donnelly, Isaac Everett, Kristyn Getty, Luke Hyder, Darwin Jordan, Bob Kauflin, Aaron Keyes, Ken Medema, Christopher Miner, Karen Mitchinson, Steve Mitchinson, Craig Musseau, Andy Park, Daphne Rademaker, Matt Redman, Greg Scheer, Paul Thé, Stuart Townend, Eelco Vos, Tommy Walker; see also responsorial settings by Gregg DeMey, Julie Howard, John Michaels, Betty Carr Pulkingham.

13. *Settings from the Spectrum of Afro-American Gospel Music*
See contributions by Lillian Bouknight, Glenn Burleigh, J. Jefferson Cleveland, Andraé Crouch, Margaret J. Douroux, Rawn Harbor, Isaiah Jones Jr., Brenda Joyce Moore, Val Parker, Leon C. Roberts, Richard Smallwood; see also 100B (p. 626).

14. *Settings from the Spectrum of Jazz Styles*
See contributions from Angel Napieralski, Daniel Richardson, Sheldon W. Sorge, Tammy Wiens.

15. *Settings from Contemporary Communities of Prayer and Renewal*
See contributions from The Iona Community, The Community of Taizé, John L. Bell, Jacques Berthier.

16. *Settings from Latin America and Southern North American Countries*
Argentina: 133D
Brazil: 30D
Caribbean: 118F, 150G (Alt. Ref. 2)
Ecuador: 145C
El Salvador: 94A
Honduras: 147A
Mexico: 42A, 150D
Paraguay: 9A
Puerto Rico: 133B
See also contributions by Simei Monteiro, Pablo Sosa, Fr. Alberto Taulé
Note: *several of the Spanish-language contributions derive from one or more Central or South American country (see below, p. 1107).*

17. *Settings from the Middle and Near East*
Israeli, Hasidic, and other Jewish melodies: 24E, 30C, 78C, 78D, 111D, 125C, 137C, 137D
Pakistan and/or India: 51G (Alt. Ref. 1), 61B, 95F, 96A, 100D, 150C, General Refrain 6 (p. 1054)

18. *Settings from Eastern Europe*
Czeckoslavakia (melody): 27J
Latvia (melody): 12A, 129A, 137A
Russia: 110B, 117F, 128A, 130F

19. *Settings from Africa*
Egypt: "The Lord's Prayer: Abana Alathi Fi Ssama" (p. 1049)
Ghana: 51K
Malawi: 4B (Alt. Ref.), 81A
Swahili/Kiyaha: 136G
Yoruba people (Nigeria): 47D
Zimbabwe: 66B

20. *Settings from Asia*
Indonesia:146B (Alt. Ref. 2), 148E
Japan: 71B (tune)
Korea: 42C, 121F
Philippines: 51L, 96E, 120B, 147B
Taiwan: 100E, 117A
Thailand: 1C
See also contributions by Francisco F. Feliciano, Swee Hong Lim, I-toh Loh

Genres and Traditions of Texts

1. *16th- to Early 20th-Century Metrical Psalmody*
   See contributions by Henry Williams Baker, Robert Grant, George Herbert, William Kethe, Henry F. Lyte, John Milton, James Montgomery, John Newton, Isaac Watts, Charles Wesley, entries from *Psalter* (1887), *Psalter* (1912), *Scottish Psalter*.

2. *Metrical Settings Written Since 1960*
   See contributions by Fred R. Anderson, Carol Bechtel, John L. Bell, Ken Bible, John Carter, Carl P. Daw Jr., David J. Diephouse, Andrew Donaldson, Arlo D. Duba, Ruth C. Duck, Timothy Dudley-Smith, John G. Dunn, Bernadette Farrell, Doug Gay, Gracia Grindal, Bev Herrema, Christopher Idle, Willard F. Jabusch, David Landegent, Richard Leach, Martin Leckebusch, Michael Morgan, David Mowbray, Helen Otte, Joy F. Patterson, Ian Pitt-Watson, Michael Perry, Bert Polman, Marie J. Post, David G. Preston, James Quinn S. J., Ada Roeper-Boulogne, Michael Saward, James E. Seddon, Calvin Seerveld, Scott Soper, Sheldon W. Sorge, Stephen P. Starke, Henrietta Ten Harmsel, Adam M. L. Tice, Stuart Townend, Clarence P. Walhout, Christopher L. Webber, Dewey Westra, Rae E. Whitney, Tammy Wiens, Stanley Wiersma, Paul Wigmore, Barbara Woollett, David Wright, Henry Zylstra.

Texts in Languages Other than English

Arabic: "The Lord's Prayer: Abana Alathi Fi Ssama" (p. 1049)
Chinese: 88A, 100A
Dutch: 100A, 148G
Filipino: 120B
French: 88A, 100A
German: 88A, 100A
Greek: 51 J, 51K
Hebrew: 92B
Hungarian: 88A, 100A
Indonesian: 100A, 146B (Alt. Ref. 2), 148E
Japanese: 100A
Korean: 23C, 42C, 88A, 100A, 121F
Latin: 71C (Alt. Ref.), 85B, 100G, 117B, 118C, 118 J, 122C (Alt. Ref.)
Muscogee: 146B (Alt. Ref.)
Paraguayan: 9A
Portuguese: 30D
Punjabi: 100D, 150C
Shona: 66B
Spanish: 1E, 20A, 23C, 23I, 27G, 29B, 30B, 31D, 34C, 42A, 46B, 51A, 51E, 51M, 65C (Alt. Ref.), 72D, 88A, 91C, 100A, 103G, 117D, 121C, 133B, 133D, 139F, 141F, 145C, 150D
Swahili: 88A, 100A, 136G
Taiwanese: 100E, 117A
Tamil: 61B
Thai: 1C
Urdhu: 51G (Alt. Ref. 1)
Xhosa: 51G (Alt. Ref. 2)

Settings Especially Appropriate for Children

23K, 24C, 24E, 31B, 46D, 49C, 57B, 73A, 81B, 92B, 100G, 118B, 118K, 120A, 121 I, 134B, 136G, 150H
In addition, the majority of refrains associated with responsorial psalms are well-suited to children.

Spoken Texts

For Litanies see "Litany," *First Lines and Common Titles*, pp. 1126-1127.
For Prayers see "Prayer," *First Lines and Common Titles*, p. 1129; see also 97D and 145A.
For Additional Spoken Texts see 2B, 22C, 28B, 81C, 118 I, 121G and 137B.
Prayers, Litanies, and the Lord's Prayer are also embedded in the *Services of Prayer*, pp. 1030-1052.

Index of Subjects and Seasons
by Biblical Psalm Number

Acrostic Psalms: 9, 10, 25, 34, 37, 111, 112, 119, 145
Advent: see CHURCH YEAR
Affliction: 4, 25, 37, 42, 43, 49, 54, 55, 56, 57, 60, 64, 73, 77, 86, 88, 91, 116, 120, 129, 140, 142
Alleluias: 145, 146, 147, 148, 149, 150
Angels: 18, 34, 73, 78, 91, 103, 148
Anniversaries: 27, 48, 90, 132
Annunciation, The: 40, 45, 113, 123, 131
Antiphonal Psalms: 118, 136
Armor of God, The: see GOD('S)/GOD AS
Ascension of Our Lord: see CHURCH YEAR
Assurance: 7, 22, 23, 27, 40, 46, 62, 121, 124
Atheism: 1, 10, 14, 53, 137
Atonement: 72, 85, 103, 116

Baptism: see WORSHIP, ELEMENTS OF
BIBLICAL NAMES, PLACES, AND THEMES
    Aaron: 77, 99, 105, 106, 115, 118, 133, 135
    Abiram: 106
    Abraham: 47, 105
    Amalek: 83
    Ammon: 83
    Amorites: 135, 136
    Assyria: 83
    Baal: 106
    Babylon: 87, 137
    Bashon: 68, 135, 136
    Benjamin: 7, 68, 80
    Canaan: 105, 106, 135
    Dathan: 106
    David: 18, 72, 78, 89, 122, 132, 144
    Edom: 60, 83, 108, 137
    Egypt: 68, 78, 80, 81, 87, 89, 105, 106, 114, 135, 136
    En-dor: 83
    Ephraim: 60, 78, 80, 108
    Ephrathah: 132
    Ethiopia: 68, 87
    Exodus: 78, 81, 105, 106, 114, 136
    Gilead: 60
    Hagrites: 83
    Ham: 78, 105, 106
    Hermon, Mount: 29, 42, 89, 133
    Horeb: 106
    Isaac: 105
    Israel: 14, 22, 25, 41, 50, 53, 59, 68, 69, 71, 72, 73, 76, 78, 79, 80, 81, 83, 89, 98, 103, 105, 106, 114, 115,
        118, 121, 122, 124, 125, 128, 129, 130, 131, 135, 136, 147, 148, 149
    Ishmaelites: 83
    Jaar: 132
    Jabin: 83
    Jacob: 14, 20, 22, 24, 44, 46, 47, 53, 59, 75, 76, 77, 78, 79, 81, 84, 85, 87, 94, 99, 105, 114, 132, 135, 146, 147
    Jerusalem: 51, 68, 79, 102, 116, 122, 125, 128, 135, 137, 147
    Jesse: 72
    Jordan: 42, 114
    Joseph: 77, 78, 80, 81, 105
    Judah: 48, 60, 63, 68, 69, 76, 78, 97, 108, 114
    Kadesh: 29
    Lebanon: 29, 92
    Levi: 135

Humility: 25, 51, 62, 113, 131, 138
Hymns of Praise: 8, 19, 29, 33, 46, 47, 48, 65, 66, 67, 68, 76, 84, 87, 93, 95, 96, 97, 98, 99, 100, 103, 104, 111, 113, 114, 117, 122, 134, 135, 136, 145, 146, 147, 148, 149, 150

Idols and Idolatry: 24, 40, 95, 96, 97, 101, 106, 115
Illness: see LAMENT
Illumination, Prayer for: see WORSHIP, ELEMENTS OF
Impatience: 4, 6, 13, 39
Incarnation, The: 47, 67, 84, 98, 102, 116, 122, 132
Innocence: 15, 17, 18, 24, 26, 35
Instruments, Musical: 33, 43, 47, 57, 68, 71, 81, 92, 98, 108, 137, 149, 150
Integrity: 7, 26, 34, 41, 44, 101

JESUS CHRIST
  Ascension: see CHURCH YEAR
  Confidence in: 23
  Cross and Crucifixion: 22
  Friend of Sinners: 8, 25, 32, 56, 57, 68, 103, 119, 122
  Good Shepherd: 1, 8, 23, 30, 42, 49, 63, 68, 111
  Healer: 103, 131, 137, 139, 142, 146, 147
  Incarnation: 47, 67, 84, 98, 102, 116, 122, 132
  Mind of: 1, 4, 19, 26, 45, 53, 55, 71, 113, 126, 127, 131, 145, 147
  Parables of: 25, 43, 75, 76, 127, 128, 133
  Teacher: 1, 8, 34, 40, 71, 73, 103, 104, 111, 119, 143
  Transfiguration: see CHURCH YEAR
  Way, Truth, and Life: 1, 8, 12, 15, 18, 19, 26, 33, 37, 43, 57, 63, 77, 119, 131, 139
Joy: 4, 7, 17, 23, 25, 27, 30, 32, 33, 36, 38, 43, 47, 51, 63, 65, 66, 67, 68, 84, 85, 86, 89, 90, 92, 95, 96, 97, 98, 100, 105, 108, 112, 114, 119, 123, 126, 128, 132, 136, 138, 143, 146, 147, 149, 150
Judgment: 1, 2, 7, 11, 18, 21, 27, 34, 38, 50, 51, 62, 67, 68, 73, 75, 76, 81, 89, 90, 92, 94, 96, 97, 98, 99, 101, 105, 119, 130, 137, 143, 149
Justice: 9, 10, 33, 58, 82, 85, 98, 149

Labor: 15, 63, 90, 127
LAMENT
  Community: 12, 44, 60, 74, 79, 80, 83, 85, 89, 94, 126, 137
  False Accusation: 7, 17, 109, 139
  General: 3, 5, 7, 9, 10, 12, 13, 17, 22, 26, 28, 31, 35, 39, 41, 44, 58, 59, 61, 69, 71, 74, 79, 80, 83, 85, 88, 94, 109, 123, 126, 137, 141 (see also Affliction)
  Illness: 6, 13, 31, 38, 39, 69, 88, 102
  Individual: 3, 4, 5, 7, 11, 22, 17, 25, 26, 27, 31, 35, 41, 42, 43, 52, 54, 55, 56, 57, 58, 59, 77, 86, 94, 102, 109, 139, 140, 142
LIFE STAGES
  Birth: 71, 139
  Children: 8, 48, 76, 78, 102, 107, 112, 128
  Death: 6, 13, 16, 18, 22, 23, 30, 31, 39, 49, 73, 83, 88, 90, 102, 104, 116, 128, 137, 139, 141
  Family: 8, 78, 103, 113, 127, 128, 148
  Generations: 78, 90, 100, 102, 103, 105, 113, 128, 145, 147
  Old Age: 39, 71, 90, 92, 101, 102, 103, 148
  Orphans: 68, 146
  Widows: 68, 146
  Youth: 25, 71, 103, 119, 148
Liturgical Year: see CHURCH YEAR
Loneliness: 22, 25, 42, 56, 69, 71, 116, 137, 142
Longing for God: 6, 13, 16, 22, 42, 61, 63, 84
LORD'S PRAYER
  1st petition (hallowed be your name): 115, 145
  2nd petition (your kingdom come): 119, 143
  3rd petition (your will be done on earth...): 103

Unity and Fellowship: 15, 24, 48, 84, 85, 89, 95, 100, 118, 122, 127, 132, 133, 147, 149, 150
Unity of the Church: 87, 102:18-22, 122, 133 (see also PEOPLE OF GOD/CHURCH: Unity of God's People)

Victory: 19, 22, 34, 46, 49, 50, 66, 73, 76, 103, 107, 111, 119, 126, 130, 142, 143
Vows: 22, 50, 56, 61, 65, 66, 76, 116

Walk with God/Christ: see Discipleship
War and Revolution: 46, 68, 76, 78, 120, 130, 138
Weddings: see OCCASIONAL SERVICES: Christian Marriage
Widows: see LIFE STAGES
Wisdom Psalms: 1, 19, 32, 34, 37, 49, 73, 111, 112, 119
Witness: 34, 40, 46, 48, 49, 66, 67, 70, 71, 73, 76, 78, 89, 96, 97, 98, 100, 103, 111, 119, 131, 138, 145, 147
Worship: 15, 19, 21, 24, 25, 26, 28, 30, 40, 47, 63, 66, 67, 75, 86, 93, 95, 97, 98, 99, 100, 104, 105, 117,
    118, 122, 123, 134, 138, 141, 145, 147, 149
WORSHIP, ELEMENTS OF
    Preparation for Worship: 15, 19:14,24
    Gathering: 15, 24, 27, 42, 43, 63, 65, 72, 84, 89, 92, 93, 95, 100, 108, 113, 117, 122, 123, 125, 135, 136,
        138, 145, 146, 147, 148, 150
    Call to Worship: 9:1-2, 24:1-4, 24:7-10, 27, 34:3, 47:1-2,5-6, 66:1-2,4, 86:8-10, 89:1-4, 92:1-2, 95, 96, 100,
        108:1-4, 113:1-3, 118:24, 124:8, 150:1-2,6
    Praise and Adoration: 1, 3, 5, 8, 18, 19, 20, 21, 25, 26, 28, 29, 42, 47, 48, 53, 57, 65, 66, 67, 72, 75, 84,
        87, 92, 93, 95, 96, 97, 98, 100, 103, 104, 105, 107, 108, 111, 113, 114, 115, 116, 117, 118, 128, 132,
        138, 145, 146, 147, 148, 149, 150
    Call to Confession: 32:1-6, 66:16,18-20, 78, 139:23-24
    Confession (Corporate): 32, 79, 123, 130, 143
    Confession (Individual): 25, 27, 38, 42, 51, 77, 86, 90, 102, 104, 123, 130, 143
    Assurance of Pardon: 32, 51, 86, 99, 103, 130
    Prayer for Illumination: 19:14, 25:4-5, 27:11, 36:9, 43:3-4, 85:8, 95, 119:105
    Testimony: 30, 107, 116,
    Baptism: 16, 23, 25, 42, 51, 71, 84, 87, 100, 103, 105, 107, 111, 115, 119, 134, 139
    Offering: 40, 50, 51, 54, 66, 112
    Lord's Supper: 15, 16, 22, 23, 24, 25, 32, 34, 36, 40, 42, 43, 51, 63, 65, 66, 72, 77, 78, 79, 81, 84, 85, 103,
        105, 107, 111, 116, 118, 123, 130, 139, 145
    Thanksgiving after the Lord's Supper: 103
    Preparation for the Blessing: 29, 67
    Sending: 20, 33, 52, 67, 72, 106, 121, 134

Youth: see LIFE STAGES

Metrical Index of Tunes

Tune Names Index

Several hymn tunes appear in abbreviated form as psalm refrains and are listed below in italics.

Index of First Lines and Common Titles

Most settings are referenced by their instance number followed by the page number in parenthesis. In the case of the New Testament canticles and settings embedded within the prayer services, only the page number is indicated. Refrains included in Responsorial Settings are indicated below by [Ref.]. *Spoken items and services of prayer are listed in italics.*